D1614874

MOUNTAIN FLOWERS

MOUNTAIN FLOWERS

IN COLOUR

ANTHONY HUXLEY

Illustrated by

Daphne Barry and Mary Grierson

BLANDFORD PRESS

POOLE   NEW YORK   SYDNEY

First published in the UK in this format 1986 by Blandford
Press
Link House, West Street, Poole, Dorset BH15 1LL

First published 1967
Revised edition 1973
Reprinted 1978
2nd Revised edition 1986

Distributed in the United States by
Sterling Publishing Co, Inc,
2 Park Avenue, New York, NY 10016

Distributed in Australia by
Capricorn Link (Australia) Pty Ltd
PO Box 665, Lane Cove, NSW 2066

British Library Cataloguing in Publication Data

Huxley, Anthony
    Mountain flowers in colour.—2nd rev. ed.
    1. Alpine flora   2. Flowers—Europe—Identification
    I. Title   II. Barry, Daphne   III. Grierson, Mary
    582.13′094   QK297

ISBN 0 7137 1846 3

Printed in Portugal by Printer Portuguesa

CONTENTS

PREFACE

WRITING about alpine plants has been going on for nearly a century. Among the earliest books designed for the layman was *Die Alpenpflanzen Deutschlands und der Schweiz* by J. C. Weber, published in Munich in 1872. It comprises four tiny volumes each containing 100 life-sized coloured illustrations. It was the acquisition of a set of these some years ago that led to this present book. I was so charmed by Weber's drawings that I considered the possibility of compiling a modern book out of them, with several of the original illustrations on each plate.

It proved that not all Weber's drawings were sufficiently accurate to justify this project, and in the course of establishing this I also discovered that there was no single volume that could be said to give any moderately comprehensive selection of the mountain plants of Europe, with the honourable exception of the late Rev. H. S. Thompson's *Alpine Plants of Europe*, published in 1911 with paintings from Joseph Seboth's work of 1879–80; but this has long been out of print. Even this volume largely passed over the Pyrenean flora and only describes some 700 species; other books on alpines mentioned 300 to 400 plants.

So was this book conceived, which illustrates 1200 plants, describes about 1640, and gives reference to a total of nearly 1900 covering all Europe from the Pyrenees to the Julian Alps, and including the Scandinavian alpines. In honour of its begetter, a few of Weber's best original illustrations are embedded in the otherwise entirely newly created plates. His fine line, deriving from the steel-engraving technique then used, and his slightly stylised approach, have been deliberately retained by the artists as being the best way to depict small botanical differences among the closely related species which it has been my aim to group together.

* * * * *

Such a task is seldom accomplished without assistance. My first and greatest debt is to the two artists, Miss Daphne Barry, and Miss Mary Grierson, the illustrator at the Royal Botanic Gardens, Kew. They laboured under my direction, sometimes from decidedly unsatisfactory material, to produce the plates which form the core of this book. I am grateful also to Miss Dora Ratman who prepared three plates (Lilies and Roses) while the project was in the pilot stage.

The late Miss T. A. Bence, then also of the Royal Botanic Gardens, Kew, put in a great deal of time-consuming research, provided constructive criticism and read the proofs, for which I remain deeply grateful.

Further invaluable help came from the late Mrs. Anna Griffith and Mr. Richard Gorer, both of them with a wide knowledge of plants in the wild as well as in cultivation who read the book in typescript and made many very helpful comments which have added to the value of the descriptions. Mr. Gorer also read the proofs.

Botanical accuracy can only be achieved in terms of the date of writing, and even then can be a matter of opinion. However, I have attempted—occasionally with something approaching desperation—to be as accurate and up to date as possible, and the nomenclature has been checked and brought into line with present-day thinking, largely by the kindness of Mr. J. E. Dandy, at that time Keeper of Botany, British Museum of Natural History, and Dr. W. T. Stearn and Dr. Melderes then on his staff.

If I have on some occasions departed from their advice it is because this book is designed for the layman rather than for the taxonomic botanist, and there seemed to me cases where the retention of a well known name was more in keeping with this aim than the use of an unfamiliar one. Such deviations have been mentioned wherever they occur so that the reader can at least know the latest thinking on these points. Further comments on taxonomy, and an outline of the problems involved, especially in this revised edition, are made in the introductory chapter.

I have necessarily made use of many books while preparing this one, and a list of the most important is given on p. 416. I am grateful to the Council of the Royal Horticultural Society for permission to use at home certain floras not normally on loan, and to Mr. P. Stageman, the then R.H.S. Librarian, for his never-failing help.

Advice and encouragement, particularly in the early stages, came from Mr. J. S. L. Gilmour, then of the Cambridge University Botanic Garden, Dr. S. M. Walters then of the Botany School, Cambridge and Miss T. E. Atkins. Prof. J. F. Kirkaldy of Queen Mary College kindly revised the geological glossary. To these, and to many other friends who gave advice on specific points, I am grateful.

Help in revising the second revised edition came from a number of friends and acquaintances, mainly members of the Alpine Garden Society, and notably Mr. and Mrs. Gerard Parker, Miss M. G. Hodgman, Mr. Richard Nutt, and Mr. B. E. Smythies.

Last but not least I must thank my long-suffering publisher and his staff for their forbearance and help.

INTRODUCTION

THE SCOPE OF THIS BOOK

THE aim of *Mountain Flowers* is to provide a reasonably comprehensive illustrated guide to the flowers of the mountains of Europe. The area covered ranges from the Pyrenees in the west to the Julian Alps in northern Yugoslavia; the Scandinavian and a high proportion of Italian alpines are also included (p. 4). Beyond this area too many different species occur, and to illustrate them with the central European ones would merely confuse. In general, the plants described are those found upwards of 1500 m. above sea-level, though a few particularly interesting plants from slightly lower levels are included, especially in Scandinavia.

There has been some selection of the plants involved. Many primarily lowland plants exceed 1500 m. In certain places, especially as one moves farther south, and where their upward range is limited, such plants are only included if they are particularly showy. On the other hand, many insignificant or weedy plants may attain considerable altitudes, and here again considerable selection has been made, though where well-known plants are involved (such as the Common Nettle) a brief mention has been made.

Again, plants which are likely to be outside the ordinary person's interests, and beyond the non-specialist's capacity to identify readily, have been omitted, or mentioned only briefly. Families involved here are notably the Grasses, *Gramineae*; Sedges, *Cyperaceae*; Cow Parsleys, *Umbelliferae*; and certain sections of the Daisy Family, *Compositae*, such as the Hawkweeds, *Hieracium*. Wherever this occurs there is a note explaining the extent of the omissions and the reasons for them.

I believe that all the more interesting and beautiful flowers likely to be seen above 1500 m. have been included. Some 1200 plants are illustrated, while close relations of these are also described in the text, which altogether covers over 1600 species and forms. Descriptions of unillustrated plants normally follow that of the most similar illustrated one, sometimes in the form of a note only. Subspecies and varieties are described only where they are likely to be of interest, notably in cases like *Saxifraga* where such forms may be of special value to the gardener, even if not botanically valid. It has not, however, been possible to mention most of the specially selected forms—often the result of collecting a single unusual specimen—which are often cultivated. To the botanist these are exceptions, and in the normal course of events such exceptions usually become reassimilated into the norm by interbreeding. Besides the plants described, some 270 plants exceeding 1500 m. are referred to.

It must be made quite clear that plants are, in general, only mentioned when they exceed 1500 m., or a rather lower altitude in Norway. Many plants may

**MOUNTAIN AREAS
REFERRED TO
IN THIS VOLUME**

GROUND OVER
1500 M. ALTITUDE

NORWAY

SWEDEN

FINLAND

DOVRE FJELL

JOTUNHEIN

JOSTEDALS BRE

HARDANGER
VIDDA

GREAT
BRITAIN

POLAND

GERMANY

CZECHOSLOVAKIA

AUSTRIA

HUNGARY

E.
ALPS

W.
ALPS

JULIAN ALPS

YUGO-
SLAVIA

FRANCE

MASSIF
CENTRAL

C.
ALPS

DINARIC ALPS

CEVENNES

Western

APUAN
ALPS

Central

PYRENEES

Eastern

ABRUZZI

APENNINES

SPAIN

CORSICA

SARDINIA

SICILY

occur below this level over other parts of their range than that specified. The only exception to this rule is that when a plant occurs at any level in Britain this is noted, since many readers will be familiar with our own wild plants.

The Plates. The aim throughout has been to illustrate all important, closely related species together. In some cases, as with *Crocus* and *Colchicum*, unrelated plants which are superficially similar have been drawn together. Partly for this reason, partly for artistic reasons, and partly for convenience, such as the placing together of two or three small families on one plate, the consecutive numbering of the plates could not be followed in the text.

In any case, the limitation on the number of colour plates made it necessary to supplement these with thirty-six black-and-white plates. In general these are restricted to white-flowered species, but they also include some insignificant plants and in some cases plants with coloured flowers which only just come within the altitude limitations. These black-and-white plates run in parallel sequence to the colour plates, a further reason for apparent inconsistency in text numbering. Besides these two sets of plates there are a number of drawings in the text. The drawings do not always depict the whole plant. In some cases only a flowering shoot is shown, often with a basal leaf adjoining it. On occasions where the leaves form the main difference between species only a leaf may be shown.

BOTANICAL NOMENCLATURE

Plants are classified into three main divisions. The *family* is a group of plants in which certain characters—almost always those of the flower—are constant or at least readily differentiated from those of other families. Within the family there are *genera* (singular *genus*) indicating subsidiary groups (sometimes of only a single plant) each of which is similar in structure and can be considered to have developed from a common ancestor. The members of a genus are called *species* (singular and plural; abbreviated sp., spp.) and these are plants which, though often variable, are basically constant in their main characters.

Where it may be desirable to subdivide a species the categories are *subspecies* (abbreviated ssp., sspp.) and, below this again, *varietates* (varieties, abbreviated var.). All such names are expressed in Latin, which is the universal scientific language. Where Lent Lily or Buckler Mustard are probably quite obscure to a Frenchman or German, *Narcissus pseudonarcissus* and *Biscutella laevigata* mean the same to all. Pheasant-eye can be applied to *Narcissus* or *Adonis*, Masterwort to *Astrantia* or *Peucedanum*; in short, English names can be misleading, although many people may find them easier and pleasanter to remember.

While I have tried to find an English name wherever possible, these have been used only where such names are in reasonably common use or where one derived from the local name in the language of the country of occurrence seemed justified. I have refrained on the whole from such transliterations of the Latin as 'Six-leaved Asperula' or 'Carinthian Wulfenia', although 'Piedmont Rampion', 'Alpine Speedwell' and 'Swiss Treacle-mustard' seemed admissible. For the sake of consistency I have, where possible without ambiguity, combined words, removing apostrophes and hyphens, as in Monkshood and Coltsfoot.

It must be realised that all these botanical divisions are man-made concepts. This fact is particularly important with respect to species. In many cases the distinctions between one species and its close relations are blurred. This is particularly noticeable where close relations are found in different areas: such groups—like the alpine willows (pp. 185–188)—are often geographical races, which may have been differentiated by geological and climatic accidents quite recently on the evolutionary time-scale. It should be noted that subspecies names are included in the captions to the plates only when the differences between subspecies are readily apparent in drawings on the scale concerned.

Mountainous areas, like islands, are particularly favourable to the development of such races. Colonies of a species, established by ordinary seeding on different mountains, proceed to develop in different ways in isolation from each other. Most alpine races are probably the outcome of movements during the ice ages. Take a hypothetical species which was widespread during an ice age, growing freely at levels below the ice-cap. As the ice retreated the plants crept up all available mountainsides to keep up with their climatic needs. During the warm interglacial period the species is then found on the high parts of isolated mountains, and these colonies again develop differently although maintaining a close similarity.

Where geographical races exist, botanists may treat them as individual species, give them subspecific rank or treat them merely as varieties, according to the degree of distinctiveness involved and also the amount of 'splitting' favoured by the particular botanist responsible.

Another cause of variation is undoubtedly habitat. Plants growing in very difficult, exposed conditions high up are apt to be smaller and more compact than those growing in warmer places lower down, often in richer soil. Names are often given to such variations, often under the title of forms (Latin *forma*), but if, as may occur, such differences are only due to habitat, and disappear if the forms are grown in identical conditions, they have no botanical validity.

In yet other cases one can only say that a species is intrinsically very variable; thus some violas produce flowers of extraordinarily different shape and colour (see p. 69); *Linaria alpina* may have an orange blotch on the flower or it may not. These appear to be seedling variations which are as likely to disappear in the next generation as not, and as such do not deserve botanical names at all. The botanist refers to such species as *polymorphic*.

Main Plant Groups. The plants described in this book fall into the following major botanical groups:

Pteridophyta: flowerless plants increasing by spores, with two distinct generations in their life-cycle (Ferns, Horsetails, Clubmosses, Selaginellas).

Gymnospermae: 'naked-seeded plants' with ovules not enclosed in an ovary; in alpine species all trees and shrubs of the group collectively known as Conifers (Pines, Firs, Larches, Junipers, Yews).

Angiospermae: flowering plants with the ovules enclosed in an ovary. These are themselves subdivided as follows:

Monocotyledons (embryo with 1 cotyledon or seed-leaf): typically with 3 or 6 divisions to the flower, usually all petal-like; leaves usually with parallel veins.

Dicotyledons (embryo with 2 cotyledons or seed-leaves): seldom with 3 or 6, more often with 1 to 4 or 5, or an irregular number, of divisions to the flower; almost always with both sepals and petals (petals sometimes wanting, sepals then petal-like); leaves seldom with parallel veins.

Order. The order of families suggested by A. Engler in *Das Pflanzenreich* is now that most widely favoured; it is adopted in *Flora Europaea*, with certain modifications, and has been followed in the present book, again with modification. It is customary to place the flowerless plants at the beginning, followed by the *Gymnospermae*, and in the *Angiospermae* to place *Dicotyledons* first and *Monocotyledons* last; this follows the supposed evolutionary development from primitive to advanced. Mainly for reasons of presentation, this order has been reversed here.

The *Monocotyledons* end with *Potamogetonaceae* (Pondweeds) on p. 185, and the *Dicotyledons* begin with *Salicaceae* (Willows) also on p. 185. Conifers start on p. 399 and the flowerless plants on p. 404.

The order of genera—the first subdivision of a family—is again fairly constant in modern floras, and is based on supposed evolutionary progress within the family. In some cases I have departed from this order; thus it seemed more desirable, for the layman, to place true Lilies at the beginning of the Lily Family; Pinks (*Dianthus*) at the beginning of the Pink Family, and so on. Apart from certain natural groupings within a family, which are usually referred to in the text, the order of genera in a Flora often seems arbitrary to the non-botanist.

This applies even more to the order of species within a genus, which varies from author to author. I have therefore followed various authorities, or sometimes placed species in an order of my own, according to which seemed best in each case; my aim being to group superficially similar plants together.

Authorities and Synonyms. Readers will note that each Latin name (printed in bold letters) is followed by another reference (printed in light italics), usually abbreviated. This identifies the person who gave that name to the plant, and is an essential part of the Latin combination, although it may appear cumbersome to the layman, because it frequently happens that different authorities have given the same specific name to different plants. These authority references must be regarded as a necessary evil.

It will also be noted that alternative names are frequently given. It may be that different authors have proposed names unknown to each other, while in the course of botanical research botanists will frequently rename plants for one reason or another; there is at present no finality in this process. Not only do views on nomenclature change with time, but authors have individual views. Some plants are, as a result, saddled with literally dozens of names. Fortunately only a few of these are usually in common use, and it has been my aim to restrict synonyms to those used in older books likely to be generally available, and to those where there is considerable disagreement between present-day botanists.

In principle the names follow those in the five volumes of *Flora Europaea*, published between 1964 and 1980 after consultation between botanists all over Europe. At the time of writing the original edition of *Mountain Flowers* (1967) only one volume of *Flora Europaea* had been published, although the text was brought into line with Volume 2. In the second edition (1973) nomenclature was adjusted according to Volume 3.

In some cases it was possible to indicate the resulting alterations in the text, but both in the second and this third revision the expense of extensive text resetting, and in particular of changing captions on the colour plates, has prevented full-scale revision of the text.

Because of these difficulties the publisher has agreed, for this edition, to print a summary of taxonomic changes arising from the publication of *Flora Europaea*, and not already summarised in the text, which will be found in the Appendix. An asterisk (*) has been inserted at the end of plant descriptions affected, so that quick reference can be made to the summary.

In some cases the changes of name result from extensive research into complex genera (*Onosma* is a good example) and resulting new thinking. In others, reconsideration of the status of a species, subspecies or variety has caused change, raising or lowering the taxonomic level. In yet other cases the rule of priority has been invoked, under which the earliest publication of a name gives that name precedence over any others however well known. Such changes, merely based on searches in botanical literature, result in the somewhat depressing situation of synonymous names in my original text now reverting to being the official names. A few names seem to have switched between a couple of alternatives over the years!

Needless to say, taxonomic research continues all the time. But I have not attempted to pursue any research subsequent to the publication of *Flora Europaea*, which has to be regarded by myself and those likely to use *Mountain Flowers* as a botanical consensus which should be adhered to for a few decades.

It should finally be added that in a few cases I have chosen to describe a plant which *Flora Europaea* considers to be merely an imprecisely defined element in another, variable species. Such cases are usually entities sufficiently distinct to be mentioned in older botanical accounts and in particular to be recognised by alpine gardeners. My deviations from *Flora Europaea* are explained in the text.

HOW TO USE THIS BOOK

This guide to *Mountain Flowers* is based unashamedly on its illustrations. The user is recommended to try to identify his plant by comparing it with the picture and then to confirm his diagnosis by reference to the text. The name of the plant must be located in the index to find the text page concerned. He can then study the descriptions of closely related plants and of subspecies where they exist. The bold numbers in the text descriptions and in the index are those of the illustrations.

Except in a few cases where only a single plant of a family is mentioned (e.g. *Rhamnus*, p. 282), or well-known plants are mentioned only in passing (e.g. Nettle and Hazel, p. 189), the characters of each family are described first, and should be borne in mind when reading the descriptions of its members. Similarly, the characters of each genus are given except where only one species exists or is described. It should be understood that family and genus characters described are usually restricted to those of European alpine representatives.

The descriptions are not always what a botanist would regard as a complete diagnosis: they contain only the information necessary to confirm identification in conjunction with the illustration. Technical words have been avoided wherever possible, but a glossary is provided (p. 411) for those which have had to be used.

Family names are printed in CAPITALS in the centre of a column; generic names in CAPITALS at the left-hand side; specific names of plants described in full in **bold characters** with their botanical authorities in *light italics*. English names are given in SMALL CAPITALS.

Where applicable, there are descriptions of sub-families, or a line giving readily recognisable group characters (e.g. flower colour) between groups of species. Within the descriptions sizes are given which represent the normal variations recorded. An exceptional size is quoted in brackets, e.g. 6–12 (20) cm. The same style is adopted for altitude records: an exceptional height is quoted in brackets. Where the plant has a distribution extending southwards, notably into Italy, this bracketed height is usually its maximum in its southern habitat, e.g. 1500–2500 (3100) m.

Habitats. Typical habitats are given in general terms as part of each descrip-

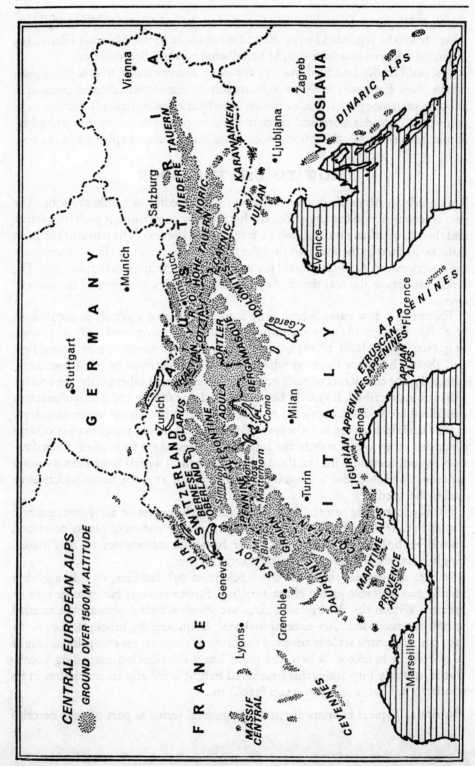

CENTRAL EUROPEAN ALPS
GROUND OVER 1500 M. ALTITUDE

AUSTRIA

Vienna

YUGOSLAVIA

DINARIC ALPS

Zagreb

Salzburg

NIEDERE TAUERN

KARAWANKEN

Ljubljana

Munich

HOHE TAUERN

NORIC

CARNIC

JULIAN

GERMANY

Innsbruck

RHAETAN

ÖTZTAL

DOLOMITES

Venice

Stuttgart

ORTLER

OTLER

Florence

APPENINES

ETRUSCAN

Zurich

BERGAMASQUE

Milan

L. Garda

APUAN
ALPS

GLARUS

ADULA

Como

SWITZERLAND

PONTINE

JURA

BERNESE
OBERLAND

Simplon

Monte
Rosa

LIGURIAN APPENINES

Genoa

Matterhorn

PENNINE

ITALY

Turin

SAVOY

Mt.
Blanc

GRAIAN

COTTIAN

Geneva

DAUPHINE

MARITIME ALPS

Grenoble

PROVENCE
ALPS

Lyons

FRANCE

MASSIF
CENTRAL

Marseilles

CEVENNÉS

tion, following the symbol ✲; it must be remembered that plants may quite often be found outside their normal habitats. The geological terms used are explained in a special glossary (p. 415).

Geographical Range. The range of each plant has again been expressed in general terms unless it is particularly restricted. The broad divisions of the central Alpine range as here used are as follows (see p. 10):

Western Alps: All the French Alps, and the Swiss and Italian Alps as far east as the Simplon Pass, including in the *south* the Provence, Maritime, Ligurian, Savoy, Dauphiné, Cottian, Graian and Pennine Alps, and in the *north* the Bernese Oberland in part, and the Jura.

Central Alps: The remainder of the Swiss Alps and as far east as the Ötztal Alps, including in the *south* the Lepontine, Adula, Rhaetian, Bergamasque and Ortler Alps, and in the *north* the eastern end of the Bernese Oberland, the Glarus and Allgau Alps, and the western part of the North Tyrol.

Eastern Alps: The remainder of the main Alpine range east of the Ötztal, as far east as the isolated Schneeberg group (2240 m.) near Vienna in the north, and the Karawanken in the south. They include, in the *south*, the Dolomites, Carnic, Noric and Dinaric Alps and Karawanken; and in the *north* the Hohe and Niedere Tauern ranges and the Salzburg and Zillertal Alps, the latter between the Hohe Tauern and Ötztal.

The term *Southern Alps* has been used, I fear, rather loosely on occasion, to denote the most southerly sections of the three main divisions.

Subsidiary areas such as the Maritime Alps, Julian Alps, etc., are usually mentioned only when a plant is localised there. Otherwise Alps, or more precisely western Alps, can be taken to include Maritime Alps and also the Jura; and N. Apennines, the Apuan Alps. The Cevennes (South France) are not normally specified as they only just exceed 1500 m. The Ariège mountains are treated as part of the Central Pyrenees. Norway has been treated separately, giving the maximum height there attained. The word (Britain) indicates that the plant exists in the British Isles, not necessarily at any altitude. Where a plant is specifically montane or local in Britain this fact is mentioned.

Rarity. On the whole it is imprudent to discuss relative abundance of plants, for this may vary enormously from one area to another, expecially where different geological formations occur. Some plants are, however, known to be generally rare or very local, and this has been stated. Where this rarity is only noticeable in part of the range it is stated in brackets (e.g. 'Pyrenees (rare); Alps' indicates relative abundance in the Alps); otherwise the word 'rare' or 'local' on its own refers to the entire geographical range.

WHAT MOUNTAIN FLOWERS ARE

As already stated, this book deals almost entirely with plants which are found growing at altitudes over 1,00 m. (about 5000 ft.). It is not, therefore, a guide

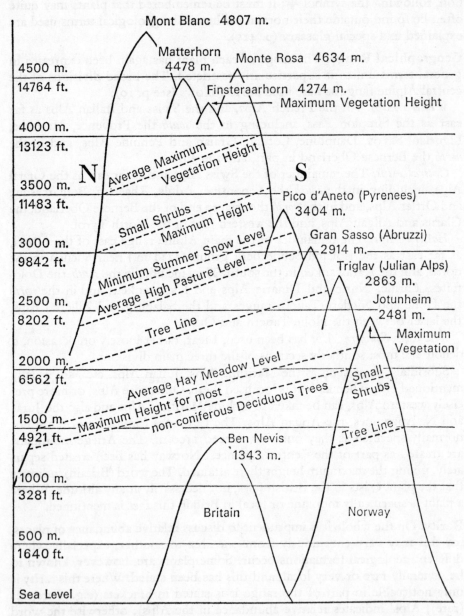

Mont Blanc 4807 m.

Matterhorn
4478 m.
Monte Rosa 4634 m.

4500 m.
14764 ft.

Finsteraarhorn 4274 m.
Maximum Vegetation Height

4000 m.
13123 ft.

N

S

Average Maximum Vegetation Height

3500 m.
11483 ft.

Pico d'Aneto (Pyrenees)
3404 m.

Small Shrubs
Maximum Height

Gran Sasso (Abruzzi)
2914 m.

3000 m.
9842 ft.

Minimum Summer Snow Level
Average High Pasture Level

Triglav (Julian Alps)
2863 m.

2500 m.
8202 ft.

Jotunheim
2481 m.

Tree Line

Maximum
Vegetation

2000 m.
6562 ft.

Average Hay Meadow Level

Small
Shrubs

1500 m.
4921 ft.

Maximum Height for most
non-coniferous Deciduous Trees

Tree Line

Ben Nevis
1343 m.

1000 m.
3281 ft.

Britain

Norway

500 m.
1640 ft.

Sea Level

Diagram illustrating height zones of vegetation on an 'average' mountain in the Central Alps. Note change of maximum heights on north and south aspects, and also the much lower levels in Norway.

The diagram also shows the highest peaks of the Central Alps and the other mountain ranges covered in this volume.

only to what the gardener calls 'alpines'. The level of 1500 m. has been selected for various reasons. It has, as will be seen later, a distinct significance to the plant geographer. It is the approximate level of many mountain resorts from which visitors tend to climb upwards. Lastly, to go below this level would mean including so many more plants that the size of the book would have reached unmanageable proportions.

Many attempts have been made to classify the climatic zones of the European mountains, and few of them agree. It is, however, possible to establish average vegetation zones for the mountains of Central Europe, and a typical arrangement is shown in the diagram (p. 12) which also indicates the heights of the tallest mountains in different ranges.

On such an 'average' mountain in the Swiss Alps, the vegetation limits on north and south aspects will vary by as much as 300 m. to start with. It must also be realised that there are innumerable local climatic variations. Thus the Swiss Valais, and to a lesser extent the Grisons, have some exceptional altitude records for basically lowland plants. Whereas on the southern side of Monte Rosa the lowest summer snow-level is 3200 m., it is 2900 m. in the Bernese Oberland and only 2700 m. in the Dolomites. The Spanish side of the Pyrenees is almost Mediterranean compared with the usually cold French side, and, of course, as one moves southwards down Italy the mountains become steadily warmer and more arid, so that, again, an almost Mediterranean type of flora can be found quite high. Conversely, in Scandinavia alpines grow at much lower levels, and those plants known as arctic-alpines (about 17 per cent of those in the Central Alps) are eventually found at sea-level in Spitzbergen.

Most alpine plants have an extensive vertical range, although this can vary considerably between areas. It can also be extended lower by seeds or fragments of plants being carried down in streams, and it is therefore often rewarding to examine river shingles quite low down in the mountains. Plants, after all, cannot choose where they grow. In Norway, virtually all the high alpines can be found down to sea-level.

In general terms, many new species start around the 1500 m. level which is also the maximum for most deciduous trees, although several sorbuses and willows exceed this. 1500 m. is therefore a very convenient starting-point for a flora of the mountains. The coniferous trees reach a maximum of about 2600 m., and above that smaller shrubs exceed the minimum summer snow-line, reaching to 3350 m.

The herbaceous plants follow a similar pattern. The hay meadows, which are cut two or three times in summer, are found up to around 2000 m., and contain tall herbaceous plants. Among the woods many other tall plants flourish, but outside and above them the stature of plants diminishes rapidly with altitude.

Grassland is found up to nearly 3000 m., and is used for summer pasturing;

above this level plants have to live exclusively among stones, in debris, screes, moraines and on rocks. Such conditions usually provide good drainage, often surprisingly high nutrition and a water supply which is often plentiful as the snow above melts, although arid conditions may occur in later summer. Variations in the soil and water conditions naturally have a marked effect on the species found.

In Norway, the only Scandinavian country with high mountains, the maximum altitudes of the different kinds of plant—trees, shrubs and herbaceous—are compressed within 1000 m., and certain shrubs exceed most herbaceous plants as the highest-reaching alpines.

It is always helpful to ascertain upon which geological formation one is botanising. Limestone is, in general, far more rich in species than acid rocks such as granite, sandstone, gneiss, schist, etc., although the latter have many specialised species. In many cases there are paired species, similar equivalents, one of which is lime-loving and one lime-hating.

Plants above the tree-line, living in debris or on rocks, tend to become far smaller and more compact than their lower-altitude relations, and the typical form of high alpines is a rosette, a low mat or a tight hummock; high-altitude shrubs are all creeping plants. In this way the plants make the most of what heat is available and are better able to withstand the great temperature changes between day and night, and the exposure to wind, brilliant sun and high ultra-violet radiation. Their compactness reduces loss of water by transpiration and is usually combined with an insulating layer of hairs or with waxy or leathery coatings to the leaves; in some cases succulence reduces the leaf area in relation to water-holding volume; the breathing pores become reduced in number and may be specially protected, as in the incurving foliage of many grasses.

In general terms there is no doubt that situation has a marked effect on plant habit, specimens from more congenial situations often having much looser habit. This must be remembered when trying to identify plants.

The stringencies of the habitat result in most alpines having far-reaching, often very strong roots; in this way both adequate moisture and security are provided in, say, an ever-moving scree, or a rocky ridge exposed to strong wind. Rock-dwelling plants often grow in the smallest crevices with very fine roots exploring unsuspected fissures and moisture reserves within; some even grow happily in overhung cliffs. It is also noticeable that if not struggling with the apparent inclemency of a tiny rock crevice, many alpines grow in fierce competition with each other, notably in turf.

High-altitude plants must be capable of flowering and seeding in a very short time. Perhaps the most amazing record is a Norwegian observation of *Ranunculus nivalis*, which flowered five days after snow melted from the plant, and was in ripe seed seventeen days later! Some seasons are so uncongenial that little seed is set, and this is why there are so few high altitude annuals or biennials, which might be eradicated after a bad summer. Even above 1500 m., only some 4–5 per cent of the plants are annuals. Many alpine plants have other means of increase than seed, notably the power of making roots from creeping stems, of producing runners above or below ground, or of making bulbils or viviparous offsets.

The climatic extremes on mountains must be emphasised: thus a typical summer sun temperature at soil level at 3000 m. can be 60°C., whereas in the shade it will be only 6°C.; both will often descend to below freezing in snow-storms and at night. A sea-level comparison in Scotland gives temperatures of 38° and 33°C. respectively. Sunny localities in the high Alps have four snow-free months, shady localities only two; in Norway the highest alpines may only have four weeks.

As H. S. Thompson once wrote, the climatic conditions of the high mountains are more or less unique, and plants which grow in the upper parts of the altitude range are highly specialised evolutionary adaptations, in the same way as cacti are highly adapted to the conditions of a desert, which are not dissimilar in effect. The capacity of alpines to push up through snow and ice is amazing; they must also be capable of spending much of the year beneath a deep heavy blanket of snow.

The number of different species to be found, not surprisingly, decreases with altitude. In Switzerland, for example, there are roughly 120 species which exceed 3000 m.; about a dozen attain 3500 m., and only six exceed 3900 m.

Over the range from 1500 m. to 4000 m., then, will be found a remarkable gamut of plant life, demonstrating very clearly the adaptability of these organisms to less and less congenial conditions. But they are not mere scientific demonstrations: most of them are beautiful by any standards, and they often possess as well the fascination of the miniature. Remembering also the wild and spectacular places where these plants grow, their study combines many kinds of pleasure. The desire to know what things are called is very strong, and I hope that this book will help many who walk and climb in the mountains of Europe to put names to the plants they find.

Conservation. If this book provides a stimulus to seek beautiful and especially rare alpine plants I hope its users will never be tempted to dig them up. The undoubted pleasure from a collected plant established in one's garden must be totally outweighed by the ever-increasing need to leave nature alone, especially in the face of tourist developments. Every plant taken from the wild reduces the chances of that species surviving, and most alpines can be bought from nurseries. In any case many alpine plants are legally protected in several European countries.

Abbreviations

C	Central	mm.	millimetre (0·04 inch)
cm.	centimetre (0·394 inch)	N	Northern
E	Eastern	S	Southern
fl., fls.	flower, flowers	sp.	species
lf., lvs.	leaf, leaves	ssp.	subspecies
m.	metre (3·281 feet)	var.	variety
		W	Western

Notes on Descriptions in Text

After each botanical description the sign ⚘ indicates physical habitats, followed by the typical altitude range, the geographical range, incidence in Britain where applicable, and finally the months when the plant is normally in flower (e.g. June–July).

An * after a plant description indicates a recommended change of name, which is listed in the Appendix.

The bold figures in or after the text description refer to the number of the plant in the plates, where the numbers run consecutively. Numbers from 1 to 884 are on the colour plates, 885 to 1175 on the black-and-white plates, and 1176 to 1251 of figures in the text, which usually adjoin the reference.

Metric Conversions

The metric system has been used to specify both plant dimensions and altitudes, as is rapidly becoming standard practice in scientific literature. Conversions into the inch-foot scale are given below.

Centimetres/Inches

cm.	in.	cm.	in.	cm.	in.
10	3·9	50	19·7	80	31·5
20	7·9	60	23·6	90	35·4
30	11·8	70	27·6	100	39·4
40	15·8				

Metres/Feet

m.	ft.
4500	14764
4000	13123
3500	11483
3000	9842
2500	8202
2000	6562
1500	4921
1000	3281

Feet/Metres

ft.	m.	ft.	m.
15000	5472	8000	2438
14000	4267	7000	2134
13000	3962	6000	1829
12000	3658	5000	1524
11000	3353	4000	1219
10000	3048	3000	914
9000	2743		

INCHES

| | 1 | | 2 | | 3 | | 4 |

CENTIMETRES

| 1 | 2 | 3 | 4 | 5 | 6 | 7 | 8 | 9 | 10 |

MILLIMETRES

ILLUSTRATED PLANTS

1. *Lilium bulbiferum ssp. croceum,* ORANGE LILY; 1a, *ssp. bulbiferum* showing bulbils. -
2. *L. pomponium,* RED LILY. - 3. *L. martagon,* MARTAGON LILY. - 4. *L. pyrenaicum,*
YELLOW TURKSCAP LILY. - 5. *L. carniolicum.*   (x$\frac{1}{2}$)

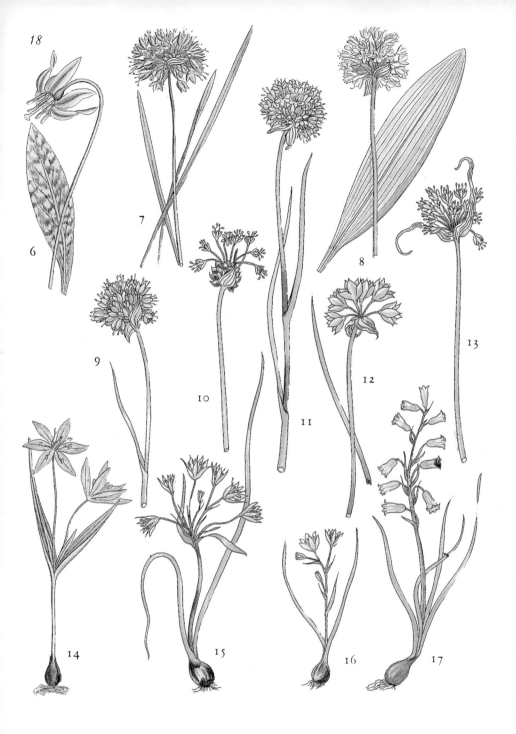

6. *Erythronium dens-canis,* DOGSTOOTH VIOLET. - 7. *Allium montanum,* MOUNTAIN ONION. - 8. *A. victorialis,* ALPINE LEEK. - 9. *A. schoenoprasum,* CHIVES. - 10. *A. vineale,* CROW GARLIC. - 11. *A. sphaerocephalon,* ROUNDHEADED LEEK. - 12. *A. narcissiflorum.* - 13. *A. flavum,* YELLOW ONION. - 14. *Gagea fistulosa.* - 15. *G. villosa.* - 16. *G. soleirolii.* - 17. *Hyacinthus amethystinus,* PYRENEAN HYACINTH. $(\times \frac{5}{8})$

18. *Fritillaria tubiformis;* 18a, bulb. - 19. *F. pyrenaica,* PYRENEAN SNAKESHEAD. - 20. *F. involucrata.* - 21. *Tulipa australis.* - 22. *Scilla bifolia,* ALPINE SQUILL. - 23. *S. liliohyacinthus,* PYRENEAN SQUILL. - 24. *S. verna,* SPRING SQUILL. - 25. *Aphyllanthes monspeliensis.* $(\times\frac{2}{5})$

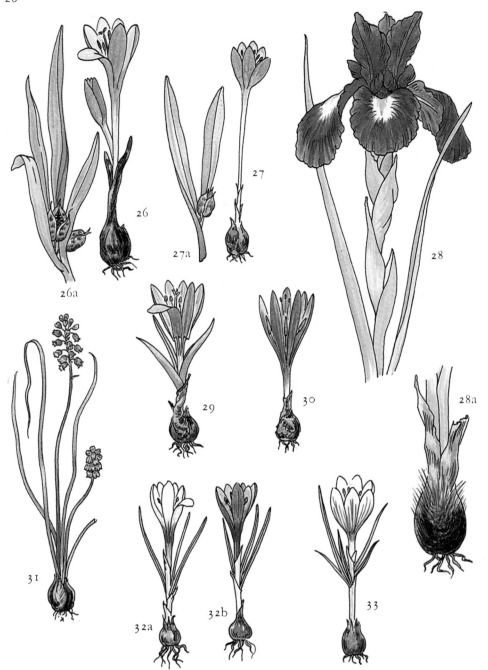

26. *Colchicum autumnale*, AUTUMN CROCUS; 26a, leaves and fruit. 27. *C. alpinum*; 27a, leaves and fruit. - 28. *Iris xiphioides*, ENGLISH IRIS; 28a, bulb. - 29. *Bulbocodium vernum*. - 30. *Merendera pyrenaica*. - 31. *Muscari atlanticum*, GRAPE HYACINTH. - 32. *Crocus purpureus*, PURPLE CROCUS; 32a, b, colour forms. 33. *C. versicolor*. (x⅖)

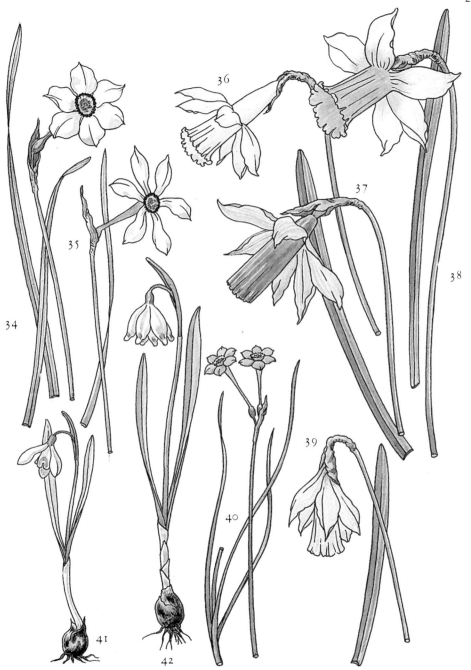

34. *Narcissus poeticus*, PHEASANT-EYE. - 35. *N. p. ssp. radiiflorus.* - 36. *N. pseudo-narcissus ssp. pallidiflorus*, PALE LENT LILY. - 37. *N. p. ssp. abscissus.* - 38. *N.p. ssp. nobilis*, PYRENEAN LENT LILY. - 39. *N.p. ssp. alpestris*, ALPINE LENT LILY. - 40. *N. juncifolius*, RUSH-LEAVED NARCISSUS. - 41. *Galanthus nivalis*, SNOWDROP. - 42. *Leucojum vernum*, SPRING SNOWFLAKE. $(x\frac{5}{8})$

43. *Juncus arcticus*, ARCTIC RUSH. - 44. *J. trifidus*, THREE-LEAVED RUSH. - 45. *J. jacquinii*. - 46. *Luzula nivea*, SNOWY WOODRUSH. - 47. *L. alpinopilosa*, BROWNISH WOODRUSH. - 48. *L. lutea*, YELLOW WOODRUSH. - 49. *L. spicata*, SPIKED WOODRUSH.
$(x\frac{1}{2})$

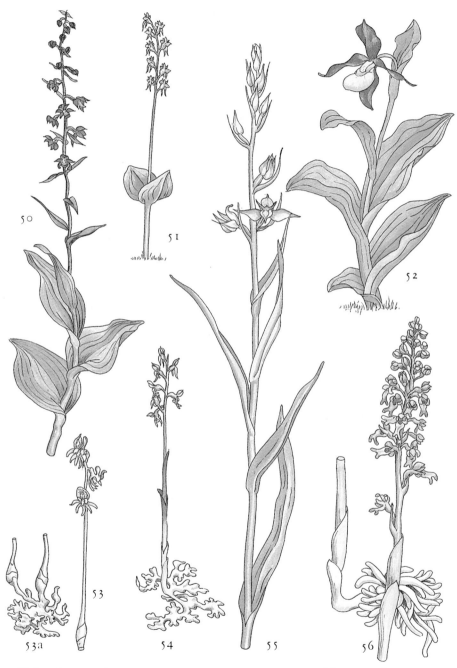

50. *Epipactis atrorubens,* DARK RED HELLEBORINE. - 51. *Listera cordata,* LESSER TWAYBLADE. - 52. *Cypripedium calceolus,* LADY'S SLIPPER ORCHID. - 53. *Epipogium aphyllum,* GHOST ORCHID; 53a, root. - 54. *Corallorhiza trifida,* CORALROOT ORCHID. - 55. *Cephalanthera rubra,* RED HELLEBORINE. - 56. *Neottia nidus-avis,* BIRDSNEST ORCHID. $(x\frac{1}{3})$

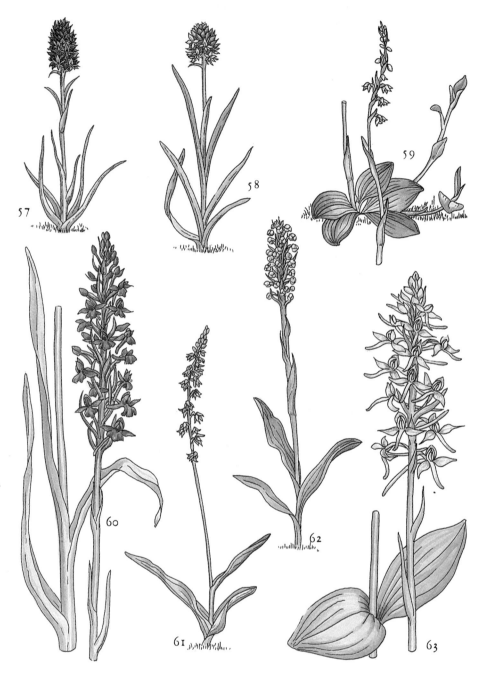

57. *Nigritella nigra,* BLACK VANILLA ORCHID. - 58. *N. rubra,* ROSY VANILLA ORCHID. -
59. *Goodyera repens,* CREEPING LADY'S TRESSES. - 60. *Gymnadenia conopsea,* FRAGRANT
ORCHID. - 61. *Herminium monorchis,* MUSK ORCHID. - 62. *Leucorchis albida.* -
63. *Platanthera bifolia,* LESSER BUTTERFLY ORCHID. $(x\frac{1}{3})$

64. *Ophrys insectifera*, FLY ORCHID. - 65. *Orchis morio*, GREEN-WINGED ORCHID. -
66. *O. mascula*, EARLY PURPLE ORCHID. - 67. *O. ustulata*, BURNT ORCHID. - 68. *O. coriophora*, BUG ORCHID. - 69. *O. spitzelii*. - 70. *O. militaris*, SOLDIER or MILITARY ORCHID. $(x\frac{1}{3})$

26

71. *Traunsteinera globosa*, ROUND-HEADED ORCHID. - 72. *Anacamptis pyramidalis*, PYRAMIDAL ORCHID. - 73. *Dactylorhiza sambucina*, ELDER ORCHID. - 74. *D. incarnata*. 75. *D. majalis*. - 76. *D. maculata*, SPOTTED ORCHID. - 77. *Orchis pallens*, PALE-FLOWERED ORCHID.

$(\times \frac{1}{3})$

78. *Alnus viridis*, GREEN ALDER. - 79. *Betula nana*, DWARF BIRCH. - 80. *Salix hastata*. -
81. *Salix glauca*, BLUISH WILLOW. - 82. *S. pyrenaica*. - 83. *S. myrsinites*. - 84. *S. alpina*. -
85. *S. lanata*, WOOLLY WILLOW. - 86. *S. arbuscula*, BUSHY WILLOW. - 87. *S. caesia*. -
88. *S. herbacea*, LEAST WILLOW. - 89. *S. reticulata*, NETTED WILLOW. - 90. *S. polaris*,
POLAR WILLOW. - 91. *S. retusa*. $(\times \frac{5}{8})$

28

92. *Polygonum viviparum.* - 93. *P. bistorta,* BISTORT. - 94. *Epilobium angustifolium,* ROSEBAY WILLOWHERB. - 95. *E. fleischeri,* ALPINE WILLOWHERB. - 96. *Euphorbia cyparissias,* CYPRESS SPURGE. - 97. *E. myrsinites,* BLUE SPURGE. $(\times\frac{5}{8})$

98. *Dianthus barbatus*, SWEET WILLIAM. - 99. *D. neglectus* (=*D. pavonius*). - 100. *D.*
superbus, SUPERB PINK. - 101. *D. monspessulanus ssp. sternbergii*, FRINGED PINK. -
102. *D. gratianopolitanus*, CHEDDAR PINK. - 103. *D. carthusianorum*, CARTHUSIAN
PINK. - 104. *D. seguieri*. - 105. *D. sylvestris*, WOOD PINK. - 106. *D. glacialis*, GLACIER
PINK. - 107. *D. alpinus*, ALPINE PINK. - 108. *D. subacaulis*. $(\times\frac{5}{8})$

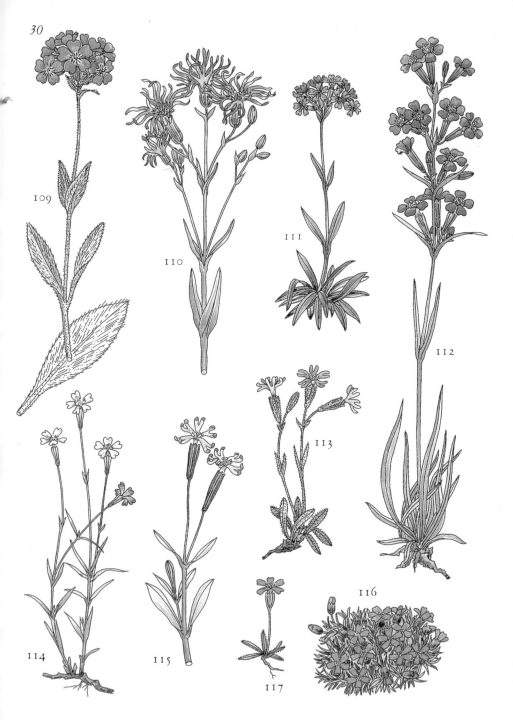

109. *Lychnis flos-jovis.* - 110. *L. flos-cuculi,* RAGGED ROBIN. - 111. *L. alpina,* RED
ALPINE CATCHFLY. - 112. *L. viscaria,* RED GERMAN CATCHFLY. - 113. *Silene borderi.* -
114. *S. saxifraga.* - 115. *S. vallesia.* - 116. *S. acaulis ssp. exscapa,* MOSS CAMPION. -
117. *S.a. ssp. longiscapa,* LONG-STALKED MOSS CAMPION. $(\times\frac{5}{8})$

118. *Gypsophila repens.* - 119. *Silene elisabetha.* - 120. *Saponaria pumilio.* - 121. *S. ocymoides,* ROCK SOAPWORT. - 122. *S. caespitosa,* TUFTED SOAPWORT. - 123. *S. bellidifolia.* - 124. *S. lutea,* YELLOW SOAPWORT. - 125. *Arenaria purpurascens,* PINK SANDWORT.

$$(x\tfrac{5}{8})$$

126. *Adonis pyrenaica*, PYRENEAN PHEASANT-EYE. - 127. *Eranthis hyemalis*, WINTER ACONITE. - 128. *Caltha palustris*, MARSH MARIGOLD, KINGCUP. - 129. *Ranunculus thora*. - 130. *R. brevifolius.**. - 131. *R. hybridus**. - 132. *R. scutatus**. - 133. *R. crenatus*. - 134. *R. bilobus*. - 135. *R.b. ssp. magellensis*, MAJELLA BUTTERCUP. - 136. *R. montanus*, MOUNTAIN BUTTERCUP. - 137. *R. aduncus**. - 138. *R. carinthiacus**. - 139. *R. nivalis*, SNOW BUTTERCUP. - 140. *R. pygmaeus*, PYGMY BUTTERCUP.   *leaf (x½)

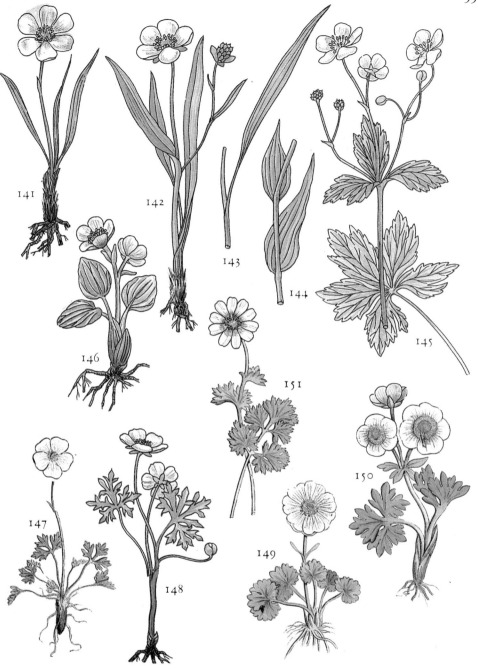

141. *Ranunculus pyrenaeus,* PYRENEAN BUTTERCUP. - 142. *R. p. ssp. plantagineus,*
PLANTAIN-LEAVED BUTTERCUP. - 143. *R. bupleuroides**. - 144. *R. amplexicaulis**. -
145. *R. aconitifolius.* - 146. *R. parnassifolius.* - 147. *R. traunfellneri.* - 148. *R. seguieri.* -
149. *R. alpestris,* ALPINE BUTTERCUP. - 150. *R. glacialis,* GLACIER CROWFOOT. -
151. *Callianthemum coriandrifolium.*   *stem leaves   (x$\frac{5}{8}$)

34

152. *Anemone narcissiflora*, NARCISSUS-FLOWERED ANEMONE. - 153. *Pulsatilla alpina ssp. alpina*, WHITE ALPINE ANEMONE; 153a, fruiting head. - 154. *P. a. ssp. apiifolia*, YELLOW ALPINE ANEMONE. - 155. *P. montana*, MOUNTAIN ANEMONE. - 156. *P. halleri*. - 157. *P. vernalis*, SPRING ANEMONE. - 158. *Anemone baldensis*, MONTE BALDO ANEMONE. 159. *A. trifolia*, THREE-LEAVED ANEMONE. - 160. *Hepatica trifolia*.

$(\times \frac{5}{8})$

161. *Trollius europaeus*, GLOBE FLOWER. - 162. *Helleborus viridis*, GREEN HELLEBORE. - 163. *H. niger*, CHRISTMAS ROSE. - 164. *Aquilegia atrata*, DARK COLUMBINE. - 165. *A. bertolonii*. - 166. *A. alpina*, ALPINE COLUMBINE. - 167. *A. pyrenaica*, PYRENEAN COLUMBINE. - 168. *A. einseleana*. $(x\frac{1}{2})$

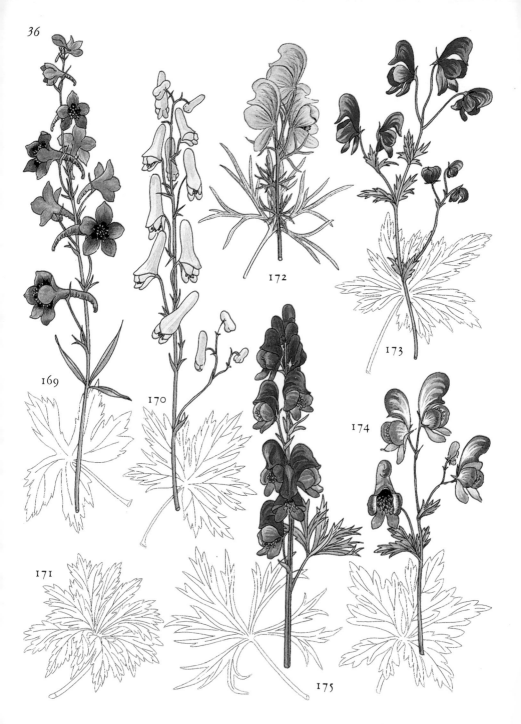

169. *Delphinium elatum*, ALPINE LARKSPUR. - 170. *Aconitum vulparia*, WOLFSBANE. - 171. *A. lamarckii* (leaf). - 172. *A. anthora*, YELLOW MONKSHOOD. - 173. *A. panicula-tum*, BRANCHED MONKSHOOD. - 174. *A. variegatum*, VARIEGATED MONKSHOOD. - 175. *A. napellus*, COMMON MONKSHOOD. $(\times \frac{5}{8})$

176. *Paeonia officinalis*, PEONY; 176a, fruit. - 177. *Isopyrum thalictroides.* - 178. *Clematis alpina*, ALPINE CLEMATIS. - 179. *Thalictrum aquilegifolium*, GREAT MEADOW RUE; 179a, b, colour forms. - 180. *T. foetidum*, STINKING MEADOW RUE. - 181. *T. simplex.* - 182. *T. alpinum*, ALPINE MEADOW RUE. - 183. *T. macrocarpum.* $(\times \frac{5}{8})$

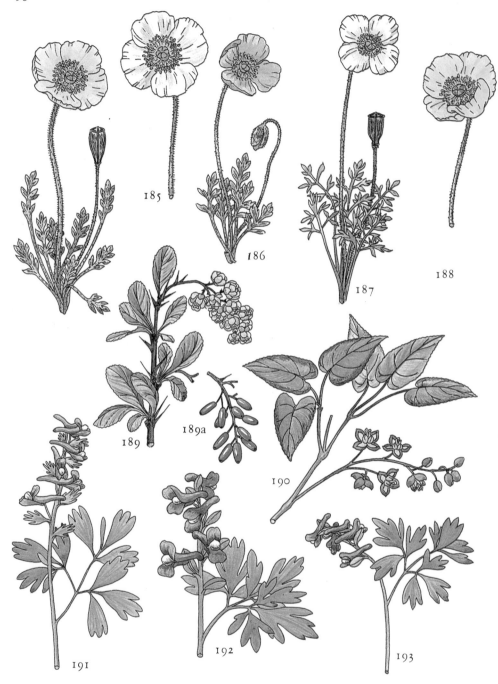

184. *Papaver rhaeticum.* - 185. *P. sendtneri.* - 186. *P. suaveolens.* - 187. *P. burseri.* -
188. *P. kerneri.* (ALPINE POPPIES). - 189. *Berberis vulgaris*, BARBERRY; 189a, fruit. -
190. *Epimedium alpinum*, BARRENWORT. - 191. *Corydalis solida.* - 192. *C. bulbosa.* -
193. *C. intermedia.* (x½)

194. *Dentaria pentaphylla;* 194a, root. - 195. *D. enneaphylla.* - 196. *D. kitaibelii* (leaf). (TOOTHWORTS). - 197. *Alyssoides utriculata.* - 198. *Cardamine pratensis,* CUCKOO FLOWER. $(\times \frac{5}{8})$

40

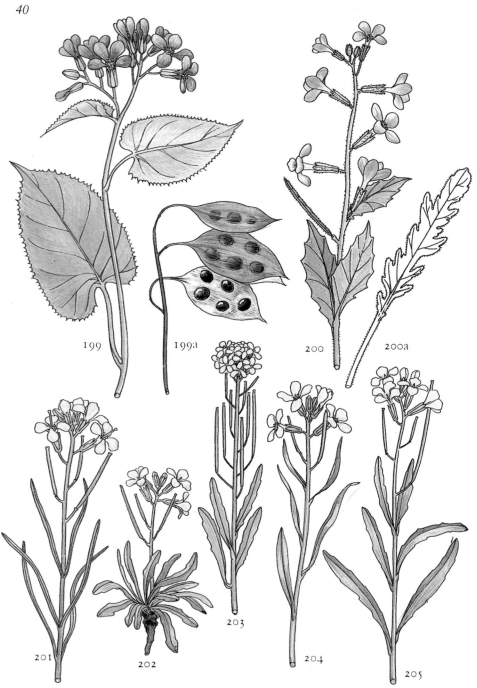

199. *Lunaria rediviva*, MOUNTAIN HONESTY; 199a, fruit. - 200. *Hesperis laciniata;* 200a, basal leaf. - 201. *Erysimum sylvestre.* - 202. *E. pumilum*, DWARF TREACLE-MUSTARD. - 203. *E. hieraciifolium.* - 204. *E. helveticum*, SWISS TREACLE-MUSTARD. - 205. *E. decumbens.* (x$\frac{1}{2}$)

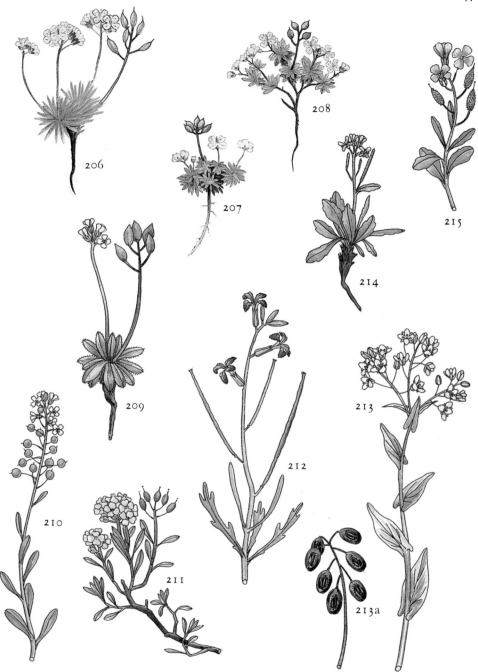

206. *Draba aizoides*, YELLOW WHITLOW-GRASS. - 207. *D. hoppeana.* - 208. *D. sauteri.* -
209. *D. alpina*, ALPINE WHITLOW-GRASS. - 210. *Alyssum montanum.* - 211. *A. wulfenianum.* - 212. *Matthiola fruticulosa*, SAD STOCK. - 213. *Isatis tinctoria*, WOAD; 213a, fruit.
214. *Arabis caerulea*, BLUISH ROCK-CRESS. - 215. *Aubrieta columnae.* $(x\frac{5}{8})$

216. *Iberis aurosica.* - 217. *I. spathulata.* - 218. *I. sempervirens,* EVERGREEN CANDYTUFT.
219. *Aethionema saxatile.* - 220. *Biscutella laevigata,* BUCKLER MUSTARD. -
221. *Thlaspi rotundifolium ssp. rotundifolium,* ROUND-LEAVED PENNYCRESS. -
222. *T.r. ssp. cepifolium.* - 223. *T. stylosum.* - 224. *Petrocallis pyrenaica.* $(\times \frac{5}{8})$

43

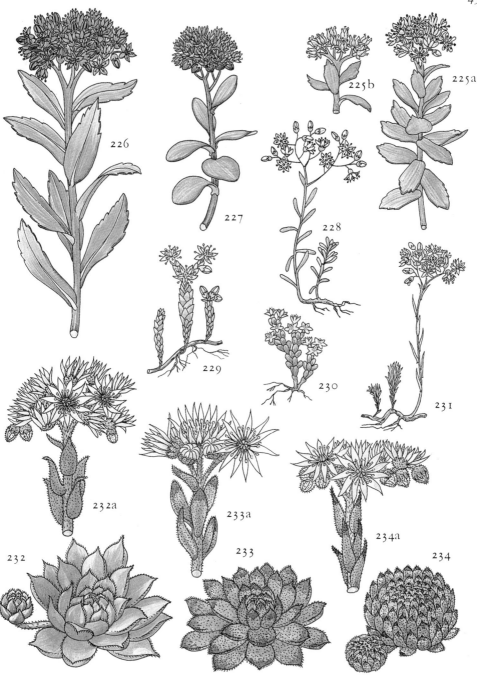

225. *Rhodiola rosea*, ROSEROOT, MIDSUMMER MEN; 225a, male; 225b, female. - 226. *Sedum telephium*, ORPINE. - 227. *S. anacampseros*. - 228. *S. album*, WHITE STONECROP. - 229. *S. acre*, WALL-PEPPER. - 230. *S. atratum*, DARK STONECROP. - 231. *S. reflexum*, ROCK STONECROP. - 232. *Sempervivum wulfenii;* 232a, flower-head. - 233. *S. grandiflorum;* 233a, flower-head. - 234. *S. pittonii;* 234a, flower-head. (HOUSELEEKS). (x$\frac{5}{8}$)

235. *Sempervivum tectorum*, COMMON HOUSELEEK; 235a, flower-head. - 236. *S. dolomiticum*, DOLOMITES HOUSELEEK. - 237. *S. funckii;* 237a, flower-head. - 238. *S. montanum ssp. montanum*, MOUNTAIN HOUSELEEK. - 239. *S.m. ssp. stiriacum*, STYRIAN HOUSE-LEEK*. - 240. *S. arachnoideum* COBWEB HOUSELEEK. - 241. *Jovibarba hirta;* 241a, flower-head. - 242. *J. sobolifera*, HEN-AND-CHICKENS HOUSELEEK*. - 243. *J. allionii;* 243a, flower-head*. - 244. *J. arenaria**.   *rosette only (x$\frac{5}{8}$)

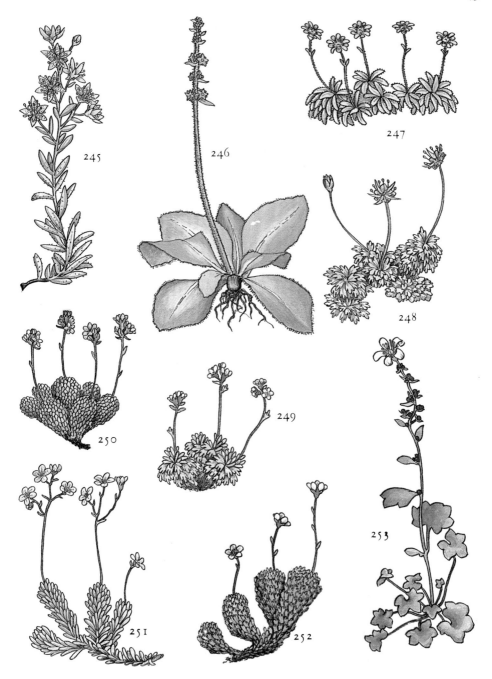

245. *Saxifraga aizoides,* YELLOW MOUNTAIN SAXIFRAGE. - 246. *S. hieracifolia,* HAWK-
WEED-LEAVED SAXIFRAGE. - 247. *S. seguieri.* - 248. *S. aphylla.* - 249. *S. moschata,*
MUSKY SAXIFRAGE: *ssp. eumoschata forma compacta.* - 250. *S.m.e. forma pygmaea.* -
251. *S.m.e. forma lineata.* - 252. *S.m. ssp. ampullacea.* 253. *S. cernua,* DROOPING
SAXIFRAGE. $(\times \frac{5}{8})$

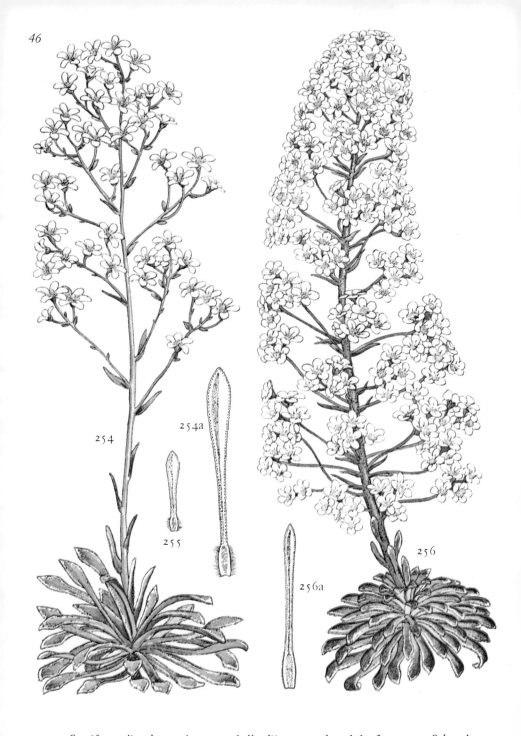

46

254. *Saxifraga lingulata sub-var. eu-bellardii;* 254a, basal leaf. - 255. *S.l. sub-var. lantoscana* (basal leaf only). (254, 255 = *S. callosa.*) - 256. *S. longifolia,* PYRENEAN SAXIFRAGE; 256a, basal leaf. $(\times \frac{5}{8})$

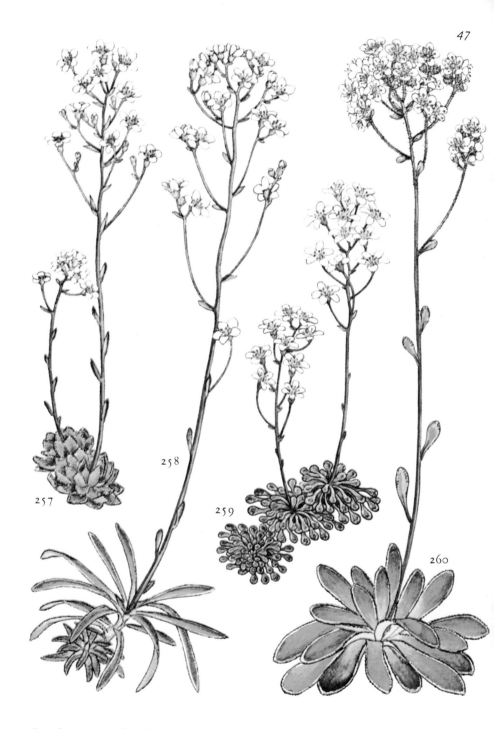

257. *Saxifraga aizoon* (= *S. paniculata*), LIVELONG SAXIFRAGE. - 258. *S. crustata*. -
259. *S. cochlearis*. - 260. *S. hostii*. $(x\frac{5}{8})$

261   262

261. *Saxifraga florulenta.* - 262. *S. cotyledon*, PYRAMIDAL SAXIFRAGE. $(\times \frac{5}{8})$

263 264 265

263. *Saxifraga mutata.* - 264. *S. porophylla normalis.* - 265. *S. media.* $(x\frac{5}{8})$

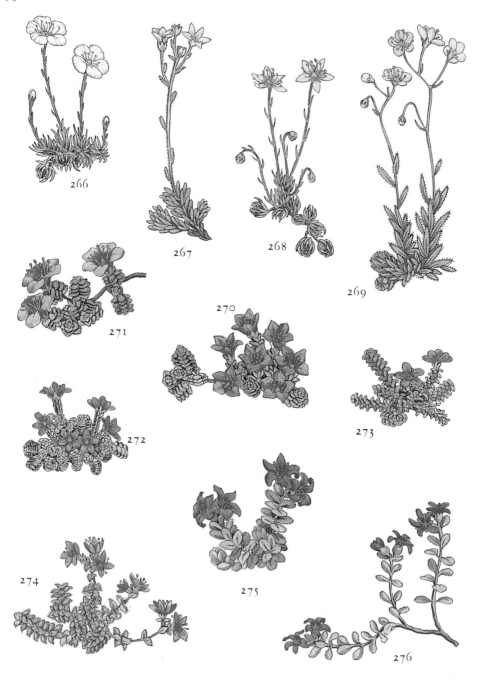

266. *Saxifraga burserana.* - 267. *S. aretioides.* - 268. *S. bryoides*, MOSS SAXIFRAGE. - 269. *S. aspera*, ROUGH SAXIFRAGE. - 270. *S. oppositifolia ssp. euoppositifolia*, PURPLE SAXIFRAGE. - 271. *S.o.e. sub-var. grandiflora.* - 272. *S.o. ssp. rudolphiana.* - 273. *S.o. ssp. speciosa.* - 274. *S. retusa.* - 275. *S. biflora.* - 276. *S. b. var. kochii.* $(x\frac{5}{8})$

277. *Rosa cinnamomea,* CINNAMON or MAY ROSE; 277a, hep. - 278. *R. pimpinellifolia,*
BURNET ROSE; 278a, hep. - 279. *R. elliptica;* 279a, hep. - 280. *R. dumalis;* 280a, hep. -
281. *R. pendulina,* ALPINE ROSE; 281a, hep. - 282. *R. abietina;* 282a, hep. $(x\frac{5}{8})$

283. *Rosa glauca*, BLUE-LEAVED ROSE; 283a, hep. - 284. *R. montana*, MOUNTAIN ROSE; 284a, hep. - 285. *R. villosa*, APPLE ROSE; 285a, hep. - 286. *R. rubiginosa*, SWEET BRIAR; 286a, hep. - 287. *R. sicula;* 287a, hep. - 288. *R. micrantha*, SMALL-FLOWERED ROSE; 288a, hep. - 289. *R. seraphinii* (hep).

$(\times \frac{5}{8})$

290. *Cotoneaster nebrodensis.* - 291. *C. integerrimus.* - 292. *Fragaria viridis.* - 293. *F. vesca,* WILD STRAWBERRY. - 294. *Geum reptans,* CREEPING AVENS. - 295. *G. montanum,* ALPINE AVENS. - 296. *G. pyrenaicum,* PYRENEAN AVENS(leaf). $(x\frac{5}{8})$

297. *Potentilla fruticosa*, SHRUBBY CINQUEFOIL. - 298. *P. multifida*. - 299. *P. argentea*, HOARY CINQUEFOIL. - 300. *P. palustris*, MARSH CINQUEFOIL. - 301. *Sanguisorba officinalis*, GREAT BURNET. - 302. *Geum rivale*, WATER AVENS. - 303. *Dryas octopetala*, MOUNTAIN AVENS.

$(\times\frac{5}{8})$

304. *Potentilla delphinensis*, DAUPHINE CINQUEFOIL. - 305. *P. crantzii*, ALPINE
CINQUEFOIL. - 306. *P. grandiflora*, LARGE-FLOWERED CINQUEFOIL. - 307. *P. nivea*,
SNOWY CINQUEFOIL. - 308. *P. frigida*. - 309. *P. aurea*, GOLDEN CINQUEFOIL. -
310. *P. tabernaemontani*, SPRING CINQUEFOIL. - 311. *P. nitida*, PINK CINQUEFOIL. -
312. *P. cinerea*. $(\times\frac{5}{8})$

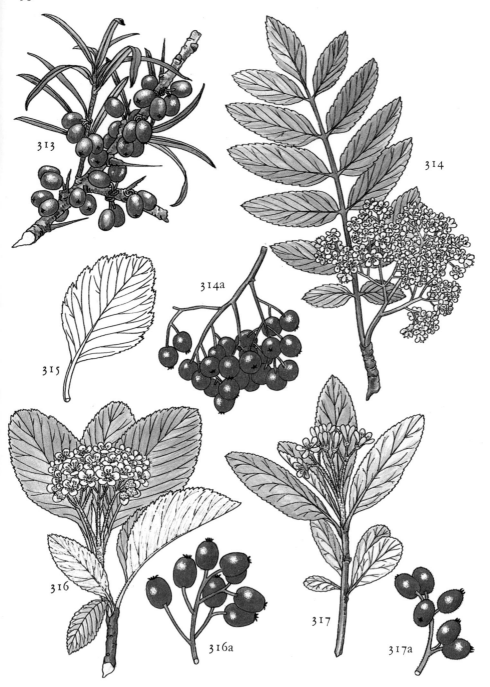

313. *Hippophaë rhamnoides*, SEA BUCKTHORN. - 314. *Sorbus aucuparia*, MOUNTAIN ASH; 314a, fruit. - 315. *S. austriaca* (leaf). - 316. *S. aria*, WHITEBEAM; 316a, fruit. - 317. *S. chamaemespilus*, FALSE MEDLAR; 317a, fruit.

$(x\frac{5}{8})$

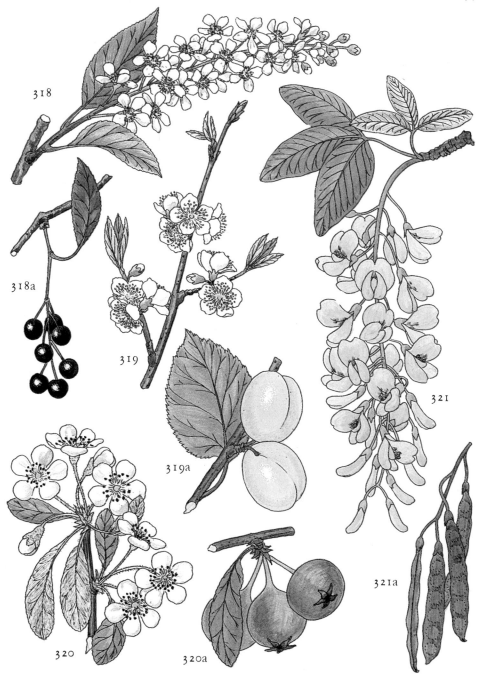

318. *Prunus padus,* BIRD CHERRY; 318a, fruit. - 319. *P. brigantina,* MARMOT PLUM; 319a, fruit. - 320. *Pyrus amygdaliformis;* 320a, fruit. - 321. *Laburnum anagyroides,* GOLDEN RAIN; 321a, fruit. $(x\frac{9}{10})$

58

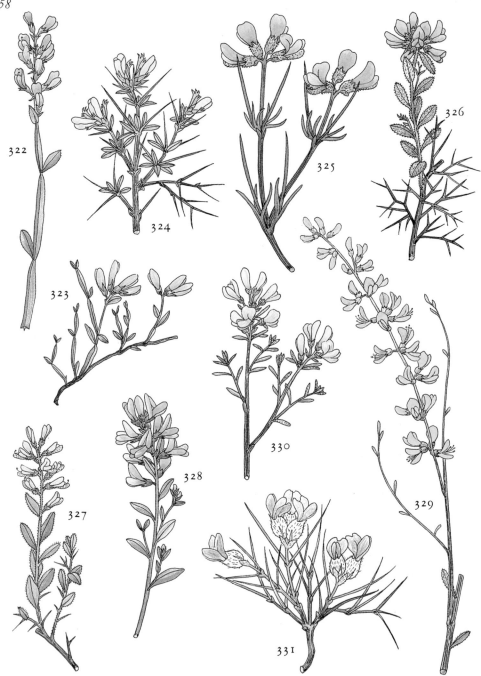

322. *Genistella sagittalis.* - 323. *G.s.ssp. delphinensis.* - 324. *Cytisanthus horridus.* - 325. *Genista radiata.* - 326. *G. hispanica*, SPANISH GORSE. - 327. *G. germanica.* - 328. *G. tinctoria*, DYER'S GREENWEED. - 329. *G. cinerea.* - 330. *Sarothamnus purgans*, PYRENEAN BROOM. - 331. *Erinacea anthyllis*, HEDGEHOG BROOM. $(x\frac{5}{8})$

332. *Ononis rotundifolia*, ROUND-LEAVED RESTHARROW. - 333. *O. cenisia*, MT. CENIS
RESTHARROW. - 334. *Trifolium rubens*, RED TREFOIL. - 335. *T. medium*, MEADOW or
ZIGZAG CLOVER. - 336. *T. badium*, BROWN CLOVER. - 337. *T. spadiceum*. - 338. *T.
incarnatum*, CRIMSON CLOVER. - 339. *T. alpinum*, ALPINE CLOVER. - 340. *Lotus alpinus*,
ALPINE BIRDSFOOT TREFOIL.

(x$\frac{5}{8}$)

60

341. *Anthyllis montana*, MOUNTAIN KIDNEY-VETCH. - 342. *A. vulneraria ssp. vulneraria*, COMMON KIDNEY-VETCH. - 343. *A.v. ssp. vulnerarioides* (leaf). - 344. *A.v. ssp. alpestris*, ALPINE KIDNEY-VETCH. - 345. *A.v. ssp. coccinea*, RED KIDNEY-VETCH. - 346. *Tetragonolobus maritimus*, WINGED PEA. - 347. *Oxytropis sericea*. - 348. *O. triflora*. - 349. *O. lapponica*. $(x\frac{5}{8})$

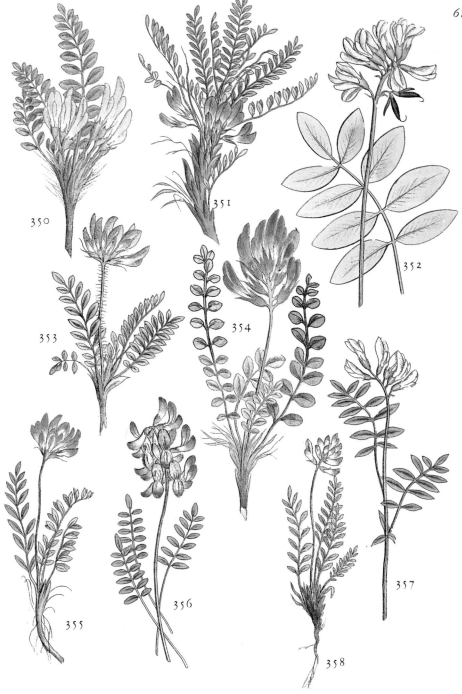

350. *Astragalus exscapus.* - 351. *A. sempervirens,* MOUNTAIN TRAGACANTH. -
352. *A. frigidus.* - 353. *A. danicus,* PURPLE MILKVETCH. - 354. *A. monspessulanus.* -
355. *A. leontinus,* TYROLEAN MILKVETCH. - 356. *A. alpinus,* ALPINE MILKVETCH. -
357. *A. australis.* - 358. *Oxytropis jacquinii,* MOUNTAIN MILKVETCH. $(\times\frac{5}{8})$

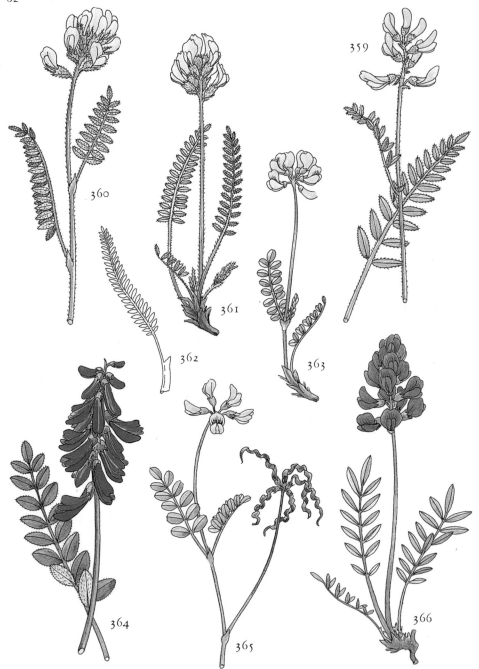

359. *Astragalus penduliflorus*, MOUNTAIN LENTIL. - 360. *Oxytropis pilosa*, WOOLLY MILKVETCH. - 361. *O. campestris*, MEADOW MILKVETCH. - 362. *O. foetida*, STINKING MILKVETCH (leaf). - 363. *Coronilla vaginalis*. - 364. *Hedysarum hedysaroides*, ALPINE SAINFOIN. - 365. *Hippocrepis comosa*, HORSESHOE VETCH. - 366. *Onobrychis montana*, MOUNTAIN SAINFOIN.   ($\times \frac{5}{8}$)

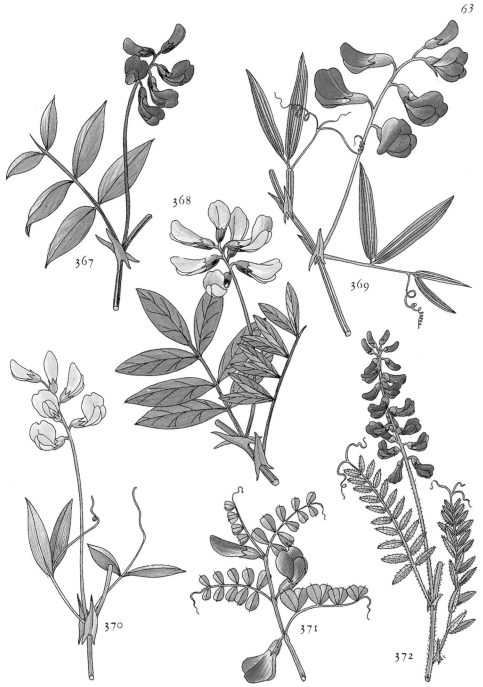

367. *Lathyrus vernus*, SPRING VETCHLING. - 368. *L. luteus*, YELLOW PEA. - 369. *L. heterophyllus*, WOOD PEA. - 370. *L. pratensis*, MEADOW VETCHLING. - 371. *Vicia pyrenaica*, PYRENEAN VETCH. - 372. *V. cracca*, TUFTED VETCH.

$(\times\frac{5}{8})$

373. *Geranium sylvaticum*, CROW FLOWER. - 374. *G. macrorrhizum*, ROCK CRANESBILL. -
375. *G. pratense*, MEADOW CRANESBILL. - 376. *G. cinereum*, ASHY CRANESBILL. -
377. *G. argenteum*, SILVERY CRANESBILL. - 378. *G. sanguineum*, BLOODY CRANESBILL.
$(x\frac{5}{8})$

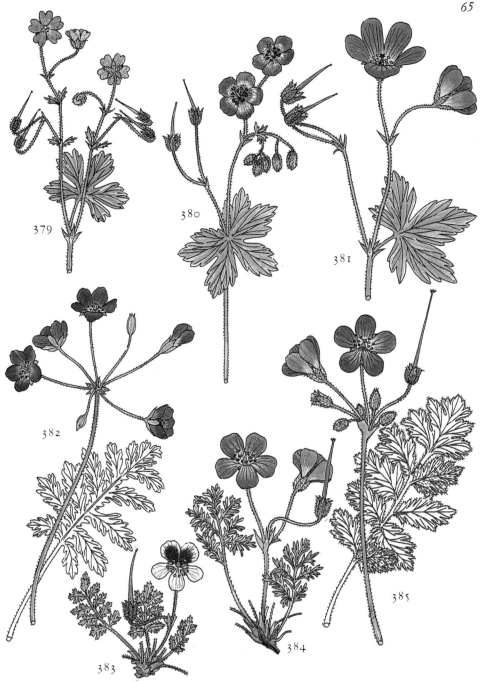

379. *G. pyrenaicum*, PYRENEAN or MOUNTAIN CRANESBILL. - 380. *G. phaeum*, MOURN-
ING WIDOW, DUSKY CRANESBILL. - 381. *G. palustre*, MARSH CRANESBILL. -
382. *Erodium alpinum*, ALPINE STORKSBILL. - 383. *E. macradenum*. - 384. *E.
petraeum*, ROCK STORKSBILL. - 385. *E. manescavi*. $(x\frac{5}{8})$

386. *Linum flavum*, YELLOW FLAX. - 387. *L. viscosum*, STICKY FLAX. - 388. *L. alpinum*, ALPINE FLAX. - 389. *L. usitatissimum*, FLAX. - 390. *Polygala alpestris*, MOUNTAIN MILKWORT. - 391. *P. comosa*, TUFTED MILKWORT. - 392. *P. amara*, BITTER MILKWORT. 393. *P. alpina*, ALPINE MILKWORT. - 394. *P. chamaebuxus*, BOX-LEAVED or SHRUBBY MILKWORT; 394a, typical form; 394b, purple-winged form. $(\times\frac{5}{8})$

395. *Hypericum montanum*, MOUNTAIN ST. JOHN'S WORT. - 396. *H. maculatum*, IMPERFORATE ST. JOHN'S WORT. - 397. *H. coris*, YELLOW CORIS. - 398. *H. richeri*, ALPINE ST. JOHN'S WORT. - 399. *H. nummularium*. - 400. *Malva moschata*, MUSK MALLOW. - 401. *M. neglecta*, DWARF MALLOW. (x$\frac{1}{2}$)

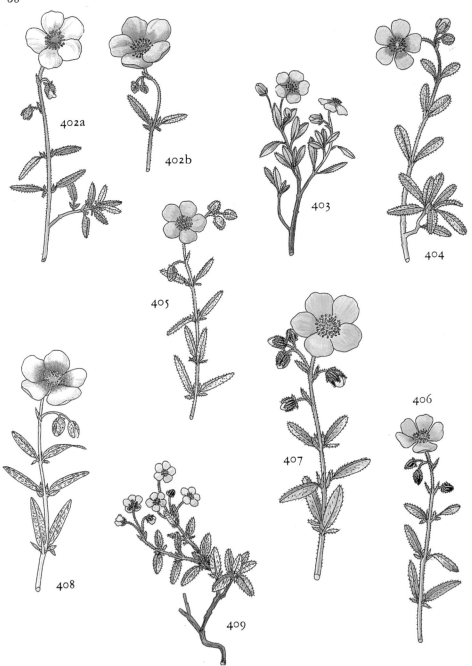

402. *Helianthemum apenninum*, WHITE ROCKROSE; 402a, typical form; 402b. pink form ("*var. roseum*"). 403. *H. lunulatum*. - 404. *H. oelandicum ssp. italicum.* - 405. *H. hirtum.* - 406. *H. nummularium*, COMMON ROCKROSE. - 407. *H.n.ssp. grandiflorum.* - 408. *H.n.ssp. tomentosum.* - 409. *H. canum*, HOARY ROCKROSE. $(x\frac{5}{8})$

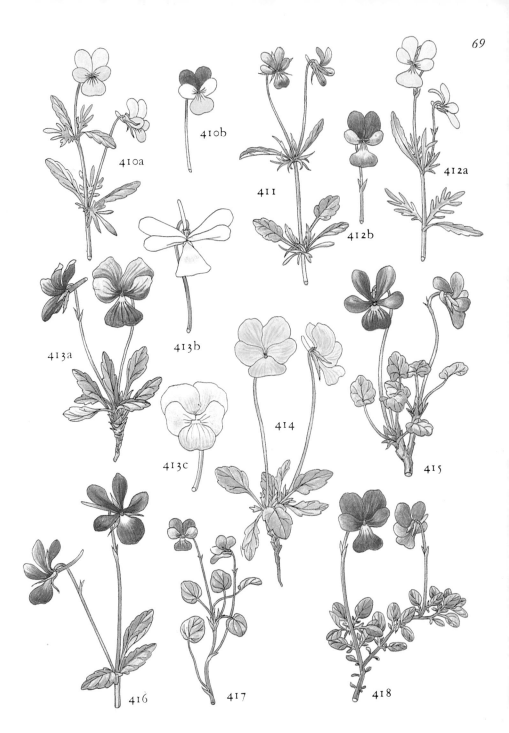

410a, b. *Viola tricolor*, HEARTSEASE (colour forms). - 411. *V. dubyana.* - 412a, b. *V. lutea*, MOUNTAIN PANSY (colour forms). - 413a. *V. calcarata*, LONG-SPURRED PANSY (typical form); b, c, variants. - 414. *V. zoysii*, DINARIC PANSY. - 415. *V. alpina*, ALPINE PANSY. - 416. *V. cornuta*, HORNED PANSY. - 417. *V. nummularifolia.* - 418. *V. cenisia*, MT. CENIS PANSY. $(x\frac{5}{8})$

419. *Viola hirta*, HAIRY VIOLET. - 420. *V. pinnata*, FINGER-LEAVED VIOLET. - 421. *V. palustris*, BOG VIOLET. - 422. *V. biflora*, YELLOW WOOD VIOLET. - 423. *V. thomasiana*. - 424. *V. riviniana*, COMMON VIOLET. - 425. *V. rupestris*, TEESDALE VIOLET. - 426. *V. pyrenaica*, PYRENEAN VIOLET. - 427. *V. collina*, HILL VIOLET. $(\times \frac{5}{8})$

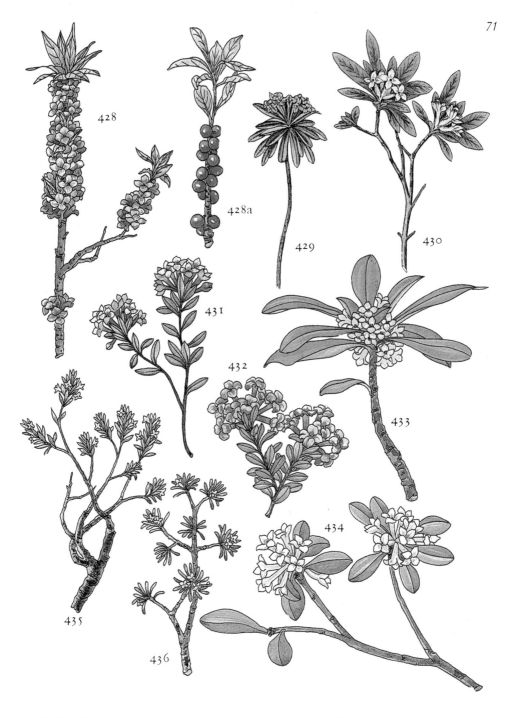

428. *Daphne mezereum*, MEZEREON; 428a, fruit. - 429. *D. striata* - 430. *D. alpina*, ALPINE MEZEREON. - 431. *D. cneorum*, GARLAND FLOWER. - 432. *D. petraea*, ROCK MEZEREON. - 433. *D. laureola*, SPURGE LAUREL. - 434. *D. blagayana*. - 435. *Thymelaea calycina*. - 436. *T. dioica*. $(\times\frac{5}{8})$

437. *Eryngium spinalba*, SILVER ERYNGO. - 438. *E. bourgatii*, PYRENEAN ERYNGO. -
439. *E. alpinum*, ALPINE ERYNGO, QUEEN OF THE ALPS. - 440. *Hacquetia epipactis*.
$(x\frac{5}{8})$

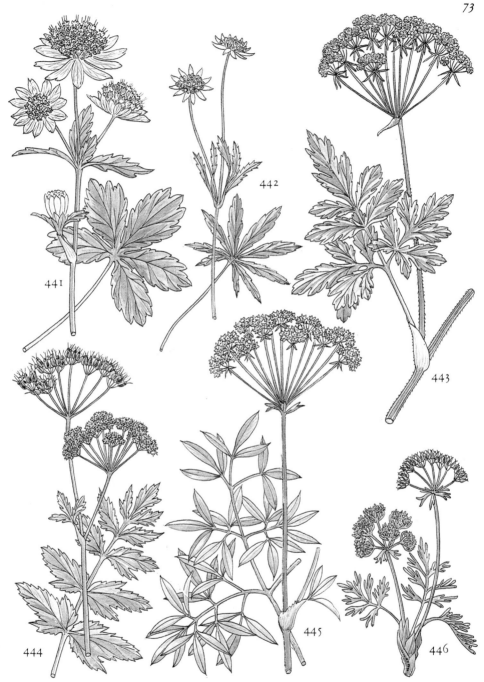

441. *Astrantia major*, GREAT MASTERWORT. - 442. *A. minor*, LESSER MASTERWORT. -
443. *Chaerophyllum hirsutum*, HAIRY CHERVIL. - 444. *Pimpinella major*, GREATER
BURNET SAXIFRAGE. - 445. *Laserpitium siler*, SERMOUNTAIN. - 446. *Ligusticum mutelli-noides*. $(x\frac{1}{2})$

74

447. *Rhododendron ferrugineum*, ALPENROSE. - 448. *R. hirsutum*, HAIRY ALPENROSE. -
449. *R. lapponicum*, LAPLAND RHODODENDRON. - 450. *Rhodothamnus chamaecistus*,
DWARF ALPENROSE. - 451. *Loiseleuria procumbens*, CREEPING AZALEA. - 452. *Erica
carnea*, SPRING HEATH. - 453. *E. tetralix*, CROSS-LEAVED HEATH. - 454. *E. vagans*,
CORNISH HEATH. - 455. *Calluna vulgaris*, LING. $(x\frac{5}{8})$

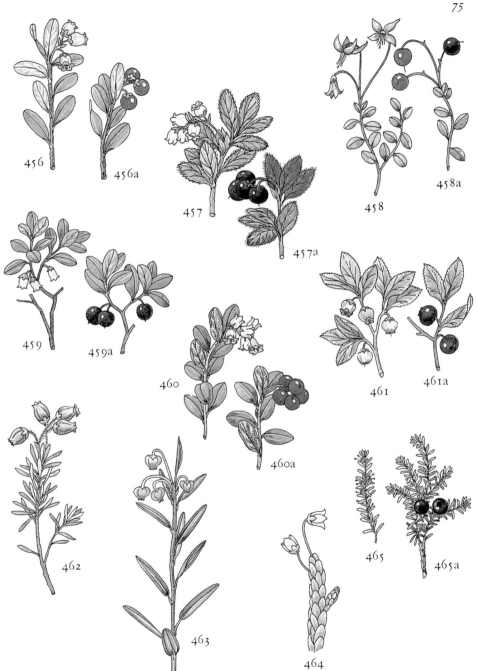

456. *Arctostaphylos uva-ursi,* BEARBERRY; 456a, fruit. - 457. *Arctous alpinus,* BLACK BEARBERRY; 457a, fruit. - 458. *Vaccinium oxycoccus,* CRANBERRY; 458a, fruit. - 459. *V. uliginosum,* BOG WHORTLEBERRY; 459a, fruit. - 460. *V. vitis-idaea,* COWBERRY; 460a, fruit. - 461. *V. myrtillus,* BILBERRY, WHORTLEBERRY; 461a, fruit. - 462. *Phyllodoce caerulea,* BLUE MOUNTAIN HEATH. - 463. *Andromeda polifolia,* MARSH ANDROMEDA. - 464. *Cassiope tetragona.* - 465. *Empetrum nigrum,* CROWBERRY; 465a, fruit. $(x\frac{5}{8})$

466. *Primula wulfeniana.* - 467. *P. viscosa.* - 468. *P. marginata.* - 469. *P. carniolica.* - 470. *P. clusiana.* - 471. *P. minima,* LEAST PRIMROSE. - 472. *P. glaucescens.* - 473. *P. spectabilis.*

$(\times \frac{5}{8})$

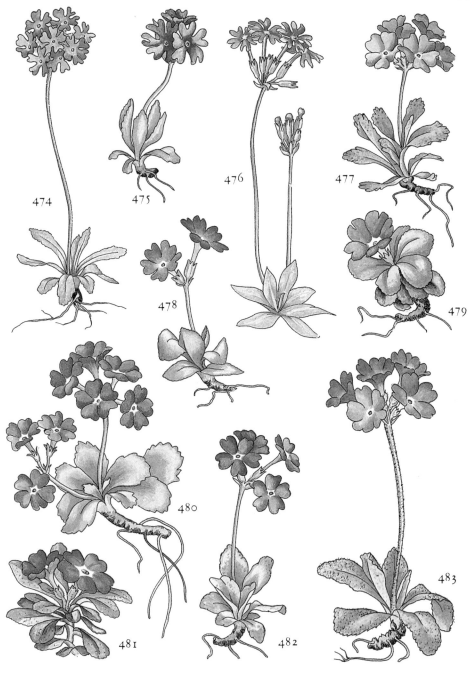

474. *P. farinosa,* BIRDSEYE PRIMROSE. - 475. *P. glutinosa,* STICKY PRIMROSE. - 476. *P. halleri,* LONG-FLOWERED PRIMROSE. - 477. *P. daonensis.* - 478. *P. integrifolia.* - 479. *P. tyrolensis,* DOLOMITES PRIMROSE. - 480. *P. hirsuta,* RED ALPINE PRIMROSE. - 481. *P. allionii.* - 482. *P. pedemontana,* PIEDMONT PRIMROSE. - 483. *P. villosa,* SHAGGY PRIMROSE.

$(\times\frac{5}{8})$

78

484. *Primula elatior*, OXLIP. - 485. *P. veris*, COWSLIP. - 486. *P. auricula*, BEARS-EAR. - 487. *Cortusa matthioli*, ALPINE BELLS. - 488. *Trientalis europaea*, CHICKWEED WINTER-GREEN. - 489. *Cyclamen europaeum* (= *C. purpurascens*), SOWBREAD. - 490. *Lysimachia nemorum*, YELLOW PIMPERNEL.

$(\times\frac{5}{8})$

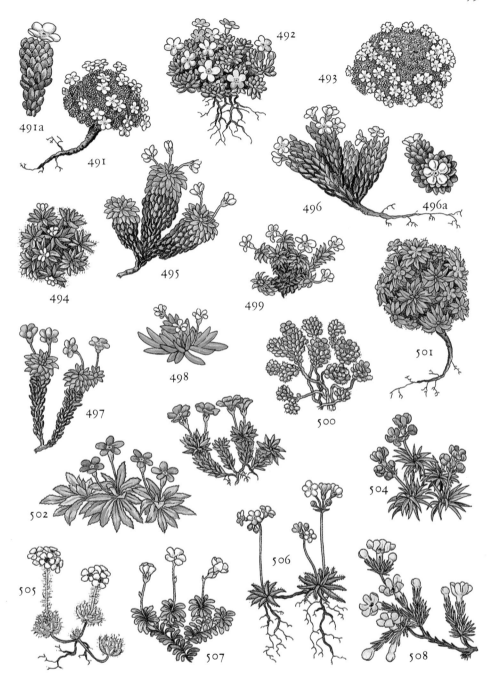

491. *Androsace helvetica;* 491a, single rosette enlarged. 492. *A. alpina.* - 493. *A. hirtella.* - 494. *A. pubescens.* - 495. *A. cylindrica.* - 496. *A. vandellii;* 496a, single rosette enlarged. - 497. *A. brevis.* - 498. *A. mathildae.* - 499. *A. pyrenaica.* - 500. *A. alpina var. tirolensis.* - 501. *A. hausmannii.* - 502. *A. ciliata* (enlarged). - 503. *A. wulfeniana.* - 504. *A. carnea var. laggeri* - 505. *A.c. villosa.* - 506. *A. carnea* (ROCK JASMINES). - 507. *Diapensia lappouica.* - 508. *Vitaliana primuliflora.*

(491a, 496a, 502, x 1; remainder x$\frac{5}{8}$)

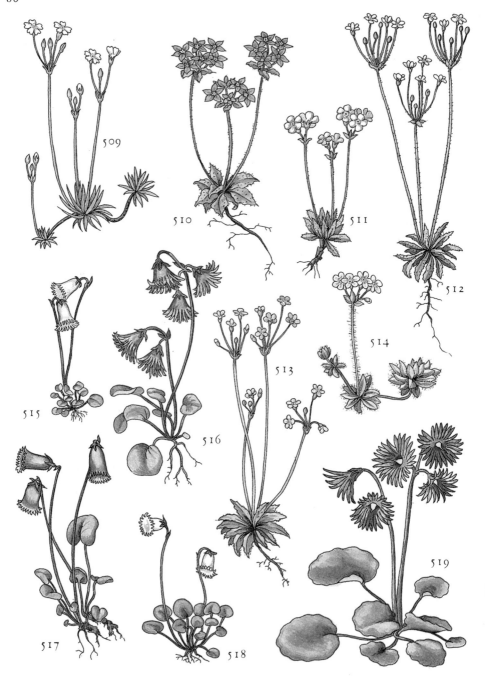

509. *Androsace lactea.* - 510. *A. maxima.* - 511. *A. obtusifolia.* - 512. *A. septentrionalis.*
513. *A. chaixii.* - 514. *A. chamaejasme.* - 515. *Soldanella minima,* LEAST SNOWBELL. -
516. *S. alpina,* ALPINE SNOWBELL. - 517. *S. pusilla,* DWARF SNOWBELL. - 518. *S.
austriaca,* AUSTRIAN SNOWBELL. - 519. *S. montana,* MOUNTAIN TASSEL-FLOWER.   ($\times\frac{5}{8}$)

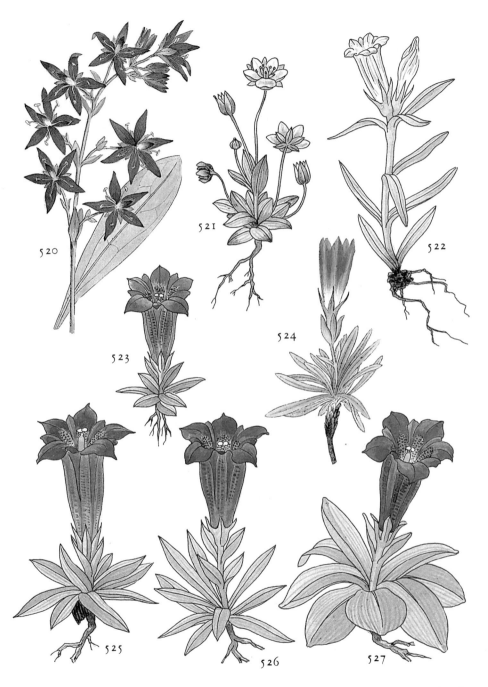

520. *Swertia perennis.* - 521. *Lomatogonium carinthiacum.* - 522. *Gentiana frigida,*
STYRIAN GENTIAN. - 523. *G. alpina,* SOUTHERN GENTIAN. - 524. *G. froelichii,* KARAWAN-
KEN GENTIAN. - 525. *G. clusii,* TRUMPET GENTIAN. - 526. *G. angustifolia,* NARROW-
LEAVED GENTIAN. - 527. *G. kochiana,* TRUMPET GENTIAN. $(\times \frac{5}{8})$

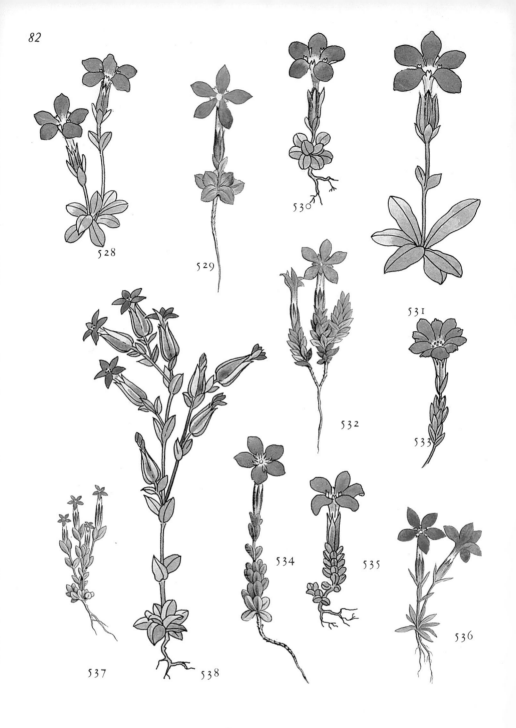

528. *Gentiana verna*, SPRING GENTIAN. - 529. *G. brachyphylla*, SHORT-LEAVED GENTIAN.
530. *G. orbicularis*, ROUND-LEAVED GENTIAN. - 531. *G. tergestina*, KARST GENTIAN. -
532. *G. terglouensis*, TRIGLAV GENTIAN. - 533. *G. pyrenaica*, PYRENEAN GENTIAN. -
534. *G. bavarica*, BAVARIAN GENTIAN. - 535. *G.b. var. subacaulis*, DWARF BAVARIAN
GENTIAN. - 536. *G. pumila*, SMALL GENTIAN. - 537. *G. nivalis*, SNOW GENTIAN. -
538. *G. utriculosa*, BLADDER GENTIAN. $(x\frac{5}{8})$

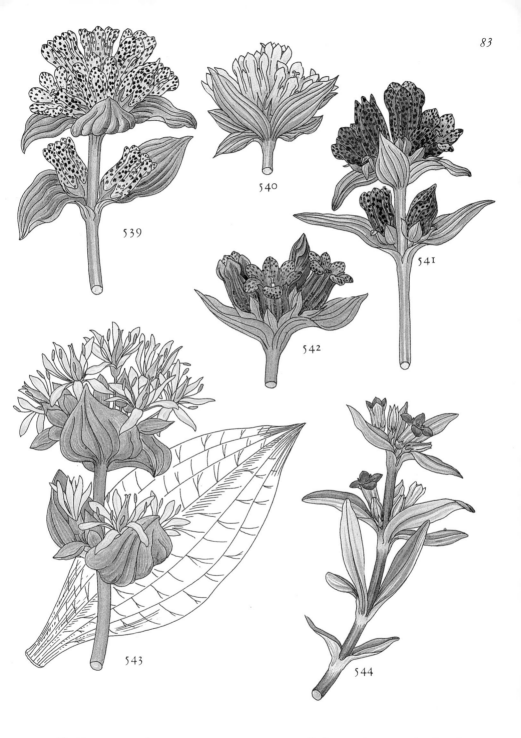

539. *Gentiana punctata*, SPOTTED GENTIAN. - 540. *G. burseri* (upper whorl only). -
541. *G. pannonica*, BROWN or HUNGARIAN GENTIAN. - 542. *G. purpurea*, PURPLE
GENTIAN. - 543. *G. lutea*, GREAT YELLOW GENTIAN. - 544. *G. cruciata*, CROSS GENTIAN.
$(x\frac{5}{8})$

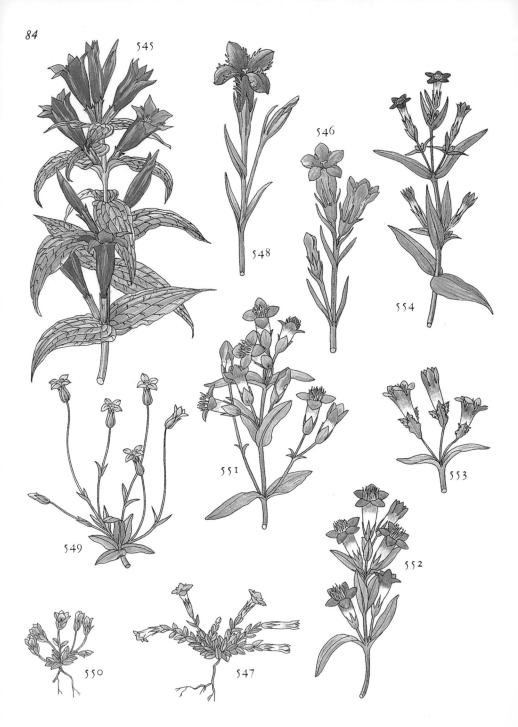

84

545. *Gentiana asclepiadea*, WILLOW GENTIAN. - 546. *G. pneumonanthe*, MARSH
GENTIAN. - 547. *G. prostrata*, CREEPING GENTIAN. - 548. *Gentianella ciliata*, FRINGED
GENTIAN. - 549. *G. tenella*, SLENDER GENTIAN. - 550. *G. nana*, DWARF GENTIAN. -
551. *G. campestris*, FIELD GENTIAN. - 552. *G. germanica*. - 553. *G. crispata*. -
554. *G. amarella*, FELWORT. $(\times \frac{5}{8})$

555. *Polemonium caeruleum*, JACOB'S LADDER. - 556. *Vincetoxicum hirundinaria*, SWALLOW-WORT; 556a, fruits and seeds. - 557. *Armeria arenaria*, PLANTAIN-LEAVED THRIFT. - 558. *A. montana*, MOUNTAIN THRIFT. - 559. *Cuscuta epithymum*, COMMON DODDER (on trefoil). - 560. *C. europaea*, LARGE DODDER. $(\times \frac{5}{8})$

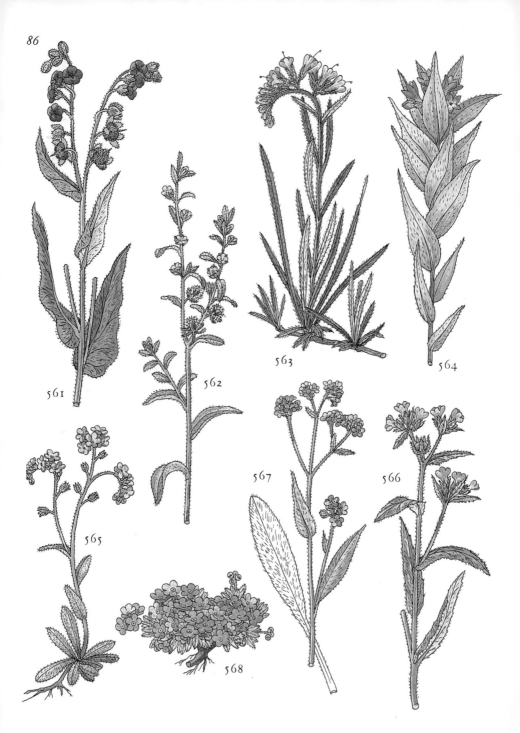

561. *Cynoglossum officinale*, HOUNDS-TONGUE. - 562. *Lappula myosotis*. - 563. *Moltkia suffruticosa*. - 564. *Lithospermum gastonis*. - 565. *Myosotis alpestris*, ALPINE FORGET-ME-NOT. - 566. *Lycopsis arvensis*, SMALL BUGLOSS. - 567. *Anchusa barrelieri*. - 568. *Eritrichium nanum*, KING OF THE ALPS. $(x\frac{1}{2})$

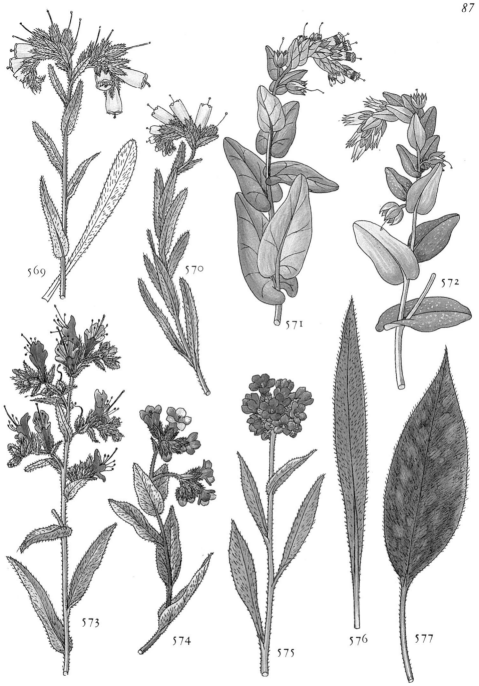

569. *Onosma echioides*, GOLDEN DROP. - 570. *O. helveticum.* - 571. *Cerinthe glabra*, SMOOTH HONEYWORT. - 572. *C. minor*, LESSER HONEYWORT. - 573. *Echium vulgare*, VIPERS BUGLOSS. - 574. *Pulmonaria montana*, MOUNTAIN LUNGWORT. - 575. *P. angustifolia*, AZURE LUNGWORT. - 576. *P. tuberosa* (leaf). - 577. *P. officinalis*, COMMON LUNGWORT (leaf). $(\text{x}\frac{1}{2})$

578. *Ajuga pyramidalis*, PYRAMIDAL BUGLE. - 579. *A. genevensis*, BLUE BUGLE. - 580.
A. reptans, COMMON BUGLE. - 581. *A. chamaepitys*, GROUND-PINE. - 582. *Scutellaria
alpina*, ALPINE SKULLCAP. - 583. *Lavandula angustifolia*, LAVENDER. - 584. *Teucrium
pyrenaicum*, PYRENEAN GERMANDER. - 585. *T. montanum*, ALPINE PENNYROYAL. $(\times\frac{5}{8})$

586. *Galeopsis ladanum.* - 587. *G. tetrahit*, COMMON HEMPNETTLE. - 588. *G. pyrenaica*, PYRENEAN HEMPNETTLE. - 589. *Dracocephalum ruyschiana*, NORTHERN DRAGONHEAD. 590. *D. austriacum*, PONTIC DRAGONHEAD. - 591. *Lamium amplexicaule*, HENBIT DEADNETTLE. - 592. *Prunella grandiflora*, LARGE SELFHEAL. - 593. *P. vulgaris*, COMMON SELFHEAL. $(x\frac{5}{8})$

594. *Stachys germanica*, DOWNY WOUNDWORT. - 595. *S. alpina*, ALPINE WOUNDWORT. - 596. *S. densiflora*, ALPINE BETONY. - 597. *Salvia glutinosa*, STICKY SAGE. - 598. *S. pratensis*, MEADOW CLARY. - 599. *S. verticillata*, WHORLED CLARY (leaf). $(\times\frac{5}{8})$

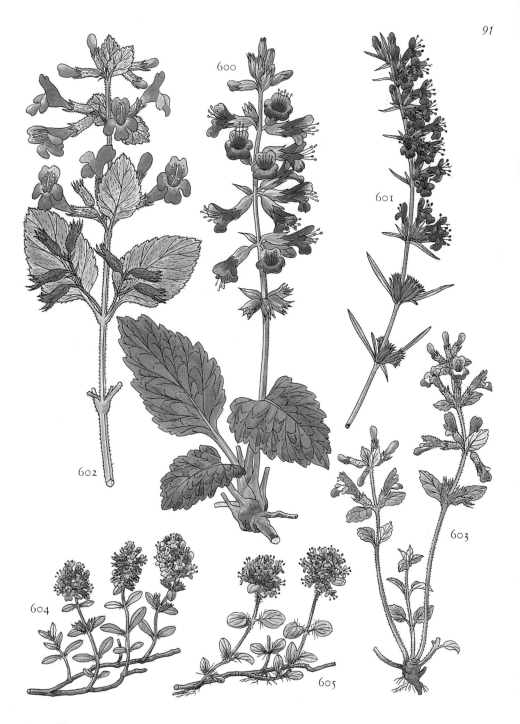

600. *Horminum pyrenaicum*, DRAGONMOUTH. - 601. *Hyssopus officinalis*, HYSSOP. -
602. *Calamintha grandiflora*, LARGE CALAMINT. - 603. *C. alpina*, ALPINE CALAMINT.
604. *Thymus serpyllum*, COMMON THYME. - 605. *T. polytrichus*, HAIRY THYME. $(\times\frac{5}{8})$

606. *Verbascum crassifolium*, MOUNTAIN MULLEIN. - 607. *V. nigrum*, DARK MULLEIN. - 608. *V. pulverulentum*, HOARY MULLEIN.

$(x\frac{1}{3})$

609. *Linaria italica,* ITALIAN TOADFLAX; 609a, floret enlarged. - 610. *L. pyrenaica,*
PYRENEAN TOADFLAX (floret, enlarged). - 611. *L. repens,* STRIPED TOADFLAX. - 612.
L. alpina, ALPINE TOADFLAX; 612a, b, colour forms. - 613. *Antirrhinum sempervirens,*
ROCK SNAPDRAGON. - 614. *A. molle,* SOFT SNAPDRAGON. - 615. *Asarina procumbens,*
CREEPING SNAPDRAGON. - 616. *Chaenorhinum origanifolium.* - 617. *Erinus alpinus.*
(609a, 610, x1; remainder x$\frac{5}{8}$)

618. *Veronica beccabunga*, BROOKLIME. - 619. *V. ponae*. - 620. *V. spicata*, SPIKED SPEEDWELL. - 621. *V. teucrium*, LARGE SPEEDWELL. - 622. *V. serpyllifolia*, THYME-LEAVED SPEEDWELL. - 623. *V. chamaedrys*, GERMANDER SPEEDWELL. - 624. *V. fruticulosa*, SHRUBBY SPEEDWELL. - 625. *V. nummularia*. - 626. *V. allionii*. $(x\frac{5}{8})$

627. *Paederota bonarota.* - 628. *P. lutea.* - 629. *Melampyrum pratense.* COMMON COW-WHEAT. - 630. *Veronica bellidioides* - 631. *V. lilacina* (leaf and floret). - 632. *V. alpina,* ALPINE SPEEDWELL. - 633. *V. fruticans,* ROCK SPEEDWELL. - 634. *V. aphylla.* - 635. *Odontites lutea.* - 636. *Digitalis grandiflora,* LARGE YELLOW FOXGLOVE. $(\times\frac{5}{8})$

96

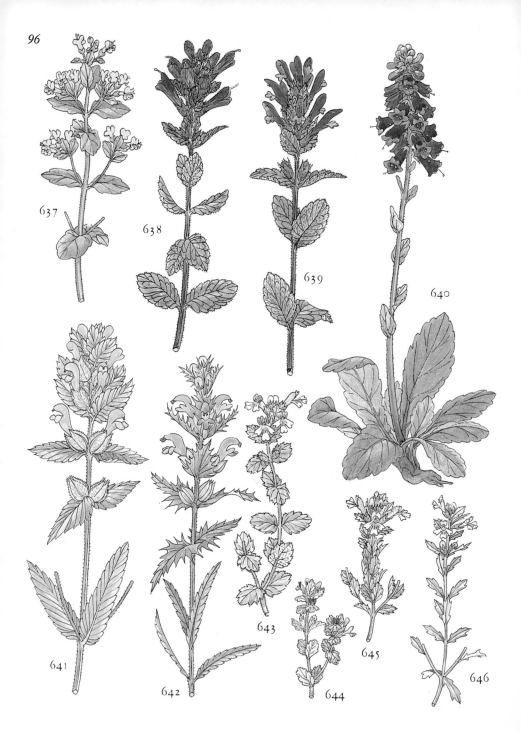

637. *Tozzia alpina.* - 638. *Bartsia alpina,* ALPINE BARTSIA. - 639. *B. spicata.* - 640.
Wulfenia carinthiaca. - 641. *Rhinanthus alectorolophus,* GREATER YELLOW-RATTLE. -
642. *R. aristatus.* - 643. *Euphrasia rostkoviana,* COMMON EYEBRIGHT. - 644. *E. minima,*
DWARF EYEBRIGHT. - 645. *E. alpina,* ALPINE EYEBRIGHT. - 646. *E. salisburgensis,*
SALZBURG EYEBRIGHT. $(\times\frac{5}{8})$

647. *Pedicularis sceptrum-carolinum*, MOOR-KING. - 648. *P. lapponica*, LAPLAND LOUSEWORT. - 649. *P. flammea*, RED-HOODED LOUSEWORT. - 650. *P. petiolaris.* - 651. *P. comosa*, CRESTED LOUSEWORT. - 652. *P. oederi.* - 653. *P. foliosa*, LEAFY LOUSEWORT. $(x\frac{5}{8})$

654. *Pedicularis elongata;* 654a, floret. - 655. *P. barrelieri;* 655a, floret. - 656. *P. palustris,* RED RATTLE, MARSH LOUSEWORT. - 657. *P. hirsuta,* HAIRY LOUSEWORT. - 658. *P. rosea,* PINK LOUSEWORT; 658a, floret. - 659. *P. sylvatica,* COMMON LOUSEWORT. - 660. *P. verticillata,* WHORLED LOUSEWORT; 660a, floret. - 661. *P. incarnata,* FLESH-PINK LOUSEWORT; 661a, floret. - 662. *P. tuberosa* (floret only).

(Florets all x 1; plants x$\frac{5}{8}$)

663. *Pedicularis acaulis*, STEMLESS LOUSEWORT. - 664. *P. portenschlagii;* 664a, floret. - 665. *P. cenisia*, MT. CENIS LOUSEWORT; 665a, floret. - 666. *P. rostrato-capitata*, BEAKED LOUSEWORT; 666a, floret. - 667. *P. kerneri*, RHAETIAN LOUSEWORT; 667a, floret. - 668. *P. gyroflexa*, TUFTTED LOUSEWORT; 668a, floret. - 669. *P. recutita;* 669a, floret. - 670. *P. pyrenaica*, PYRENEAN LOUSEWORT (floret only). - 671. *P. mixta* (floret only). - 672. *P. asplenifolia*, FERN-LEAVED LOUSEWORT (floret only). - 673. *P. elegans* (floret only).　　　　　　　　　　　(Florets all x 1 ; plants x$\frac{5}{8}$)

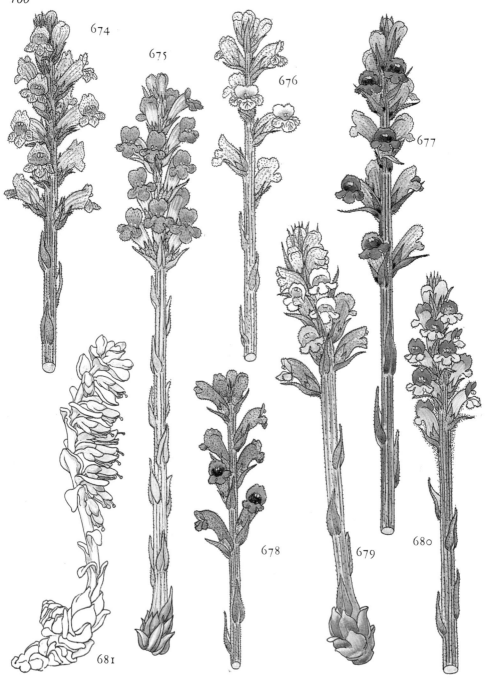

674. *Orobanche purpurea*, PURPLE BROOMRAPE. - 675. *O. arenaria*, SAND BROOMRAPE. - 676. *O. alba*, THYME BROOMRAPE. - 677. *O. reticulata*, SCABIOUS or NETTED BROOM-RAPE. - 678. *O. teucrii*, GERMANDER BROOMRAPE. - 679. *O. salviae*, SAGE BROOMRAPE. - 680. *O. flava*, YELLOW BROOMRAPE. - 681. *Lathraea squamaria*, TOOTHWORT. $(x\frac{1}{2})$

682. *Pinguicula alpina*, ALPINE BUTTERWORT. - 683. *P. vulgaris*, COMMON BUTTERWORT.
684. *P.v. var. alpicola* (flower). - 685. *P. villosa*, DOWNY BUTTERWORT. - 686. *P. grandiflora*, LARGE BUTTERWORT. - 687. *P.g. var. reuteri* (flower). - 688. *P. leptoceras.* - 689. *P. longifolia.* - 690. *Ramonda myconi.* - 691. *Globularia cordifolia.* - 692. *G.c. var. nana.* - 693. *G. incanescens* (leaf). - 694. *G. nudicaulis.* - 695. *G. aphyllanthes.* $(\times\frac{5}{8})$

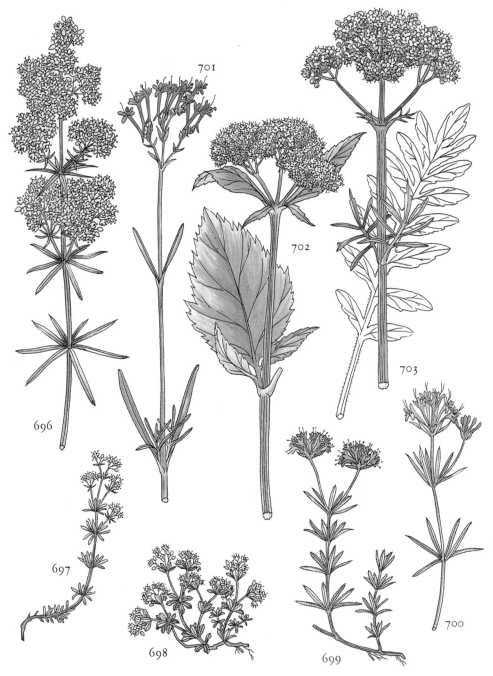

696. *Galium verum*, LADY'S BEDSTRAW. - 697. *G. baldense*, TYROL BEDSTRAW. -
698. *G. helveticum*, SWISS BEDSTRAW. - 699. *Asperula hirta*. - 700. *A. hexaphylla*. -
701. *Centranthus angustifolius*. - 702. *Valeriana pyrenaica*, PYRENEAN VALERIAN. -
703. *V. officinalis*, VALERIAN. $(\times\frac{5}{8})$

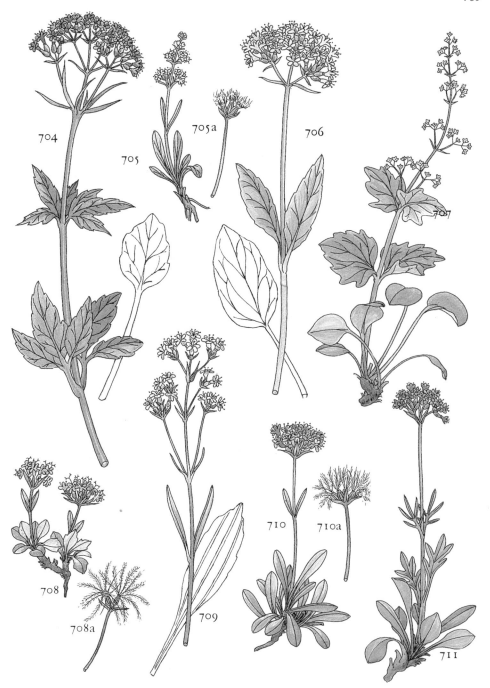

704. *Valeriana tripteris*, THREE-LEAVED VALERIAN. - 705. *V. celtica*, CELTIC SPIKENARD; 705a, fruiting head. - 706. *V. montana*, MOUNTAIN VALERIAN. - 707. *V. elongata*. - 708. *V. supina*, DWARF VALERIAN; 708a, fruiting head. - 709. *V. saxatilis*, ROCK VALERIAN. - 710. *V. saliunca*; 710a, fruiting head. - 711. *V. globulariifolia*. (x⅝)

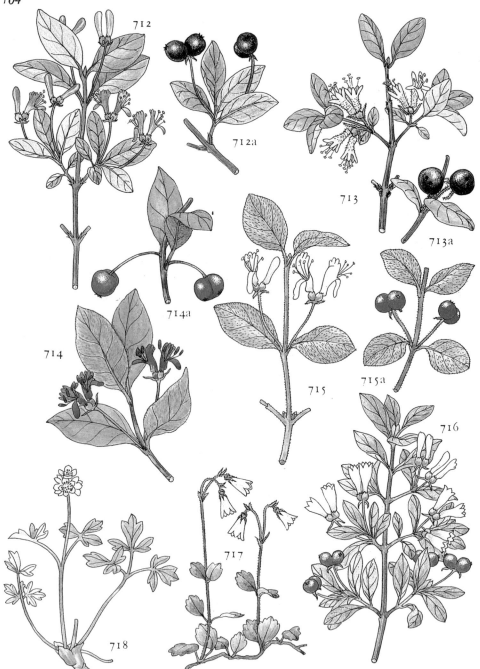

712. *Lonicera nigra*, BLACK-BERRIED HONEYSUCKLE; 712a, fruit. - 713. *L. coerulea*, BLUE-BERRIED HONEYSUCKLE; 713a, fruit. - 714. *L. alpigena*, ALPINE HONEYSUCKLE; 714a, fruit. - 715. *L. xylosteum*, FLY HONEYSUCKLE: 715a, fruit. - 716. *L. pyrenaica*, PYRENEAN HONEYSUCKLE. - 717. *Linnaea borealis*, TWINFLOWER. - 718. *Adoxa moschatellina*, MOSCHATEL. (x$\frac{5}{8}$)

719. *Sambucus racemosa,* ALPINE ELDER; 719a, fruit. - 720. *Scabiosa lucida,* SHINING SCABIOUS. - 721. *S. pyrenaica,* PYRENEAN SCABIOUS (stem leaves). - 722. *Knautia sylvatica,* WOOD SCABIOUS. - 723. *K. baldēnsis,* MT. BALDO SCABIOUS. - 724. *Cephalaria alpina,* ALPINE SCABIOUS. - 725. *Succisa pratensis,* DEVILS-BIT SCABIOUS $(x\frac{5}{8})$

726. *Campanula barbata*, BEARDED BELLFLOWER. - 727. *C. foliosa*. - 728. *C. alpina*, ALPINE BELLFLOWER. - 729. *C. speciosa*, PYRENEAN BELLFLOWER. - 730. *C. spicata*, SPIKED BELLFLOWER. - 731. *C. thyrsoides*, YELLOW BELLFLOWER.

(729 x$\frac{5}{8}$; remainder x$\frac{2}{5}$)

732. *Campanula persicifolia*, PEACH-LEAVED BELLFLOWER. - 733. *C. linifolia*, FLAX-LEAVED BELLFLOWER. - 734. *C. rhomboidalis*. - 735. *C. rapunculoides*, CREEPING BELL-FLOWER. - 736. *C. elatinoides*. - 737. *C. rotundifolia*, HAREBELL. - 738. *C. scheuchzeri*. - 739. *C. cochlearifolia*, FAIRY'S THIMBLE. $(x\frac{5}{8})$

740. *Campanula allionii*. - 741. *C. excisa*, PERFORATE BELLFLOWER. - 742. *C. uniflora*, NORTHERN BELLFLOWER. - 743. *C. zoysii*, CRIMPED BELLFLOWER. - 744. *C. caespitosa*, TUFTED BELLFLOWER. - 745. *C. raineri*. - 746. *C. morettiana*, DOLOMITES BELLFLOWER. 747. *C. pulla*. - 748. *C. cenisia*, MT. CENIS BELLFLOWER. - 749. *Edraianthus graminifolius*. $(\mathrm{x}\frac{5}{8})$

750. *Phyteuma halleri*, DARK RAMPION. - 751. *P. betonicifolium*. - 752. *P. spicatum*, SPIKED RAMPION. - 753. *P. balbisii*. - 754. *P. scorzonerifolium*. - 755. *P. scaposum* (basal leaf). - 756. *P. michelii* (basal leaf). - 757. *P. sieberi*, DOLOMITES RAMPION. - 758. *P. orbiculare*, ROUND-HEADED RAMPION. $(x\frac{1}{2})$

759. *P. charmelii*, PYRENEAN RAMPION. - 760. *P. hedraianthifolium*, RHAETIAN RAMPION. - 761. *P. hemisphaericum*. - 762. *P. confusum*, TONGUE-LEAVED RAMPION. - 763. *P. scheuchzeri*, HORNED RAMPION. - 764. *P. comosum*, DEVIL'S CLAW. - 765. *P. pedemontanum*, PIEDMONT RAMPION. - 766. *P. pauciflorum*. - 767. *P. globularifolium* (leaves). - 768. *P. humile*, DWARF RAMPION. - 769. *Jasione perennis*, SHEEPSBIT. - 770. *J. humilis*, DWARF SHEEPSBIT.   (x$\frac{1}{2}$)

771. *Antennaria dioica*, CATSFOOT; 771a, female; 771b, male. - 772. *Aster alpinus*, ALPINE ASTER. - 773. *A. pyrenaeus*, PYRENEAN ASTER. - 774. *Solidago virgaurea*, GOLDEN-ROD. - 775. *Erigeron alpinus*, ALPINE FLEABANE. - 776. *E. uniflorus*. - 777. *E. unalaschkensis*.

$(\times\frac{5}{8})$

778. *Tussilago farfara*, COLTSFOOT. - 779. *Leontopodium alpinum*, EDELWEISS. -
780. *L. nivale*, SNOW EDELWEISS. - 781. *Achillea tanacetifolia*, TANSY MILFOIL. -
782. *A. millefolium*, YARROW, COMMON MILFOIL (leaf). - 783. *Homogyne alpina*, ALPINE
COLTSFOOT. - 784. *H. discolor*. - 785. *Artemisia glacialis*, GLACIER WORMWOOD. -
786. *A. norvegica*, NORTHERN WORMWOOD. $(\times\frac{5}{8})$

787. *Doronicum austriacum*, AUSTRIAN LEOPARDS-BANE. - 788. *D. clusii*, TUFTED
LEOPARDS-BANE. - 789. *D. grandiflorum*, LARGE-FLOWERED LEOPARDS-BANE. -
790. *D. columnae*, HEART-LEAVED LEOPARDS-BANE. $(x\frac{5}{8})$

791. *Senecio alpinus*, ALPINE RAGWORT. - 792. *S. doronicum*, CHAMOIS RAGWORT. -
793. *S. tournefortii* (leaf). - 794. *S. ovirensis* (leaf). - 795. *Arnica montana*, ARNICA. -
796. *Buphthalmum salicifolium*, YELLOW OX-EYE. $(\times\frac{5}{8})$

797. *Senecio abrotanifolius.* - 798. *S. uniflorus*, ONE-FLOWERED ALPINE GROUNDSEL. - 799. *S. incanus*, GREY ALPINE GROUNDSEL. - 800. *S.i. ssp. insubricus* (leaf). - 801. *S.i. ssp. carniolicus.* - 802. *S. leucophyllus*, WHITE ALPINE GROUNDSEL. - 803. *S. capitatus.*

$(x\frac{5}{8})$

804. *Jurinea bocconii.* - 805. *Saussurea depressa.* - 806. *S. alpina.* - 807. *S. pygmaea,* wavy-leaved form; 807a, straight-leaved form. - 808. *S. discolor.* - 809. *Berardia subacaulis.*   (809 x$\frac{1}{3}$; remainder x$\frac{5}{8}$)

810. *Carduus carlinoides,* PYRENEAN THISTLE. - 811. *C. defloratus,* ALPINE THISTLE. -
812. *C. personatus,* MOUNTAIN THISTLE. - 813. *Cirsium acaulon,* STEMLESS THISTLE.
$(x\frac{5}{8})$

118

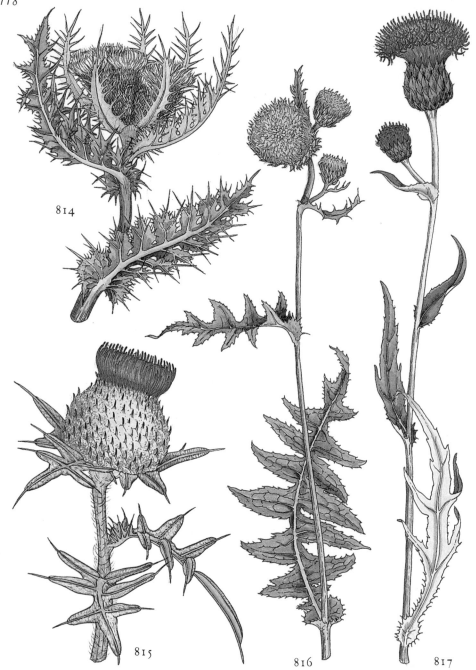

814. *Cirsium spinosissimum*, SPINIEST THISTLE. - 815. *C. eriophorum*, WOOLLY THISTLE.
816. *C. erisithales.* - 817. *C. heterophyllum*, MELANCHOLY THISTLE.   (x$\frac{1}{2}$)

818. *Centaurea montana*, MOUNTAIN CORNFLOWER. - 819. *C. scabiosa ssp. alpestris*, ALPINE KNAPWEED. - 820. *C. nervosa*, PLUME KNAPWEED. - 821. *Rhaponticum cynaroides*, CARDOON KNAPWEED. - 822. *R. scariosum*, GIANT KNAPWEED. $(x\frac{1}{2})$

823. *Prenanthes purpurea.* - 824. *Cicerbita alpina*, BLUE SOW-THISTLE. - 825. *Lactuca perennis*, MOUNTAIN LETTUCE. - 826. *Hypochoeris uniflora*, GIANT CATSEAR. - 827. *Aposeris foetida.*

$$(x\tfrac{5}{8})$$

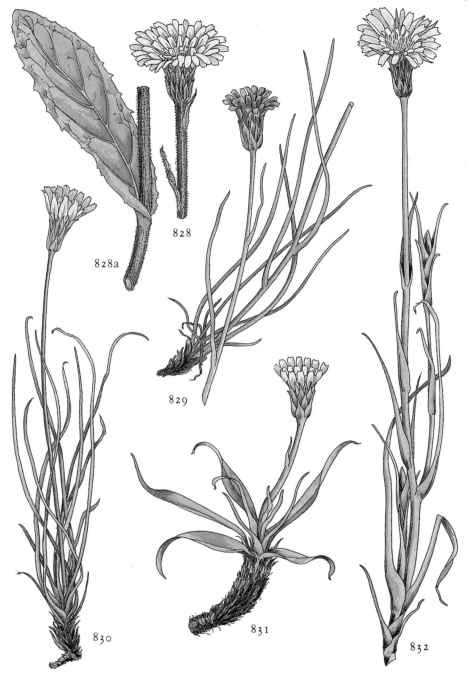

828. *Crepis pontana*, MOUNTAIN HAWKSBEARD; 828a, lower stem-leaf. - 829. *Scorzonera rosea*, PINK VIPERGRASS. - 830. *S. aristata*, BEARDED VIPERGRASS. - 831. *S. austriaca*, AUSTRIAN VIPERGRASS. - 832. *Tragopogon pratensis*, GOATSBEARD. $(x\frac{5}{8})$

122

833. *Taraxacum alpinum*, ALPINE DANDELION. - 834. *Leontodon montanus*, MOUNTAIN
HAWKBIT. - 835. *L. pyrenaicus*, PYRENEAN HAWKBIT. - 836. *Crepis raetica*, PLUMED
HAWKSBEARD. - 837. *C. terglouensis*, TRIGLAV HAWKSBEARD. - 838. *C. aurea*, GOLDEN
HAWKSBEARD. - 839. *C. pygmaea*, PYGMY HAWKSBEARD. $(x\frac{5}{8})$

840. *Crepis incarnata*, PINK HAWKSBEARD. - 841. *C. jacquinii*, ROCK HAWKSBEARD.
842. *Hieracium humile*, DWARF HAWKWEED. - 843. *H. alpinum*, ALPINE
HAWKWEED. - 844. *H. lanatum*, WOOLLY HAWKWEED. - 845. *H. aurantiacum*, GRIM
THE COLLIER. $(\times\frac{5}{8})$

846. *Equisetum fluviatile,* WATER HORSETAIL. - 847. *E. pratense,* FIELD HORSETAIL;
847a, fruiting shoot, 847b, sterile shoot. - 848. *E. palustre,* MARSH HORSETAIL. -
849. *E. variegatum,* VARIEGATED HORSETAIL. - 850. *E. hyemale,* DUTCH RUSH. - 851.
Selaginella selaginoides. - 852. *S. helvetica.* - 853. *Lycopodium annotinum.* - 854. *L. selago,*
FIR CLUBMOSS. - 855. *L. alpinum,* ALPINE CLUBMOSS. - 856. *L. clavatum,* STAGSHORN
CLUBMOSS.   (x$\frac{5}{8}$)

857. *Ceterach officinarum,* RUSTY-BACK. - 858. *Woodsia ilvensis.* - 859. *W. alpina.* -
860. *Polypodium vulgare,* POLYPODY. - 861. *Cryptogramma crispa,* PARSLEY FERN. -
862. *Cystopteris fragilis,* BRITTLE BLADDER-FERN. · - 863. *C. montana,* MOUNTAIN
BLADDER-FERN. - 864. *Polystichum lonchitis,* HOLLÝ FERN.   (x½)

865. *Ophioglossum vulgatum*, ADDERS-TONGUE. - 866. *Botrychium lunaria*, MOON-FERN. - 867. *B. boreale*. - 868. *B. lanceolatum*. - 869. *B. simplex*. - 870. *Asplenium viride*, GREEN SPLEENWORT. - 871. *A. adiantum-nigrum*, BLACK SPLEENWORT. - 872. *A. septentrionale*, FORKED SPLEENWORT. - 873. *A. ruta-muraria*, WALL RUE. - 874. *Thelypteris phegopteris*, BEECH FERN. $(\times \frac{5}{8})$

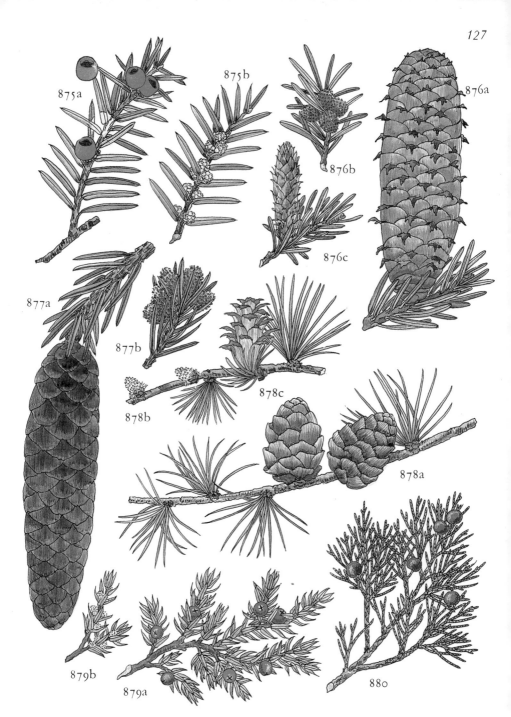

875. *Taxus baccata,* YEW; 875a, fruit, 875b, male flowers. - 876. *Abies alba,* SILVER
FIR; 876a, cone, 876b, male flowers, 876c, female flowers. - 877. *Picea abies,*
NORWAY SPRUCE; 877a, cone, 877b, male flowers. - 878. *Larix decidua,* LARCH;
878a, cone, 878b, male flowers, 878c, female flowers. - 879. *Juniperus communis
ssp. nana,* DWARF JUNIPER; 879a, fruit, 879b, male flowers. - 880. *J. sabina,* SAVIN (in
fruit). $(\times \frac{5}{8})$

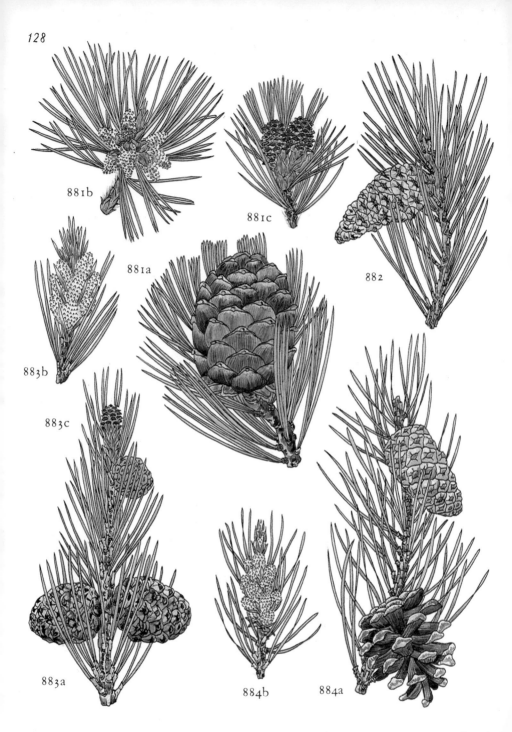

881. *Pinus cembra*, AROLLA PINE; 881a, cone. 881b, male flowers, 881c, female flowers. - 882. *Pinus nigra*, AUSTRIAN PINE (cone). - 883. *Pinus mugo*, MOUNTAIN PINE; 883a, cone, 883b, male flowers, 883c, female flowers. - 884. *Pinus sylvestris*, SCOTS PINE; 884a, cones, 884b, male flowers. $(x\frac{5}{8})$

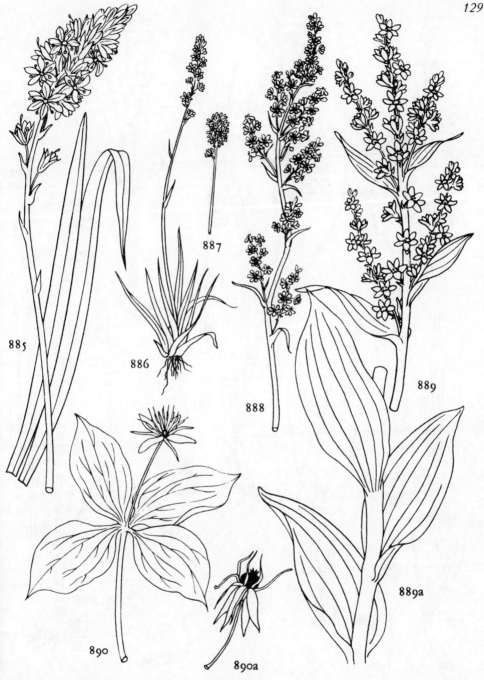

885. *Asphodelus albus,* ASPHODEL. - 886. *Tofieldia calyculata.* - 887. *T. pusilla,* SCOTTISH ASPHODEL (flower head). - 888. *Veratrum nigrum,* BLACK FALSE HELLEBORINE. - 889. *V. album,* WHITE FALSE HELLEBORINE; 889a, lower leaves. - 890. *Paris quadrifolia,* HERB PARIS; 890a, fruit.

$(\times\frac{5}{8})$

891. *Convallaria majalis*, LILY OF THE VALLEY. - 892. *Anthericum liliago*, ST. BERNARD'S LILY. - 893. *A. ramosa*. - 894. *Lloydia serotina;* 894a, multi-flowered form. - 895. *Dipcadi serotinum*. - 896. *Maianthemum bifolium*, MAY LILY. - 897. *Paradisea liliastrum*, ST. BRUNO'S LILY.

$(\times\frac{2}{5})$

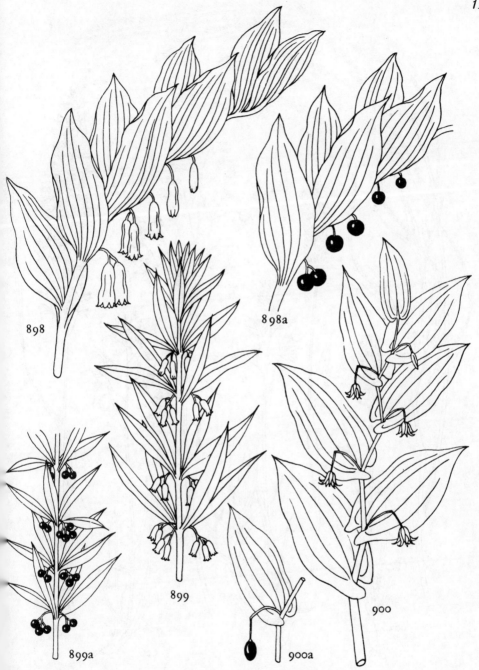

898. *Polygonatum odoratum,* COMMON SOLOMON'S SEAL; 898a, fruits. - 899. *P. verticilla-tum,* WHORLED SOLOMON'S SEAL; 899a, fruits. - 900. *Streptopus amplexifolius;* 900a, fruit. $(x\frac{2}{5})$

132

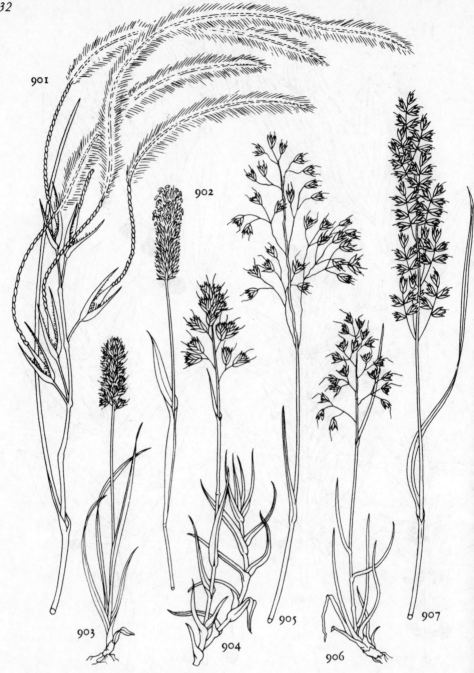

901. *Stipa pennata*, FEATHER GRASS. - 902. *Phleum alpinum*, ALPINE CATSTAIL. -
903. *Trisetum spicatum.* - 904. *T. distichophyllum.* - 905. *Deschampsia flexuosa*, WAVY
HAIR GRASS. - 906. *Agrostis alpina*, ALPINE BENT. - 907. *Calamagrostis villosa*,
SHAGGY SMALLREED. $(\times\frac{1}{2})$

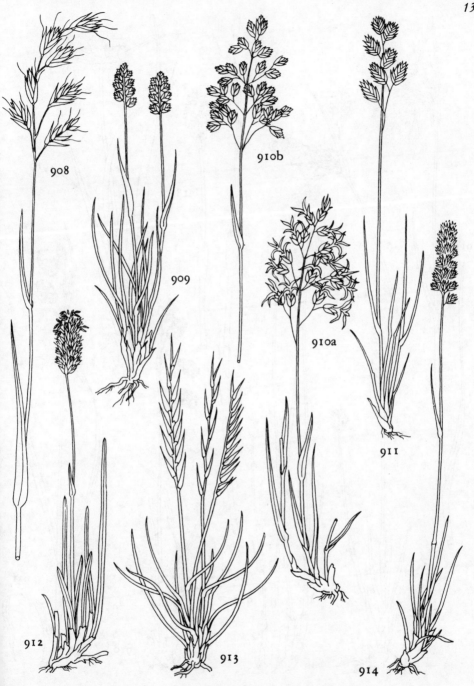

908. *Helictotrichon versicolor*, VARIEGATED OAT. - 909. *Oreochloa disticha*. - 910. *Poa alpina*, ALPINE POA; 910a, viviparous form; 910b, seed-bearing form. - 911. *Festuca varia*, COLOURED FESCUE. - 912. *Sesleria coerulea ssp. calcarea*, BLUE SESLERIA. - 913. *Nardus stricta*, MAT GRASS. - 914. *Koeleria hirsuta*. (x$\frac{1}{2}$)

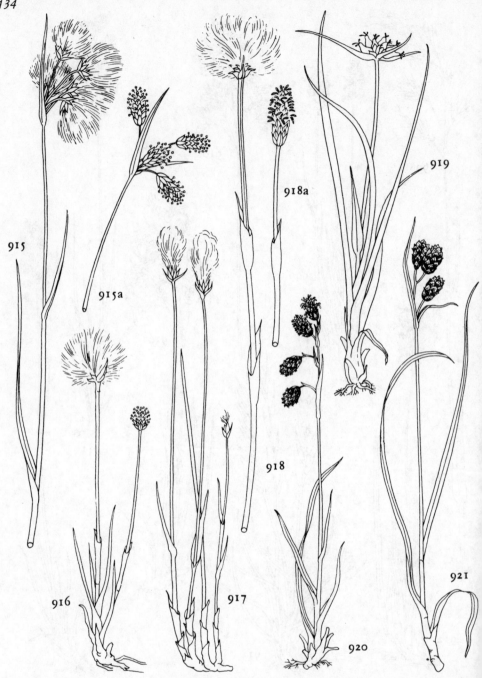

915. *Eriophorum angustifolium*, COMMON COTTONGRASS, with seeding head; 915a, flowers. - 916. *E. scheuchzeri*. - 917. *E. alpinum*, ALPINE COTTONGRASS. - 918. *E. vaginatum*, HARESTAIL, with seeding head; 918a, flowers. - 919. *Carex baldensis*, MONTE BALDO SEDGE. - 920. *C. atrofusca*, BLACK SEDGE. - 921. *C. atrata*, DARK SEDGE. $(\times \frac{5}{8})$

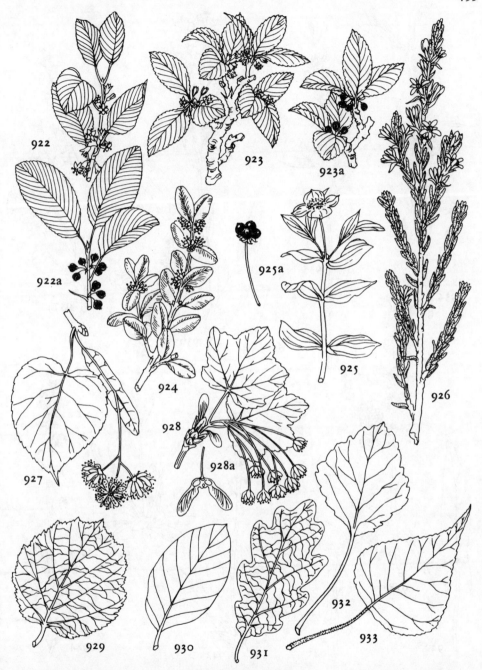

922. *Rhamnus alpinus*, ALPINE BUCKTHORN; 922a, fruit. - 923. *R. pumilus*, DWARF
BUCKTHORN; 923a, fruit. - 924. *Buxus sempervirens*, BOX. - 925. *Chamaepericlymenum
suecicum*, DWARF CORNEL; 925a, fruit. - 926. *Myricaria germanica*. - 927. *Tilia platyphyllos*, LARGE-LEAVED LIME. - 928. *Acer opalus;* 928a, seed. - 929. *Corylus avellana*,
HAZEL (leaf). - 930. *Fagus sylvatica*, BEECH (leaf). - 931. *Quercus petraea*, DURMAST OAK
(leaf). - 932. *Populus tremula*, ASPEN (leaf). - 933. *P. nigra*, BLACK POPLAR (leaf).   (x⅝)

136

934. *Thesium alpinum*, ALPINE BASTARD TOADFLAX. - 935. *T. pyrenaicum*, PYRENEAN BASTARD TOADFLAX. - 936. *Polygonum alpinum*, ALPINE KNOTGRASS. - 937. *Oxyria digyna*, MOUNTAIN SORREL. - 938. *Rumex scutatus*, RUBBLE DOCK. - 939. *R. arifolius* (leaf). - 940. *R. acetosa*, SORREL-DOCK (leaf). - 941. *R. acetosella*, SHEEPS SORREL (leaf). - 942. *R. nivalis*, SNOW DOCK. - 943. *Sesamoides pygmaea*. - 944. *Reseda glauca*, BLUISH MIGNONETTE. (x$\frac{5}{8}$)

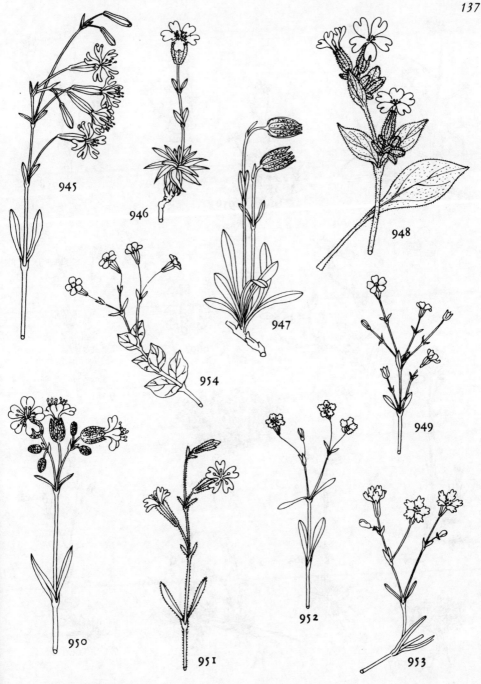

945. *Silene nutans*, NOTTINGHAM CATCHFLY. - 946. *S. auriculata*, EARED CATCHFLY. -
947. *S. wahlbergella*. - 948. *S. dioica*, RED CAMPION. - 949. *S. rupestris*, ROCK CAMPION.
950. *S. vulgaris ssp. prostrata*, ALPINE BLADDER CAMPION. - 951. *S. ciliata*. - 952. *S. pusilla*. - 953. *S. alpestris*. - 954. *Petrocoptis pyrenaica*. $(x\frac{5}{8})$

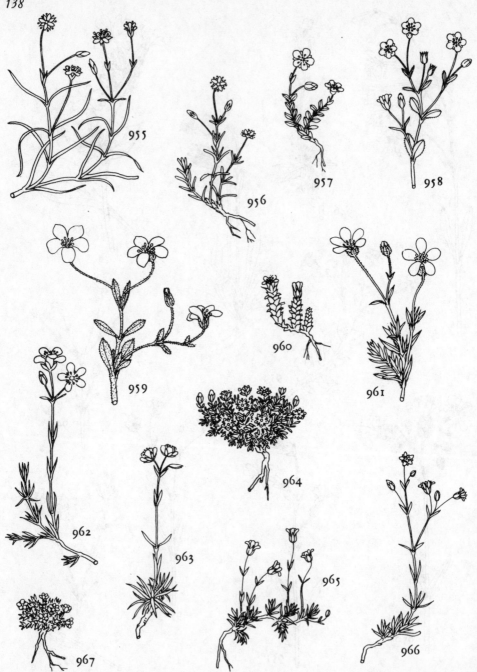

955. *Moehringia muscosa.* - 956. *M. ciliata.* - 957. *Arenaria norvegica,* NORWEGIAN
SANDWORT. - 958. *A. ciliata.* - 959. *A. huteri.* - 960. *A. tetraquetra.* - 961. *A. grandi-
flora.* - 962. *Minuartia laricifolia.* - 963. *M. graminifolia.* - 964. *M. sedoides,* MOSSY
CYPHEL. - 965. *M. biflora.* - 966. *M. verna,* VERNAL SANDWORT. - 967. *Sagina caespitosa,*
CUSHION PEARLWORT.
$(\times \frac{5}{8})$

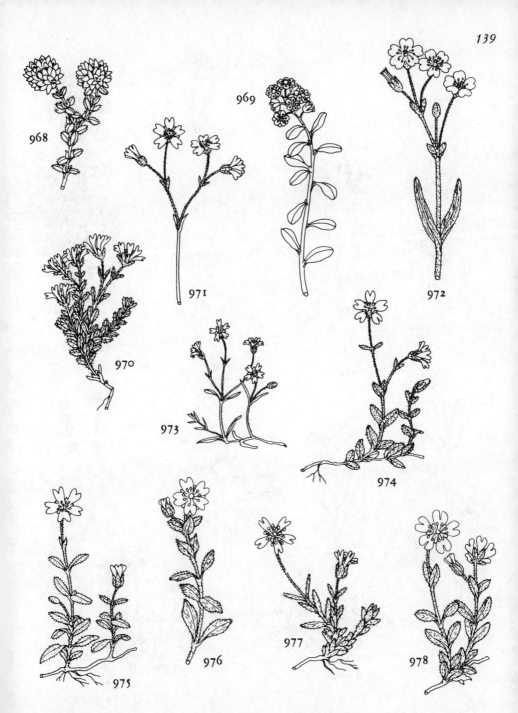

968. *Paronychia kapela ssp. serpyllifolia.* - 969. *Telephium imperati.* - 970. *Cerastium arvense ssp. thomasii.* - 971. *C.a. ssp. strictum.* - 972. *C. tomentosum,* SNOW-IN-SUMMER. - 973. *C. cerastoides.* - 974. *C. alpinum,* ALPINE MOUSE-EAR CHICKWEED. - 975. *C. arcticum,* ARCTIC MOUSE-EAR CHICKWEED. - 976. *C. pyrenaicum,* PYRENEAN MOUSE-EAR CHICKWEED. - 977. *C. uniflorum,* GLACIER MOUSE-EAR CHICKWEED. - 978. *C. latifolium.* $(x\frac{5}{8})$

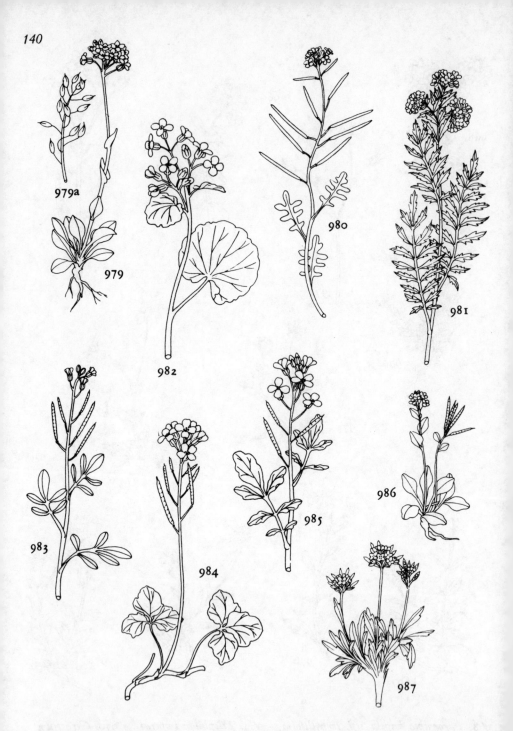

979. *Thlaspi alpinum*, ALPINE PENNYCRESS; 979a, fruits. - 980. *Murbeckiella pinnatifida*.
981. *Hugueninia tanacetifolia*. - 982. *Cardamine asarifolia*. - 983. *C. resedifolia*. -
984. *C. trifolia*. - 985. *C. amara*, LARGE BITTERCRESS. - 986. *C. bellidifolia ssp. alpina*,
ALPINE BITTERCRESS. - 987. *Braya alpina*. $(\times\frac{5}{8})$

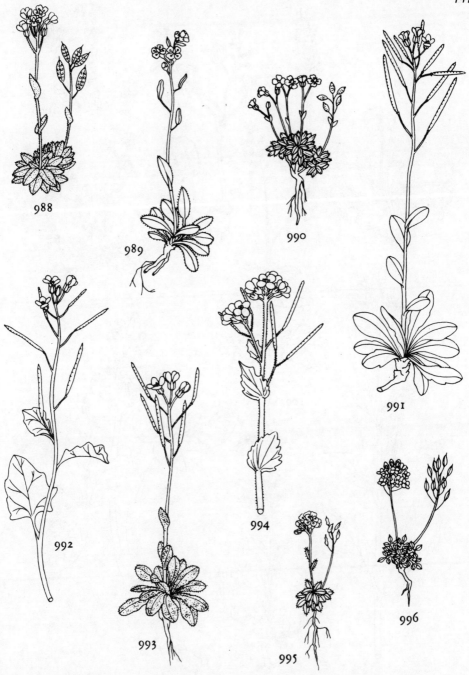

988. *Draba tomentosa*, DOWNY WHITLOW-GRASS. - 989. *D. carinthiaca*. - 990. *D. fladnizensis*. - 991. *Arabis soyeri ssp. jacquinii*. - 992. *A. pedemontana*, PIEDMONT ROCKCRESS. - 993. *A. pumila*, DWARF ROCKCRESS. - 994. *A. alpina*, ALPINE ROCK-CRESS. - 995. *A. scopoliana*. - 996. *Hutchinsia alpina*, CHAMOIS CRESS. $(x\frac{5}{8})$

142

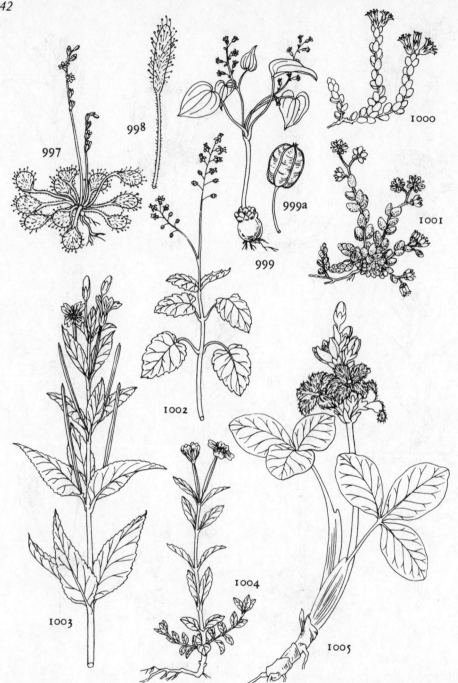

997. *Drosera rotundifolia,* COMMON SUNDEW. - 998. *D. anglica,* LONG-LEAVED SUNDEW
(leaf). - 999. *Dioscorea pyrenaica;* 999a, fruit. - 1000. *Mucizonia sedoides.* - 1001. *Sedum
dasyphyllum,* THICK-LEAVED STONECROP. - 1002. *Circaea alpina,* ALPINE ENCHANTERS
NIGHTSHADE. - 1003. *Epilobium trigonum.* - 1004. *E. alpinum.* - 1005. *Menyanthes
trifoliata,* BOGBEAN.

$(\times\frac{5}{8})$

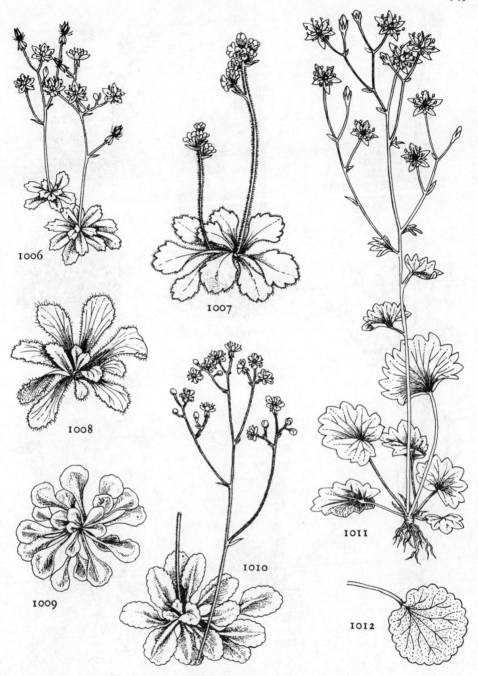

1006. *Saxifraga stellaris,* STARRY SAXIFRAGE. - 1007. *S. nivalis,* ALPINE SAXIFRAGE. - 1008. *S. clusii* (rosette). - 1009. *S. cuneifolia* (rosette). - 1010. *S. umbrosa,* WOOD SAXIFRAGE. - 1011. *S. rotundifolia,* ROUND-LEAVED SAXIFRAGE. - 1012. *S. hirsuta,* KIDNEY SAXIFRAGE (leaf). $(\times\frac{1}{2})$

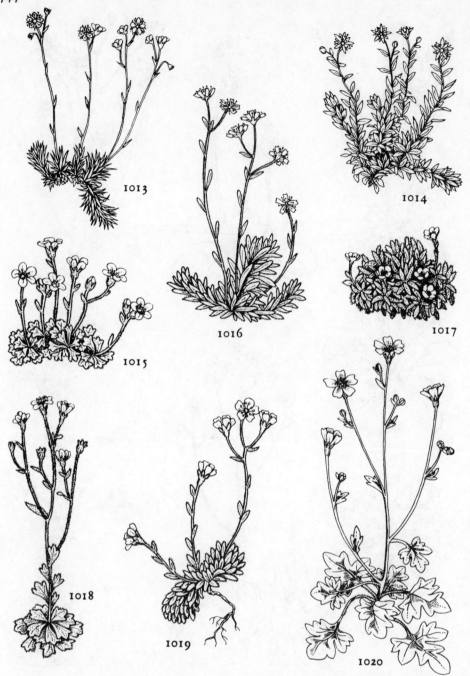

1013. *Saxifraga tenella.* - 1014. *S. sedoides.* - 1015. *S. groenlandica.* TUFTED SAXIFRAGE. -
1016. *S. presolanensis.* - 1017. *S. fachinii.* - 1018. *S. adscendens.* - 1019. *S. muscoides.* -
1020. *S. petraea,* ROCK SAXIFRAGE. $(\times\frac{5}{8})$

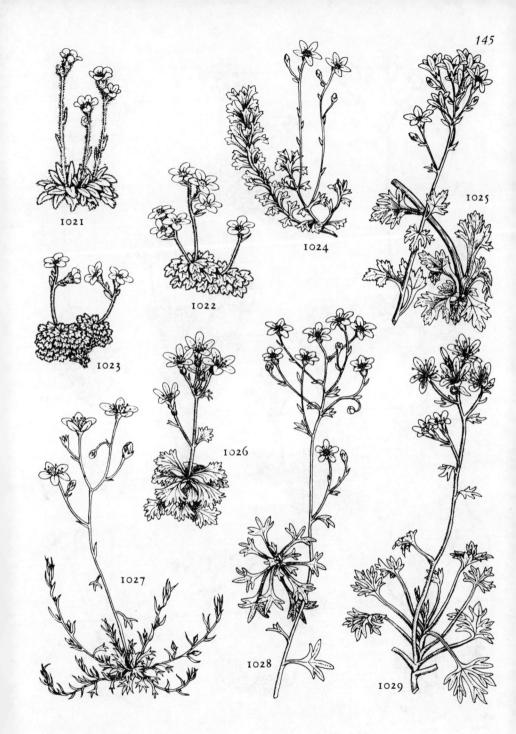

1021. *Saxifraga androsacea var. integrifolia.* - 1022. *S.a. var. tridentata.* - 1023. *S. italica.*
1024. *S. praetermissa.* - 1025. *S. aquatica,* WATER SAXIFRAGE. - 1026. *S. pedemontana,*
PIEDMONT SAXIFRAGE. - 1027. *S. hypnoides,* DOVEDALE MOSS. - 1028. *S. pentadactylis.* -
1029. *S. geranioides,* GERANIUM-LIKE SAXIFRAGE. $(x\frac{5}{8})$

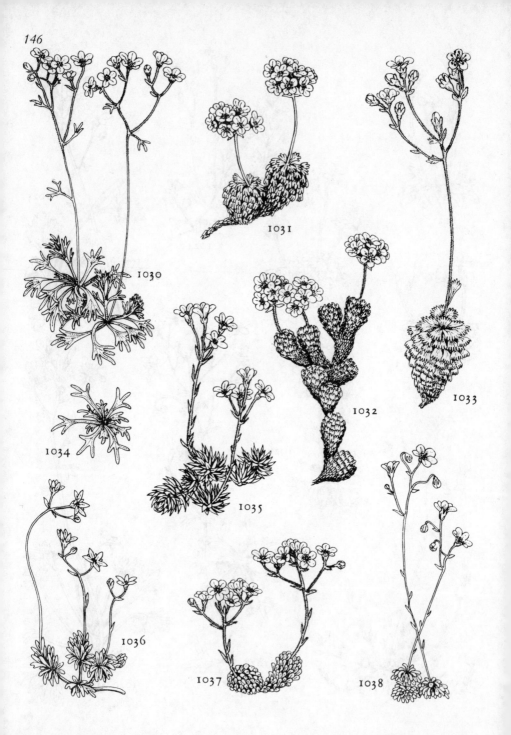

1030. *Saxifraga pubescens,* HAIRY SAXIFRAGE: *ssp. pubescens forma elata.* - 1031. *S. p. p. forma cephalantha.* - 1032. *S. p. ssp. iratiana forma vulgaris.* - 1033. *S. p. i. forma polyantha.* 1034. *S. exarata* (rosette). - 1035. *S. vandellii.* - 1036. *S. hariotii.* - 1037. *S. valdensis.* 1038. *S. caesia,* BLUE SAXIFRAGE. $(\times \frac{5}{8})$

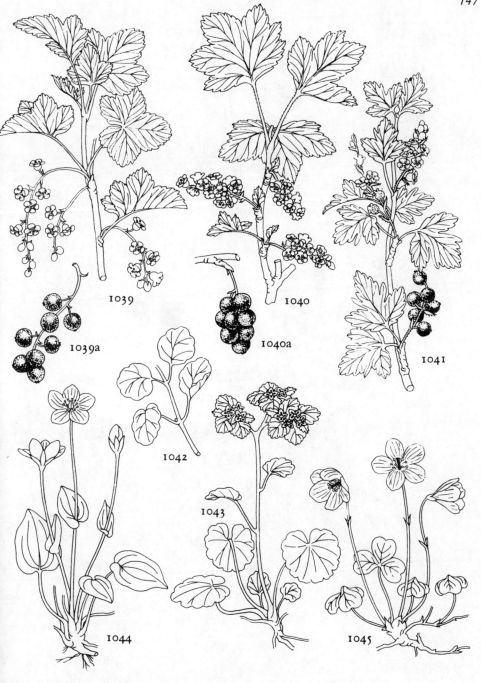

1039. *Ribes rubrum,* RED CURRANT; 1039a, fruits. - 1040. *R. petraeum,* ROCK RED
CURRANT; 1040a, fruits. - 1041. *R. alpinum,* MOUNTAIN CURRANT. - 1042. *Chrysosplenium oppositifolium,* OPPOSITE-LEAVED GOLDEN SAXIFRAGE (leaves). - 1043. *C.
alternifolium,* ALTERNATE-LEAVED GOLDEN SAXIFRAGE. - 1044. *Parnassia palustris,*
GRASS OF PARNASSUS. - 1045. *Oxalis acetosella,* WOOD-SORREL.   (x$\frac{5}{8}$)

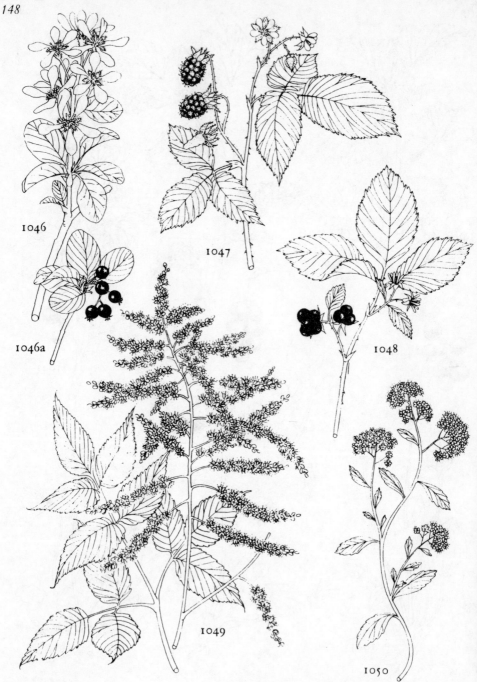

1046. *Amelanchier ovalis;* 1046a, fruits. - 1047. *Rubus idaeus,* RASPBERRY. - 1048. *R. saxatilis,* ROCK BRAMBLE. - 1049. *Aruncus vulgaris,* GOATSBEARD, with upper leaf. - 1050. *Spiraea decumbens.*

$(x\frac{5}{8})$

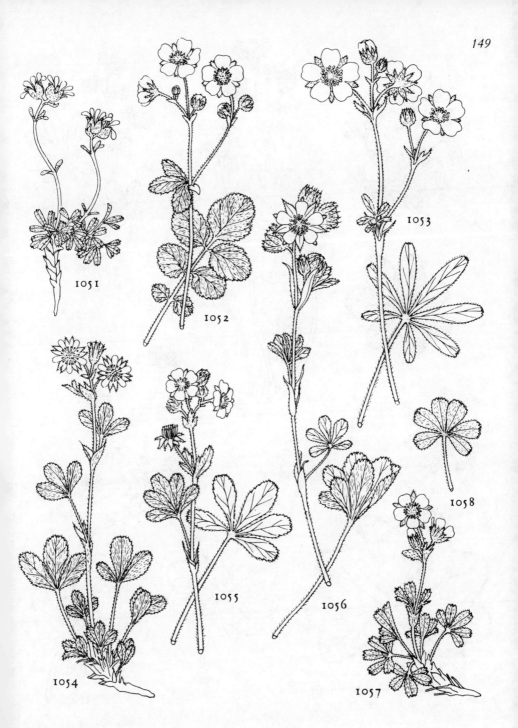

1051. *Potentilla apennina.* – 1052. *P. rupestris*, ROCK CINQUEFOIL. – 1053. *P. alche-milloides.* – 1054. *P. grammopetala.* – 1055. *P. caulescens.* – 1056. *P. valderia.* – 1057. *P. clusiana.* – 1058. *P. nivalis*, WOOLLY CINQUEFOIL (basal leaf). $(\times \frac{5}{8})$

1059. *Sibbaldia procumbens.* - 1060. *Alchemilla glabra.* - 1061. *A. alpina ssp. subsericea,*
ALPINE LADY'S MANTLE. - 1062. *A. hoppeana ssp. asterophylla*.* - 1063. *A.h. ssp.
conjuncta*.* - 1064. *A. hybrida*.* - 1065. *A. glomerulans*.* - 1066. *A. murbeckiana*.*
1067. *A. splendens*.* - 1068. *A. pentaphyllea.*   (* basal leaf only) (x$\frac{5}{8}$)

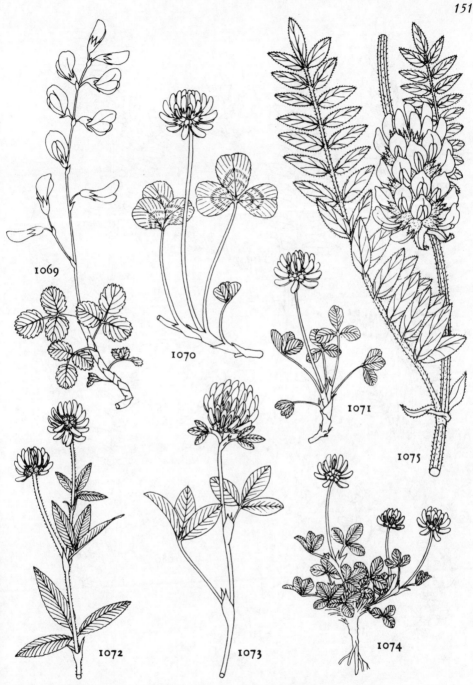

1069. *Ononis aragonensis.* - 1070. *Trifolium repens,* WHITE CLOVER. - 1071. *T. thalii.* -
1072. *T. montanum,* MOUNTAIN CLOVER. - 1073. *T. pratense var. frigidum,* ALPINE RED
CLOVER. - 1074. *T. pallescens.* - 1075. *Astragalus alopecuroides.* $(\times\frac{5}{8})$

152

1076. *Onobrychis saxatilis*, ROCK SAINFOIN. - 1077. *Astragalus cicer*, WILD LENTIL. -
1078. *Vicia sepium*, BUSH VETCH. - 1079. *V. argentea*, SILVERY VETCH. - 1080. *V.
sylvatica*, WOOD VETCH. - 1081. *Medicago suffruticosa*. - 1082. *Lathyrus aphaca*, YELLOW
VETCHLING.   (x$\frac{5}{8}$)

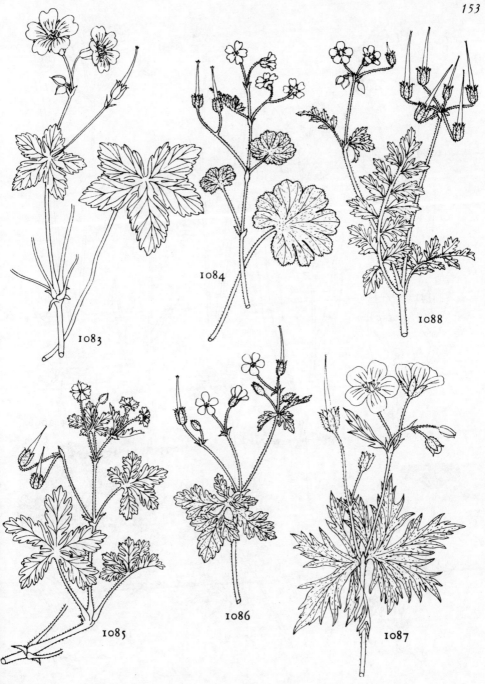

1083. *Geranium nodosum.* - 1084. *G. molle,* DOVESFOOT CRANESBILL. - 1085. *G. divari-*
catum. - 1086. *G. robertianum,* HERB ROBERT. - 1087. *G. sylvaticum ssp. rivulare.* -
1088. *Erodium cicutarium,* COMMON STORKSBILL. $(x\frac{5}{8})$

1089. *Bupleurum longifolium.* - 1090. *B. angulosum.* - 1091. *B. stellatum,* STARRY HARES-
EAR. - 1092. *B. petraeum,* ROCK HARES-EAR. - 1093. *B. ranunculoides.* - 1094. *Endressia
pyrenaica.* - 1095. *Ligusticum mutellina.* - 1096. *Xatartia scaber;* 1096a, single seed-
head.
$(\times \frac{5}{8})$

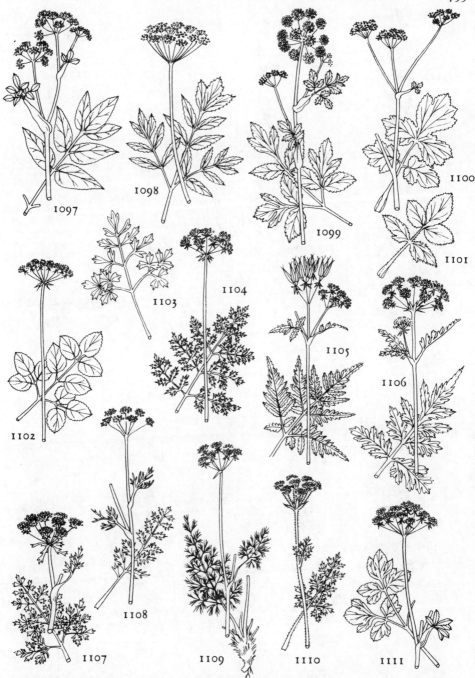

1097. *Angelica sylvestris*, WILD ANGELICA. - 1098. *A. razulii.* - 1099. *A. archangelica* ssp. *norvegica*, ANGELICA. - 1100. *Heracleum sphondylium*, COW PARSNIP. - 1101. *H. austriacum.* - 1102. *Laserpitium latifolium.* - 1103. *L. gallicum.* - 1104. *L. halleri.* - 1105. *Myrrhis odorata*, SWEET CICELY. - 1106. *Molopospermum peloponnesiacum.* - 1107. *Ligusticum ferulaceum.* - 1108. *Carum carvi*, CARAWAY. - 1109. *Meum athamanticum*, SPIGNEL. - 1110. *Athamanta cretensis.* - 1111. *Peucedanum ostruthium*, MASTER- WORT. (Leaf segments only shown in most cases) (x$\frac{1}{2}$)

156

1112. *Orthilia secunda*, NODDING WINTERGREEN. - 1113. *Moneses uniflora*, ONE-
FLOWERED WINTERGREEN. - 1114. *Pyrola chlorantha*, GREENISH WINTERGREEN. - 1115.
P. norvegica, NORTHERN WINTERGREEN (leaf). - 1116. *P. minor*, SMALL WINTERGREEN.
1117. *P. media*, INTERMEDIATE WINTERGREEN (leaf). - 1118. *P. rotundifolia*,
ROUND-LEAVED WINTERGREEN. - 1119. *Monotropa hypopitys*, YELLOW BIRDSNEST.
(x$\frac{5}{8}$)

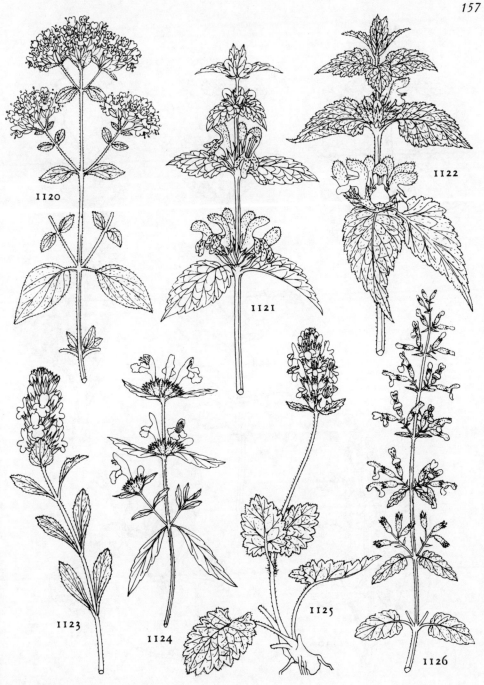

1120. *Origanum vulgare*, MARJORAM. - 1121. *Galeobdolon luteum*, YELLOW ARCHANGEL.
1122. *Lamium album*, WHITE DEADNETTLE. - 1123. *Sideritis hyssopifolia*. - 1124.
Galeopsis angustifolia, NARROW-LEAVED HEMPNETTLE. - 1125. *Stachys alopecuros*,
YELLOW BETONY. - 1126. *Nepeta nepetella*.
$(x\frac{5}{8})$

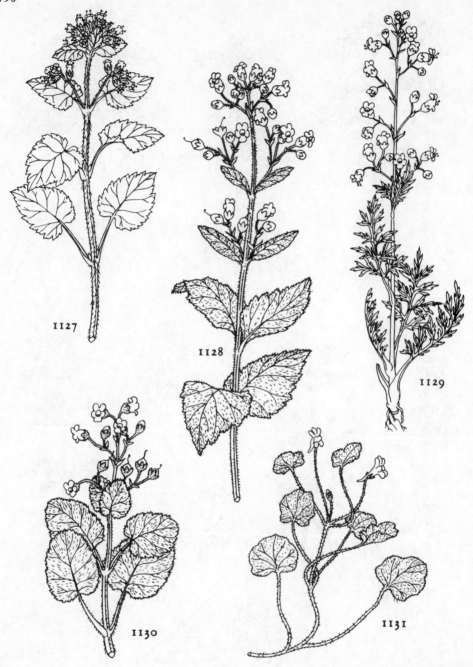

1127. *Scrophularia vernalis*, YELLOW FIGWORT. - 1128. *S. scopolii.* - 1129. *S. hoppei*, ALPINE FIGWORT. - 1130. *S. pyrenaica*, PYRENEAN FIGWORT. - 1131. *Cymbalaria pallida.* (1131 x$\frac{1}{2}$; remainder x$\frac{1}{3}$)

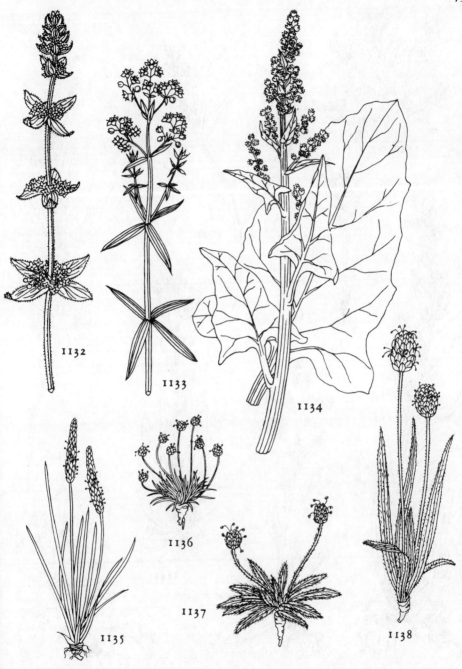

1132. *Galium cruciata*, CROSSWORT. - 1133. *G. boreale*, NORTHERN BEDSTRAW. - 1134. *Chenopodium bonus-henricus*, GOOD KING HENRY. - 1135. *Plantago alpina*, ALPINE PLANTAIN. - 1136. *P. alpina var. capitellata.* - 1137. *P. monosperma.* - 1138. *P. atrata.*

$(\times\frac{5}{8})$

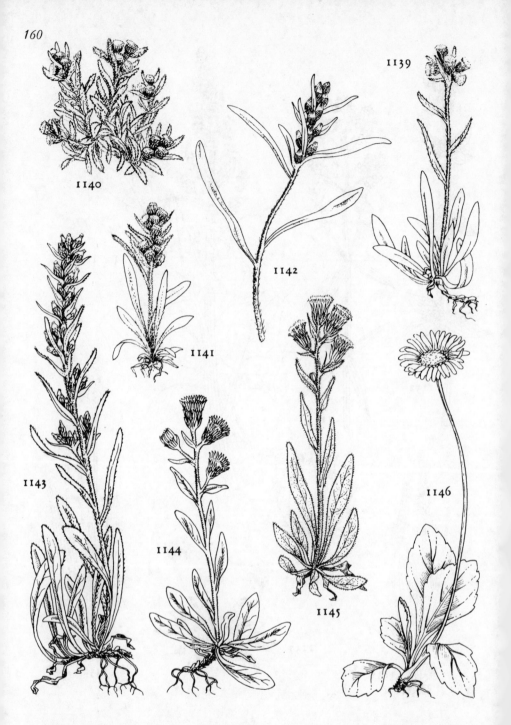

1139. *Antennaria carpatica*, CARPATHIAN CATSFOOT. - 1140. *Gnaphalium supinum*,
DWARF CUDWEED. - 1141. *G. hoppeanum*. - 1142. *G. norvegicum*, HIGHLAND CUD-
WEED. - 1143. *G. sylvaticum*, WOOD CUDWEED. - 1144. *Erigeron atticus*. - 1145. *E.
acris*, BLUE FLEABANE. - 1146. *Bellidiastrum michelii*, FALSE DAISY. $(\times\frac{5}{8})$

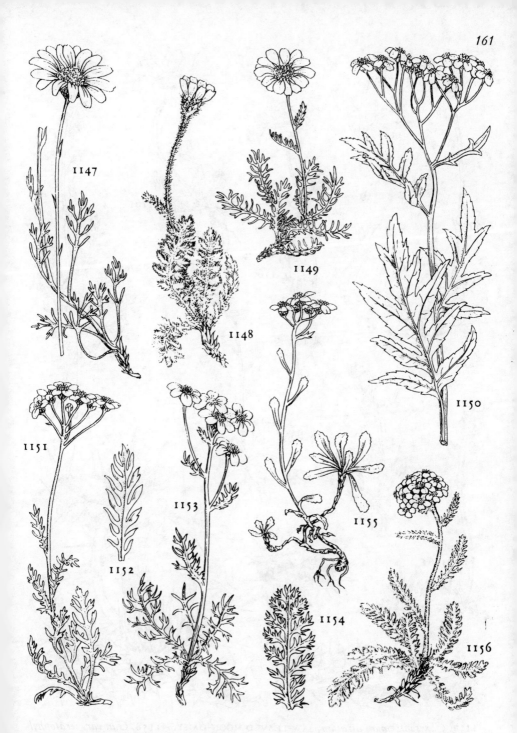

1147. *Anthemis montana*, MOUNTAIN DOG-DAISY. - 1148. *A. barrelieri*. - 1149. *Achillea oxyloba*, ALPINE SNEEZEWORT. - 1150. *A. macrophylla*, LARGE-LEAVED SNEEZEWORT. - 1151. *A. clavennae* - 1152. *A. moschata*, MUSK MILFOIL (leaf). - 1153. *A. atrata*. - 1154. *A. clusiana* (leaf). - 1155. *A. erba-rotta*. - 1156. *A. nana*, DWARF MILFOIL. (x⅝)

162

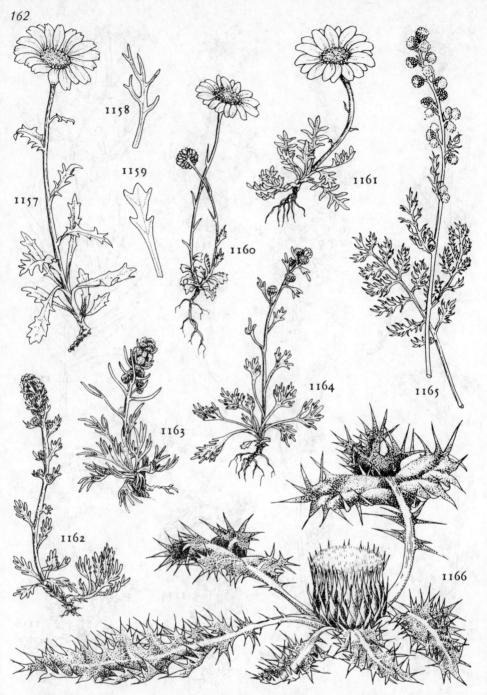

1157. *Chrysanthemum atratum*, SAW-LEAVED MOON-DAISY. - 1158. *C.a. var. ceratophyl-loides* (leaf). - 1159. *C.a. var. tridactylites* (leaf). - 1160. *C. pulverulentum*, DOWNY MOON-DAISY. - 1161. *C. alpinum var. hutchinsiifolium*, ALPINE MOON-DAISY. - 1162. *Artemisia genipi*, GENIPI. - 1163. *A. borealis var. nana*, ARCTIC MUGWORT. - 1164. *A. mutellina*, YELLOW GENIPI. - 1165. *A. atrata*, DARK ALPINE WORMWOOD. - 1166. *Onopordum acaulon*. (1166, x$\frac{1}{3}$; remainder x$\frac{5}{8}$)

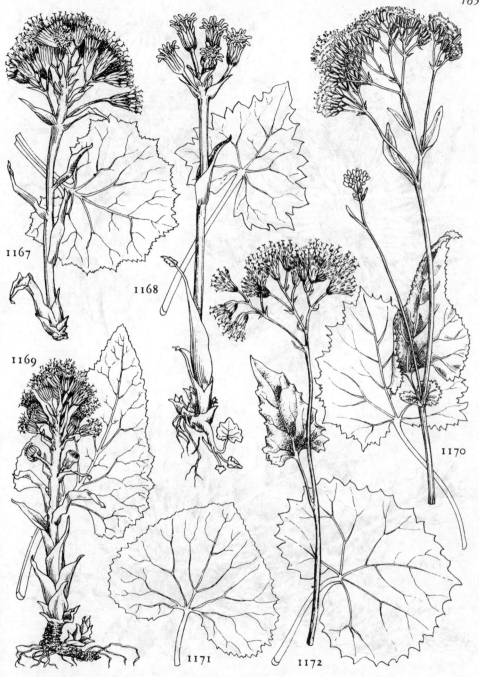

1167. *Petasites albus,* WHITE BUTTERBUR, - 1168. *P. frigidus.* - 1169. *P. paradoxus,* ALPINE BUTTERBUR. - 1170. *Adenostyles alliariae.* - 1171. *A. glabra* (leaf). - 1172. *A. leucophylla.* (x$\frac{1}{2}$)

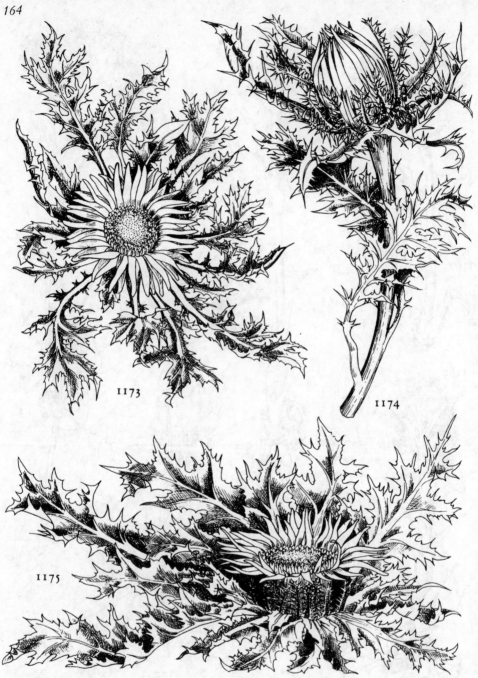

1173. *Carlina acaulis,* STEMLESS CARLINE·THISTLE. - 1174. *C.a. var. alpina,* ALPINE
CARLINE THISTLE. - 1175. *C. acanthifolia.*   (x$\frac{2}{5}$)

LILIACEAE—LILY FAMILY

Alpine representatives all perennial, with bulbous or swollen creeping roots. Fls. usually in a raceme (in *Allium*, an umbel), usually composed of 6 similar lobes or segments (perianth-petals and sepals not differentiated); both sexes normally present; style normally 1, but 3 in *Tofieldia, Veratrum, Bulbocodium, Merendera* and *Colchicum*, which are grouped into the tribe *Colchiceae*. Stamens 6; fruit usually a 3-celled capsule or berry.

LILIUM *L.* LILY. Erect plants with a few showy fls. with prominent stamens and style; fls. in alpine species either pendulous with recurved segments ('turkscap') or open and up-facing; lvs. all carried on stem, alternate or in whorls. Bulb composed of numerous separate scales.

L. martagon *L.* MARTAGON LILY. Turkscap fls., dull pink to purplish, usually purple-spotted, sometimes very numerous, on stout 30–150 cm. stem; leaves tapered at each end, in whorls.
❋ Meadows, woods. To 2800 m. Pyrenees; Alps; Apennines. (Britain: naturalised.) June–August. **3**

L. pomponium *L.* (**L. rubrum** *Lam.*). RED LILY. Turkscap fls., scarlet, lightly black-spotted, fragrant, on slender 30–50 cm. stem. Lvs. narrow, alternate, ciliate on edges.
❋ Rocky places. Seldom above 1000 m. Provence Alps; Maritime Alps; Ligurian Alps. Rare. May–July. **2**

L. pyrenaicum *Gouan.* YELLOW TURKS-CAP LILY. Turkscap fls., bright yellow, brown-spotted, with unpleasant odour, on stout 40–80 cm. stems. Lvs. narrow, alternate, closely packed, ciliate on edges.
❋ Meadows, clearings, cliff pockets. 800–2200 m. Pyrenees. Rare. (Britain: naturalised.) June–July. **4**

L. carniolicum *Bernh.* (**L. chalcedonicum** *Jacq., non L.*). Turkscap fls., cinnabar red, with greenish flush and light spotting, usually few on stout 50–40 cm. stems. Lvs. 8 cm. long, alternate, sparse, downy below.
❋ Meadows, scrub. To 2300 m. S. E. Alps. N. W. Yugoslavia. June–July.

L. bulbiferum *L.* (**L. croceum** *Chaix*). ORANGE LILY. With 1–5 large, open, upward-facing fls., orange or orange-red, sometimes lightly spotted, scentless fls. on stout 40–60 cm. stems which are downy at the base, as are sometimes the alternate lvs. The form known as *ssp.* **bulbiferum** *Baker* carries black bulbils between the lvs. and stem, while *ssp.* **croceum** (*Chaix*) *Baker* has no bulbils; but observations suggest that this character is neither constant in the field nor genetically.
❋ Rocks, woods, meadows. To 2400 m. Pyrenees; W. and C. Alps; Apennines. May–July. **1**

GAGEA *Salisb.* Small plants with bulbs in a tunic and several small starry yellow fls. on one stem. Number of fl. segments may vary.

G. villosa *Duby* (**G. arvensis** (*Pers.*) *Dumort*). A silky-hairy plant 5–20 cm. tall with 2–20 fls., 2–3½ cm. across, in a long-stalked head rising from 2 wide, unequal bracts. Basal lvs. 2, rush-like, channelled. Bulb usually with many bulbils within the tunic. *****
❋ Pastures, waste ground. To 2200 m. C. and S. Alps; Apennines. February–May. **15**

G. soleirolii *Schultz.* With up to 10 fls., 1½–2 cm. across, with narrow segments, yellow inside, flushed green outside, on a branching 5–15 cm. stem with 2–5 narrow lvs. Basal lvs. 2, almost thread-like, often with silky hairs, arising from 2 bulbs in common tunics. *

✣ Meadows; rocky debris. 1000–2500 m. C. and E. Pyrenees. Rare. March–April. **16**

G. minima *(L.) Ker.* Not unlike *G. soleirolii*. Slender, 7–20 cm. tall, with usually 1, rarely 2, linear lvs., hooked at the top, longer than fl. stem, which carries unequal, narrow bracts under the fl.-heads. Fls. few with narrow, very pointed segments 1–1½ cm. long. 2 bulbs in common tunic.

✣ Alpine and sub-alpine pastures, especially near cow-huts. To 1600 m. Alps. Rare: not France. May–June.

G. fistulosa *(Ram.) Ker.* (**G. liotardii** *(Sternb.)* R. *& Sch.*). Carrying 1–5 fls., each 1½–3 cm. across, in head arising from 2 wide, pointed, opposite bracts; fl. stalks usually silky-hairy. Early fls. frequently 4-parted, later ones 5-parted. Basal lvs. 1–3, usually 2, rush-like, hollow; 2 bulbs in common tunic. 5–15 cm. tall.

✣ Pastures, often near cow-huts. 1200–2800 m. Pyrenees; Alps; Apennines. May–July. **14**

G. pratensis *(Pers.) Dumort.* With 1–5 fls. 2–3 cm. across, arising from 4 uneven, strongly ciliated bracts, and with very long single basal lf.; 6–20 cm. tall. 2 loose bulbs with flowering bulb in tunic.

✣ Pastures. Only at alpine levels in the Cottian Alps and (*var.* **spathacea** *Parl.*) in Apennines. March–April.

G. lutea *(L.) Ker.* YELLOW STAR OF BETHLEHEM. With 1–5 fls. 2–3 cm. across; stem 8–25 cm., with small bract below fl.-head and larger one below this

and a single wide basal lf., abruptly hooded and pointed at tip, usually shorter than fl. stem.

✣ Pastures, woods. To 1700 m. Pyrenees (rare); Alps. (Britain.) March–May.

LLOYDIA *Salisb.* **L. serotina** *(L.) Rchb.* (**L. alpina** *Salisb.*). Bulbous, with narrow basal lvs. as long as 5–12 cm. fl. stem, which carries a few narrow lvs. Fls. cup-shaped, white with brownish pink veins, usually solitary but sometimes 2–3 together.

✣ Short turf, rocky debris, on granite. 1800–3100 m. Alps. (Britain.) June–August. **894**

ALLIUM *L.* GARLIC, ONION. Bulbous plants with strong garlic smell when bruised. Fls. usually small, numerous, in an umbel at first enclosed in a spathe and then arising from 1 or more bracts formed by the split spathe. Fl. segments all similar, separate almost to the base. Bulbils sometimes present among fls., or may even replace them.

Flowers usually pink or purple, not yellow

A. vineale *L.* CROW GARLIC. Fl.-head small, with numerous bulbils which sometimes entirely replace the fls. These are few, pale pink, with projecting stamens, on stalks 4–5 times longer than fls. Stem 30–120 cm. Lvs. cylindrical, slightly channelled, hollow.

✣ Waste places. To 1900 m. Pyrenees; French Alps. (Britain.) June–August. **10**

A. sphaerocephalon *L.* ROUND-HEADED LEEK. Fl.-head dense, round, on 30–90 cm. stem. Fls. numerous, reddish purple, stamens projecting, external stalks as long as fls., central ones longer. Lvs. semi-circular in section, deeply channelled, hollow.

Var. **pygmaeum** *Perr.:* Dwarf plant with small fls.

✣ Dry places. To 2630 m. Alps; Apennines. (Britain.) *Var. pygmaeum:* Savoy (very rare). June–August. **11**

A. strictum *Schrad.* Fls. small, close-packed, the narrow segments pink or purplish with purple keel; stamens prominent. Lvs. on lower third of stem, linear, with rounded back; stem 20–50 cm., arising from bulb up to 10 cm. long.   *

✣ Rocky and grassy places. 1500–3000 m. W. Alps. Very local. July–August.

A. montanum *L.* (A. senescens *L.*, **A. fallax** *Roem. & Schultes*). MOUNTAIN ONION. Head dense, sub-spherical, on 15–30 cm. stems. Fls. small, purplish, stamens projecting. Lvs. with rounded back. Looks like Thrift.   *

✣ Dry places, rocks. To 2275 m. Pyrenees (rare); Alps; N. Apennines. June–August.   7

A. suaveolens *Jacq. non Duby.* Head very dense on 20–60 cm. stem. Fls. scented, pink with purple keels, stamens prominent. Lvs. narrow, rounded on back, on lower third of stem.

✣ Scrub, rocky and grassy places. At alpine levels in Piedmont Apennines. August–October.

A. schoenoprasum *L.* CHIVES. Head dense on 8–50 cm. stem, usually dwarf in mountains. Fls. violet-pink. Lvs. cylindrical, forming tufts.

✣ Damp meadows, rocks. To 2600 m. Alps; Apennines. Often cultivated. (Britain.) June–July.   9

A. oleraceum *L.* FIELD GARLIC. Head usually with many bulbils. Fls. few, pink, greenish or whitish, on long stalks. Lvs. linear, channelled, hollow at base, glaucous. 30–80 cm. tall; *var.* alpestre *Bruegg.* is a dwarf plant less than 30 cm. tall.

✣ Waste and cultivated places. To 2140 m. (*var. alpestre* at this level). Alps. (Britain.) June–August.

A. carinatum *L.* Very similar to *A. oleraceum*, with a sparse, long-stalked head of bright pink fls.

✣ Waste places. To 2000 ft. E. Pyrenees (very rare); S. and E. Alps; N. and C. Apennines. (Britain.) June–August.

A. narcissiflorum *Vill.* (A. pedemontanum *W.*). Unmistakable with its very large, bright pink fls. 1½ cm. across, 3–8 in head, pendulous before fls. open. Stem 20–30 cm. Lvs. flat, green.

Var. insubricum *B. & R.:* fl.-head always pendulous; lvs. glaucous.   *

✣ Calcareous debris. 1500–2000 m. W. Alps. Rare. *Var. insubricum:* only near Lakes Como and Lecco, Italy. July–August.   12

A. saxatile *M.B.* Fl.-head with very long bracts. Fls. pink or white, stamens projecting. Lvs. thread-like. 10–12 cm. tall.

✣ Rocky places. To 2100 m. Abruzzi. August–September.

Flowers yellow or whitish

A. victorialis (*L.*) *P.F.* ALPINE LEEK. With round head on 30–75 cm. stem. Fls. on short stalks, bell-shaped, greenish or yellowish white, with wide segments, stamens projecting.

✣ Woods and rocky places. 1400–2600 m. Pyrenees; Alps. June–August.   8

A. ochroleucum *W. & K.* (A. ericetorum *Thore.*, **A. suaveolens** *Duby non Jacq.*). Head 2–3 cm. across on 15–40 cm. stem. Fls. yellowish or whitish, sometimes pink-tinted. Lvs. thin and wide.   *

✣ Rocky and grassy places. To 2000 m. Pyrenees; S.E. Alps; Apennines. July–August.

A. flavum *L.* YELLOW ONION. Fls. clear yellow, on stalks of varying length, pendulous at some stages; bracts under head very long and curving over it. Stem 20–60 cm. tall.

✣ Meadows, woods, rocky places. Just reaching alpine levels in S. French Alps. June–August.   13

168

A. ursinum L. RAMSONS. With large white fls. in a loose flat-topped head. Lvs. 4–7 cm. wide, bright green. Stem 15–30 cm. tall.

✤ Woods and shady places. To 1900 m. E. Alps. (Britain.) April–June.

ERYTHRONIUM L. **E. denscanis** L. DOGSTOOTH VIOLET. A striking, unmistakable plant with large, solitary, rich pink fls., the segments pointing backwards and the stamens and style projecting. Stem 6–30 cm. Lvs. all basal, elliptical, pointed, marbled red and sometimes white, arising from white bulb supposedly like a dog's tooth.

✤ Meadows, woods, clearings. 500–2000 m. S. Pyrenees; S. Alps; Julian Alps. Local. February–April. **6**

FRITILLARIA L. FRITILLARY, SNAKES-HEAD. Bulbous plants, the alpine species having large, bell-shaped fls., usually solitary, sometimes 2.

F. pyrenaica L. PYRENEAN SNAKESHEAD. Lvs. 6–10, 4–8 cm. long, alternate, often closer together nearer the top of the 20–50 cm. stem, the lower third of the stem leafless. Fls. dusky purple, chequered, the inner segments wider than the outer, with tiny recurved tips.

✤ Meadows. 500–2000 m. Pyrenees. Local. June–July. **19**

F. tubiformis G. & G. (**F. delphinensis** Gren.). Lvs. alternate, all in upper third of 15–30 cm. stem, 8–15 mm. wide. Fls. large, glaucous dusky purple, faintly chequered, the oval segments all the same size.

Var. **moggridgei** Boiss. & Reut.: with very wide lvs. and yellow, purple-blotched fls.

Var. **burnati** Planch.: a frailer plant with narrow, channelled lvs. and pale purple fls. (Some authorities refer to F. tubiformis under the name F. burnati, but this suppresses the

paler, frailer variety mentioned, which appears to be well attested.)

✤ Meadows. 800–2000 m. Rare in S. Alps from Savoy to Tirol; Maritime Alps. *Vars. moggridgei* and *burnati*: Maritime Alps: very rare. March–June. **18**

F. tenella M. Bieb. Upper and lower lvs. opposite or in whorls, middle ones alternate; glaucous, linear. Stem 20–40 cm., with small fls. (2½–3 cm.), chequered brownish purple and yellowish; segments narrow, tending to diverge at tips. *

✤ Rocky meadows. Not above 1000 m. in Maritime Alps (very rare); at alpine levels in Apennines, where 2 or 3 variants are recorded. April–May.

F. involucrata All. Lvs. mostly all in whorls, lower opposite, the uppermost usually 3, grouped round the fl. stalk. Stem 20–40 cm., with large fl. (3½–4 cm.), greenish or yellowish, speckled purple.

✤ Rocky woods. Up to 1500 m. in Provence, Alps; Maritime and Ligurian Alps; Monte Viso. Rare. April–May. **20**

TULIPA L. TULIP. **T. australis** L. This and its variety **alpestris** Jord. & Fl. (now considered to = **T. sylvestris** L. ssp. **australis** (Link) Pamp.) are the only tulips found at alpine levels. The small, solitary fls., opening from pendant buds, are yellow, often tipped red, with outer segments stained brownish red. The species has yellow anthers and lvs. shorter than the 15–30 cm. fl. stems. The variety has brownish anthers and lvs. about as long as the fl. stems.

✤ Meadows, rocky places. To 2000 m. French Alps; Valais (Switzerland); Apennines. Rare. *Var. alpestris:* E. Pyrenees; Savoy and Dauphiné. Rare. April–July. **21**

T. didieri Jord. This purple tulip with deep blue, yellow-edged base to the long-pointed segments is an endemic of Savoy below alpine levels, dubiously recorded at 1750 m. in Valais. April–May.   *

SCILLA *L.* SQUILL. Bulbous plants with usually blue or purple fls. in a racemose spike; segments quite separate, spread out, with marked midrib.

S. bifolia *L.* ALPINE SQUILL. Usually with 2 (rarely 3) lvs., stem-clasping up to half the length of the 10–25 cm. stem. Fl. stalks without bracts; fls. bright blue, 3–8 in loose spike.
✴ Meadows, damp woods. To 1500 (2260) m. S. Alps. (local); Apennines. March–May.   22

S. verna *Huds.* SPRING SQUILL. Lvs. 3–6, narrow, arising from the base, shorter than the 5–15 cm. stem which carries a few small blue-violet fls. arising almost from the same level, each stalk with a bract at the base.
✴ Meadows, woods. To 2000 m. Pyrenees. (Britain.) March–June.   24

S. liliohyacinthus *L.* PYRENEAN SQUILL. With a large bulb from which arise several glossy lvs. 1½–3 cm. wide. The 10–40 cm. stem carries 6–20 blue fls. in a conical spike, each stalk with a bract at the base.
✴ Grassy slopes. To 2000 m. Pyrenees. April–May.   23

ORNITHOGALUM *L.* Bulbous plants with fls. usually white and green-marked, with separate segments. Stamen filaments flattened.

O. umbellatum *L.* STAR OF BETHLE-HEM. With 5–15 narrow-segmented, starry fls. clustered at about the same level on 10–30 cm. stem; lower fl. stalks longer than upper. Lvs. 15–30 cm. long, ½ mm. wide, channelled, with white central stripe. Bulb small, surrounded by bulbils.
✴ Grassy places, scrub. To 1600 m. Alps; Apennines. (Britain.) April–June.

O. pyrenaicum *L.* With 50–100 cm. stem carrying numerous small, starry greenish white fls. on short stalks of roughly equal length, in a long, narrow, tapering spike. Lvs. 30–60 cm. long, ½–1½ cm. wide.
✴ Meadows, woods. To 1000 (1500) m. Pyrenees; S. Alps; Apennines. May–July.

APHYLLANTHES (*Tourn.*) *L.* **A. monspeliensis** *L.* Tufted plant with lvs. reduced to sheaths, arising from hard rootstock. Fls. bright blue, 1–3 on thin stiff rush-like stalks 10–25 cm. tall.
✴ Dry, rocky and grassy places. Only reaching 1500 m. in Spanish Pyrenees and N. Italy. April–July.   25

ASPHODELUS *L.* ASPHODEL. **A. albus** *Mill.* (**A. macrocarpus** *Parl.*; the alpine form has been called **A. delphinensis** *G. & G.* or **A. subalpinus** *G. & G.*, and the Pyrenees form **A. sphaerocarpus** *G. & G.*). Fls. white or pink-flushed, up to 2 cm. across, tight-packed in large spikes with dark bracts on stout, rarely branched, leafless 50–150 cm. stems. Lvs. long, channelled, forming clumps; roots tuberous.
✴ Meadows, rocky slopes, woods. 900–1600 m. Pyrenees; W. and S. Alps; Apennines. May–July.   885

PARADISEA *Mazz.* **P. liliastrum** (*L.*) *Bertol.* (**Anthericum liliastrum** *L.*). ST. BRUNO'S LILY. With pure white, scented, 5 cm. long lily-like fls., of which there are up to 5, all facing the same way; segments separated. Stems leafless, 20–50 cm. tall. Basal lvs. narrow, arising from short rootstock.
✴ Meadows, rocky places. 900–2400 m. Pyrenees; Alps; N. and C. Apennines. June–August.   897

ANTHERICUM *L.* (**PHALAN-GIUM** *auct.*). Many smallish white fls.

on stiff stems above narrow basal lvs. arising from fleshy rootstock.

A. liliago *L.* **(Phalangium liliago** *Schreb.*). ST. BERNARD'S LILY. Lvs. as long as unbranched 30–60 cm. stems which carry several small lily-like fls. 3–6 cm. across.
⚜ Dry slopes, debris, in warm places. To 2000 m. Pyrenees; S. Alps. May–July. **892**

A. ramosum *L.* **(Phalangium ramosum** *Poir.*). Lvs. much shorter than branched 30–80 cm. stems which carry 2½ cm. fls.
⚜ Dry slopes, rocky places. To 2000 m. S. and Apuan Alps. June–August. **893**

DIPCADI *Medic.* **D. serotinum** (*L.*) *Medic.* **(Uropetalum serotinum** *Ker-Gawl.*). A curious plant with yellowish brown or amber 1½ cm. bell-shaped fls. with the outer segments recurved, each with a bract at the base, and all turned in the same direction on the 10–40 cm. stem. Lvs. long and narrow.
⚜ Rocks and hot, stony places. To 2400 m. C. and S. Pyrenees. Rare. July–August. **895**

HYACINTHUS (*Tourn.*) *L.* **H. amethystinus** *L.* PYRENEAN HYACINTH. Fls. blue, funnel-shaped, small, on short stalks each with a basal bract. Lvs. 1–3 cm. wide, bulb small, stem 10–30 cm. tall. *
⚜ Meadows, screes. To 1500 m. C. Pyrenees. May–July. **17**

MUSCARI *Mill.* With small urn-shaped fls., lobes very small, upper fls. sterile.

M. atlanticum *Boiss. & Reut.* **(M. racemosum** (*L.*) *Mill.*). GRAPE HYACINTH. With numerous drooping, violet-blue fls., twice as long as wide, in dense spike, on stalks shorter than the fls., with tiny bracts. Fl. lobes white, aperture minute; lvs. 3–5, very narrow,

lightly grooved, longer than 10–25 cm. stem, often recurving at top. *
⚜ Fields, vineyards. To 1800 m. S. French Alps; Engadine. (Britain.) March–May. **31**

M. botryoides (*L.*) *Mill.* With numerous nearly round blue or violet fls. in dense spike; aperture fairly large. Lvs. 4 mm. wide, widening towards summit, shorter than 10–30 cm. stem.
⚜ Fields, woods. To 2000 m. S. French Alps; S. Italian Alps (near Lake Garda), C. Appenines. March–May.

M. comosum (*L.*) *Mill.* TASSEL HYACINTH. This familiar garden fl. with its 'tassel' of sterile, violet fls. may be found at up to 1400 m. in S. France; Valais. (Casual in Britain.) April–July.

MAIANTHEMUM *Weber.* **M. bifolium** (*L.*) *Schm.* MAY LILY. A delicate plant arising from a thin creeping rhizome, readily recognised by its two alternate heart-shaped lvs. on 8–20 cm. stem terminating in a dense head of very small white fls., followed by red berries.
⚜ Woods. To 2100 m. Alps; Apennines. Norway to 1160 m. (Britain.) May–July. **896**

CONVALLARIA *L.* **C. majalis** *L.* LILY OF THE VALLEY. A well-known garden plant with creeping rhizome, with a pair of oblong, pointed, bright green lvs. surrounding the 8–20 cm. stem which carries on one side only 6–12 white, fragrant, open bell-shaped fls. with recurved lobes, followed by red berries.
⚜ Woods and scrub. To 2300 m. Alps; Apennines. Norway to 1240 m. (Britain.) May–July. **891**

POLYGONATUM *Mill.* SOLOMON'S SEAL. Erect plants arising from thick horizontal rootstock; lvs. all on stem; fls. white, 3-parted, pendulous, tubular-bell-shaped, 1 or 2 in lf. axils or a few together in whorls.

P. odoratum (*Mill.*) *Druce* (**P. officinale** *All.*). COMMON SOLOMON'S SEAL. Lvs. in 2 ranks, alternate, elliptical, 5–10 cm. long, on 15–50 cm. slightly arching stem. Fls. 2 cm. long, 1 or 2 on the same stalk in lf. axils, followed by blue-black berries.
⚜ Woods, rocky places. To 2200 m. Alps; Apennines. Norway to 1200 m. (Britain.) May–June. **898**

P. verticillatum (*L.*) *All.* WHORLED SOLOMON'S SEAL. Lvs. narrow lance-shaped, in whorls of 4 or 5, on vertical 30–100 cm. stem. Fls. 6–8 mm. long, narrow, in groups of 1–3, arising from leaf whorls, followed by blue-black berries.
⚜ Woods, meadows, rocky places. To 2400 m. Pyrenees; Alps; Apennines. Norway to 1200 m. (Britain: very rare.) May–July. **899**

STREPTOPUS *Mich.* **S. amplexifolius** (*L.*) *DC.* With zigzag 30–60 cm. stem carrying alternate lvs., heart-shaped and clasping at the base, each with a solitary 6-parted open bell-shaped white fl. on angled stalk in the axil, followed by a red berry.
⚜ Woods, damp rocky places. To 2300 m. Pyrenees; Alps; Apennines. July–August. **900**

PARIS *L.* (sometimes placed in the recently suggested family *Trilliaceae*). **P. quadrifolia** *L.* HERB PARIS. Unmistakable with its usually 4 broad, pointed lvs., in a whorl on 15–40 cm. stem bearing single green fls., usually with 4 sepal-like and 4 narrower petal-like segments, succeeded by a black berry-like fruit.
⚜ Damp woods. To 2000 m. Pyrenees to Bavarian Alps; Apennines. Norway to 1240 m. (Britain.) May–June. **890**

TOFIELDIA *Huds.* Small plants with flattened, grass-like lvs., mainly in a tufted clump, arising from a creeping rootstock; fls. tiny, yellow, in short spikes.

T. calyculata (*L.*) *Wahl.* Fls. yellow, rarely reddish (*forma* **rubra**), in an elongated spike 2–8 cm. long with 3-lobed involucre and 1 lanceolate bract. Fl. stem 10–30 cm. Lvs. with 5–10 veins.
Var. **glacialis** *Thomas:* a dwarf plant to 10 cm. wide with rounded fl.-head. *
⚜ Marshes, damp meadows, among rocks. To 2500 m. *Var. glacialis:* 1700–2800 m. Pyrenees; Alps; Apennines. Local. June–September. **886**

T. pusilla (*Miln.*) *Pers.* (**T. palustris** *Huds.*, **T. borealis** *Wahl.*, **T. alpina** *Hoppe & Stern*). SCOTTISH ASPHODEL. A smaller edition of the preceding, 5–10 cm. tall, with 3 veins to the lvs. and a more compact, ovoid fl.-head, with 3-lobed involucre but no bract. *
⚜ Marshes, damp meadows, wet sandy places. 1800–2700 m. Alps. Norway to 1600 m. (Britain to 1000 m.) July–August. **887**

VERATRUM *L.* FALSE HELLEBORE. Tall plants with creeping rootstock; lvs. large, oval, strongly veined; fls. in branched spikes. Poisonous.

V. album *L.* WHITE FALSE HELLEBORE. Fls. greenish, up to 1½ cm. across, on 50–150 cm. stem. Lvs. joined to stem by long sheaths, downy beneath (this distinguishes it from *Gentiana lutea* in the unflowered state).
⚜ Meadows and clearings light woodland. 700–2700 m. Pyrenees; Alps; Apennines. June–August. **889**

V. nigrum *L.* BLACK FALSE HELLEBORE. Similar to last but fls. purplish black, only to 1 cm. across; lvs. with short stalk ending in sheath; fl. stem 60–130 cm.

172

✠ Meadows, clearings. To 1600 m. S. and E. Alps; Apennines. June–August. **888**

BULBOCODIUM *L.* **B. vernum** *L.* (**Colchicum bulbocodium** *Ker.*). A crocus-like plant 5–15 cm. tall with lilac-pink fls., 1–3 together in the centre of the lvs. which appear at the same time, arising from corm with long blackish sheath. Distinguished from crocuses by the 6 stamens and entirely separate segments, curiously hooked together at the base, which soon recurve to form a flat 6-pointed star and do not form a tube. Style only divided into 3 near top.
✠ Meadows. To 1900 (2400) m. E. Pyrenees (rare); French Alps; Valais only in Switzerland; Val d'Aosta; Apennines. February–May. **29**

MERENDERA *Ram.* **M. pyrenaica** (*Pourr.*) *P.F.* (**M. bulbocodium** *Ram.*). Like an autumn crocus (*Colchicum*), arising from a corm, 5–15 cm. tall, with rose-pink fls., single or in pairs, with strap-shaped segments not joined into tube, soon recurving to form flat 6-pointed star. Anthers as long as filaments; stigma divided into 3 all the

way down. Lvs. grooved, usually appearing in spring.
✠ Meadows, screes. 1500–2500 m. C. Pyrenees. Local. August–September. **30**

COLCHICUM *L.* AUTUMN CROCUS. Cormous, autumn-flowering plants, the segments joined into a tube at base; anthers much shorter than filaments. Readily distinguished from *Crocus* by having 6 stamens, not 3. Poisonous.

C. autumnale *L.* AUTUMN CROCUS. Fls. mauve-pink or white, 10–25 cm. high, 1 or sometimes 2 together, stamens at 2 levels. Lvs. 4–6, appearing in spring, 20–30 cm. long, wide and glossy, surrounding the large capsule.
✠ Damp meadows. To 2000 (2200) m. Pyrenees; Alps; Apennines. (Britain.) August–October (very rarely in spring). **26**

C. alpinum *DC.* A smaller version of the preceding, 6–12 cm. high, with slender tube, much narrower segments and stamens on one level. Lvs. 2 only, appearing in spring, 6–8 cm. long.
✠ Meadows on acid soils. 600–2000 m. W. Alps, Var, Apennines. Very local. August–September (always earlier than *C. autumnale* if in same localities). **27**

IRIDACEAE—IRIS FAMILY

Alpine representatives perennial, with bulb or corm. Fls. with parts in 3's; divisions petal-like, in 2 series. Stamens and styles 3; ovary below fl.; fruit a capsule.

CROCUS *L.* Lvs. and fls. arising from a corm; fl. with long thin tube, enclosed in 1 or 2 sheaths (spathes) in bud, with 6 similar divisions. Stamens 3 (which readily distinguishes crocuses from *Colchicum, Bulbocodium,* and *Merendera,* which have 6 stamens). The violet,

autumn-flowering, British *C. nudiflorus* Sm. reaches 1200 m. in the Pyrenees.
C. purpureus *Weston* (**C. vernus** (*L.*) *Wulf.,* **C. albiflorus** *Kit.*). PURPLE CROCUS. Fls. in spring with the lvs., emerging from 2 sheaths; white or violet or sometimes combining both

colours; throat with hairs. 6–10 cm. tall. *

⚜ Wet meadows, often flowering as the snow melts. To 2700 m. Pyrenees; Alps; Apennines. (Britain.) February–June. 32

C. versicolor *Ker*. Fls. in spring with the lvs., emerging from a single sheath which splits in 2; white with violet streaks. Throat hairless. 10 cm. or more tall.

⚜ Meadows, dry places. To 1600 m. Provence and Maritime Alps; Dauphiné. February–March. 33

IRIS *L*. **I. xiphioides** *Ehrh*. ENGLISH IRIS (so-called because introduced to European gardens via England). Fls. with 2 sets of 3 parts, the outer (falls) broad and pendant, the inner (standards) erect and shorter. Colour brilliant blue to violet, with white and orange marks on falls. Fls. 2 or 3, on stout 30–70 cm. stem encased in short sheathing lvs., with long narrow basal lvs. arising from large bulb surrounded with brown fibres. *

⚜ Meadows. To 2200 m. Pyrenees. July–August. 28

AMARYLLIDACEAE—DAFFODIL FAMILY

Bulbous perennials, many being well-known garden plants. Fls. with parts in 3's, divisions petal-like, sometimes in 2 series, sometimes with central disk or trumpet (corona). Ovary below fls.; fruit a capsule.

GALANTHUS *L*. **G. nivalis** *L*. SNOWDROP. Fl. solitary, pendant, with outer bell of 3 white divisions and inner tube of 3 smaller white, green-tipped divisions. Lvs. 2, to 25 cm. long, 4 mm. broad, bluish.

⚜ Damp woods, meadows. To 1600 (2200) m. Pyrenees; S. Alps; Apennines (rare). (Britain.) February–May. 41

LEUCOJUM *L*. **L. vernum** *L*. SPRING SNOWFLAKE. Fl. usually solitary, pendant, bell-shaped, with 6 equal white, green-tipped divisions. Lvs. 30–40 cm. long, 1 cm. broad, bright green.

⚜ Damp woods and meadows. To 1600 m., but usually much lower. Alps; N.W. Italy. (Britain.) February–April. 42

NARCISSUS *L*. DAFFODIL. Fls. with 6 usually outspread divisions and central disk or trumpet (corona).

N. pseudonarcissus *L*. LENT LILY. A trumpet daffodil, native in Britain as a smallish plant with sulphur-yellow, rather bicoloured fls., which has many

subspecies, of which the following are likely to be seen in mountain regions.

⚜ All grow on grassy slopes or in rocky places. To 2150 m. Flowering March–June according to locality. *

Ssp. **abscissus** (*Schultes f.*) *Fernandes* (**N. muticus** *Baker*). 20–30 cm. tall, with large fls.; divisions pale yellow, trumpet orange-yellow with almost straight edge, as if cut off. Pyrenees. 37

Ssp. **bicolor** (*L.*) *Baker var.* **lorifolius** (*Herbert*) *Fernandes* (**N. lorifolius** *Schultes f.*). Similar to *ssp. abscissus*, but trumpet with 6 wavy lobes. Pyrenees.

Ssp. **nobilis** (*Schultes f.*) *Fernandes*. PYRENEAN LENT LILY. The biggest of the group, reaching 40 cm. tall, with very large fls., frequently bicoloured with white divisions and deep yellow or pale orange recurving trumpet. N. Spanish Pyrenees. 38

Ssp. **pallidiflorus** (*Pugsley*) *Fernandes* (*var.* **pallidus praecox** *Parl.*). PALE LENT LILY. 10–30 cm. tall, with medium-sized, pale yellow, sometimes bi-coloured, usually rather drooping fls.

with a marked tube behind the wavy divisions. Pyrenees. **36**

Ssp. **alpestris** *(Pugsley) Fernandes.* ALPINE LENT LILY. Only 10–15 cm. tall, with drooping creamy white fls., the divisions drooping around the longer, narrow trumpet. Pyrenees, especially Spanish. **39**

N. poeticus *L.* PHEASANT-EYE NARCISSUS. Fl. white with central red-edged disk. Lvs. bluish, 7–8 mm. wide. 30–60 cm. tall. **34**

Ssp. **radiiflorus** *(Salisb.) Baker* (**N. angustifolius** *Curtis*) has lvs. 3–4 mm. wide and fl. divisions narrowed at the base. **35**

✤ Damp meadows. To 2300 m. Pyrenees; Alps. *Ssp. radiiflorus:* to 2000 m. Apennines. (Naturalised in Britain.) April–May. **34, 35**

N. juncifolius *Lag.* RUSH-LEAVED NARCISSUS. Fls. golden yellow, 2 cm. across, 2 or rarely up to 5 together, with central disk or cup, fragrant. Lvs. semi-cylindrical, very thin. 10–20 cm. tall. *

✤ Stony places. To 1600 m. Pyrenees. April–May. **40**

DIOSCOREACEAE—YAM FAMILY

One curious member of this mainly tropical family is found in the Pyrenees.

DIOSCOREA *Plum. ex Ling.* **D. pyrenaica** *Bub. & B.* (**Borderea pyrenaica** *(Bub.) Mièg.*). Arises from a blackish tuber surrounded by bulbils at the top, with an angular, hollow 5–25 cm. stem with short branches in the upper third; lvs. heart-shaped. Fls. unisexual, green, buds bell-shaped, of 6, equal segments, only 1–2 mm. across; the males in small spikes, the females 1–3 together; fruit a dry 3-winged capsule. *

✤ Rocks, debris. To 2500 m. Pyrenees. Very local. June–September. **999**

Tamus communis *L.* BLACK BRYONY. A British native, reaches 1200 m. in the Alps and Pyrenees.

JUNCACEAE—RUSH FAMILY

Typically perennial, tufted or creeping-rooted plants, superficially grass-like but often with lvs. of rounded section with sheaths at the base. Fls. like those of the Lily family in miniature, with 6 segments in 2 series, usually greenish or brownish; 6 stamens and 3 brush-like stigmas. The fls. are carried in crowded cymes or in dense heads.

Examples are given of members of this small family which reach alpine levels.

JUNCUS *L.* RUSH. Lvs. smooth, variously shaped but seldom flat; capsule many-seeded. At least 15 alpine species, of which 3 are described.

J. jacquinii *L.* Forming dense tufts of slender 10–30 cm. stem-like lvs. with pointed basal sheaths. Fls. 4–12 together, purplish brown, in a long-stalked head carried in the upper quarter of the stem.

✤ Damp meadows on acid soils. 1500–3180 m. Alps; Apennines. July–September. **45**

J. arcticus *Willd.* ARCTIC RUSH. With fairly thick, channelled, 15–30 cm. stem-like lvs. spaced out along long creeping rhizomes. Fls. 2–8 together, brownish, in stalkless heads in the upper quarter of the stem.

⚘ Damp, sandy places. 1600–2500 m. Pyrenees (rare); French and Swiss Alps (rare), eastwards into Tyrol; Apennines. Norway to 1300 m. June–August. **43**

J. trifidus *L.* THREE-LEAVED RUSH. Forming dense tufts, often in circular patches, of soft, slender, 10–30 cm. stem-like lvs. with a mass of sheaths at the base. Fls. 1–4, dark brown, in a tight cluster, with 2–3 thread-like bracts 2–8 cm. long.

⚘ Rocky meadows, debris, rock ledges, usually on acid soils. 1500–3200 m. Pyrenees; Alps; Apennines. Norway to 1850 m. (Britain: Scottish mountains.) June–August. **44**

LUZULA *DC.* WOODRUSH. Lvs. usually with sparse hairs, flat or grooved, and grass-like; capsule 3-seeded. About 12 alpine species of which 4 are described.

L. lutea (*All.*) *Lam. & DC.* YELLOW WOODRUSH. A handsome plant with yellow fls. in a group of long-stalked clusters on 10–30 cm. stems. Lvs. bluish, 4–8 cm. long, 6 mm. wide.

⚘ Debris, grassy places, on acid soils. 1800–3500 m. C. and E. Pyrenees; Alps; N. Apennines. July–August. **48**

L. nivea *Lam. & DC.* SNOWY WOODRUSH. A striking plant 30–90 cm. high with silvery white fls., each 5–6 mm. across, 6–20 in stalked clusters. Stems stiff, erect, with arching hairy-edged lvs. up to 30 cm. long, 4 mm. wide.

⚘ Grassy clearings. To 2270 m. Pyrenees; Alps; N. Apennines. June–August. **46**

L. alpinopilosa (*Chaix*) *Breistr.* (**L. spadicea** (*All.*) *Lam. & DC.*). BROWNISH WOODRUSH. 10–30 cm. tall, with almost hairless lvs., 1–3 mm. wide. Fls. small, brownish, in small much-branched clusters.

⚘ Damp meadows, debris, scrub. 1100–3260 m. Pyrenees; Alps; Apennines. July–August. **47**

L. spicata (*L.*) *Lam. & DC.* SPIKED WOODRUSH. A tufted plant, 10–20 (50) cm. high, with sparsely hairy lvs. 2–8 cm. long, 2 mm. wide. Fls. dark brown in dense, drooping, spike-like clusters.

⚘ Meadows, debris, heaths, on acid soils. 1600–3500 m. Pyrenees; Alps. Norway to 2200 m. (Britain: northern mountains.) June–August. **49**

GRAMINEAE—GRASS FAMILY

A very large family with at least 100 alpine species, of which only a handful are illustrated as examples. These plants are difficult to identify and full descriptions are not attempted.

Typically perennial, sometimes annual, the perennials having both sterile and flowering stems, the latter usually hollow between solid nodes. Lvs. narrow, with a base forming a sheath around the stem; at the junction of blade and sheath there is often a flap-like structure or ring of hairs called a *ligule*. Fls. arranged in spikelets, each of which usually carried 2 scale-like bracts (*glumes*) at the base and includes 1 or more *florets*. The spikelets may have footstalks, or have short or no stalks and be packed into a tight spike. The florets each have an outer bract (*lemma*), an inner bract (*palea*), 2 or usually 3 stamens, and a 1-celled ovary carrying usually 2 feathery stigmas. The lemma may carry a stiff bristle-like *awn* on its back or tip.

ANTHOXANTHUM *L.* **A. odoratum** *L.* SWEET VERNAL GRASS. A tufted grass 20–50 cm. tall, interesting as an important component of meadows and, with its smell of coumarin, providing the typical odour of new-mown grass. Lvs. flat, short, pointed, sparsely hairy; sheaths smooth; ligule 4 mm. long. Fls. in a narrow compact panicle with stemless spikelets, in which the translucent, keeled glumes are prominent.
❀ Meadows. To 3000 m. Pyrenees; Alps; Apennines. Norway to 1960 m. (Britain.) April–June.

STIPA *L.* (sometimes spelt **STYPA**). **S. pennata** *L.* FEATHER GRASS. 40–100 cm. tall, with long, thin-channelled lvs.; unmistakable with its feathery, silvery awns 15–30 cm. long, twisted at the base, which bear the seed aloft in the wind when ripe.
❀ Stony or sandy places, grassy slopes. To 2500 m. Alps; Apennines. May–August. **901**

PHLEUM *L.* With dense ovoid or cylindrical spikes (panicles). Spikelets of 1 compressed floret.

P. pratense *L.* TIMOTHY. A stout grass 50–100 cm. tall, with dense cylindrical spike 6–15 cm. long (exceptionally to 30 cm.), 6–10 mm. wide. Lemma much shorter than glumes.
❀ Meadows. To 2650 m. Pyrenees; Alps; Apennines. (Britain.) June–July.
The similar but shorter-spiked **P. commutatum** *Gaud.* reaches 1800 m. in Norway. *

P. alpinum *L.* ALPINE CATSTAIL. Similar to *P. pratense*, but not exceeding 50 cm., and with ovoid, violet spike. Lemma as long as glumes.
❀ Meadows. 1000–2900 m. Pyrenees; Alps; Apennines. (British mountains.) June–August. **902**

AGROSTIS *L.* **A. alpina** *Scop.* ALPINE

BENT. With fibrous rootstock, 10–20 cm. tall. Spikelets of 1 floret, in a loose panicle on spreading stalks. Glumes unequal.
❀ Rocky debris, meadows, on acid soils. To 3100 m. Pyrenees; Alps; Ligurian Apennines. July–October. **906**

CALAMAGROSTIS *Adans.* **C. villosa** (*Chaix*) *Mutel.* (**C. halleriana** *P.B.*, **C. alpina** *Host.*). SHAGGY SMALLREED. A tall but slender grass 60–100 cm. high, with long, loose compound panicle. Spikelets 4 mm. long.
❀ Woodland clearings, damp meadows, on acid soils. To 2550 m. Alps (very rare in French Alps). July–August. **907**

DESCHAMPSIA *P.B.* **D. flexuosa** (*L.*) *Trin.* (**Aira flexuosa** *L.*). WAVY HAIR GRASS. A slender grass 25–40 cm. tall with loose 5–10 cm. panicle in which some of the long branches are wavy. Spikelets of 2 florets, shining.
Var. **montana** *Huds.:* a smaller plant with panicle not exceeding 5 cm., spikelets large but fewer, which is more likely to be seen at high altitudes.
❀ Woods, meadows, rocky places, on acid soils. To 2700 m. Pyrenees; Alps; Apennines. Norway to 2050 m. (Britain.) May–August. **905**

TRISETUM *Pers.* With compound panicle of shining compressed spikelets carrying 2–4 florets. Lemma with 2 bristly points and an angled awn on the back.

T. spicatum (*L.*) *Rich.* (**T. subspicatum** *P.B.*). With thick 5–20 cm. stems, downy near top, and flat or folded lvs. Panicle violet, yellow and green, almost spike-like; spikelets nearly stalkless.
❀ Meadows, debris, moraines. 1900–3800 m. Pyrenees; Alps (rather local). Norway to 2220 m. July–October. **903**

T. distichophyllum (*Vill.*) *P.B.* With short glaucous lvs. in 2 ranks on the long, rampant sterile shoots. Sheath of uppermost lf. very long on the 10–30 cm. fl. stem.

❀ Rocky places, screes, on limestone. 1200–3300 m. E. Pyrenees (very local); Alps (local). July–August. **904**

HELICTOTRICHON *Bess.* ex *Roem. & Schult.* H. versicolor (*Vill.*) *Pilg.* (Avena versicolor *Vill.*, A. scheuchzeri *All.*). VARIEGATED OAT. With stiff, hairless, white-edged lvs. on 20–60 cm. stems, bearing a 3–6 cm. ovoid panicle of large shining spikelets splashed with violet, yellow and green, each with 4–5 florets; glumes with a long, bent awn on the back. *

❀ Meadows, rocky places. 1400–3250 m. Pyrenees; Alps; Apennines. Local. July–September. **908**

OREOCHLOA *Link.* O. disticha *Link.* (Sesleria disticha (*Wulf.*) *Pers.*). Lvs. slender, inrolled, forming a compact clump with 10–20 cm. fl. stems. Panicle 1–3 cm. long, somewhat 1-sided with stalkless spikelets in 2 rows. Exterior glumes streaked with blue.

❀ Pastures, rocky places. 1900–3300 m. Pyrenees (local); Alps. July–August. **909**

SESLERIA *Scop.* With stiff lvs. and bluish, ovoid, dense panicles. Spikelets with 3–5 florets.

S. ovata (*Hoppe*) *Kern.* Like a smaller version of *Oreochloa disticha* with 5–7 mm. panicle. Lemmas with 5 awns.

❀ Debris, moraines. 2200–2800 m. French Alps (very rare); C. and E. Alps. July–August.

S. caerulea (*L.*) *Ard.* ssp. calcarea *Čel.* BLUE SESLERIA. Lvs. forming large clumps; long, parallel-sided, abruptly pointed, 2–4 mm. wide; highest lf. very short. Panicle 1–3 cm. long. Lemmas with 3 awns.

❀ Rocky slopes. To 3200 m. Pyrenees; Alps; Apennines. (A form in Britain.) March–August. **912**

KOELERIA *Pers.* (sometimes spelt **KOEHLERIA**). K. hirsuta (*DC.*) *Gaud.* With 10–25 cm. stem, downy at top and on the nodes; spikelets also downy, of 2–3 florets, short-stalked, forming a narrow spike-like panicle.

❀ Rocky places. 1700–3150 m. S. and S.E. Alps (very rare in Switzerland). June–August. **914**

POA *L.* P. alpina *L.* ALPINE POA. Forming tufts from a stout rootstock surrounded by the fibrous remains of old lvs. Lvs. short, 4 mm. broad, stiff, abruptly pointed, partly or entirely folded. Panicle on 10–40 cm. stem, ovoid to pyramidal, rather loose, 2–5 cm. Spikelets nearly as broad as long, with 2–4 florets, often purple or purple and green (sometimes called *var.* **seminifera**—910a); but very often viviparous, e.g. producing plantlets which on falling to the ground take root (sometimes called *var.* **vivipara** —910b).

❀ Dry meadows. 1400–2500 (4225) m. Pyrenees; Alps; Apennines. Norway to 2000 m. (Britain.) May–October.

910 a, b

P. bulbosa *L.*, which has elliptic, woolly spikelets, is also viviparous. It is a plant of the more southerly mountains, reaching 2500 m.

FESTUCA *L.* F. varia *Haenke.* COLOURED FESCUE. Lvs. glaucous, thread-like, oval-sectioned, forming a tussock. Stems 15–30 cm. tall, tending to bend over under the weight of the large ovoid spikelets which have 3–5 florets.

❀ Grassy and rocky places. 1500–3000 m. Pyrenees; Alps (rare); Apennines. July–August. **911**

NARDUS *L.* N. stricta *L.* MAT GRASS. A very wiry plant with hard spiky lvs., at first upright, later spreading sideways, forming a tuft surrounded by the whitish remains of old lvs. Stems thin,

10–50 cm. tall, carrying on one side a 2–10 cm. spike with 2 ranks of spikelets of 1 floret each with only a tiny lower glume.

✤ Moors and grassy places, on peat or acid soils. 900–2200 (3000) m. Pyrenees; Alps; Apennines. Norway to 1750 m. (Britain.) May–June.   **913**

CYPERACEAE—SEDGE FAMILY

Grass-like, usually perennial plants, often with rhizomes, and narrow, flattened lvs., sometimes reduced to sheaths. Fls. small, with either one or both sexes present, very variable, with no floral segments except sometimes bristles in the male fls., but stamens and stigmas visible. Stems frequently triangular in section.

A very large family, with scores of alpine species, too specialised for extensive treatment here. Most of the showy alpine cotton grasses (*Eriophorum*) are described here, but only 3 of the true sedges (*Carex*) as examples. Besides these genera, *Scirpus*, *Kobresia* or *Cobresia*, and *Elyna* have alpine species.

ERIOPHORUM L. COTTONGRASS. Perennials forming tufts or with creeping rhizome. Lvs. green in winter, but usually dead at fl. time. Fls. with both sexes present, with silvery membranous glumes, and many bristles which lengthen and become cottony in seed.

E. vaginatum L. HARESTAIL. Forming tussocks of stiff, 3-angled lvs. 1 mm. wide. Fl. stems 20–70 cm., triangular at top, carrying pointed bracts forming a swollen funnel which entirely clasp the stem at their base. Fl.-head cylindrical, becoming in fruit a large round mass of cottony hairs 2–3 cm. long.
✤ Acid marshes. To 2600 m. Pyrenees; Alps. (Britain.) June–August.   **918**

E. scheuchzeri Hoppe. Similar to *E. vaginatum*, but with softer lvs. and entirely rounded stems 10–40 cm. tall, carrying narrow tubular bracts enclosing the stem. Cottony hairs 1½–2½ cm. long.
✤ Marshes. 1500–2900 m. Pyrenees; Alps; Apennines. Norway to 1800 m. June–October.   **916**

E. angustifolium Honck. COMMON COTTONGRASS. A wide-creeping plant with rounded 20–60 cm. stem carrying long clasping stem-lvs., 3–6 mm. wide, the topmost with a funnel-shaped sheath. Basal lvs. keeled and channelled, 3-angled at the pointed tip. Fl. spikes 3–7 on slender, smooth branches, narrow-oval, pointed, developing into 3–4 cm. cottony hairs.
✤ Acid bogs, pools, marshes. To 2700 m. Pyrenees; Alps. Norway to 1700 m. (Britain.) April–July.   **915**

E. latifolium Hoppe. Very similar to *E. angustifolium*, but with flat lvs. up to 8–9 mm. wide, arising from a rootstock. Fl. branches very rough.
✤ Calcareous bogs, marshes. To 2100 m. Pyrenees; Alps. (Britain.) April–June.

E. alpinum L. (**Trichosporum alpinum** (L.) Pers.). ALPINE COTTONGRASS. A more or less creeping plant with most of the sheaths leafless, a few having a short blade. Stem 10–30 cm. tall with single fl.-head, carrying in fruit a few crumpled cottony hairs up to 2 cm. long.   *

❀ Bogs, marshes. 1500–2280 m. Alps. (Recorded in Britain, but now believed extinct.) April–May.   **917**

CAREX L. SEDGE. Perennials with rhizomes, extremely variable, with 1-sexed fls., 1 to each spikelet, each with a glume at the base, and no fl. segments nor bristles; fl.-heads sometimes branched, sometimes spike-like. Only 3 species are described here as examples of a very large number.

C. baldensis L. MONTE BALDO SEDGE. A distinctive species with its whitish fl.-head 2½ cm. across and long horizontal bracts around it. 15–25 (40) cm. tall, with narrow, pointed lvs.

❀ Meadows, stony places. To 2400 m. E. Alps. May–July.   **919**

C. atrata L. DARK SEDGE. With grass-like lvs. 5 mm. wide. Stem 10–50 cm. long, often nodding, with 2–4 or more blackish, rounded fl. spikes 1–2 cm. long.

❀ Meadows, rocky places. 1800–3000 (3500) m. Pyrenees; Alps. Norway to 1920 m. (Britain: northern mountains.) June–August.   **921**

C. atrofusca Schkuhr (also spelt **atrifusca**). BLACK SEDGE. With grass-like lvs. 3–5 mm. wide. Stem 10–35 cm. tall, with 2–4 reddish black fl. spikes 1–1½ cm. tall.

❀ Micaceous marshes. 1500–2700 m. Pyrenees; Alps (very rare in French and Swiss Alps). Norway to 1700 m. (Britain: very rare.) July–August.   **920**

ORCHIDACEAE—ORCHID FAMILY

Perennials, usually with tuberous roots, sometimes rhizomes or rootstocks; occasionally saprophytic (living on decaying matter) and then without lvs. or green colouring matter (*Epipogium, Corallorhiza, Neottia*). Lvs. variously arranged, usually at the base of the stem and also on it. Fls. usually in spikes, sometimes only 1 or 2 together, often with bracts among them. Fls. symmetrical if divided vertically, with 3 outer segments (described as sepals), one vertical and the others lateral (except in *Cypripedium*); 2 inner segments (described as petals) placed in the angles between the sepals; and the sixth segment, the lip, usually much larger, often lobed, or forming a pouch in *Cypripedium*. The lip is usually the lowest point of the fl. except in *Epipogium* and *Nigritella*. In many orchids there is a nectar-containing spur at the back of the lip. Stamens and stigma are combined into a *column*, a structure unique to the orchid family. The ovary, placed below the fl., is often twisted, and in fruit becomes a dry capsule with numerous minute seeds.

CYPRIPEDIUM L. **C. calceolus** L. LADY'S SLIPPER ORCHID. The most impressive of European orchids, with horizontal rhizome and 15–50 (70) cm. stem, carrying 3–4 large ovate-oblong, furrowed lvs. Fls. 1, rarely 2, 6–9 cm. across, projecting from a lf.-like bract on an arching stalk. Sepals and petals reddish maroon, the lateral sepals usually combined into a single down-pointing segment; lip yellow, forming a large pouch. Now becoming scarce due to excessive picking and collecting, but still abundant in some localities.

❀ Grassy clearings, woods. To 2000 m.

180

Pyrenees (rare); Alps. Norway to 1120 m. (Britain: almost extinct.) May–July.
52

CEPHALANTHERA *Rich.* **C. rubra** (*L.*) *Rich.* RED HELLEBORINE. A slender, stately orchid, 20–60 cm. tall, with creeping rhizomes, long narrow lvs. and a loose spike of carmine-pink fls. 3 cm. across, with large segments and lip of similar size; no spur; each fl. with a long bract at the base.
❧ Stony woods. To 1800 m. Pyrenees (rare); Alps (local). (Britain: very rare.) May–July.
55

EPIPACTIS *Sw.* HELLEBORINE. Leafy-stemmed plants, with short rhizomes and fleshy roots. Fls. typically hanging, with triangular segments of similar size, and a lip jointed in the centre; no spur; ovary not twisted, but fl. stalk is.

E. atrorubens (*Hoffm.*) *Schultes* (**E. atropurpurea** *Raf.*). DARK RED HELLE-BORINE. 15–60 (100) cm. tall, stem downy; lvs. large and numerous in 2 opposite ranks; fls. in a loose spike, dark red or reddish violet, often greenish inside, each with a bract at the base; lip shorter than other segments.
❧ Woods, grass, scree, sand, rock crevices. To 2185 (2380) m. Pyrenees; Alps; Apennines. Norway to 1250 m. (Britain.) May–August.
50

E. helleborine (*L.*) *Crantz* (**E. lati-folia** (*L.*) *All.*). Similar to *E. atrorubens*, but lvs. in a spiral and fls. greenish, often with red or purple flush. Stem 25–60 (90) cm. tall, with short hairs towards top.
❧ Woods, clearings. To 1750 m. Pyrenees; Alps. (Britain.) June–September.

EPIPOGIUM *Gmel.* (also spelt **EPI-POGON**). **E. aphyllum** *Sw.* GHOST ORCHID. A saprophyte, always local and erratic in appearance, arising from a much-lobed fleshy rhizome, the 5–20

(30) cm. stem swollen at the base. Stem translucent, with a few tightly sheathing scales, bearing 1–4 fls. with narrow yellowish white petals and sepals and pinkish lip, the latter up-turned, with curious serrated crests; spur short and broad.
❧ Beech and pine woods. To 1900 m. Pyrenees; Alps; Apennines. (Britain: very rare.) June–September.
53

LISTERA *R.Br.* TWAYBLADE. With short rhizomes and erect stems, nor-mally bearing a single pair of more or less opposite lvs.

L. cordata (*L.*) *R.Br.* LESSER TWAY-BLADE. An insignificant orchid 4–20 cm. tall, arising from a creeping rhizome, with the pair of lvs. in the lower part of the stem, and a spike (raceme) of 6–12 small fls. with tiny bracts at the base. Segments green; lip reddish, forked at the base and with 2 strap-shaped side lobes.
❧ Woods, usually pine, in moss and on decaying trees, or in wet places; sometimes on heath moors. 1400–2300 m. Pyrenees; Alps; Apennines. Nor-way to 1100 m. (Britain: especially on mountains.) May–September.
51

L. ovata (*L.*) *R.Br.* TWAYBLADE. In-stantly recognisable by its pair of 5–20 cm., rounded, ribbed lvs. on the lower part of the 20–60 cm. stem, which carries a loose spike (raceme), up to 25 cm. long, of numerous greenish fls., the narrow, deeply forked 1–1½ cm. lip being their most prominent part.
❧ Woods, woodside meadows. To 2100 (2300) m. Pyrenees; Alps; Apen-nines. (Britain.) May–July.

NEOTTIA *Ludw.* **N. nidus-avis** (*L.*) *Rich.* BIRDSNEST ORCHID. This sapro-phyte gets its name from the mass of twisted, fleshy, pale buff roots sur-rounding the rhizomes. The 20–45 (60) cm. stem has sheathing scales only and a large head (raceme) of pale brown

fls. with segments forming a loose 'hood' above the prominent lip, divided at the apex into 2 lobes; no spur.
⚜ Shady woods, mainly beech, especially over calcareous soil. To 1700 m. Pyrenees; Alps. (Britain.) May–August. 56

CORALLORHIZA *Chat.* (also spelt **CORALLIORRHIZA**). C. trifida *Chat.* (**C. innata** *R.Br.*). CORALROOT ORCHID. A saprophyte with much-branched coral-like rhizomes. Stem 7–25 cm., yellowish, with long sheathing scales and a loose spike (raceme) of 4–12 small, hanging, yellowish green fls., with strap-shaped segments curving down towards the strap-shaped, 3-lobed lip; no spur.
⚜ Woods, occasionally in meadows. 1400–2700 m. Pyrenees; Alps; Apennines. Norway to 1150 m. (Britain.) May–August. 54

GOODYERA *R.Br.* G. repens (*L.*) *R.Br.* CREEPING LADY'S TRESSES. With creeping rhizomes ending in leafy rosettes. Stems 10–35 cm. tall with small white, fragrant fls. in a spiral, 1-sided spike (raceme). Side sepals somewhat spreading; top sepal and petals coming together; lip concave, in 2 distinct parts; no spur.
⚜ Woods, especially of conifers; mossy places; preferring acid soils. To 2200 m. Pyrenees; Alps. (Britain.) July–September. 59

CHAMORCHIS *L.* (also spelt **CHAMAEORCHIS**). C. alpina *Rich.* FALSE ORCHID. An insignificant orchid 6–12 cm. tall. Tuberous; lvs. narrow and grass-like, often exceeding the stem which carries a few fls. 7 mm. long, with very small green segments arching together and a larger, yellowish lip.
⚜ Damp short grass. 1600–2700 (2900) m. Alps. July–August. 1176

HERMINIUM *Schaeff.* H. monorchis (*L.*) *R.Br.* MUSK ORCHID. Another

insignificant orchid, 7–15 (30) cm. tall, with 2–4 lvs. 2–7 cm. long; spike slender, of tiny greenish fls., more or less bell-shaped and drooping, smelling of musk. With small tubers, 1 sessile, 2–5 on separate subterranean stems.
⚜ Dry meadows on calcareous soils. To 1800 (2000) m. Pyrenees; Alps; Apuan Alps. (Britain.) May–August. 61

COELOGLOSSUM *Hartm.* C. viride (*L.*) *Hartm.* FROG ORCHID. 6–25 (35) cm. tall, with lobed tubers. Lvs. 3–5, bluish, rounded to oblong, stem lvs. narrow and pointed. Spike with a few fls. and prominent bracts; segments greenish, forming a hood, above the 3-lobed green or reddish lip; spur 2 mm. long.
⚜ Meadows, scrub, rocky places. To 2700 (3000) m. Pyrenees (rare); Alps; Apennines. Norway to 1740 m. (Britain.) May–August. 1177

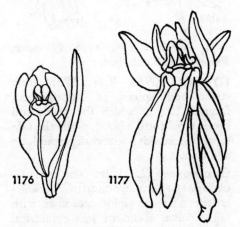

1176. *Chamorchis alpina.* 1177. *Coeloglossum viride.* Florets, over life size.

NIGRITELLA *L.* VANILLA ORCHID. With rounded or slightly egg-shaped, very tight-packed blackish red or pink fl. spike on an angular stem; lip turned upwards. Lvs. narrow, grass-like. Tubers lobed. Hybrids with *Gymnadenia* spp. often occur.

N. nigra (*L.*) *Reichb. f.* (**N. angusti-folia** *Rich.*). BLACK VANILLA ORCHID. Spike usually rounded, sometimes elongated; fls. usually blackish red; segments and lip all much the same size, forming a rough 6-pointed star.
✤ Meadows. To 2780 m. Pyrenees; Alps; Apennines. Norway to 1270 m. May–September. **57, 1178**

N. rubra (*Wettst.*) *Rich.* (**N. suaveolens** *Dall.*). ROSY VANILLA ORCHID. Similar to *N. nigra* but fls. flesh-pink to rose; segments narrow; lip broadly triangular, pointed. Sometimes considered a hybrid with *Gymnadenia*.   *
✤ Meadows. 1600–2300 (2500) m. E. and S.E. Alps. May–July.   **58, 1179**

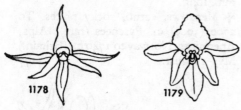

1178. *Nigritella nigra.* 1179. *N. rubra.* Florets, much enlarged.

GYMNADENIA *R.Br.* With leafy stems and spikes of tight-packed, fragrant fls., in which the petals and upper sepal form a hood, while the side sepals spread out horizontally; spur long and thin.

G. conopsea (*L.*) *R.Br.* (also spelt **G. conopea**). FRAGRANT ORCHID. A characteristic plant of alpine meadows with fairly dense, more or less cylindrical spike 6–10 cm. long on stout 15–40 (60) cm. stem. Lvs. long and narrow; stem lvs. small, closely pressed to the stem. Fls. about 1 cm. across, a rather bluish pink or red, with rather sickly fragrance; each fl. accompanied by a long bract; spur about 12 mm. long, curving downward, usually twice as long as ovary.
✤ Meadows, edges of woods. To 2450

m. Pyrenees; Alps; Apennines. Norway to 1400 m. (Britain.) May–August. **60**

G. odoratissima (*L.*) *Rich.* A smaller, frailer edition of *G. conopsea,* 15–40 cm. tall, with 5–7 mm., paler fls., and spur only as long as ovary. Very fragrant of vanilla.
✤ Meadows, light woodland. To 2700 m. N. Pyrenees; Alps; Piedmont Apennines; Apuan Alps. May–August, always later than *G. conopsea* where they occur together.

LEUCORCHIS *E.Mey.* **L. albida** (*L.*) *E.Mey.* (**Gymnadenia albida** (*L.*) *Rich.*, **Bicchia albida** *Parl.*). 10–35 cm. tall; similar to *Gymnadenia,* but all sepals and petals forming a hood; fls. very small—2–2½ mm.—greenish white, in a dense, narrow, cylindrical spike. Spur relatively thick, down-pointing, less than ½ length of ovary. Tubers divided into cylindrical sections.   *
✤ Meadows. To 2550 m. Pyrenees (rare); Alps; Apennines. Norway to 1800 m. (Britain.) May–September. **62**

PLATANTHERA *Rich.* BUTTERFLY ORCHID. Fl. spikes loose, with no bracts, of large, strongly fragrant whitish fls. with long strap-shaped lip and long thin spur. The relative position of the pollinia is diagnostic. The latter, the pollen-masses, are horn-shaped structures 2–4 mm. long in the centre of the fl. under the hood formed by the upper sepal and petals. The tubers are tapering.

P. bifolia *Rich.* LESSER BUTTERFLY ORCHID. 15–50 cm. tall, with more or less cylindrical spike; fls. white, 11–18 mm. wide; lip 6–10 mm. long; spur 15–20 mm. long; pollinia 2 mm. long, vertical and parallel.
✤ Woods, meadows, occasionally marshes (in typically small form). To 2300 m. Pyrenees; Alps; Apennines; Norway to 1240 m. (Britain.) May–July. **63, 1180**

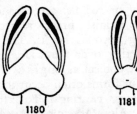

1180. *Platanthera chlorantha.* 1181. *P. bifolia.* Relative positions of pollinia, much enlarged.

P. chlorantha (*Cust.*) *Reichb.* GREATER BUTTERFLY ORCHID. 20–60 cm. tall, with more or less pyramidal spike; fls. creamy white or greenish white, 18–23 mm. wide; lip 10–16 mm. long; spur 19–28 mm. long; pollinia 4 mm. long, not vertical, and leaning together at their upper ends.
✤ Woods, meadows. To 1800 m. S. Alps, Apennines. (Britain.) May–July. **1181**

OPHRYS *L.* **O. insectifera** *L.* (**O. muscifera** *Huds.*). FLY ORCHID. A tuberous orchid with leafy stems 15–60 cm. tall, carrying 4–12 well-spaced fls. Sepals greenish; petals very narrow, purplish brown; lip 12 mm. long, fly-like, with narrow side lobes and divided central lobe, purplish brown with central shining blue patch.
✤ Grassy places, woods, on calcareous soils. To 1850 m. Alps. (Britain.) May–July. **64**

ORCHIS *L.* With fls. in a spike; lip usually 3-lobed, with a hood above it formed by the sepals and petals, or at least the petals, arching together; spur pointing up or down. Bracts membranous. Basal lvs. forming a rosette; stem lvs. sheathing. Tubers rounded.

O. mascula (*L.*) *L.* EARLY PURPLE ORCHID. 15–60 cm. tall, with stout stem, arising from a tight rosette of narrow, sometimes purple-spotted lvs. Fls. in a loose spike, purplish crimson, with a rather disagreeable catty odour, which is lacking in the typical alpine

form *var.* **speciosa** *Mutel.* Side sepals outspread; central sepal and petals forming a hood over the large, 3-lobed lip, which has a pale basal zone dotted with dark purple; spur straight, blunt-ended, horizontal or up-pointing.
✤ Woods, meadows. To 2650 m. Pyrenees; Alps; Apennines. (Britain.) April–June; *var. speciosa* into August. **66**

O. spitzelii *Saut.* 20–40 cm. tall, with wide sheathing lvs. Fls. purple-red, in a loose spike. Side sepals arching out and up; central sepal and petals forming a hood over the large, wide, 3-lobed lip; spur down-pointing.
✤ Woods, meadows, on dolomite. To 2000 m. Maritime Alps; S.E. and E. Alps. May–July. **69**

O. militaris *L.* SOLDIER or MILITARY ORCHID. 20–60 cm. tall, with large, shining lvs. Fls. in a dense spike. Segments forming a tight, forward-pointing hood, grey with pink or violet flush. Lip relatively large, with strap-shaped side lobes and short basal lobes with a small tooth between them; lip whitish, with pink or violet flush on edges and violet spots in centre; spur short, down-pointing.
✤ Woods, meadows. To 1800 m. Pyrenees (rare); Alps; Apennines. (Britain: very rare.) April–June. **70**

O. ustulata *L.* BURNT ORCHID. 8–30 (50) cm. tall, with narrow, channelled lvs. and a dense spike of small, fragrant fls. Spike at first dark maroon at the top, as if burnt, due to the colour of the small fl. hoods tightly packed together. This often gradually pales to white. Lip short, with side and basal lobes, white with dark red dot. Spur very short, thin, down-pointing.
✤ Meadows. To 2100 m. Pyrenees; Alps; Apennines. (Britain.) May–June. **67**

O. morio *L.* GREEN-WINGED ORCHID. 10–40 cm. tall, with narrow lvs., and a

rather loose fl. spike. Segments forming a hood, purple with marked green veins on side sepals; occasionally flesh-pink or white. Lip broader than long, slightly 3-lobed, wavy-edged, more or less folded back, reddish purple on sides, centre paler with deep purplish dots. Spur horizontal or up-pointing, slightly swollen at end.
✤ Meadows. To 1800 m. Pyrenees; Alps. (Britain.) April–June.   65

O. coriophora L. BUG ORCHID. 15–40 cm. tall, slender, with long narrow lvs. and a dense spike of smallish fls. with an unpleasant odour like that of a bed bug. Sideways on, the pointed hood gives the fls. the look of birds; it is usually brownish red above the narrow, 3-lobed lip, which is usually reddish purple, but varies to pink; spur short, down-pointing.
✤ Damp meadows. To 1800 m. Pyrenees; Alps; Maritime Alps. April–July.   68

O. pallens L. PALE-FLOWERED ORCHID. 10–35 cm. tall, with broad lvs. Fls. large in an egg-shaped to cylindrical head, pale yellow, rarely red, fragrant; outer sepals broad, pointing up and out, central sepal and petals forming a hood over the brighter yellow, 3-lobed lip; spur shorter than ovary, horizontal or up-pointing.
✤ Meadows, woods. To 2000 m. Pyrenees; Alps; Maritime Alps. Rare. April–June.   77

DACTYLORHIZA *Nevski* (**DACTY-LORCHIS** (*Klinge*) *Vermeul.*). Resembling *Orchis* (and often included in that genus), but fl. segments not combining to form a hood, spur always down-pointing, bracts leafy. Lvs. not forming a clear-cut rosette at fl. time. Tubers lobed or divided.

D. sambucina (*L.*) *Vermeul.* (**O. sambucina** *L.*). ELDER ORCHID. 10–30 cm. tall, with large shining lvs. and a spike

of yellow or red fls. accompanied by green or reddish bracts respectively, projecting beyond the fls. The petals arch together over the wide, flat lip; spur stout, conical, as long as ovary. The two colour forms often occur together.
✤ Meadows, clearings. To 2100 m. Pyrenees; Alps; Apennines. April–July.   73

D. maculata (*L.*) *Vermeul.* (**O. maculata** *L.*). SPOTTED ORCHID. A variable plant often segregated into subspecies. 15–60 (90) cm. tall, with solid stem, lvs. keeled, folded upwards, usually spotted with dark maroon; fl. spike long and pointed until the topmost fls. open. Bracts usually shorter than fls. Outer sepals outspread, horizontal; lip 3-lobed; spur straight, cylindrical. Colour varying from purple to bright pink and white, the lip variously marked with dots or continuous lines of darker shade.
✤ Meadows, woods, moorland. To 2200 (2325) m. Pyrenees; Alps; Apennines. Norway to 1200 m. (Britain.) May–August.   76

D. incarnata (*L.*) *Vermeul.* (**O. latifolia** *L.* in part). A variable plant often segregated into subspecies. 15–50 (100) cm. tall, with hollow stem. Lvs. yellowish green, long and narrow, more or less keeled, tapering to a hooded tip. Fl. spike dense, oblong. Bracts much longer than fls. Outer sepals pointing upwards, especially at their base; lip folded, barely lobed, wavy-edged; spur conical. Colour pink or purplish, lip often marked with darker dots or lines.
✤ Damp meadows, marshes. To 2100 (2300) m. Alps; Apennines. (Britain.) May–July.   74

D. majalis *Reichb.* (**D. alpestris** *Pugsl.*, **O. latifolia** *L.* in part). A variable plant usually segregated into individual species; the European alpine form has been named *D. alpestris*. 20–50 (80) cm. tall, stem slightly hollow. Lvs. deep green, usually spotted or ring-marked with dark brown. Fl. spike dense, egg-shaped. Bracts longer than fls. Outer sepals outspread; lip broad, strongly 3-lobed, the side lobes often notched, the central lobe smaller; spur cylindrical, often curved at tip. Colour bright purple or reddish, lip with darker dots or lines.

✶ Damp meadows, marshes, woods. To 2500 m. Pyrenees; Alps; Apennines. Britain.) May–July.　　　　**75**

TRAUNSTEINERA Reichb. **T. globosa** (L.) Rchb. (**Orchis globosa** L.). ROUND-HEADED ORCHID. 15–65 cm. tall, with bluish lvs. carried on the stem and only a few brownish sheaths at the base. Fls. packed tightly into a rounded or slightly pyramidal head, lilac to pink. Fls. small, with nearly equal-sized segments, broad at base, each ending

in a little spoon-like projection; lip 3-lobed, pale pink with purple spots; spur thin, cylindrical, down-pointing. ✶ Meadows, woods. 900–2600 m. Pyrenees (rare); Alps; Apennines. May–August.　　　　**71**

ANACAMPTIS Rich. **A. pyramidalis** (L.) Rich. (**Orchis pyramidalis** L.). PYRAMIDAL ORCHID. 20–50 (75) cm. tall, with leafy stems and narrow, keeled lvs. Fls. small, densely packed into a conical spike, purplish pink, with foxy smell. Outer sepals curved, outspread; upper sepal and petals forming a hood; lip small, 3-lobed, with 2 erect 'guide-plates' leading to the opening of the very long, slender, down-pointing spur.

✶ Meadows, clearings, on chalk or limestone. To 1900 m. Pyrenees; Alps (local). (Britain.) May–August.　　**72**

POTAMOGETONACEAE—PONDWEED FAMILY

Aquatic plants; at least a dozen species of *Potamogeton* L., the PONDWEED, reach considerable altitudes. They live in water up to 12 m. deep; in many the lvs. are submerged, but in some cases there are floating lvs. of different character. One feature of the family is the presence of a membranous scale in the lf. axils, sometimes growing from the lf. base, sometimes free, which sheaths the stem. The fls. are small, with 4 curiously shaped segments, 4 stamens and 4 carpels each with a stigma on its surface; the fls. are carried in spikes, ovoid to cylindrical, sometimes above the water, sometimes submerged.

Individual species are not described here, but in alpine pools long-stalked water plants with alternate lvs., usually translucent and finely netted or veined, though sometimes thread-like, are almost certainly Pondweeds.

SALICACEAE—WILLOW FAMILY

Deciduous trees and shrubs, the latter sometimes prostrate, with alternate lvs.; fls. in catkins of separate sexes. In *Salix* each bud has 1 outer scale and the bracts between fls. are entire; in *Populus* there are several outer scales and the bracts are toothed or fringed. Fruit a capsule; seeds surrounded by silky hairs.

SALIX L. WILLOW. An enormous genus, the species often variable, often difficult to identify unless both male and female catkins are available together with lvs. Identification is further complicated by much natural hybridisation. The creeping and dwarf species are the most interesting, and only these, which are truly alpine (not found at lower levels at all), are described here. At least a dozen larger species may exceed 1500 m., some reaching 2300 m.

With several species botanists have fairly recently proposed new specific names to take geographical races into account. These groups are described under the original name and indicated by *.

The fls. which comprise the catkins have no petals or sepals but each is accompanied by a bract which may be prominent. Females with 2 stigmas, males with 2, 3, 5 or more stamens to each fl.

S. reticulata *L.* NETTED WILLOW. To 8 cm., creeping, stems often half buried and rooting. Lvs. few on erect twigs, 2–4 cm. long, rounded to shortly egg-shaped, often heart-shaped at base; at first woolly, later glossy, dark green on top, with marked network of veins; whitish below. Catkins many-flowered, 1–3 cm. long, narrow, males orange to reddish, females greyish green, appearing after lvs. Capsule hairy.
♣ Damp screes, rocks. 1300–2500 (3400) m. Pyrenees; Alps. Norway to 1940 m. (Britain: Scotland to 1200 m.; rare.) June–August. **89**

S. herbacea *L.* LEAST WILLOW. Creeping, with branching underground stems. Lvs. few on short twigs, ½–2 cm. long, rounded, sometimes broader than long, sometimes heart-shaped at base, with toothed edge; shining bright green, with marked veins. Catkins 2–12 flowered, ½–1½ cm. long, greenish yellow. Capsules often reddish. In Scandinavia and Scotland this species often hybridises, but seldom elsewhere.
♣ Damp meadows, rocky places, on primary rocks. 1800–2800 (3400) m. Pyrenees; Alps; Apennines. Norway to

2170 m. (Britain: mountains to 1200 m.) June–August. **88**

S. polaris *Wahl.* POLAR WILLOW. Very dwarf, with creeping underground stems and very slender twigs. Lvs. few, ½–1½ cm. long, rounded, usually egg-shaped, often slightly indented at apex. Catkins small, with up to 15 fls., with blackish bracts and noticeable hairs. May hybridise with *S. herbacea*.
♣ Damp meadows, rocky places. To 1700 m. Norway. July. **90**

S. retusa *L.* More or less creeping, with stems above ground. Lvs. numerous, ¾–2 cm. long, oblong, pointed or flattened or indented at apex. Catkins oval, 2 cm. long, with 10 or more fls. Style ⅛–⅓ length of ovary.
♣ Damp meadows, rocky places. 1200–2700 (3400) m. Pyrenees; Alps; Apennines. July–August. **91**

S. serpyllifolia *Scop.* Sometimes regarded as a subspecies of *S. retusa*, and almost identical but smaller, tightly pressed to the soil, with more rounded lvs. ½–1 cm. long and roundish catkins ½ cm. long with 3–8 fls. Style ¼ length of ovary.
♣ Damp meadows, rocky places. To 1800–3180 m. E. and C. Alps. July–August.

***S. myrsinites** *L.* (including **S. breviserrata** *Flod.* and **S. alpina** *Scop.*) (**S. jacquiniana** *Willd.*, **S. jacquini** *Host.* are synonyms of the latter). Varying from prostrate to a twiggy bushlet, with 10–50 cm. stems. Lvs. 1–2 cm. long, oval, hairy on edges, shining green on both surfaces, clustered at shoot tips. Catkins stout, on long stalks, males to 2 cm. long, females to 3 cm., tight-packed, purplish.

S. myrsinites (83): lvs. slightly toothed; dead lvs. persisting till the end of the following season.
S. breviserrata: lvs. slightly toothed; dead lvs. falling in autumn.

S. alpina (84): lvs. entire, deciduous; catkins slender.

🌿 Marshy meadows, streamsides, moraines. *S. myrsinites:* to 1750 m. Norway. (Scotland to 1250 m.) May–June. *S. breviserrata:* 1700–2400 (3040) m. C. and E. Pyrenees (local); Maritime Alps; C. Alps; Apennines, June–July. *S. alpina:* to 2000 (2600) m. E. Alps. June–July. **83, 84**

*S. glauca L. (including **S. glaucosericea** *Flod.*) BLUISH WILLOW. 50–150 cm. tall, bushy, with thick, grey-brown, shiny, hairy stems. Lvs. to 8 cm. long. Catkins long and stout, ovary grey-woolly.

S. glauca (81): obovate, bright green lvs. with rather tangled silky hairs and 5–7 pairs of side veins; capsule 10–12 mm. long.

S. glaucosericea: oblanceolate lvs. grey-green above, blue-green below, with flattened silky hairs and 7–10 pairs of side veins; capsule 6–9 mm. long.

🌿 Damp and stony places. *S. glauca:* to 1760 m. Norway. June. *S. glaucosericea:* 1700–2560 m. C. Alps. June–July. **81**

S. pyrenaica *Gouan.* More or less prostrate with 20–50 cm. stems. Twigs reddish brown. Lvs. oval to elliptical, to 3 cm. long, slightly hairy above, white-felted below when young, hairy on edges. Catkins loose, long and thin; anthers at first violet; bracts hairy, blackish.

🌿 Damp places. 1200–2500 m. Pyrenees. July. **82**

S. lanata L. WOOLLY WILLOW. ½–3 m. tall, usually prostrate. Twigs felted. Lvs. oval, thick, to 2 cm. long, yellow when young, densely white-woolly. Catkins stout, 4–5 cm. long. Anthers yellow. This species hybridises freely with *S. hastata* and *S. caprea.*

🌿 Damp, stony places. To 1750 m.

Norway. (Scotland to 1000 m.; very rare.) June. **85**

*S. phylicifolia L. (including **S. hegetschweileri** *Heer*). ½–2 m. tall, sometimes prostrate. Lvs. shining green above, bluish below. Anthers yellow.

S. phylicifolia: dark brown buds; lvs. pointed-oval, tapered at both ends, lightly toothed; catkins 2–4 cm. long, 1 cm. wide.

S. hegetschweileri: chestnut-brown buds; lvs. broadest above middle, with few, very small teeth; catkins 2½ cm. long, 1¾ cm. wide.

Confusion may arise with the *S. arbuscula* group, q.v.: in the *S. phylicifolia* group the stalk of the ovary is 2–4 times as long as nectary.

🌿 Wet stony places, watersides. *S. phylicifolia:* to 1760 m. Norway. (Britain to 750 m.) April–May. *S. hegetschweileri:* 1500–2200 m. Pyrenees (very rare); C. Alps. May–June.

*S. arbuscula L. (including **S. foetida** *Schleich.* and **S. waldsteiniana** *Willd.*). 20–50 cm. tall. Stems brown and shining. Lvs. shining green above, bluish below. Anthers bluish.

S. arbuscula. BUSHY WILLOW (86): lvs. ½–4 cm. long, narrow-elliptic, toothed; catkins 3 times longer than wide, short-stalked.

S. foetida: lvs. ½–3 cm. long, deeply toothed, with pronounced white glands; catkins twice as long as wide, short-stalked.

S. waldsteiniana: lvs. 3–5 cm. long, indistinctly toothed; catkins 4–5 times longer than wide, long-stalked.

🌿 Damp meadows, stony places, moraines. *S. arbuscula:* to 1300 m. Norway. (Scotland to 850 m.; local.) May–June. *S. foetida:* on primary rocks. 1700–2800 m. Pyrenees; W. and C. Alps. June–July. *S. waldsteiniana:* on limestone and micaceous schist. 1700–2800 m. E. Alps. June–July. **86**

S. hastata *L.* 50–150 cm. tall, bushy. With thin, brittle, shining, greenish or brownish stems. Lvs. very variable, elliptic to lance-shaped, more or less toothed, thin, pale dull green above, paler below. Catkins cylindrical, with long white hairs, long-stalked; anthers yellow; females 6 cm. long.
❀ Wet meadows, streamsides, stony places. 1000–2500 (2775) m. C. Pyrenees (rare); Alps. Norway to 1500 m. May–August. **80**

S. helvetica *Vill.* 50–70 cm., usually prostrate, with grey to brown twigs. Lvs. to 4 cm. long, narrow-oval, shiny on top, densely white-felted below. Catkins 1½–3 times longer than wide, females elongating in fruit; anthers pink, then tawny.
❀ Wet places. 1700–2600 (3000) m. C. and E. Alps. June–July.

S. lapponum *L.* LAPLAND WILLOW. 30–100 cm. tall, often prostrate, with grey to brown twigs. Lvs. to 9 cm. long, crowded at shoot tips, fairly hairy above, silky-hairy below. Catkins dense and not elongating in fruit; anthers violet, females densely silky-hairy.

❀ Wet heaths, watersides, stony places. 1000–2600 m. E. Pyrenees (very local). Norway to 1750 m. (N. Britain to 1150 m.) May–July.

S. caesia *Vill.* 30–100 cm., bushy or prostrate. Twigs brown. Lvs. 1–1½ cm., obovate or elliptical, not toothed, dull bluish green on both sides. Catkins 1–2 cm. long, round to oval, reddish brown with violet anthers. Ovary woolly.
❀ Damp meadows, streamsides. 1700–2300 (2630) m. C. Alps. Uncommon. June–July. **87**

POPULUS *L.* **P. tremula** *L.* ASPEN. Tree 20 m. high, producing many suckers. Readily recognised by its long-stalked, rounded, coarsely toothed lvs., often whitish beneath, which tremble continuously in the slightest breeze. Male catkins 4–8 cm. long; females 3–8 cm. long, purple.
❀ Damp woods. To 2100 m. Pyrenees; Alps; Apennines. Norway to 1200 m. (Britain to 500 m.) March–May. **932**

P. nigra, the BLACK POPLAR, may reach 1800 m. **933**

BETULACEAE—BIRCH FAMILY

Deciduous trees and shrubs with alternate lvs. Fls. in catkins, of separate sexes, females lacking perianth; males 3 to each bract, with perianth; fruit a nutlet.

BETULA *L.* BIRCH. Fruiting catkins cylindrical, with 3-lobed scales which fall with the fruit; stamens 2, divided under anthers.

B. nana *L.* DWARF BIRCH. Shrub 30–100 cm. tall, often procumbent. Lvs. ½–1½ cm. long, nearly circular, deeply toothed. Female catkins ½–1 cm. long, erect.

❀ Bogs, moors. To 2200 m. Alps. Very rare. Norway to 1570 m. April–June. **79**

B. pubescens *Ehrh.* (**B. odorata** *Bechst.*). 1–20 m. tall, with brownish or greyish bark, not fissured. Lvs. rounded-triangular, coarsely toothed.
❀ Moors: sometimes the dominant tree. To 2000 m. Pyrenees; Alps; N.

Apennines. (Britain to 800 m.) March–May.

B. pendula *Roth.* (**B. alba** *L.*, **B. verrucosa** *Ehrh.*). SILVER BIRCH. Very similar to preceding, but lower bark divided into rectangular bosses, upper bark white and peeling.
⚜ Heaths, sandy places. To 2000 m. Pyrenees; Alps; Apennines. (Britain.) March–May.

ALNUS *Mill.* ALDER. Fruiting catkins ovoid, with 5-lobed scales persisting after fruit has fallen as cone-like structure; stamens 4.

A. viridis *DC.* GREEN ALDER. Shrub ½–4 m. tall, sometimes prostrate. Buds stalkless. Lvs. bright green, round to elliptical, doubly toothed. Male catkins long, yellowish; females 8–15 mm. long, usually 3 together.
⚜ Woods, meadows, rocky places. 1500–2300 (2800) m. Maritime Alps; Alps; N. Apennines. April–May. 78

A. incana *Moench.* 5–10 m. tall, rarely more. Buds short-stalked. Lvs. rounded to oval lance-shaped, doubly toothed,

grey-green below. Female catkins 1–1¾ cm. long, round to oval, 3–5 together.
⚜ Rocky places, riversides. To 1600 m. Alps; N. Apennines. Norway to 1040 m. (Britain: introduced.) February–March.

CORYLACEAE—HAZEL FAMILY

Corylus avellana *L.* HAZEL. This familiar small tree reaches 1800 m. in many mountainous areas. (Britain to 700 m.) 929

FAGACEAE—BEECH FAMILY

Fagus sylvatica *L.* BEECH. Reaches 1800–1900 m. in many areas, especially in E. Alps; occasionally (e.g. Julian Alps) in markedly columnar forms. 930

Quercus petraea (*Matt.*) *Lieb.* (**Q. sessiliflora** *Salisb.*). DURMAST OAK. Reaches 1600–1800 m. in C. and S. Swiss Alps. 931

URTICACEAE—NETTLE FAMILY

Both **Urtica dioica** *L.*, the COMMON NETTLE, and **U. urens** *L.*, the ANNUAL NETTLE, reach great heights, the maximum recorded being 3125 m. for the former, 2700 m. for the latter, both at Zermatt, Switzerland.

SANTALACEAE—SANDALWOOD FAMILY

Alpine representatives herbaceous; perianth of one whorl, with 4–5 lobes. Stamens 4–5, stigma 1.

THESIUM *L.* Slender, rather insignificant, reputedly semi-parasitic plants with linear alternate lvs., and fl. stem usually carrying 2–3 sub-bracts with a larger bract at the base. Fls. very small, whitish; persisting when dry above the fruit, a small green nut.

T. alpinum *L.* ALPINE BASTARD TOADFLAX. 10–20 cm. tall, seldom branched. Fl. stem often 1-sided; bracts 3 times as long as fl. and fruit; persistent perianth normally 4-lobed, tubular, 2–3 times as long as nut.
⚜ Dry meadows, stony places. To

2600 m. Pyrenees; Alps; Apennines. May–August. **934**

T. pyrenaicum *Pourr.* (**T. pratense** *Ehrh.*). PYRENEAN BASTARD TOADFLAX. 10–20 cm. tall, often branched; fl. stem tending to zigzag; bracts twice as long as fl. and fruit; persistent perianth typically 5-lobed, but often 4-lobed, tubular-bell-shaped, equalling to twice as long as nut. *

✵ Dry meadows. To 2500 m. Pyrenees; Alps; Apennines. June–July. **935**

T. divaricatum *Jan.* 10–30 (60) cm. tall, branching from the base, with very narrow lvs. and a pyramidal fl.-head; bracts shorter than fl. or fruit; persistent perianth 5-lobed, bell-shaped, 5 times longer than nut.

✵ Dry meadows, scrub. To 2150 m. S.E. Alps; Apennines; S. Italian mountains. June–August.

POLYGONACEAE—DOCK FAMILY

An extensive family, many species all too familiar as weeds, some species being genuine alpines. These are all herbaceous perennials, with simple alternate lvs. and membranous stipules usually forming a tubular sheath enclosing the stem-nodes. Fls. 3–6-parted, small, clustered, white, green or reddish, followed by flat, winged seeds.

Besides the species mentioned, *P. aviculare* L., the KNOTGRASS, reaches 2300 m., and its dwarf *var. nana* Boiss. (*var. minimum* Murith.) 2700 m.

POLYGONUM *L.* Lvs. always longer than wide; fls. with 1 whorl of 3–6 (usually 5) segments.

P. bistorta L. BISTORT. 20–100 cm. tall, with thick rootstock giving rise to stout erect stem with triangular-lanceolate lvs., lower with winged stalk, upper stemless. Fls. pale to bright pink, with projecting stamens, in a dense cylindrical spike. Usually grows in large colonies.

✵ Meadows, especially on primary formations. To 2500 m. Pyrenees; Alps; Apennines. (Britain.) May–August. **93**

P. viviparum L. 5–40 cm. tall; stem unbranched; lvs. long, narrow, wavy, with thick cross-veins and recurved edges. Fl. spike dense, narrow and cylindrical; fls. white or pale pink, usually replaced in lower part of spike by brown or purplish bulbils which drop and grow into new plants.

✵ Pastures, rocky places. 1500–3200 m.

Pyrenees; Alps; Apennines. Norway to 2280 m. (Britain to 1300 m.) June–August. **92**

P. alpinum *All.* ALPINE KNOTGRASS. 30–80 cm. tall, with branching stem, lvs. lance-shaped, tapered at both ends. Fls. white or pale pink in a loose head (panicle).

✵ Damp meadows, debris, usually on primary formations. To 2200 m. Pyrenees; Alps; Apennines. July–August. **936**

OXYRIA *Hill.* **O. digyna** L. MOUNTAIN SORREL. 8–20 (30) cm. tall. Lvs. usually all basal, 1–3 cm. long, kidney-shaped, long-stalked. Fls. with 2 whorls or 2 segments each, greenish, on upright, sometimes branched stem, with thin, jointed stalks. Seeds red, flat and round.

✵ Rocks, debris, on granite. 1700–3000 (3800) m. Pyrenees; Alps. Norway to 2150 m. (Britain: mountains.) July–August. **937**

RUMEX *L.* DOCK, SORREL. Fls. with 2 whorls of 3 segments each, the outer small, the inner enlarging and usually becoming hard in fruit, when they are known as valves. Lvs. acid-tasting except in *R. alpinus* (of species described).

R. scutatus *L.* RUBBLE DOCK. 25–50 cm. tall, with subterranean shoots forming branches. Lvs. of helmet outline, with distinct outward-pointing basal lobes, as long as broad, sometimes bluish. Fls. few on erect, branched stems; male and female on same plant. ❧ Rocks, debris. To 2500 (3000) m. Pyrenees; Alps; Apennines. (Britain: naturalised.) May–August.   **938**

R. acetosella *L.* SHEEPS SORREL. To 30 cm. tall, erect, lvs. on stem typically arrow-shaped, with narrow basal lobes often pointing sideways. Fls. greenish, with the 2 whorls closely pressed together, on stems up to 15 cm. long, branched from above the middle; male and female on separate plants. Perianth segments enlarging a little at fruiting time. ❧ Meadows, heaths, typically on acid soil. To 2400 m. Pyrenees; Alps; Apennines. Norway to 1580 m. (Britain.) May–August.   **941**

R. acetosa *L.* SORREL-DOCK. 30–100 cm. tall. Like a larger edition of *R. acetosella*, but perianth segments larger than nut at fruiting time; valves with a small basal tubercle. Male and female fl. on separate plants. Lf. lobes always down-pointing; upper lvs. tending to clasp stem; sheaths fringed. ❧ Woods, meadows. To 2300 m. Pyrenees; Alps; Apennines. Norway to 1880 m. (Britain.) May–June.   **940**

R. nivalis *L.* SNOW DOCK. 7–30 cm. tall. Lvs. usually all basal, typically rounded at apex and often without basal lobes. Fls. red, on seldom branched erect stem; male and female on separate plants. ❧ Debris, snow-beds. 1500–2800 m. C. and E. Alps. Local. July–September.   **942**

R. arifolius *All.* (**R. montanus** *Desf.*) 30–100 cm. tall. A rather coarse sorrel with thin, strongly veined lvs., those on stem arrow-shaped, basal lvs. (illustrated) ovate, heart-shaped at base. Fls. greenish, in loose branching head; male and female on separate plants. ❧ Meadows, woods, usually on acid soils. To 2500 (2740) m. Pyrenees; Alps; Apennines. June–September. **939**

R. alpinus *L.* MONKS RHUBARB. A giant sorrel up to 100 cm. (exceptionally 200 cm.) tall, with a long, dense, yellowish, barely branched fl. spike; male and female fls. on same plant. Lvs. up to 10 cm. long, basal ones as long as wide, heart-shaped at base; stalks channelled, red-edged. Sheaths large and parchment-like. Valves triangular. ❧ Meadows and around cow-sheds. 800–2500 (2800) m. Pyrenees: Alps; Apennines. (Britain: introduced.) June–August.

CHENOPODIACEAE— GOOSEFOOT FAMILY

Chenopodium bonus-henricus *L.* GOOD KING HENRY. A fleshy, mealy plant up to 80 cm. tall, with arrow-shaped lvs., and greenish fl. spikes; reaches 3100 m. and occurs in most mountainous areas. Often found near buildings, it was and probably still is eaten like spinach.   **1134**

CARYOPHYLLACEAE—PINK FAMILY

Alpine species all herbaceous; sometimes annual. Lvs. never lobed, in opposite-facing pairs. Fls. radially symmetrical; both sexes usually present; sepals and petals usually 5, rarely 4, stamens 10 or 8, stigmas usually 2–5. Fruit usually a toothed capsule.

Besides the species described, *Agrostemma githago* L., the CORN COCKLE, may reach 1980 m.

Sub-family Silenoideae: sepals 5–6 joined to form a tubular or bell-shaped calyx; an outer structure of scales (*epicalyx*) sometimes present. Petals usually well developed, with a long 'claw' at base inserted in calyx, and often with scales in the throat.

DIANTHUS L. PINK. Petals 5, sometimes toothed or fringed but never 2-lobed, and with long 'claw' at base inserted in calyx. Epicalyx present; calyx tubular, with 5 teeth. Stamens 10; styles 2. Capsule with 4 teeth.

Dwarf male-sterile plants with smaller fls. than usual may occur, and plants flowering later than normal may also have abnormally smaller or fewer fls. Hybrids occur readily where species grow together.

Flowers in a head with a pair of bracts below it

D. barbatus L. SWEET WILLIAM. A well-known garden plant, 30–70 cm. tall, with stout erect stems carrying pairs of lance-shaped lvs. 7–9 cm. long, and a terminal head made up of several sub-heads of 3–30 purple, pink or red, often spotted fls. Bracts below head long and narrow. Epicalyx of 4 ovate, pointed scales, at least as long as calyx; both structures greenish.

Ssp. **compactus** (*Kit.*) *Heuffel:* with short bracts under fl.-head; calyx and epicalyx usually brownish purple.

☘ Meadows, clearings. 900–2500 m. Pyrenees; S. Alps; Apennines. *Ssp. compactus:* Apennines, Yugoslavia. (Britain: as a garden escape.) June–August. **98**

D. carthusianorum L. CARTHUSIAN PINK. A very variable plant 3–50 cm. tall, but always distinguishable by the narrow, pointed lvs., and stiff, pointed bracts below fl.-head. Epicalyx about ½ length of purplish, 1–2 cm. calyx which is narrowed above the middle. Fls. deep pink, red or purple, 3–30 in head.

Ssp. **vaginatus** (*Chaix*) *Hegi:* has short-pointed pale red epicalyx scales, and is usually low-growing.

☘ Dry meadows, stony places, woods. To 2500 m. Pyrenees; Alps (mainly S.); Apennines. (Britain: escaped.) May–August. **103**

Flowers not in heads; petals deeply cut (Fringed Pinks)

D. monspessulanus L. (**D. sternbergii** *Sieber*, **D. hyssopifolius** L.). FRINGED PINK. 5–60 cm. tall, with thin, flexible lvs. and 1–5 fragrant pink or white fls. 2–4 cm. across; the petals cut about halfway into narrow lobes; central part of petal much wider than lobes. Epicalyx of 4 scales, ⅓—½ length of cylindrical, 18–25 mm. calyx.

Ssp. **monspessulanus:** plant tall and robust (20–60 cm.); fls. usually several; epicalyx ½ length of calyx.

Ssp. **marsicus** (*Ten.*) *Novak:* plant

slender (5–20 cm.), green; fls. usually 1;
epicalyx ½ length of calyx.
Ssp. **sternbergii** *Hegi* (**101**): plant
slender (5–20 cm.), bluish; fls. 1;
epicalyx less than ½ length of calyx.
⚜ Meadows, stony places, woods. To
2000 m. *Ssp. monspessulanus:* Pyrenees;
Alps. *Ssp. marsicus:* Abruzzi. *Ssp. sternbergii:* Pyrenees (doubtful record); E.
Alps. May–August. 101

D. plumarius *L.* COMMON PINK.
Similar to *D. monspessulanus,* but lvs. and
stems always bluish, 10–40 cm. tall, with
larger fls. and stiff, pointed lvs.
⚜ Meadows, scrub. To 1900 (2400) m.
C. and E. Alps. (Britain: naturalised.)
April–August.

D. superbus *L.* SUPERB PINK. 30–60
(90) cm. tall, branching above; lvs.
¼–1 cm. broad. Fls. fragrant, pink or
purplish, often green at the throat, 4–6
cm. across. Petals much fringed, cut
well beyond the middle, the central part
2–3 times wider than the long narrow
lobes. Epicalyx of 2–4 scales, ¼–⅓ length
of calyx, which narrows towards top.
The plant usually seen at higher altitudes is *ssp.* **speciosus** (*Reichb.*) *Pawl.,*
which is bluish with 6 cm. fls.; the
lowland form—*ssp. superbus*—is green
with 4 cm. fls.
⚜ Dry meadows, woods. To 2400 m.
Pyrenees; Alps; N. Apennines. June–
October. 100

*Flowers not in heads; petals plain or
toothed*

D. alpinus *L.* ALPINE PINK. A showy,
tufted plant 2–20 cm. tall with deep
green, glossy, oblong to lance-shaped,
blunt-ended lvs. 3–5 mm. wide. Fls.
3–3½ cm. across, with jagged petal
edges, pink or purplish with red and
white spots, and greenish white reverse.
Epicalyx of 2–4 scales at least ½ length
of 15–18 mm. calyx, which widens
upwards and has broad, whitish teeth.

⚜ Limestone rocks, meadows. 1000–
2500 m. E. Alps (not France or Switzerland). Local. June–August. 107

D. glacialis *Haenke.* GLACIER PINK.
5–10 cm. tall, forming tufts, with
narrow fleshy lvs., widest above the
middle, often longer than fl. stems; lf.
pairs very close. Fls. solitary, 1½ cm.
across, pink with white throat, greenish
white under petals. Epicalyx of 2–4
pointed scales with white edge, as long
as 12–16 mm. calyx or longer.
⚜ Meadows, stony places, on granite.
1900–2900 m. C. and E. Alps (Switzerland only in Grisons). Local. July–
August. 106

D. neglectus *Lois.* (**D. pavonius**
Tausch.). 3–15 cm. tall, lvs. narrow,
pointed, grass-like, usually making tufts.
Fls. usually solitary, 3 cm. across,
pink with buff reverse; petals not overlapping. Epicalyx scales pointed, spreading out, as long as calyx, which is
reddish with whitish teeth and narrows
upwards.   *
⚜ Meadows, stony places. 1200–3000
m. E. Pyrenees (rare); S.W. Alps
(local); E. Alps (very rare). (Not
Switzerland.) July–August. 99

D. seguieri *Vill.* A sprawling, branching plant 25–60 cm. tall with narrow
lvs. in tufts; sheaths where lvs. join
stem rather swollen. Fls. 1–4, 2–4 cm.
across, fragrant, pink or purplish with
a ring of dark spots, paler below;
hairy at throat. Epicalyx of 2–6 pointed,
spreading scales ⅓–¾ length of 14–20
mm. calyx, which has brown teeth.
⚜ Meadows, stony places. 800–1600
m. Pyrenees; W. Alps (local). June–
September. 104

D. gratianopolitanus *Vill.* (**D. caesius**
Sm.). CHEDDAR PINK. 6–30 cm. tall,
bluish, with soft narrow lvs. forming
dense tufts. Fls. usually solitary, 1½–3
cm. across, fragrant, pink or purplish.
Epicalyx of 4–6 very short-pointed

scales, $\frac{1}{4}-\frac{1}{3}$ length of 13–20 mm.
cylindrical, brownish purple calyx. *Var.*
montanus *Gaud.* is a dwarf plant.
✤ Meadows, stony places. 700–2200
m. Alps. Rare. (Britain: Cheddar
Gorge.) May–July. **102**

D. deltoides L. MAIDEN PINK. 10–45
cm. tall, forming loose tufts with
creeping flowerless stalks. Stems covered
with short hairs, lvs. linear or narrow
lance-shaped, 1–2½ cm. long, with short
hairs on midrib and edges. Fls. under
2 cm. across, pink or white, spotted,
with a darker ring in centre. Epicalyx
of 2–4 scales, ½ length of 12–17 mm.
cylindrical calyx, which has narrow
pointed teeth.
✤ Dry meadows and woods. To 2000
m. Pyrenees; Alps; Apennines. Norway
to 900 m. (Britain.) June–October.

D. scaber *Chaix* (**D. hirtus** *Vill.*).
10–20 (40) cm. tall, forming loose tufts.
Stems rough-hairy. Lvs. stiff, keeled,
pointed. Fls. 1 cm. across, up to 5 in a
tight cluster, but without bracts below.
Epicalyx of 6 scales, ½ length of 17–22
mm. tapering calyx.
✤ Stony places. To 1800 m. Pyrenees.
June–September.

D. sylvestris *Wulf.* WOOD PINK. A
variable plant normally around 10 cm.
tall, sometimes branched, forming tufts.
Lvs. very narrow. Fls. 1 or 2, 1½–2½
cm. across, pink. Epicalyx of 2–4
scales, $\frac{1}{6}-\frac{1}{4}$ length of 2½–3 cm. cylindrical
calyx.
✤ Meadows, stony places. 1400–2800
m. Pyrenees; Alps; Apennines. July–
August. **105**

D. subacaulis *Vill.* A neat tufted plant
with woody stock, 3–20 cm. tall, with
short, stiff, keeled lvs. and angular
stem. Fls. solitary, pink, up to 1½ cm.
across; petals toothed or plain-edged.
Epicalyx of 4 broad scales ⅓ length of
6–10 mm., slightly swollen, blunt-

toothed calyx. The alpine plant is
usually *ssp.* **brachyanthus** (*Boiss.*) P.F.
✤ Meadows, stony places, rocks. To
1700 m. Pyrenees; Dauphiné. June–
August. **108**

D. furcatus *Balb.* (including **D. re-
quienii** *G. & G.*). A dense tufted
plant 5–30 cm. tall. Lvs. soft, linear.
flat. Fls. 1–3, red, pink or whitish, 1–2
cm. across; petals toothed or plain-
edged. Epicalyx of 4–6 scales about ½
length of 14–19 mm. calyx. A variable
species often divided into subspecies.
✤ Dry meadows, stony places, rocks.
To 2300 m. Pyrenees (*ssp. geminiflorus*
(Lois.) Tutin.); Maritime Alps; S.W.
Alps (France) (*ssp. furcatus*). June–
August.

LYCHNIS L. Erect perennials with
opposite lvs.; fls. in spikes or heads.
Petals with long 'claw' within calyx;
scales in throat; stamens 10; calyx
tubular, toothed; no epicalyx.

L. flos-cuculi L. RAGGED ROBIN. 20–90
cm. tall, with wide lance-shaped lvs.
Fls. in groups on paired branches, each
3–4 cm. across, petals deep pink,
deeply cut into 4 narrow segments.
Calyx 6–10 mm. long.
✤ Damp meadows, thickets. To 2500
m. Pyrenees; Alps; Apennines. Norway
to 960 m. (Britain to 650 m.) May–June.
110

L. flos-jovis (*L.*) *Braun.* 40–90 cm. tall,
unbranched, with lance-shaped lvs.,
altogether white-cottony. Fls. strong
pink, on short footstalks, 4–10 in dense
heads, petals notched into 2 lobes.
Calyx with very short teeth.
✤ Rocks, screes, meadows. 1000–2400
m. S. Alps. June–July. **109**

L. viscaria L. (**Viscaria viscosa**
(*Scop.*) *Asch.*). RED GERMAN CATCHFLY.
15–90 cm. tall, with mostly basal lvs.
and red or purplish fls. in opposite

groups of 3–6 up the sticky, sometimes branched stem.

✤ Dry, sandy meadows and clearings, avoiding limestone. To 1800 m. Alps. (Britain: very local.) May–June. **112**

L. alpina *L.* (**Viscaria alpina** (*L.*) *Don.*). RED ALPINE CATCHFLY. A tuft-forming plant 5–15 cm. tall with small deep reddish pink fls., 6–20 in dense heads, petals markedly 2-lobed. Calyx bell-shaped.

✤ Meadows, stony places, usually on siliceous rocks. 2200–3100 m. Pyrenees; Alps; Apennines (two localities only). Norway to 1900 m. (Britain to 900 m.; very rare.) June–August. **111**

PETROCOPTIS *Braun.* **P. pyrenaica** *Braun.* (**Lychnis pyrenaica** *Berg.*). A fragile, loosely tufted plant 5–15 cm. tall, arising from long-stalked rosettes of ovate-lance-shaped lvs. Fls. white, sometimes pale pink, 1–2 cm. across, petals not lobed. Calyx whitish, 5–8 mm. long.

✤ Banks, rocks. 1300–2800 m. W. and C. Pyrenees. May–August. **954**

SILENE *L.* (including **Heliosperma** *Reichb.*, **Melandrium** *Röhl.*). A very large and varied genus of annuals and perennials. Fls. solitary or grouped. Sepals joined at base, with 5 teeth and noticeable veins. Petals with long basal 'claw' within calyx. No epicalyx. Stamens 10.

S. nutans *L.* NOTTINGHAM CATCHFLY. 20–80 cm. tall, with woody stock; basal lvs. stalked, spoon-shaped; upper not stalked, narrow-lance-shaped. Fls. whitish, sometimes reddish below, to 18 mm. across, with scales in throat; drooping from paired sticky branches to form 1-sided head. Calyx with 10 purplish veins. Petals split deeply in 2.

✤ Meadows, banks, stony places. To 2200 (2450) m. Pyrenees; Alps; Apennines. (Britain.) May–July. **945**

S. paradoxa *L.* Not unlike *S. nutans*, but fls. held erect when open. 20–50 cm. tall, very sticky near top of stem. Basal lvs. lance-shaped. Fls. white, yellowish below, with scales in throat.

✤ Meadows, open woods, stony places. To 2200 m. Dauphiné. Rare. May–September.

S. dioica (*L.*) *Clairy.* (**Melandrium dioicum** (*L.*) *Coss. & Germ.*, **M. rubrum** (*Weigel*) *Garcke*, **M. silvestre** (*Schkuhr*) *Roehl.*). RED CAMPION. 30–90 cm. tall. Lvs. broad, ovate, lower with long stalk; whole plant hairy, sometimes slightly sticky. Fls. red, 18–25 mm. across, 1-sexed, several together in clusters; petals deeply 2-lobed. Calyx 10–15 mm., cylindrical in male fls., swollen in female, with small teeth.

✤ Woods, typically on limestone. To 2360 m. Pyrenees; Alps; Apennines. Norway to 1780 m. (Britain.) May–September. **948**

S. auriculata *S. & S.* EARED CATCHFLY. 8–30 cm. tall, with woody stock, forming tufts of thickly hairy lvs., sometimes up to 12 cm. long, but usually much shorter. Fls. solitary, 1–1½ cm. across, white; petals lobed, with a pair of small side lobes just above the densely hairy, 12–15 mm. calyx.

✤ Rocks. To 1930 m. Apuan Alps. July–August. **946**

S. elisabetha *Jan.* (**Melandrium elisabethae** (*Jan.*) *Rohrb.*). 5–15 cm. tall, with woody stock, forming tufts; basal lvs. almost hairless. Fls. 3–4 cm. across, usually solitary, sometimes 2–3, red or pink, with fringed scales in throat; petals toothed, lobed. Calyx densely hairy, 20 mm. long.

✤ Limestone rocks, screes. 1000–2450 m. S. Alps from Lombardy to S. Tyrol (rare); dubiously recorded from Mt. Viso. July–August. **119**

S. cordifolia *All.* 10–20 cm. tall, with

woody stock; lvs. pointed, heart-shaped to oval, clasping the stem. Fls. terminal, 1-4, white or pink, with deeply lobed petals, no throat scales. Calyx 12-15 mm. long, slightly swollen. ✲ Rocks, screes. 1200-2400 m. Maritime and Ligurian Alps. Local. July-August.

S. wahlbergella *Chow.* **(Lychnis apetala** *L.,* **Melandrium apetalum** *(L.) Fenzl.).* To 15 cm. tall, with solitary, nodding fls. apparently consisting only of the whitish, netted, swollen calyx, which usually conceals the short, reddish petals.
✲ Damp meadows, watersides, wet debris. To 1920 m. Norway. June-July.
947

S. vulgaris *(Moench) Garcke* **(S. inflata** *Sm.,* **S. cucubalus** *Wibel.).* BLADDER CAMPION. A variable plant 10-25 cm. tall, with slender stems and usually a woody stock. Lvs. ovate, often bluish. Fls. 1-5, white; petals deeply lobed: calyx swollen, 20-veined, grey-green, often flushed pink or mauve.
Ssp. **glareosa** *(Jord.) M.-J. & Turrill:* lvs. 2-5 mm. wide, fls. with scales in throat.
Ssp. **prostrata** *(Gaud.) C. & W. (ssp.* **alpina** *(Lam.) S. & K.)* **(950):** ALPINE BLADDER CAMPION: lvs. 3-10 mm. wide, no throat-scales.
✲ Meadows, rocks, screes. To 3100 m. *Ssp. glareosa:* Pyrenees; Alps. *Ssp. prostrata:* Alps; Apennines. The species in Norway to 1330 m. (The species in Britain.) July-August. 950

S. vallesia *L.* A sticky, mat-forming plant with 5-15 cm. stem and short hairy lvs. Fls. 1-3 together, pink, the 2 pronounced petal lobes curling up to show the red reverse.
Ssp. **vallesia** **(115):** lvs. oblong-lance-shaped.

Ssp. **graminea** *(Vis.) Asch. & Graebn.:* lvs. narrow-strap-shaped.
✲ Siliceous rocks, screes. 1100-2100 (3100) m. *Ssp. vallesia:* W. & S. Alps; Apuan Alps; Apennines. *Ssp. graminea:* Mt. Ventoux; Dauphiné; Piedmont; Yugoslav mountains. July-August. 115

S. saxifraga *L.* A slender plant, usually forming dense tufts, with 10-20 cm. stems, sticky at top. Lvs. linear, sometimes narrow-spoon-shaped, pointed. Fls. 1 or 2, whitish above, reddish or greenish below; petals lobed; calyx whitish, 8-13 mm. long.
✲ Limestone rocks, screes. To 2400 m. Pyrenees; Alps; Apennines. May-August. 114

S. campanula *Pers.* Similar to *S. saxifraga,* but not sticky, with very slender stems, longer, grassy lvs., and reddish calyx 7-8 mm. long.
✲ Damp, shady rocks. 900-2200 m. Maritime and Ligurian Alps. Rare. July-August.

S. ciliata *Pourr.* A variable plant forming dense rosettes of linear to narrow-spoon-shaped lvs., with 5-30 cm. stems. Plant finely hairy, not sticky. Fls. 1-7, 1½ cm. across, white or pink, greenish or reddish below; throat-scales present, claw lobed; calyx conical, 11-20 mm. long.
✲ Meadows, rocks. 1000-3000 m. Pyrenees (rare); C. Apennines. July-September. 951

S. borderi *Jord.* Mat-forming, with woody stock, and 5-15 cm. stems sticky at top; basal lvs. narrow-spoon-shaped, with minute raised dots on surface, hairy on margins. Fls. 1-4, pink; petals deeply lobed, claw hairy; calyx 8-10 mm. long, finely hairy, with blunt teeth.
✲ Rocks. 2000-2200 m. Pyrenees. Very rare. August. 113

S. acaulis *L.* MOSS CAMPION. Forming

dense low mats of pointed, linear, 6–12 mm. lvs. with cartilaginous, hairy edges. Fls. pink to reddish, occasionally white; plants vary much in colour and size of fls. and several subspecies have been named, but they do not seem to be geographical races. Length of fl. stem also varies, although the stem elongates when fruiting in any case. The extremes have been named as follows:

Ssp. exscapa (*All.*) *Braun* (116): almost stemless, with conical base to calyx.

Ssp. longiscapa (*Kern.*) *Hayek*. LONG-STALKED MOSS CAMPION (117): with 2–6 cm. stem and flattened base to calyx.

✤ Damp rocks, debris, short turf. 1900–3680 m. Pyrenees; Alps; Apennines. Norway to 2150 m. (Britain to 1250 m.) June–August.   116, 117

S. rupestris *L*. ROCK CAMPION. A slender 5–25 cm. plant, branching below; lower lvs. spoon-shaped, stem-lvs. lance-shaped to oval, numerous. Fls. small, white or pink, in very loose heads; petals shallowly notched, throat-scales pointed; calyx 4–6 mm. long, 10-veined.

✤ Rocks, screes, usually acid. To 2900 m. Pyrenees; Alps; N. Apennines. Norway to 1360 m. June–September.   949

S. pusilla *W. & K.* (**S. quadrifida** *auct.*, **Heliosperma quadrifidum** (*L.*) *Rchb.*, **H. quadridentatum** (*Murr.*) *S. & K.*). Rather resembling *S. rupestris*, but petals 4-toothed. 10–20 cm. tall, frail, sticky near top; lvs. linear to lance-shaped, 2–4 mm. wide. Fls. in loose heads, white, sometimes pinkish, 6–8 mm. across; calyx 3½–7 mm. long.

✤ Damp limestone rocks. 1300–2900 m. C. Pyrenees; Alps; Apennines. July–August.   952

S. alpestris *Jacq.* (**S. quadrifida** *L.*, **Heliosperma alpestre** (*Jacq.*) *Reichb.*).

Like *S. pusilla*, but more robust, 10–30 cm. tall; lvs. narrow lance-shaped to oval, 9 mm. wide. Fl.-head often sticky; fls. white, 1 cm. across or more, petals 4–6-toothed; calyx 5–7 mm. long.

✤ Damp calcareous rocks, stony places. Maritime Alps (very rare); S.E. Alps (local). 1000–2500 m. June–August. **953**

GYPSOPHILA *L*. **G. repens** *L*. Perennial, with branched rhizome giving rise to many sprawling stems to 25 cm. long, with more or less erect fl. stems carrying white or pale pink fls. in loose heads of 5–30. Lvs. bluish, 1–3 cm. long, ½–3 mm. wide, linear or lance-shaped. Calyx 2½–3½ mm. long, bell-shaped, 5-veined; petals twice as long; stamens 10, styles 2.

✤ Rocks, debris, grass. 1000–2860 m. Pyrenees; Alps; Apennines; Apuan Alps. May–September.   **118**

SAPONARIA *L*. Alpine species perennial, with woody stock and multi-fld. heads. Calyx cylindrical, 5–15-veined; petals with long 'claw' within calyx, usually with scales at throat; stamens 10, styles 2.

Petals yellow

S. bellidifolia *Sm.* A tufted plant with erect, unbranched 20–50 cm. fl. stems, usually with 1 pair only of narrow stem-lvs. Fls. about 8 mm. across, stalkless, in a head with a pair of narrow bracts below. Petals notched; stamen filaments yellow.

✤ Stony places, grass, dolomitic sand. To 2000 m. Pyrenees; Alps (local); Apennines. June–July.   **123**

S. lutea *L*. YELLOW SOAPWORT. A dwarf tufted plant with 2–12 cm. unbranched fl. stems, hairy, with 2 or more pairs of narrow stem-lvs. Fls. about 8 mm. across on short hairy stalks, in a loose head. Petals rounded, with dark blotch on claw; stamen filaments black.

198

✤ Limestone rocks. 1500–2600 m. S.W. and C. Alps; Switzerland only in Valais and Tessin. July–August.   124

Petals red or pink, occasionally white

S. caespitosa *L.* TUFTED SOAPWORT. Densely tufted, with 4–15 cm. fl. stems carrying 2 or more pairs of narrow lvs. Fls. bright pink, 8–14 mm. across, few in neat heads; petals rounded, with horn-like scales at throat; calyx very hairy, purplish. ✤ Rocks, screes. C. Pyrenees. Uncommon. July–August.   122

S. pumilio (*L.*) *Fenzl.* (**Saponaria pumila** (*St. Lag.*) *Janch.*, **Silene pumilio** *Wulf.*). Tufted, with linear lvs. and very short stems carrying large solitary rose-red fls. shading deeper at the centre, or occasionally white. Petals broad, lightly notched, noticeably separated; calyx hairy, rather swollen. ✤ Pastures on acid soils; often associated with *Loiseleuria procumbens*. 1900–2600 m. E. Alps. August–September.   120

S. ocymoides *L.* ROCK SOAPWORT. A sprawling, much-branched, hairy plant, with stems up to 20 cm. long. Lvs. elliptic or spoon-shaped. Fls. ½–1 cm. across, pink, red or purplish; petals rounded, with horn-like scales at throat; calyx glandular. ✤ Stony places, debris, grass, walls. To 2000 (2400) m. Pyrenees; Alps; Apennines. March–October.   121

Sub-family Alsinoideae: sepals 4–5, separate. Petals with very short 'claw' or none; throat scales never present. In the genera *Arenaria*, *Moehringia* and *Minuartia* most of the species have at some time been named in each genus, and also in the now generally suppressed genus *Alsine*; these synonyms are not usually given below.

ARENARIA *L.* SANDWORT. Usually insignificant plants, perennials or rarely annuals; lvs. very variable in shape; fls. sometimes solitary, more often few in clusters (cymes). Petals and sepals usually 5; petals white, seldom pink. There are 3 or 4 alpine species besides those described here.

Flowers purplish or pink

A. purpurascens *Ram.* PINK SANDWORT. Mat-forming, with 4–10 cm. more or less ascending stems. Lvs. lance-shaped, to elliptic lance-shaped, 5–10 mm. long, hairy at base. Fls. 2–4, 7–14 mm. across, on downy footstalks as long as sepals; usually purplish, rarely pink, occasionally white. ✤ Damp rocks, debris. 1800–2800 m. Pyrenees. July–August.   125

Flowers white

A. tetraquetra *L.* Forming tight cushions 1–2 cm. high, up to 25 cm. across, the stems hidden by closely overlapping round lvs. 1–4 mm. long, hairy at base. Fls. solitary, often 4-parted, 5–9 mm. across. on short stems. ✤ Dry places. 1800–2700 m. C. and E. Pyrenees. July–August.   960

A. grandiflora *L.* A straggling, more or less tufted plant 5–15 cm. tall, with short-haired stems and narrow, pointed, hairy, 5–10 mm. lvs. Fls. 1–3 (6), ½–1½ cm. across on downy footstalks 2–6 times length of sepals. ✤ Dry limestone rocks and debris. To 2000 (2600) m. Pyrenees; S. and E. Alps (not Switzerland); Apennines. May–August.   961

A. huteri *Kern.* More or less tufted, with 5–12 cm. branching stems. Lvs. lance-shaped, broadest near tip, downy. Fls. 1–3, to 2 cm. across, on footstalks 3–5 times length of sepals. ✤ Crevices of dolomitic rocks. E. Alps. June–August.   959

A. biflora *L.* With thin sprawling stems up to 20 cm. long, rooting as they go, and 2–3 cm. fl. stems. Lvs. rounded, blunt, 3–4 mm. long, with hairy footstalks. Fls. 1–2, ½ cm. across, on footstalks 1–2 times length of sepals. ❋ Granitic rocks, often in snow-beds. 1800–3200 m. E. Pyrenees (rare); Alps; Apennines. July–August.

A. norvegica *Gunn.* NORWEGIAN SAND-WORT. A loosely tufted annual or perennial 3–7 cm. tall. Lvs. lance-shaped, broadest near tip, not exceeding 1 cm. Fls. 1–2 (4), about 5 mm. across, on faintly hairy footstalks 1–3 times length of sepals. ❋ Screes, shingle. To 1440 m. Norway. (Britain: north.) June–July. **957**

A. ciliata *L.* A very variable plant with several subspecies. Tufted, with rough, 5–25 cm. prostrate stems. Lvs. elliptical or spoon-shaped, hairy at edges at least in lower half. Fls. 1–5 (7), 5–10 mm. across. ❋ Meadows, rocky debris, on basic soil. 1400–3200 m. Pyrenees; Alps; N. Apennines. (N.W. Ireland to 600 m.) July–August. **958**

MOEHRINGIA *L.* SANDWORT. In-significant plants very similar to *Arenaria*, with white, usually 5-parted fls. There are several more alpine species besides the three commonest described here.

M. bavarica *(L.) Gren.* (including **M. ponae** *Fenzl.*). Sprawling or erect, bluish, with thin stems up to 20 cm. long. Lvs. narrow, thick, to 2 cm. long, pairs fairly close together. Fls. white, solitary or few, 5-parted. Petals 4–8 mm. long, 1–2 times length of sepals. ❋ Limestone rocks. Probably seldom above 1500 m. S.E. Alps, from Mt. Baldo eastwards. *Ssp.* **insubrica** *Degen* (Sauer): Brescian Alps only. May–July.

M. muscosa *L.* A very variable plant

with weak, often sprawling 8–30 cm. stems, forming dense bright green patches. Lvs. 1½–2½ cm. long, thread-like, pointed. Fls. 2–6, white, usually 4-parted, 4–8 mm. across, on footstalks 3–6 times length of sepals. ❋ Damp rocks, mossy places, in shade, preferring limestone. To 2360 m. Pyrenees; Alps; Apennines. May–September. **955**

M. ciliata *(Scop.) D.T.* (**M. poly-gonoides** *(Wulf.) M. & K.*). A tufted plant with thin, brittle, creeping 5–20 cm. stems. Lvs. 3–10 mm. long, narrow, fleshy, with a few hairs at the base. Fls. 1–3, white, 5-parted, 4–5 mm. across, petals barely exceeding sepals. *Ssp.* **nana** *(St. Lag.) S. & K.:* fls. to 1 cm. across, with petals twice as long as sepals; a cushion plant 2–5 cm. tall, with small, overlapping triangular-sectioned lvs. ❋ Damp meadows, rocky debris, on limestone. 1000–2700 m. Alps (rare). *Ssp. nana:* 2000–3000 m. June–August. **956**

MINUARTIA *L.* Mossy plants, re-sembling *Arenaria*, but with very nar-row lvs., often bristle-like or awl-shaped. There are at least 9 other alpine species besides those described here.

M. graminifolia *(Ard.) Jav.* Forming a dense cushion from which arise un-branched 4–14 cm. fl. stems. Plant downy in *ssp.* **graminifolia**, hairless in *ssp.* **clandestina** *(Port.) Mattf.* Lvs. 1–4 cm. long, narrow, stiff. Fls. 2–7, white, 1 cm. across. ❋ Rocks. 1400–2000 m. *Ssp. gramini-folia:* N. and C. Apennines. *Ssp. clan-destina:* C. and S. Apennines; C. and S. Yugoslav mountains. July–August. **963**

M. verna *(L.) Hiern.* VERNAL SAND-WORT. A very variable plant forming a loose tuft, with 4–15 cm. downy fl. stems. Lvs. to 2 cm. long, narrow, pointed, keeled. Fls. few to many, with footstalks longer than sepals, petals white, shorter or longer than sepals.

✣ Screes, grassy and stony places. 1200–3000 (3300) m. Pyrenees; Alps; Apennines. (Britain.) May–September. **966**

M. laricifolia (*L.*) *S. & K.* (**M. striata** (*L.*) *Mattf.*). Loosely tufted, woody at base, with 8–20 cm. fl. stems. Lvs. narrow, stiff, bristle-like, rough. Fls. 1–6, large, footstalks and calyx downy in *ssp.* **laricifolia** (*ssp.* **diomedis** (*Br.-Bl.*) *Mattf.*), hairless in *ssp.* **kitaibelii** (*Nym.*) *Mattf.* Petals white, 1½–2 times length of red-edged sepals.

✣ Dry grassy and stony places, especially on serpentine and granite. 1300–2000 (3000) m. *Ssp. laricifolia:* C. Pyrenees; S. Alps; Apennines. *Ssp. kitaibelii:* E. Austrian Alps. Both very local. July–August. **962**

M. biflora (*L.*) *S. & K.* Tufted, with thin fl. stems to 10 cm. tall. Lvs. to 1 cm. long, narrow, blunt. Fls. 1–3. Petals white, sometimes pale pink, narrow.

✣ Damp open places, sometimes in snow-beds. 2000–2800 m. C. and E. Alps. Norway to 2120 m. June–August. **965**

M. sedoides *Hiern.* (**Cherleria sedoides** *L.*, **Alsine cherleri** *Fenzl.*). MOSSY CYPHEL. Forming dense yellow-green, moss-like cushions up to 25 cm. across and 8 cm. tall, of short, crowded stems, with closely overlapping, linear, rough-edged lvs. 5 mm. long. Fls. on very short footstalks, solitary, with narrow greenish sepals and usually no petals.

✣ Grassy and stony places, rocks, screes. 1800–3800 m. Pyrenees; Alps. (Scotland to 1300 m.) July–August. **964**

STELLARIA *L.* **S. alsine** *Grimm* (**S. uliginosa** *Murr.*). BOG STITCHWORT. A weak, thin-stemmed plant 10–40 cm. tall with 4-angled stems and small white starry fls., with deeply 2-lobed petals, in loose clusters. Its *var.* **glacialis** *Lagg.* (*var.* **alpina** (*Schur*) *Gürke*) is a true alpine forming dense tufts with lanceolate lvs. ciliate at base.

✣ Clay and sand by streamsides, wet places; *var. glacialis* often in icy pools and streams. To 2300 m. Pyrenees; Alps; Apennines. (Britain to 1000 m.) June–August. **962**

S. media (*L.*) *Vill.*, the COMMON CHICKWEED, reaches 2500 m.; *S. nemorum* *L.*, the WOOD STITCHWORT, with 1 cm. fls., reaches 2400 m. Both are widespread and occur in Britain.

CERASTIUM *L.* MOUSE-EAR CHICKWEED. Alpine species perennials, usually hairy; lvs. opposite, stalkless, uncut. Fls. solitary or more often in clusters (cymes), 5- or 4-parted. Sepals separate, petals white, usually 2-lobed or notched. Stamens 5, 8 or 10; styles usually 5 (3 in *C. cerastoides*).

A confusing group with several very similar species. Among alpine species not described here are *C. carinthiacum* Vest, *C. fontanum* Baumg., *C. julicum* Schellm., *C. lineare* All. and *C. scaranii* Ten.

C. cerastoides (*L.*) *Britt.* (**C. trigynum** *Vill.*). A loose mat-forming perennial with more or less erect 5–15 cm. fl. stems which root as they go, and have a single line of small hairs. Lvs. narrowly elliptic to lance-shaped, ½–2 cm. long, pale green, often curving to one side. Fls. 1–3 on footstalks to 8 cm. Petals deeply 2-lobed; styles usually 3.

✣ Damp grass and debris, on granite. 1500–3000 (3200) m. Pyrenees; Alps; Abruzzi. Norway to 2080 m. (Britain: N. mountains.) July–August. **973**

C. tomentosum *L.* SNOW-IN-SUMMER. A familiar garden plant, entirely white-

woolly, forming a large tuft with erect or spreading stems 15–45 cm. long, and linear to lance-shaped lvs. 1–3 cm. long. Fls. up to 2 cm. across, 3–15 in an elongated cluster; petals notched.
✲ Dry, exposed places. 1000–2270 m. C. and S. Apennines. May–July. **972**

C. arvense *L.* FIELD MOUSE-EAR CHICK-WEED. A variable plant, tufted or mat-forming, with sprawling, rooting, much-branched 5–40 cm. stems; more or less covered in short hairs. Lvs. linear to elliptic; petals 2–3 times length of sepals; bracts with thin dry edges.

Several subspecies are recognised, including the tufted *ssp.* **thomasii** (*Ten.*) *Rouy & Fouc.* (970), with elliptic lvs., and *ssp.* **strictum** (*Haenke*) *Gaud.* (971), with lance-shaped lvs.; the mat-forming *ssp.* **pallasii** (*Vest*) *Walt.* and *ssp.* **suffruticosum** (*L.*) *Hegi* with stiff, pointed, linear lvs.; and the densely matted *ssp.* **ciliatum** (*W. & K.*) *Reichb.* (*ssp.* **rigidum** *Vitm.*) with narrow lance-shaped lvs.
✲ Dry fields, rocky places. To 3100 m. *Ssp. ciliatum:* E. Alps; *ssp. strictum* Alps; *ssp. suffruticosum:* Alps; *ssp. pallasii:* Apennines; *ssp. thomasii:* C. Apennines. (The type in Britain.) April–September. **970, 971**

C. alpinum *L.* ALPINE MOUSE-EAR CHICKWEED. A variable, mat-forming, woody-based plant 6–20 cm. tall, rather similar to *C. arvense,* but with elliptic to nearly circular 1–1½ cm. lvs. all woolly (as in *ssp.* **squalidum** (*Lam.*) *Huet.*) or with long soft hairs, at least at tips of young lvs. (as in *ssp.* **alpinum**). Fls. 1–5, 2–2½ cm. across; petals twice length of calyx, deeply notched.

This plant is recorded from 83° 24′ N. in N. Greenland, the 'northernmost botanical locality on earth' (Clapham, Tutin and Warburg).
✲ Rocks, grassy places, mainly on granite and schist. 1800–2860 m. Pyrenees (uncommon); Alps (rare). Norway to 2270 m. *Ssp. squalidum:* Pyrenees only. (Britain to 1300 m.) June–August. **974**

C. arcticum *Lange* (including **C. edmonstonii** (*Wats.*) *Murb. & Ostf.*). ARCTIC MOUSE-EAR CHICKWEED. A variable, mat-forming plant, covered in short, stiff, whitish, hairs, with prostrate woody stems carrying erect shoots to 15 cm. Lvs. varying from narrow-elliptic to broadly elliptic (usually narrower than in *C. alpinum*). Fls. 1–3, 2–3 cm. across; petals at least twice length of sepals, deeply notched.
✲ Rocks, debris. Norway to 1680 m. (Britain: mountains to 1150 m.) June–August. **975**

C. uniflorum *Clairv.* (also *Thom.*) (**C. glaciale** *Gaud.*). GLACIER MOUSE-EAR CHICKWEED. A mat-forming, woody-based perennial 3–10 cm. tall with soft, bright green, 1–2 cm. obovate lvs. Fls. solitary or 2–3 (despite name!), 1–1½ cm. across, creamy white, rather bell-shaped; petals narrow, deeply 2-lobed, twice length of sepals. Seed capsule curved.
✲ Rocks, debris, moraines, on schist and granite. 1900–3400 m. Alps. July–August. **977**

C. latifolium *L.* Loosely tufted, more or less erect, 5–20 cm. tall; usually downy and glandular. Lvs. bluish, thick, ovate, pointed, stiff. Fls. 1–4, 1½–2 cm. across, rather bell-shaped; petals broad, notched, at least twice length of sepals.
✲ Rocks, debris, moraines, on limestone. 1600–3500 m. Alps; Apennines. July–August. **978**

C. pyrenaicum *Gay.* PYRENEAN MOUSE-EAR CHICKWEED. Similar to *C. lati-folium,* but with smaller fls., petals almost heart-shaped, hairy at base, only slightly longer than sepals. Lvs. oval-lance-shaped.

⚘ Rocks, debris. 1500–3000 m. E. Pyrenees (very rare on French side). August–September. **976**

C. pedunculatum *Gaud.* Loosely tufted, 3–10 cm. tall, not unlike *C. latifolium*, but with bright green lance-shaped lvs., sometimes sparsely hairy. Fls. solitary, bell-shaped, 7–8 mm. across, on 4–6 cm. footstalks; petals 2-lobed, slightly longer than sepals.

⚘ Rocks, debris, moraines, on primary formations. 2000–3600 m. C. and E. Alps. June–August.

SAGINA L. PEARLWORT. Small, usually tufted annuals or perennials, with awl-shaped or linear lvs. in pairs joined at the base. Fls. 4–5-parted, globular in bud, solitary or in small clusters (cymes); petals white, often tiny, sometimes absent.

Besides the two examples of these insignificant plants given, species found at alpine levels include *S. intermedia* Fenzl, *S. procumbens* L., *S. pyrenaica* Rouy. and *S. saginoides* (L.) Karst. (*S. linnaei* Presl).

S. caespitosa (*J. Vahl.*) *Lge.* CUSHION PEARLWORT. A tufted perennial forming small round cushions 1–3 cm. high, up to 5 cm. across, of 3–6 cm. linear, pointed lvs., with dead lvs. persisting

underneath. Fls. 1–2, barely exceeding the lvs., usually 5-parted, about 8 mm. across; petals a little longer than sepals.

⚘ Debris, snow-beds, gravels. To 1670 m. Norway. Rare. June. **967**

S. glabra (*Willd.*) *Fenzl* (**S. repens** *Burnat*). ALPINE PEARLWORT. Bright green, loosely mat-forming, with thin stems to 2 cm. high, and 3–5 mm. thread-like lvs. in fairly close pairs. Fls. solitary, white, 5-parted, ½–1 cm. across, on 1–2 cm. footstalks; petals 1½–2 times length of sepals.

⚘ Meadows, debris, on acid soils. 1600–2400 (2700) m. E. Pyrenees; Alps; Apennines. July–August.

SCLERANTHUS L. KNAWEL. **S. perennis** L. Perennial with woody base, more or less erect and with branching 5–22 cm. stems with linear to lance-shaped, grooved, pointed 5–9 mm. lvs. in fairly close pairs, sometimes apparently in whorls of 4. No stipules. Fls. up to 7 in the taller plants, small, in terminal clusters with small bracts below, each fl. consisting of pale green, white-edged sepals; no petals.

Ssp. **polycnemoides** (*W. & C.*) *F.Q.*: forming a dense 3 cm. cushion; fls. more than 7 in cluster.

⚘ Fields on acid and granitic soils. To 2260 m. Pyrenees; Alps; Apennines. *Ssp. polycnemoides:* Pyrenees only. (The species in Britain.) May–October.

Sub-family Paronychioideae. With stipules (leaf-like or scale-like appendages) at base of opposite, alternate or whorled lvs. Petals often tiny or none; sepals separate.

PARONYCHIA *Mill.* With prominent papery stipules to the opposite lvs., and silvery papery bracts concealing the tiny fls., with very minute petals or none, which are carried in round heads.

P. kapela (*Hacq.*) *Kern.* With stout stock; stems much branched, 5–15 cm. long; stipules narrow lance-shaped,

nearly as long as crowded, ciliate lvs. Fls. tiny, whitish, in 7–15 mm. clusters conspicuous with 3–5 mm. silvery bracts. The montane plant is *ssp.* **serpyllifolia** (*Chaix*) *Graebn.* (**968**), which is mat-forming with elliptic to ovate 1½–3½ mm. lvs., often flattened in one plane.

⚘ Hot, dry, stony places. To 2500 m.

Ssp. serpyllifolia: Pyrenees; Alps (not Switzerland); Ligurian Alps; Apennines. May–June. **968**

P. polygonifolia (*Vill.*) *DC.* With stout stock; forming a sprawling, often dense mat with much-branched 5–30 cm. stems; lvs. ½–1 cm., ovate-lance-shaped, with smaller, whitish, lance-shaped stipules. Fls. in heads about ½ cm. across, with 2–4 mm. lanceolate bracts among the minute green fls.
⚜ Sandy and rocky places, on granite. 1300–2600 m. Pyrenees; Alps (not Switzerland). (Britain: casual.) July–September.

HERNIARIA *L.* RUPTURE-WORT. Completely flat, mat-forming plants with tiny opposite lvs., the upper often apparently alternate, and minute fls. in clusters in lf. axils, with 5 sepals attached to a bowl-shaped disk, and 5 shorter, bristle-like petals, the whole giving a greenish-yellow effect like a tiny fern or selaginella.

H. alpina *L.* Forming dense mats of 5–15 cm. stems with yellowish lvs., to 4½ mm. long, elliptic-obovate. Fls. to 2½ mm., 1–3 near stem-ends; sepals hairy.
⚜ Sandy and stony places, moraines, turf, on acid soils. 1900–3000 (3400) m. Pyrenees; Alps; Apennines. Uncommon. July–August.

H. latifolia *Lap.* Stems 10–40 cm. long, with hairs on one side; lvs. green, to 1 cm. long, broadly elliptic. Fls. to 2 mm. in clusters of 3–6, sometimes on leafless stems; sepals hairy.
⚜ Sandy and rocky places, paths, on granite. To 2500 m. Pyrenees. July–September.

The British *H. glabra* L., which has hairless sepals, reaches 2000 m.

TELEPHIUM *L.* **T. imperati** *L.* 15–40 cm. tall, with sprawling stems arising from woody base. Lvs. oval, fleshy, bluish, alternate, to 1½ cm. long. Fls. small, white, with 5 petals as long as 5 white-edged sepals, short-stalked in rounded terminal clusters of 5–20.
⚜ Limestone rocks and debris. To 1900 m. French Jura; Hautes Alps; Maritime Alps; S.W. Switzerland; Tyrol. Very local. May–August. **969**

NYMPHAEACEAE—WATER-LILY FAMILY

Perennial water plants with large floating lvs. and sometimes submerged lvs. of different shape, and solitary fls., floating or above water, with 4–6 sepals, numerous petals and numerous stamens.

Nymphaea alba *L.*, the WHITE WATER-LILY, with large white multi-petalled fls. to 10–20 cm. across, having 4 green sepals, occasionally exceeds 1500 m. (e.g. 1660 m. in Grisons).

Nuphar lutea (*L.*) *S. & S.*, the YELLOW WATER-LILY or BRANDYBOTTLE, is recorded to 1484 m., and **Nuphar pumila** (*Timm*) *DC.*, the LEAST YELLOW WATER-LILY, to 1685 m. These have 5–6 yellowish sepals and numerous much smaller yellow petals surrounding a bottle-shaped fruit encircled by stamens. *N. lutea* has fls. 4–6 cm. across, *N. pumila* fls. 1½–3½ cm. across. The last is a glacial relic and the only true alpine of these water-lilies, all of which are native to Britain.

RANUNCULACEAE—BUTTERCUP FAMILY

Alpine species perennials, or woody climbers (*Clematis*). Fls. usually radially symmetrical (actinomorphic) but sometimes only vertically so (zygomorphic: *Delphinium, Aconitum*). The parts are of varying numbers, only occasionally with distinctive green sepals (*Ranunculus, Callianthemum*), more often with all segments petaloid. There is often only one rank of fl. segments, in which case they are technically regarded as sepals; the petals are sometimes reduced to tiny proportions (*Isopyrum*), often dropping at an early stage (*Thalictrum, Actaea*); or they are reduced to insignificant nectaries (*Helleborus*). Modern authors, indeed, refer to the petals as honey-leaves. In *Aquilegia* they are spurred. The stamens are numerous, spirally arranged, and the female organs are carpels varying from 1 to many, usually separate and spirally arranged, giving rise to various kinds of fruit.

CALTHA *L.* **C. palustris** *L.* MARSH MARIGOLD, KINGCUP. A stout, fleshy plant 15–30 (60) cm. tall, arising from a creeping rhizome, with lvs. mainly basal, rounded to heart-shaped, toothed or notched. Fls. 2–5 cm. across, with 5–8 golden-yellow segments, sometimes greenish below. Carpels 5–13, fruit a follicle.

❧ Marshy places. To 2530 m. Pyrenees; Alps; Apennines. (Britain to 1100 m.) March–July.   **128**

ERANTHIS, *Salisb.* **E. hyemalis** (*L.*) *Salisb.* WINTER ACONITE. Fl. stems 5–15 cm. tall, elongating after flowering, arising from tuberous rhizome; fls. 2–3 cm. across, usually of 6 narrow yellow sepals and about 6 short nectaries, about 30 stamens and 6 (3–11) carpels giving rise to follicles. Stem lvs. 3, deeply lobed, in a whorl just below the fl., giving the appearance of a green ruff. Basal lvs. appearing after the fls., long-stalked, much-lobed. Poisonous.

❧ Hedgerows, grass, scrub. Just reaching 1500 m. Much cultivated: naturalised in various places (e.g. Switzerland), probably native in Jura, Dauphiné, Provence Alps, and here and there in

S. Europe. (Britain: naturalised.) January–March.   **127**

ADONIS *L.* **A. pyrenaica** *DC.* PYRENEAN PHEASANT-EYE. 10–40 cm. tall, with ferny lvs. cut into thin segments, the lower lvs. long-stalked. Fls. golden yellow, 4–6 cm. across, with 12–20 petals and about 5 hairless sepals. Carpels numerous, fruit an elongated head of achenes.

❧ Stony places, screen, rocks. 1300–2400 m. French and Spanish Pyrenees (rare); Maritime Alps (one locality). June–July.   **126**

A. distorta *Ten.* is a smaller plant with curved stems and lvs., and downy sepals, from the C. Apennines.

The scarlet spring-fl. annual. **A. aestivalis** *L.*, with 1½–3 cm. fls., reaches 1500 m. in the Pyrenees.

RANUNCULUS *L.* BUTTERCUP. Fls. usually solitary, sometimes in clusters, yellow, white or pinkish. Sepals 3–5; petals 3, 5 or more; stamens and carpels numerous; fruit a head of achenes. All species are acrid and poisonous.

Besides the alpine species described,

the following common lowland species may be found up to 2500 m. or even more: R. *acris* L., R. *arvensis* L., R. *auricomus* L., R. *bulbosus* L., R. *polyanthemos* L., R. *repens* L.

The aquatic, white-fld. R. *tricho-phyllus* Chaix (R. *flaccidus* Pers.), with much-cut, thread-like lvs., reaches 2500 m.

Flowers yellow; leaves lobed

R. montanus *Willd.* (R. **geraniifolius** *Pourr.*). MOUNTAIN BUTTERCUP. A variable plant 16–30 cm. tall. Lvs. of 3–5 lobes with blunt teeth and rounded sinuses. Upper stem-lvs. usually strap-shaped, sometimes toothed. Fls. 2–3 cm. across; sepals downy. Carpels with arched beak $\frac{1}{3}$–$\frac{1}{4}$ length of achene.
❀ Meadows, woods, screes, snow-beds. To 2800 (3100) m. Pyrenees; Alps; Apennines. May–August. **136**
This species is the type of a confused and variable group to which the following 3 species belong, together with the similar R. *oreophilus* Bieb. and R. *grenieranus* Jord.

R. carinthiacus *Hoppe.* Similar to R. *montanus* (of which it is sometimes regarded as a subspecies), but only 6–15 cm. tall, lvs. with more, narrower lobes, notably the upper stem-lvs. which are much divided into strap-shaped segments. Fls. 1–3 cm. across; sepals barely downy. Achenes with minute beak.
❀ Meadows, woods, screes. To 2800 m. Pyrenees; Alps, especially E. May–August. **138**

R. aduncus *Gren.* Very similar to R. *carinthiacus*, but with smaller, less-divided lvs. of 3–5 lobes, downy; fls. to 3 cm. across; sepals with 2 mm. hairs and achenes with hooked beak at least $\frac{1}{2}$ as long.
❀ Meadows. To 2800 m. S.W. (Swiss) Alps. June–July. **137**

R. gouanii *Willd.* Like R. *aduncus*, but

fls. up to 5 cm. across; sepals densely downy, achenes with hooked beak at least $\frac{1}{3}$ as long.
❀ Meadows. To 2800 m. Pyrenees. June–July.

R. pygmaeus *Wahl.* PYGMY BUTTERCUP. A minute plant 1$\frac{1}{2}$–4 (7) cm. tall with lvs. deeply cut into 3–5 relatively wide, blunt lobes. Fls. $\frac{1}{2}$–1 cm. across, 5-parted.
❀ Turf, snow-beds. 1800–2800 m. C. Alps (rare). Norway to 2100 m. July–August. **140**

R. hyperboreus *Rottb.* A low plant to 5 cm. tall, creeping or even floating, with lvs. like those of R and 3 sepals and petals.
❀ Turf, snow-beds, glacial streams. To 2100 m. Norway. July.

R. nivalis *L.* An erect plant 5–10 (25) cm. tall, with basal lvs. like those of R. *pygmaeus*, but stem-lvs. much longer, with 3–5 strap-shaped lobes. Fls. 1$\frac{1}{2}$ cm. across, 5-parted, with shaggy brownish sepals.
❀ Turf, snow-beds. To 1550 m. Norway. July. **139**

Flowers yellow; leaves rounded, or broader than long, toothed not lobed

R. thora *L.* 10–30 cm. tall, arising from elongated, fleshy, bundled roots, with large, waxy, kidney-shaped lvs. a little broader than long, upper edge toothed, more noticeably towards centre; upper stem-lvs. small, lance-shaped, or with 3 pointed lobes. Fls. 1–5, 5-parted, 1–2 cm. across; achenes rounded. Very poisonous.
❀ Rocks, stony places, meadows, on limestone. To 2200 m. Pyrenees; Alps; Abruzzi. Local. May–July. **129**

R. scutatus *W. & K.* Like R. *thora*, and possibly only a form of it; usually taller; lvs. more markedly toothed, lower stem-lf. heart-shaped, stem-clasping. Fls. usually several.

206

✿ Stony places, meadows. To 2000 m.
E. Alps; Yugoslav Alps. June–July. 132

R. hybridus *Biria* (**R. pseudothora**
Host). Like R. *thora*, but only 10–15 cm.
tall; lvs. greyish green, rather straight-
edged at base, with a few broad lobe-
like teeth on upper edge. Fls. 1–3,
1–2½ cm. across; beak of achene short.
✿ Stony places, debris, on limestone.
1000–2500 m. E. Alps; Yugoslav Alps;
Apennines. Local. June–July. 131

R. brevifolius *Ten*. Like R. *hybridus*, and
sometimes regarded as a variety of it;
lvs. small-toothed on outer edges, more
deeply in centre. Fl. solitary; beak of
achene long.
✿ Stony places, debris. To 2200 m.
C. Apennines; Yugoslav Alps. June–
July. 130

Flowers white; leaves toothed or lobed

R. crenatus *W. & K.* 4–10 cm. tall, with
rounded, long-stalked, toothed lvs., the
central teeth on upper edges sometimes
grouped in 3 larger sub-lobes. Stem-lvs.
linear, bract-like. Fls. 1–2, 2–2½ cm.
across, with broad, oblong, wavy-edged
petals. Achenes longer than broad, long-
beaked.
✿ Rocks, damp debris. 1700–2400 m.
E. Alps. Rare. June–July. 133

R. bilobus *Bert.* (**134**) Similar to R.
crenatus, but lvs. with more prominent
veins and rounder, larger sub-lobes;
petals heart-shaped with shallow notch.
Achenes longer than broad, long-
beaked.
Ssp. **magellensis** *Ten.*, MAJELLA
BUTTERCUP (**135**): with narrow-heart-
shaped, shallowly notched petals and
achenes as broad as long, with curved
beak.
✿ Stony places. To 2000 m. Tyrol and
Lombard Alps. *Ssp. magellensis*: Abruzzi,
including Mt. Majella. June–July.
134, 135

Flowers white, rarely pink; leaves not lobed

R. pyrenaeus *L.* PYRENEAN BUTTERCUP
(**141**). 10–20 cm. tall, with fibrous
stock; lvs. usually 1–3, long, linear to
lance-shaped, tapered at both ends. Fl.
stems downy near top; fls. 1–3 (10), 1–2
cm. across, with rounded petals.
Ssp. **plantagineus** *All.* PLANTAIN-
LEAVED BUTTERCUP. (**142**). More robust,
more branched and with broader lvs.
Probably not a valid ssp.
The narrow-lvd. form from the
Pyrenees is sometimes called *var.*
angustifolius *DC.* and has hairless fl.
stalk.
R. *pyrenaeus* hybridises freely with
other white-fld. spp.
✿ Damp meadows, earthy slopes,
usually on limestone. 1700–2800 (3050)
m. Pyrenees; Alps. *Ssp. plantagineus*:
Alps only. May–July. **141, 142**

R. bupleuroides *Brot.* Like R. *pyrenaeus*,
but with broader lvs., ovate or ovate
lance-shaped, with distinct basal stalk;
plant more branched.
✿ Damp meadows. 1700–2800 m.
Pyrenees (doubtful record: see below).
May–July. **143**
There is some doubt about the
distribution of this plant. Marret
regards it as a form of R. *pyrenaeus*
restricted to the Pyrenees and Iberian
Peninsula; it is also recorded from the
Pyrenees by Farrer and (as a form of
R. *pyrenaeus*) by Acloque. 'Flora
Europaea', however, confines it to
N.W. Spain and Portugal and states that
it has pale yellow fls.

R. amplexicaulis *L.* Resembling R.
pyrenaeus, but with stem-lvs. ovate-
lance-shaped and clasping the stem.
Basal lvs. ovate-lance-shaped, on
distinct stems.
✿ Meadows. 1000–2500 m. C. and E.
Pyrenees. June–July. **144**

R. parnassifolius *L.* 5–20 (30) cm. tall

with basal lvs. ovate, pointed, with a distinct stalk (like a spade on playing cards); stem-lvs. narrow, clasping. Fls. 1–5 (exceptionally to 25), 2–2½ cm. across, white or reddish, pink-flushed on back, with rounded petals and downy sepals; often missing some or all petals. ❀ Rocks, moraines, on limestone and schist. 1900–2900 m. Pyrenees; Alps (rare). July–August. **146**

Flowers white, pink or reddish; basal leaves lobed

R. alpestris L. ALPINE BUTTERCUP. 3–12 cm. tall, tufted, with shiny basal lvs. often apparently rounded in outline, but, in fact, of 3–5 deeply cut but overlapping toothed lobes. Stem-lvs. linear, 1 or 2, lower 3-parted, upper simple. Fls. 1–3, 2 cm. across, normally white, with heart-shaped, shallowly notched petals; achenes hairless. ❀ Damp meadows, snow-patches, stony places. 1300–2970 m. C. and E. Pyrenees; Alps (rare in France); N. and C. Apennines. June–October. **149**

R. traunfellneri Hoppe. Similar to R. *alpestris* and often considered a ssp., but more straggling, to 10 cm., with matt lvs. more distinctly cut into 3 lobes which are divided to the central vein; stem-lf. usually 1, simple. Fl. usually solitary, 1½ cm. across, normally white; achenes hairless. ❀ Grassy and stony places. 1300–2800 m. S.E. Alps. June–July. **147**

R. seguieri *Vill.* 10–20 cm. tall, downy, with 3–5 deeply cut lobes, each divided into angular segments; stem-lvs. similar, smaller. Fls. 1–2, 1½–2½ cm. across, white; petals very shallowly notched; achenes downy. ❀ Damp meadows, stony places, screes, on limestone. 1800–2400 m. W. and E. Alps (rare in Switzerland); C. Apennines. Very local. June–July. **148**

R. glacialis L. GLACIER CROWFOOT.

4–25 cm. tall, rather fleshy, smooth. Basal lvs. dark green, metallic-looking, 3-parted, each section usually stalked and subdivided into elliptic or oblong lobes; stem-lvs. similar but smaller, less divided. Fls. 1–3, white, pink or purplish red (reputedly pink or red only after pollination), with central boss of carpels and stamens prominent. Petals persistent; sepals with rusty red hairs.

Found near the top of the Finsteraarhorn at 4275 m., the highest record for a European plant.

❀ Debris, moraines, streamsides, on acid soils. (1500) 2300–4275 m. Pyrenees (rare); Alps, mainly W. Norway to 2370 m. July–October. **150**

R. aconitifolius L. 20–50 (100) cm. tall, with 1–2 cm. white fls. in branching heads (cymes); sepals reddish purple, falling as flowers open. Basal lvs. cut into 3–5 lobes to centre vein. ❀ Meadows, woods. 1000–2600 m. Pyrenees; Alps; Apennines. May–August. **145**

R. platanifolius L. Similar to R. *aconitifolius* and sometimes considered a subspecies, but up to 130 cm. tall with rather larger fls. and lvs. 5–7-lobed, the central lobes not cut to the centre vein. ❀ Scrub, dry places. Seldom above 1500 m. Pyrenees; Alps, more common towards E. Norway to 1400 m. May–August.

CALLIANTHEMUM *C. A. Meyer.* Perennials, with lvs. cut into paired side lobes and a terminal lobe, each lobe further cut 2 or 3 times. Fls. with 5 sepals and 5–20 petals, numerous stamens, and numerous short-stalked carpels.

C. coriandrifolium *Reichb.* (**C. rutifolium** (*L.*) *Reichb.* in part, **Ranunculus rutaefolius** *L.* in part, **R. berardi** *Vill.*). 5–25 cm. tall, with long-stalked basal lvs. cut into narrow oblong segments; stem lvs. similar, but stalkless and less cut. Fls. 1½–3½ cm. across, white with orange central ring and sometimes pink exterior; petals broadly ovate; carpels 3 mm. long, veined.

✻ Turf and stony places, especially by melting snow, usually avoiding limestone. 1800–3000 m. Pyrenees; C. and S. Alps. Rare. July–August.   151

C. anemonoides *Zahl.* (also *Schott.*) (**C. rutifolium** (*L.*) *Reichb.* in part, **Ranunculus rutaefolius** *L.* in part). Very like *C. coriandrifolium*, but with narrower, strap-shaped petals and carpels 5 mm. long, veined.

✻ Turf, stony places, light woodland. To 2100 m. Austrian Alps. March–May.

C. kerneranum *Freyn* (also spelt **kernerianum**). Resembling *C. coriandrifolium*, but usually only 2–6 cm. tall, with short-stalked basal lvs., fls. about 2½ cm. across, carpels 3–4 mm. long, smooth.

✻ Stony places on limestone. To 1500 m. Monte Baldo, S. Italian Tyrol. May–July.

ANEMONE *L.* Perennials with rhizomes or woody stocks, basal lvs. usually lobed (if present), and 3 stem-lvs. in a whorl some distance below the fl. which is usually solitary (clustered in *A. narcissiflora*). Fl. with 4–20 petaloid sepals, many stamens and fruit a cluster of achenes. Poisonous. Besides the species mentioned the golden *A. ranunculoides* L. just reaches 1500 m.

A. trifolia *L.* THREE-LEAVED ANEMONE. 10–30 cm. tall, with brown creeping rhizome; usually no basal lvs.; stem-lvs. 3-parted into elliptical, toothed segments. Fls. white, sometimes flushed blue or pink, flattish, 2–4 cm. across, of 6–7 (5–9) segments.

✻ Woods, rocky places. To 1860 m. Pyrenees (very local); S. and E. Alps (not Switzerland); Apennines. May–July.   159

A. nemorosa *L.* WOOD ANEMONE. Similar to *A. trifolia*, but with 1–2 basal lvs. with deeply lobed segments, stem-lvs. similar but smaller, fls. more cupped.

✻ Woods. To 1800 m. Pyrenees; Alps. (Britain.) March–May.

A. baldensis *L.* MONTE BALDO ANEMONE. 5–12 cm. tall, elongating in fruit. Lvs. divided into 3, each segment again cut into 3, and each final division of 2–3 lobes. Fl. white, often bluish outside, slightly cupped, 2½–4 cm. across, of 8–10 segments, rarely fewer, on woolly stalk. Fruit reddish, very woolly, with projecting styles.

✻ Rocky places, screes. 1800–3055 m. Alps (local); Yugoslav mountains. July–August.   158

A. narcissiflora *L.* NARCISSUS-FLOWERED ANEMONE. A handsome plant 20–50 cm. tall, arising from a thick stock, with 2–8 white, often pink-backed, 2–3 cm. fls. in a terminal cluster. Basal lvs. long-stalked, deeply divided; stem-lvs. forming a 'ruff' of long narrow segments from which the fl. stems radiate.

✻ Meadows, preferring limestone. 1500–2600 m. Pyrenees; Alps; Apennines. June–July.   152

PULSATILLA *Mill.* Very similar to *Anemone* and originally included in that genus, but with stem-lvs. close to the fl. and sometimes resembling a calyx; fl. solitary, usually of 5–8 segments, and with persistent styles which elongate and become feathery when the fruit ripens. Poisonous.

P. alpina (*L.*) *Delarbre* (also *Schrank*) (**Anemone alpina** *L.*). ALPINE ANEMONE. 15–35 cm. tall, elongating to 45 cm. in fruit. Basal lvs. long-stalked, downy, of 2 opposed pairs of deeply cut, pointed leaflets, terminal segments not cut to midrib; stem-lvs. similar but smaller. Fl. 4–8 cm. across, cupped, more or less erect. Fruiting head large, feathery, conspicuous in late summer.

Ssp. alpina: WHITE ALPINE ANEMONE (153): with white fl., sometimes bluish. (This bluish form has been called *P. subalpina Song.*)

Ssp. alpina: *var.* myrrhidifolia (*Vill.*) *Rouy & Fouc.*: a stout plant with much larger lvs. with more, dissected segments and 4–6 cm. white, rosy-backed fls., from the Alps. This is probably the same as *var.* millefoliata (*Bert.*) *Fiori*, recorded in the Apennines to 2150 m.

Ssp. apiifolia (*Scop.*) *Nym.* (*Ssp.* sulphurea (*L.*) *DC.* Anemone sulphurea *L.*). YELLOW ALPINE ANEMONE (154): with yellow fl.

✳ Meadows, *ssp. alpina* preferring limestone; *ssp. apiifolia* usually avoiding it. 1000–2730 m. Pyrenees; Alps; Apennines (not *ssp. apiifolia*). May–July.

153, 154

P. alba *Reichb.* (P. alpina *ssp.* austriaca *Schw.*). Resembling *P. alpina*, but only 10–20 cm. tall, not elongating in fruit, with 2½–4½ cm. white or bluish fls. and terminal lf. segments cut to midrib, which is hairless.

✳ Meadows, usually avoiding limestone. 1000–2200 m. Pyrenees; Alps. May–July.

P. vernalis (*L.*) *Mill.* (Anemone vernalis *L.*). SPRING ANEMONE. 5–15 cm. tall, elongating to 35 cm. in fruit. Basal lvs. evergreen, with fine hairs, short-stalked, cut into toothed segments; stem-lvs. of long, very narrow segments, forming a 'collar' close below the fl., and like stem covered in long, yellowish, woolly hairs. Fls. 4–6 cm. across, nodding in bud, erect when open, deeply cup-shaped; inner sepals usually white, sometimes pink to claret coloured; outer with pink, violet or blue flush, woolly on exterior. Sometimes difficult to distinguish from *P. halleri* when sepals

are fading but have not fallen and stem is elongating, but lvs. are distinct.

✳ Meadows, stony places, often flowering as the snow melts. 1300–3600 m. Pyrenees; Alps; Norway to 1840 m. April–July. **157**

P. montana (*Hoppe*) *Reichb.* (Anemone montana *Hoppe*). MOUNTAIN ANEMONE. 10–25 cm. tall, elongating to 30 cm. in fruit. Basal lvs. deeply cut into long narrow segments; stem-lvs. of around 25 long, very narrow segments. Entirely downy, including exterior of the pendant dark blue to purple fl., at first bell-shaped, later opening starlike, usually of 5–6 sepals.

✳ Meadows, woods. To 2150 m. Alps (local). April–May. **155**

P. halleri (*All.*) *Willd.* (Anemone halleri *All.*). Resembling *P. montana*, but with basal lvs. very white-woolly, divided into narrow-oblong lobes, themselves cut into 2–3 lobes. Fl. purple to lilac, bell-shaped at first, opening to a flat star, more erect. Resembling our native Pasque Flower, *P. vulgaris*, but much more woolly; may be considered its nearest Alpine relation.

Ssp. styriaca *Pritz.* is described as having lvs. almost always with 3 secondary lobes, appears to be more woolly and to have longer persistent styles on fruit (6–7 cm. as against 5–6 cm.), but these are only minor variations of a curiously isolated geographical race.

✳ Meadows, stony places. 1000–3000 m. *Ssp. halleri*: S.W. to W.C. Alps. *Ssp. styriaca*: S.E. Austria. Always very local. June–July. **156**

HEPATICA *L.* H. trifolia *Mill.* (H. nobilis *Mill.*, H. triloba *Chaix*, Anemone hepatica *L.*). 5–15 cm. tall, arising from thick short stock, with evergreen lvs., heart-shaped at base, sometimes white-blotched, of 3 rounded, shallow lobes. Fls. 1½–2½ cm. across, starry, blue, purple, pink or white, usually of 6–7 narrow segments, with 3 small undivided bracts below.

The name *H. nobilis* as used by Miller referred only to the blue form, and its use for the entire species in 'Flora Europaea' would therefore seem misguided.

❋ Stony places, usually in woods, preferring limestone. To 2200 m. Pyrenees; Alps; Apennines. March–April.   **160**

TROLLIUS *L.* **T. europaeus** *L.* GLOBE FLOWER. Perennial, 10–70 cm. tall, hairless, usually unbranched, with long-stalked basal lvs. cut into 3–5 lobes themselves further divided; stem-lvs. smaller, stalkless. Fls. 1–3, globular, yellow, to 5 cm. across, with about 10 petaloid sepals and 5–15 short petals or honey-lvs. within. Fruit of several follicles. Poisonous.

Var. humilis (*Crantz*) *DC.* (**T. minimus** *Med.*) is the name given to a 1-fld. montane form 10–15 cm. tall.

❋ Damp meadows, woods. To 2800 m. Pyrenees; Alps; N. and C. Apennines. Norway to 1080 m. (Britain: mountains to 1500 m.) May–August.   **161**

HELLEBORUS *L.* BEAR'S FOOT. Perennials arising from a blackish stock, with toothed lvs. divided into more or less radiating segments. Fls. solitary or clustered, of 5 large petal-like sepals and 8–12 small, often insignificant petals or honey-lvs. Sepals often persistent around the fruit of several follicles. Very poisonous.

H. viridis *L.* GREEN HELLEBORE. 20–40 cm. tall, stem not overwintering; basal lvs. usually of 7–13 narrow elliptical segments; stem-lvs. smaller, stalkless. Fls. 2–4, pale green, open, 4–5 cm. across.

❋ Woods, scrub, rocky places, preferring limestone. To 1600 m. Pyrenees; Alps. (Britain: *ssp. occidentalis* (Reut.) Schiffn). March–April.   **162**

H. foetidus *L.* STINKING HELLEBORE. 20–80 cm. tall, with overwintering stem; no basal lvs.; stem-lvs. sheathing at the base, of 3–9 narrow lance-shaped segments, lower long-stalked, upper stalkless. Fls. 1–3 cm. across, many in a drooping head, rounded or cup-shaped, yellowish green with red margin.

❋ Woods, scrub, on shallow chalky soil or screes. To 1600 (1800) m. Pyrenees; Alps, C. Apennines. (Britain.) January–April.

H. niger *L.* CHRISTMAS ROSE. A familiar garden plant 10–30 cm. tall, with 1–2 white or pink-tinged fls., 3–10 cm. across, and dark green, overwintering basal lvs. of usually 7–8 elliptical segments; stem-lvs. usually none. Fruit persisting well into summer.

❋ Woods, scrub, on limestone. To 1850 m. C. and E. Alps (French Alps: very rare; Switzerland: only in Tessin); N. Apennines. January–April.   **163**

AQUILEGIA *L.* COLUMBINE. Perennials, with erect stems and lvs. of 3 distinct segments themselves further divided. Fls. 1-several, nodding, of 5 petal-like sepals and 5 petals each with a long hollow nectar-producing spur pointing backwards. Stamens numerous; some without anthers (staminodes). Fruit of several (usually 5) follicles. Poisonous.

Spur hooked at apex, usually curving inwards

A. atrata *Koch* (**A. atroviolacea** (*Ave-Lall.*) *Beck.*; sometimes regarded as a subspecies of *A. vulgaris*). DARK COLUMBINE. The only alpine columbine with stamens protruding markedly beyond petals. 30–80 cm. tall, with hairy stems. Fls. dark purple, 3–4 cm. across; spur 10–15 mm. long, hooked; staminodes blunt.

❋ Clearings, rocky places, on limestone. To 2000 (2800) m. Alps; Apennines. May–July.   **164**

A. vulgaris *L.* COMMON COLUMBINE. A variable plant 40–100 cm. tall, stems smooth or hairy. Fls. 3–5 cm. across, violet-blue, occasionally white or reddish; stamens often protruding slightly beyond petals; staminodes white, blunt; spur 15–22 mm. long, markedly hooked and swollen at the tip.
♣ Woods, meadows, rocky places, preferring limestone. To 2000 m. Pyrenees; Alps. (Britain to 1000 m.) May–July.

A. bertolonii *Schott.* (**A. reuteri** *Boiss.*). 10–30 cm. tall, stems downy above; stem-lvs. narrow-strap-shaped. Fls. 2–3 cm. across, dark blue; stamens not exceeding petals; staminodes pointed; spur 10–14 mm. long, straight or curved, hooked.
♣ Woods, rocks. To 1700 m. S. French Alps; Maritime Alps; Ligurian Alps; Piedmont Apennines. June–July. **165**

Spur not hooked at apex, nearly straight

A. einseleana *Schultz.* 10–45 cm. tall, barely downy above; stem-lvs. linear. Fls. 2–3 cm. across, purplish; stamens not exceeding petals; spur 7–10 mm. long, straight or slightly curved.
♣ Grassy and stony places, woods, only on limestone. To 1800 (2800) m. E. Alps. June–July. **168**

A. pyrenaica *DC.* PYRENEAN COLUMBINE. 10–30 cm. tall, sometimes slightly hairy. Fls. 3–4 cm. across, blue or lilac; stamens about as long as petals; staminodes pointed; spur 10–16 mm. long, slender, straight or slightly curved.
♣ Rocks, stony places. 1800–2500 m. Pyrenees. Uncommon. (Britain: naturalised in Angus.) July–August. **167**

A. alpina *L.* ALPINE COLUMBINE. 20–80 cm. tall, with long hairs below, densely downy above. Fls. 5–8 cm. across, purple-blue, centre sometimes pale blue or creamy. Stamens about as long as petals; staminodes pointed; spur 18–25

mm. long, straight or curved, slightly swollen at tip.
♣ Meadows, woods, rocky places. 1200–2600 m. Alps, mainly W.; N. Apennines. Uncommon: excessively picked. July–August. **166**

DELPHINIUM *L.* LARKSPUR. Alpine species perennial, with spirally arranged lvs. and a spike of large, stalked fls. symmetrical only in vertical plane (zygomorphic), with 5 petal-like sepals, the upper with a prominent spur, and 4 separate, reduced petals (honey-lvs.), the upper 2 spurred, inside sepals. 8 stamens; fruit 3–5 follicles. Poisonous.

D. elatum *L.* ALPINE LARKSPUR. A variable species 40–200 cm. tall, with upper stems more or less hairy; 2 bracts under each fl. stalk. Fls. of various shades of blue or bluish violet. Sepals 14–21 mm. long. Carpels usually hairless.
Ssp. **elatum** (including **D. alpinum** *W. & K*; **D. tiroliense** *Kern.*) (**169**) has spur usually longer than sepals; lower sepals 1½–2½ times longer than wide; petals blackish or brownish; bracts, stalks and calyx hairless or lightly hairy.
Ssp. **helveticum** *Pawl.*: similar, but with spur about same length as sepals; lower sepals 2½–3½ times longer than wide.
Ssp. **austriacum** *Pawl.*: has larger fls., with sepals and spur about same length; petals blue to yellowish.
♣ Meadows, stony places. 1280–2000 m. *Ssp. elatum*: Pyrenees; Alps. *Ssp. helveticum*: W. Alps. *Ssp. austriacum*: C.E. Alps. June–August. **169**

D. montanum *DC.* Similar to *D. elatum*, and often considered a subspecies. 15–65 cm. tall, all densely velvety-hairy, including carpels. Sepals usually 12–20 mm. long.
♣ Meadows, stony places. To 2000 m. Pyrenees; S. Tyrol (doubtful record). June–August.

ACONITUM L. Perennials with tuberous rootstocks, stout stems, spirally arranged lvs., and a more or less branched spike (raceme) of fls. symmetrical only in vertical plane (zygomorphic), of 5 petal-like sepals, the upper forming a helmet-shaped hood, and 2–5 reduced petals (honey-lvs.), the rear pair spurred and long-clawed, remainder tiny or absent, within the sepals. Stamens many; fruit 2–5 follicles. Extremely poisonous.

All species are variable and often tend to grade into each other, with the result that nomenclature is confused. Ill-defined species include *A. angustifolium* Bernh., often regarded as a subspecies of *A. napellus* and very like *A. tauricum*, from Yugoslavia; *A. burnatii* Gáyer, local to the Maritime Alps; and *A. zahlbruckneri* Gáyer, from the E. Alps. The latter two share characters of *A. paniculatum* and *A. compactum* and may be hybrids.

Flowers usually yellow

A. vulparia Reichb. (**A. lycoctonum** auct. in part). WOLFSBANE. 50–150 cm. tall. Extremely variable, and by some authors divided into many subspecies, but basically easily recognised by its elongated helmet 15–25 mm. long and 3–8 mm. wide (a character shared by several non-alpine species), and its dark green lvs. of 5–7 lobes, each lobe 3-parted, cut to the middle only. Fl.-spike rather sparse, with side-spikes at an angle from the main stem.
♣ Woods, stony places, meadows. To 2400 m. Pyrenees; Alps; Apennines. June–August.   170

A. lamarckii Reichb. (**A. ranunculifolium** Reichb., **A. lycoctonum** auct. in part, **A. pyrenaicum** L. in part). 50–100 cm. tall. Fls. similar to those of *A. vulparia* but numerous, carried in large spikes with side spikes erect, if present. Forms exist in which the helmet has a 'waist' or is narrowly conical. Lvs. 7–8-lobed, each lobe cut beyond the middle into several sections. The name *A. pyrenaicum* Lam. was given to a large-lvd., long-haired plant found only in the Pyrenees, the other forms being short-haired.
♣ Woods, stony places, meadows. To 2300 m. Pyrenees; S. Alps. Rare. July–August.   171

The name *A. lycoctonum* used by older authors must now be considered ambiguous: it covered both the above species, which undoubtedly grade into each other.

A. anthora L. YELLOW MONKSHOOD. 25–90 cm. tall. Fls. sometimes orange-yellow, very rarely blue, with helmet 1½–2½ cm. high, usually as high as broad, but sometimes taller than broad (the latter form has been called var. **jacquinii** Reichb.). Fl.-head rarely branched. Lvs. cut right to midrib, into very narrow segments.
♣ Dry meadows, rocky places, usually on limestone. To 2200 m. Pyrenees; Alps; Ligurian Apennines. July–September.   172

Flowers blue or mauve

A. paniculatum Lam. BRANCHED MONKSHOOD. 60–150 cm. tall, with branched, rather zigzag glandular-hairy fl.-head and no definite spike. Lvs. lobed to the midrib. Fls. violet to mauve, sometimes whitish or greenish at base; helmet round, usually as high as broad, strongly recurved. The form illustrated, with leafy bracts, is close to what has been called *A. hebegynum* DC., with helmet taller than broad. 'Flora Europaea' considers *A. paniculatum* proper to have linear bracts, although other authorities disagree. There are doubtless various intermediate forms.
♣ Woods, clearings, damp meadows. 1000–2400 m. Alps (rare); N. Apennines. July–September.   173

A. variegatum *L.* (including **A. rostratum** *Bernh.*) VARIEGATED MONKSHOOD. Similar to *A. paniculatum*, but with fl.-head hairless or with short wavy hairs; fls. usually blue with white streaks; helmet twice as high as broad.
❀ Woods, clearings, meadows. To 2000 m. C. Alps (very rare in France). July–September. **174**

A. napellus *L.* COMMON MONKSHOOD. 50–150 cm. tall, with stout fl. spike and often smaller subsidiary spikes of large, deep blue, violet or reddish violet fls., with helmet as high as broad, or higher. Lvs. divided almost to midrib into narrow lobes, not crowded below fl. spike. Variable in lf. and fl. shape but always basically recognisable.
❀ Damp meadows. To 2500 (2925) m. Pyrenees; Alps. July–September.
The form sometimes called *A. anglicum Stapf.* is found in Britain. **175**

A. compactum *Reichb.* Similar to *A. napellus*, and often considered a subspecies, but with lvs. crowded below the seldom-branched fl. spike.
❀ Damp meadows. To 2500 m. Pyrenees; W. Alps. (Britain: naturalised.) July–September.

A. tauricum *Wulf.* Similar to *A. compactum*, also often considered a subspecies of *A. napellus*, but lvs. rather broader-lobed.
❀ Damp meadows. To 2400 m. E. Alps. July–September.

A. septentrionale *Koelle.* LOUSEHAT. 75–150 cm. tall, with stout, downy stem and 20–40 cm. spike of lavender-blue fls., sometimes becoming creamy or yellowish, 2–2½ cm. long, with narrow upright helmet rather like that of *A. vulparia*, but projecting more at base. Lvs. large, divided into 3–5-toothed segments.
❀ Birch forests, willow thickets. To 1300 m. S. Norway. July. **1182**

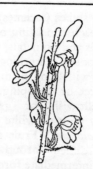

1182. *Aconitum septentrionale.* Part of flower spike.

ISOPYRUM *L.* **I. thalictroides** *L.* A slender, bluish, hairless perennial 10–30 cm. tall, arising from a creeping rhizome, with 3-parted lvs. and solitary 1–2 cm. fls. of 5 white sepals, 5 tiny (1–1½ mm.) petals (honey-lvs.) and numerous short stamens. Fruit of 1–3 follicles. Poisonous.
❀ Damp, shady places. Seldom above 1000 m. Pyrenees (rare); Savoy; E. Alps; N. and C. Apennines. March–May. **177**

ACTAEA *L.* **A. spicata** *L.* BANEBERRY, HERB CHRISTOPHER. A stout perennial with thick blackish rhizome and stout, hairless 30–80 cm. stem. Basal lvs. large, long-stalked, divided into 3 or 5 separate, saw-toothed segments; stem-lvs. smaller; all lvs. dark green above, pale below. Fls. in a dense head (raceme), each of 4 (3–6) small greenish white sepals and 4–6 very short petals, shorter than the numerous white stamens; as the sepals fall early the fls. usually look like a head of stamens only. Fruit a cluster of 1 cm. berries, at first green, sometimes turning red, later glossy black. Very poisonous.
❀ Damp woods. To 1900 m. Pyrenees (rare); Alps. Norway to 1050 m. (Britain.) May–July.

THALICTRUM *L.* MEADOW RUE. Erect perennials, usually with lvs. 3-parted or repeatedly divided, and with small fls. in spikes (racemes) or clusters (panicles), each consisting of 4–5 early-falling sepals and no petals, so that they appear to consist of nothing but a mass of stamens with long filaments, which may be erect or drooping. These are usually yellowish or greenish, or occasionally pink or white (*T. aquilegifolium*, *T. alpinum*.) Fruit a group of achenes. A difficult group botanically, with many intermediate forms.

T. aquilegifolium L. GREAT MEADOW RUE. 40–100 (150) cm. tall, hairless, with lvs. 2- or 3-parted into large, toothed segments, like those of *Aquilegia*. Fls. numerous in a large cluster, with pink or purplish, rarely white stamens with wide filaments.

✤ Damp places, open or wooded. To 2500 m. Pyrenees; Alps; Apennines. May–July.   **179**

T. macrocarpum *Gren.* 30–60 cm. tall, hairless, with large 3- or 4-parted lvs., like those of *T. aquilegifolium*. Fls. few, yellowish, on long stalks in little-branched heads, followed by large, long-beaked, curved achenes.

✤ Damp limestone rocks. 800–2200 m. Pyrenees. Rare. June–September. **183**

T. alpinum L. ALPINE MEADOW RUE. An insignificant plant 5–20 cm. tall, hairless, with lvs. mainly basal, small, usually 5-parted, of rounded, toothed segments, whitish below. Fls. in a spike, drooping in fruit. Sepals 4, purplish, 3 mm. long; stamens 8–20, pendulous, with thread-like violet filaments and yellowish anthers.

✤ Bogs, damp stony meadows. 1900–2900 m. Pyrenees (rare); Alps (very rare). Norway to 1920 m. (Britain to 1200 m.) June–July.   **182**

T. foetidum L. STINKING MEADOW RUE. 10–40 (50) cm. tall, ash-grey, foetid, glandular, with a few hairs, stem not or only faintly grooved; lvs. 3 or 4 times divided into rounded, toothed, 2–4 mm. leaflets. Fls. yellow, hanging, in much-branched clusters; stamens with slightly thickened filaments.

✤ Rocks and stony places, preferring limestone. 1500–2400 m. E. Pyrenees (rare); Alps; C. Apennines. June–August.   **180**

T. minus L. An extremely variable species with many subspecies, not unlike *T. foetidum*, but with well-marked grooves on stem, making it angular; also usually larger, 15–150 cm. tall, either hairless or glandular, not usually foetid. Lower leaflets usually larger than upper ones. Fls. in long-branched clusters.

✤ Rocky and dry grassy places, preferring limestone. To 2850 m. Pyrenees; Alps; Apennines; Norway to 850 m. (Britain to 800 m.) May–July.

T. simplex L. A variable plant with many subspecies, 20–120 cm. tall, hairless, with lvs. cut into 3–5 long, narrow, usually toothed segments. Fls. yellowish, at first drooping, later erect, in a short-branched, erect, elongated head.

✤ Meadows. 1500–2000 m. Maritime Alps; Dauphiné. Very rare. July–August.   **181**

CLEMATIS L. **C. alpina** (L.) *Mill.* (*Atragene alpina* L.) ALPINE CLEMATIS. A handsome climber to 2 m., with twice-cut lvs. of toothed, ovate-lance-shaped segments, and solitary, nodding, blue to violet fls. (rarely white) with 4 sepals 2½–4 cm. long; no petals.

✤ Woods, rocks, preferring limestone. 1000–2400 m. Alps; Apennines. June–July.   **178**

C. vitalba L., the familiar OLD MAN'S BEARD or TRAVELLER'S JOY, reaches 2100 m. in the Alps and 1800 m. in the Pyrenees.

PAEONIACEAE—PEONY FAMILY

The peonies were formerly included in *Ranunculaceae*, but owing to differences both in anatomy and morphology have been given their own family. The main anatomical difference is that the ovules within the 2–8 separate carpels each have 2 skins (integument), while the carpels have fleshy walls and are seated on a fleshy disk. The obvious visible difference is that the normally solitary fl., which has 5 separate sepals and 5–10 separate petals, is at least 7 cm. across, usually red or pink, sometimes white or yellow.

PAEONIA *L.* **P. officinalis** *L.* PEONY. 30–60 cm. tall, with large lvs., hairless above, downy below, of 17–30 narrow segments cut almost to the base. Fls. red, rarely pink or whitish, 7–13 cm. across, with 5–8 petals. Fruit of 2–3 large follicles which when ripe open to expose the red seeds.

⚘ Meadows, woods. To 1700 m. S. Alps (only Tessin in Switzerland); C. Apennines. Uncommon. May–June. 176

BERBERIDACEAE—BARBERRY FAMILY

Shrubs or herbaceous plants. Fls. regular, with 6–9 perianth segments, the inner ones usually petal-like; 4–6 honey-lvs. and 4–6 stamens. Fruit various.

BERBERIS *L.* **B. vulgaris** *L.* BARBERRY. A shrub 1–2½ (6) m. tall, with yellowish, grooved twigs and 1–2 cm. spines, usually much divided. Lvs. obovate to oblong, spiny-toothed, 2–6 cm. long; deciduous. Fls. 15–30 in a 4–6 cm. pendulous cluster (raceme), each 6–8 mm. across, yellow, with 3 outer sepaloid segments and 6 inner petaloid ones. Fruit a bright red narrow-oblong berry (edible).

⚘ Hedgerows, rocky hillsides, preferring limestone. To 2300 (3000) m. Pyrenees; Alps; Apennines. (Britain: possibly introduced.) April–June. (Fruiting August–November.) 189

EPIMEDIUM *L.* **E. alpinum** *L.* BARRENWORT. A perennial herbaceous plant 6–30 cm. tall, with long creeping rhizome. Lvs. of 2 or 3 heart-shaped, pointed leaflets to 13 cm. long. Fls. 8–26 in a loose cluster (panicle), each 9–13 mm. across, dark red, with 2 outer sepaloid segments and 4 inner petaloid ones. Fruit a capsule.

⚘ Damp woods. Seldom above 1200 m. S.E. and E. Alps, sometimes naturalised elsewhere. (Britain: escaped.) March–May. 190

PAPAVERACEAE—POPPY FAMILY

Alpine species perennial, herbaceous, with radially symmetrical fls. of 2–3 sepals, falling early, and 4 petals; numerous stamens; fruit a capsule.

Modern authors include *Fumariaceae* in this family as sub-family *Fumarioideae*, but it is so different in superficial appearance that it has been treated separately here (see p. 217). Under the modern scheme the genera here included under *Papaveraceae* are classified under the sub-family *Papaveroideae*.

PAPAVER L. POPPY. Usually with white latex (milky juice). Lvs. toothed or divided, all basal in alpine species, forming a tuft, with old lf. bases persistent around base, from which arise the fls., solitary of long stalks. Ovary with a disk on top of which the stigmas radiate in rays; capsule more or less cylindrical, releasing seeds through pores beneath the stigmatic disk.

The alpine poppies are a confused group with many minute variations and local populations. Some authors group all the European alpine species as sub-species under the name *P. alpinum* L., or under *P. alpinum* and *P. pyrenaicum* (Willd.) Kern.; both these names must now be considered ambiguous. The latest treatment, followed here, gives each form specific rank, though some themselves now have subspecies. *P. radicatum* is a Scandinavian plant.

The arable weeds *P. rhoeas* L., the red-flowered CORN POPPY, and the orange-pink *P. dubium* L., reach 1750 m. and 1900 m. respectively.

🌱 All the alpine species are found in similar habitats—limestone rocks, screes, moraines, river gravels.

P. suaveolens *Lap.* To 10 cm. tall, bristly; lf. bases persistent, loosely arranged. Lvs. divided into irregular oval-lance-shaped lobes, 2–4 mm. across. In *ssp.* **suaveolens** the lvs. are slightly hairy and the lobes undivided; in *ssp.* **endressii** Asch. the lvs. are distinctly hairy and the lobes often themselves divided. Fls. yellow or rarely red, 2½–3 cm. across; petals longer than wide, not overlapping; stamens shorter than ovary.
🌱 1800–2500 m. Spanish Pyrenees. July–August. **186**

P. rhaeticum *Leresche.* 8–20 cm. tall, bristly with dark hairs; lf. bases forming a compact basal tunic; lvs. asymmetrically cut into 2–4 pairs of short, ovate, blunt lobes 1–6 mm. wide. Fls. 4–5 cm. across, golden-yellow, rarely red or white. Stigmatic disk flat or rarely pyramidal, with 5–7 stigmatic rays running down ovary for about ⅔ of its length.
🌱 1500–3040 m. E. Pyrenees; S.W. and E. Alps; C. Apennines. July–August. **184**

P. sendtneri *Kern.* Very similar to *P. rhaeticum*, but 5–15 cm. tall, with 3–4 (6) cm. white fls., flat stigmatic disk and 5 rays running down ⅔ length of ovary. Lvs. with pointed lobes 1½–2½ mm. wide.
🌱 2000–2700 m. C. and E. Alps; Abruzzi. July–August. **185**

A plant called **P. alpinum** *ssp.* **ernesti-mayeri** *Mark.* is probably only a form of *P. sendtneri*, but has blunt lf. lobes and a pyramidal stigmatic disk with rays running down ⅔ length of ovary.
🌱 900–2400 m. C. and S.E. Alps; C. Apennines (Mt. Majella). July–August.

P. burseri *Crantz.* (**P. alpinum** *ssp.* **alpinum** *auct.*). 10–20 cm. tall, barely hairy; lf. bases loose around stem. Lvs. symmetrically cut into 3–4 pairs of narrow segments ½–2 mm. wide, themselves further divided once or twice into narrow pointed lobes. Fls. 1½–2 (4) cm. across, white. Stigmatic disk pyramidal, rays 4, running down about ½ length of ovary.
🌱 1200–2000 m. N. Alps. Rare. July–August. **187**

P. **kerneri** *Hayek.* Very similar to *P. burseri,* but petals yellow; stigmatic rays 5.
❉ 1200–2000 (2650) m. S.E. Alps; Yugoslav Alps. July–August. **188**

P. **radicatum** *Rottb.* An extremely variable plant with numerous local subspecies, 5–30 (usually 15–25) cm. tall, forming tufts; latex usually yellow. Lvs. 3–10 cm. long, with 2–5 pairs of narrow, pointed, rather crowded lobes, sometimes further subdivided. Fl. stalk more or less hairy. Fls. 2–5 cm. across,

usually yellow, sometimes white or pink.
❉ Screes, gravels. To 1850 m. Norway. July.

MECONOPSIS *Vig.* **M. cambrica** (*L.*) *Vig.* WELSH POPPY. A perennial 30–60 cm. tall with leafy stems, the large lvs. twice divided. Fls. yellow, 3–4 (7½) cm. across, arising from the axils of the upper lvs. Capsule elliptic, topped by a short stout style with 4–6 stigma-lobes.
❉ Woods, shady places. To 2000 m. Pyrenees. (Britain.) June–August.

FUMARIACEAE—FUMITORY FAMILY

Brittle herbaceous plants with no latex (milky juice), lvs. usually much divided, and fls. symmetrical transversely only (zygomorphic), in spikes. Sepals 2, soon falling; petals 4, 2 outer, one of which is twisted to appear at the top of the fl. and is spurred; 2 inner smaller, sometimes joined. Modern authorities regard this family as the sub-family *Fumarioideae* of *Papaveraceae.*

CORYDALIS *Vent.* FUMITORY. Alpine species perennials with tuberous root; hairless, usually bluish. Inner petals joined at tip. Upper outer petal spurred, lower usually sac-like. Fruit a more or less elliptic capsule.

C. **bulbosa** (*L.*) *DC.* (**C. cava** (*L.*) *Schw. & Koerte*). Tuber hollow. 10–35 cm. tall with erect stem, elongating after flowering. Lvs. twice cut into 3, the final segments rather fan-shaped, lobed at tip; no scale on stem. Fls. dull purple, 18–30 mm. long, with spur curved at tip; usually 10–20 fls. in a spike with oval, entire bracts. Fruit 20–25 mm. long, hanging when ripe.
❉ Woods, hedgerows, orchards, cultivated ground. To 2000 m. E. Pyrenees; S.W. Alps; Apennines. (Britain: escaped.) March–May. **192**

C. **solida** (*L.*) *Swartz.* Similar to *C. bulbosa,* but tuber solid, 7–20 cm. tall,

with prominent scale on stem below lowest lf.; lf. segments wedge-shaped, lobed; bracts deeply lobed; fls. 15–25 (30) mm. long, with long, rarely curved spur. Fruit 10–25 mm. long.
❉ Woods, hedgerows, orchards. To 2000 m. Pyrenees; Alps; Apennines. (Britain: escaped.) March–May. **191**

C. **intermedia** (*L.*) *Merat* (**C. fabacea** *Pers.*). 6–10 cm. tall, with slender spike of 2–8 fls. and ovate, entire bracts; spike leaning when mature; an ovate scale on stem below lowest lf. Lvs. like those of *C. solida.* Fls. purple, 10–15 mm. long; spur straight or curved. Fruit 15–20 mm. long.
❉ Woods, pastures, preferring limestone. To 2000 m. Alps; Norway to 1075 m. March–April. **193**

C. **lutea** (*L.*) *DC.* YELLOW FUMITORY. 10–40 cm. tall, with fairly large lvs. 2 or

3 times divided, rather like those of a maidenhair fern, bluish beneath. Fls. 6–16 in dense spikes, yellow, 12–18 mm. long, upper petal with short, blunt, down-pointing spur. Fruit 1 cm. long.

bluish; fls. 5–6 mm. long, pale pink, tips of side petals blackish red, 6–16 in a spike longer than its stalk, but individual fls. on short stalks barely longer than bracts.

1183. *Corydalis lutea.*

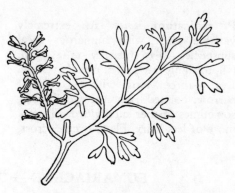

1184. *Fumaria vaillantii.*

❀ Rocks, walls, shady places. To 1700 m. Often naturalised: probably only native at alpine levels in S.C. Alps. (Britain: naturalised.) May–October.

1183

FUMARIA L. FUMITORY. Hairless, often bluish annuals, with much-divided, feathery lvs. Fls. in spikes (racemes); upper petal spurred. Fruit a nutlet.

F. vaillantii *Lois.* A sprawling plant with 10–25 cm. stems, usually very

❀ Waste and cultivated ground, walls, preferring calcareous soils. To 2100 m. Pyrenees; Alps. (Britain.) May–October.

1184

F. schleicheri *Soy.-W.* Similar to *F. vaillantii,* but with 12–20 fls. in spike little longer than its stalk, individual fl. stalks 3 times longer than bracts. Fls. deep pink with wings of upper petal and tip of inner petal dark purple.

❀ Waste and cultivated ground, walls. To 1700 (2100) m. C. Alps; Apennines. May–October.

CRUCIFERAE—CRESS FAMILY

Annual and perennial herbaceous plants, occasionally woody. Lvs. alternate, spirally arranged, entire to lobed. Fls. bisexual, usually in a loose terminal cluster. Sepals 4, in pairs alternately at right-angles to each other, the inner pair sometimes pouched at base and collecting nectar. Petals 4, free, clawed, variously coloured, alternating with sepals. Stamens 6, sometimes 4 or less, one pair shorter than the rest. Style single; stigma round, disk-shaped or slightly bilobed, or with 2 long lobes. Fruit a specialised capsule, usually 2-celled, with one to many seeds and opening from below by 2 valves, which is either called a *siliqua* or, if it is less than 3 times as long as wide, a *silicula*. In many cases the capsules are quite distinctive and provide the easiest way of diagnosing genera.

Many lowland species exceed 1500 m., e.g. in the genera *Subularia, Lepidium, Erophila* and *Capsella*. These have been omitted, as have the insignificant alpine members of *Kernera* and *Cochlearia*, while in the genera *Arabis, Alyssum, Draba* and *Thlaspi* there are a number of insignificant alpine species beyond those described.

MURBECKIELLA *Rothm.* **M. pinnatifida** *(Lam.) Rothm.* **(Sisymbrium pinnatifidum** *(Lam.) DC.,* **Braya pinnatifida** *(Lam.) Koch).* Perennial, 5–20 cm. high, slightly to densely covered in star-shaped hairs. Basal lvs. entire to divided. Stem-lvs. deeply divided with up to 6 lobes on each side. Fls. small, shortly stalked, petals white, slightly notched. Sepals unequal, the inner pair slightly pouched. Stamens 6; style very short, stigma slightly 2-lobed. Fruit a siliqua, 1–2½ cm. long, 1 mm. wide; seeds small, numerous, arranged in one rank in each cell.
♣ Rocky places on acid soils. 1000–3000 (3350) m. Pyrenees; Alps; Apennines. June–August. **980**

HUGUENINIA *Reich.* **H. tanacetifolia** *(L.) Reich.* **(Sisymbrium tanacetifolium** *L.).* A stout perennial, 30–60 cm. tall or more, densely hairy or hairless, hairs more or less star-shaped when present. Lvs. to 30 cm. long, deeply divided into up to 10 pairs of toothed segments. Fls. small, numerous, in loose clusters. Petals yellow, longer than sepals. Sepals not pouched at base. Stigma slightly 2-lobed, style very short. Fruit a siliqua, ½–1½ cm. long, 1–2 mm. wide.
♣ Rocky places, grassy waste land, streamsides. 1700–2500 m. Pyrenees; Alps; Apennines. Rather rare. June–August. **981**

BRAYA *Sternb. & Hoppe.* **B. alpina** *Sternb. & Hoppe.* Perennial, often tufted. Fl. stem up to 10 cm. Lvs. undivided; lower lance-shaped, sometimes minutely toothed. Fls. small; petals white or purplish. Sepals not pouched.

Stigma more or less 2-lobed, style short. Fruit a siliqua, about ½–1 cm. long, 1–1½ mm. wide. Seeds small, up to 18 in 1 row (occasionally 2) in each cell.
♣ Dry waste places, preferring limestone. 1500–3000 m. Alps. Uncommon. July–August. **987**

B. linearis *Rouy.* Similar to *B. alpina,* but fl. stem reaching 20 cm.; lower lvs. linear, and the siliqua is about 1 cm. long, 1 mm. wide.
♣ Limestone rock and gravel. To 800 m. Norway. Local. July.

ISATIS *L.* Annual to perennial, often bluish, hairless or with unbranched hairs. Stem-lvs. stalkless, arrow-head-shaped, the base clasping the stem. Fls. in loose clusters, usually branched. Petals yellow, sepals not pouched. Stamens 6, stigma slightly 2-lobed, style absent. Fruit a winged, flattened silicula with 1 (seldom 2) large, unwinged seeds.

I. tinctoria *L.* WOAD. Biennial or perennial, rosette-forming with stout taproot. Fl. shoots 50–120 cm. tall, leafy, branched above, bluish, hairless above, softly hairy below. Basal lvs. lance-shaped, narrowing to a long stalk. Fls. 2½–4 mm. across, petals up to twice as long as sepals. Silicula purple-brown, a 1-seeded cell surrounded by a wide thickened wing, 1–3 cm. long, ½–1 cm. wide. This plant is the source of the ancient blue pigment, woad.
♣ Waste ground, roadsides, grassland, rocky places. To 2000 m. Pyrenees; Alps; Apennines. (Britain: introduced, now naturalised in places.) July–August. **213**

I. allionii *Ball.* Similar to *I. tinctoria*, but the silicula is not more than twice as long as wide, 1½–2½ cm. long, ¾–1½ cm. wide. The plant has leafy non-fl. shoots and 10–30 cm. fl. stems.

✿ Stony pastures. To 2350 m. S.W. Alps; N. and C. Apennines. July–August.

I. alpina *Vill.* Sometimes included in *I. tinctoria*, but apparently distinct: a perennial with sprawling stems, basal lvs. with blunt basal 'ears', rather larger fls. and oval siliculae 1½–2 cm. long, 8–13 mm. wide.

✿ Meadows, stony places, preferring schistous soils. 1800–2500 m. W. Alps; Apennines. Rare. July–August.

ERYSIMUM *L.* TREACLE-MUSTARD. Plants with branched hairs. Lvs. usually narrow, entire. Inner pair of sepals pouched, outer pair often with a horny projection beneath the tip. Petals yellow, seldom purple. Stamens 6. Stigma round, slightly 2-lobed, style short. Fruit a siliqua, more or less 4-sided, hairy. Seeds numerous, 1 row in each cell. A confusing group, with several very similar species. Most of the species have also been named under *Cheiranthus*.

E. sylvestre (*Crantz*) *Scop.* A silvery-grey, tufted perennial, 10–60 cm. tall. Lower lvs. to 7 mm. across; margins smooth to wavy and toothed. Fl. stalks 2–4 mm. long, to 7 mm. when fruiting. Sepals pouched, 9–15 mm. long. Petals lemon yellow, 1½–2½ cm. long, 5–10 mm. wide. Siliqua 6–8 cm. long, 1–1½ mm. wide, grey-green, square-sectioned; style not exceeding width of siliqua.

✿ Rocks, debris, gravels. To 1600 m. C. and E. Alps; N. Apennines. May–August. **201**

E. helveticum (*Jacq.*) *DC.* SWISS TREACLE-MUSTARD. Similar to *E. syl-*

vestre, but often less silvery. Siliqua 3–9 cm. long, 1–1½ mm. wide, square-sectioned; style 1–3 times longer than width of siliqua.

✿ Rocks, debris, gravels. To 2800 m. Pyrenees; Alps; Apennines. June–August. **204**

E. pumilum *Gaud.* (**E. alpestre** *Jord.*, **Cheiranthus pumilus** *Schleich.*). DWARF TREACLE-MUSTARD. Very similar to *E. helveticum* and included in that species by some authorities, but much smaller, not exceeding 12 cm., forming a congested tuft covered with relatively large fls. Lvs. mostly at base of stem, with about 3–5 lvs. on stem. Siliqua 5–7 cm. long, held almost parallel to stem.

✿ Waste and rocky places, preferring limestone. 1500–3100 m. Pyrenees; Alps. May–August. **202**

E. hieraciifolium *L.* (**E. strictum** *Gaertn., Meyer & Scherb.*, **E. marschallianum** *Andrz. ex Bieb.*). Biennial or occasional perennial, 110 cm. or more tall, with star-shaped hairs. Lvs. greyish or green, linear or oblong with wavy-toothed margins. Sepals 4–6 mm., inner slightly or not pouched at base. Petals to 1 cm. long, hairy, downy on back. Siliqua 2–5½ cm. long, ½–1½ mm. wide, 4-sided, grey, or grey with green edges, held nearly parallel to stem. *

✿ Woods, rocky places, preferring calcareous soils. To 1700 m. Alps. Norway to 1265 m. May–August. **203**

E. decumbens (*Schleich. ex Willd.*) *Dennst.* (**E. ochroleucum** *DC.*, **E. dubium** (*Suter*) *Thell.*). A greyish perennial with long sprawling sterile shoots, fl. stems up to 40 cm. tall, hairy; lower lvs. 1½–5 mm. wide, green; old lvs. persisting. Sepals 10–15 mm., pouched at base. Petals pale yellow, 15–27 mm. long, 6–10 mm. wide. Siliqua 3½–8 cm. long, 1½–2 mm. wide, square-sectioned but irregular; style 1–3 times longer than width of siliqua.

❀ Rocky places, on limestone. To 2300 m. Pyrenees; S.W. Alps (not above 1500 m.). May–June. **205**

HESPERIS L. H. **laciniata** *All.* (H. **glutinosa** *Vis.*). Biennial or perennial, to 80 cm. tall, downy. Lower lvs. divided especially at the base, wavy-toothed; stem-lvs. stalkless. Petals yellow, sometimes purple-tinged, or lilac, pink, red or purple. Fl. stalks shorter than sepals, but to 1½ cm. long when in fruit. Sepals 5–12 mm. long. Siliqua 5–15 cm. long, 1½–3 mm. wide. ❀ Rocks, stony places. To 1500 m. Alps; Apennines. (Britain: introduced.) May–July. **200**

MATTHIOLA R. *Br.* STOCK. M. **fruticulosa** (L.) *Maire* (M. **tristis** (L.) R. *Br.*, **Cheiranthus fruticulosus** L.). SAD STOCK. Perennial, to 60 cm. tall, slightly to densely white-hairy, hairs branched. Lvs. linear or oblong, margins smooth to wavy-lobed. Petals purple-red, occasionally yellow. Stigma 2-lobed, style absent. Fruit a siliqua, 2–12 cm. long, 1–2 mm. wide, cylindrical. Seeds in 1 row in each cell. ❀ Rocky places, preferring calcareous soils. To 1500 (2200) m. Maritime Alps; Apennines. May–August. **212**

CARDAMINE L. Annuals to perennials, with unbranched hairs or none. Lvs. divided or not. Inner pair of sepals slightly pouched. Petals purple or white, seldom yellow. Style short or distinct, stigma slightly 2-lobed. Fruit a siliqua. Seeds in 1 row in each cell.

Modern authorities include *Dentaria* in this genus, but retain the name as a sub-genus division. It seems simpler here to separate the two: *Cardamine* has a root or rhizome growing above ground with few or no scale-lvs.; *Dentaria* has an underground rhizome with scale-lvs.

C. trifolia L. Perennial, 20–30 cm. tall.

Rhizome 2–4 mm. across, branched, creeping, with nodules (swellings) and few scale-lvs. Stem simple, upright, more or less hairless. Basal lvs. long-stalked, leaflets 3, roundish lobed, slightly hairy above, tinged violet to purple below. Stem-lvs. 0–3, small, not stalked, lobed or not. Petals white to pink. Sepals green with white edges, inner pair pouched, ¼ of length of petals. Anthers yellow. Siliqua 2–2½ cm. long, to 2 mm. wide, held upright. ❀ Moist shady places, woods, especially on limestone. To 1400 m. E. Alps; N. Apennines. (Britain: introduced.) April–June. **984**

C. asarifolia L. Perennial, to 40 cm. tall. Rhizome short, thick, horizontal. Basal lvs. kidney-shaped with wavy margins, long-stalked. Stem-lvs. similar but with shorter stalks, rarely with 3 rounded segments. Petals white, rarely pink; anthers violet to purple. Siliqua to 3 cm. long, ½–2 mm. wide. ❀ Moist pastures, streamsides. To 2000 m. Pyrenees; Alps; Apennines. July–August. **982**

C. amara L. LARGE BITTERCRESS. Perennial, 20–60 cm. tall; stems angular; seldom hairy. Rhizome with many slender stolons. Basal lvs. thin, stalked, divided into 5–9 oval to oval-oblong leaflets, the terminal one usually larger. Upper lvs. similar but with shorter stalks. Cluster of 10–24 fls. Petals white, rarely purple; anthers deep violet, rarely yellow-white. Siliqua 2–4 cm. long, 1–2 mm. wide ❀ Streamsides, damp woodlands and pastures, preferring acid soils. To 1800 (2500) m. Pyrenees (rare); Alps; Apennines. Norway to 1000 m. (Britain.) April–July. **985**

C. opizii *Presl.* (also spelt **opicii**). Very similar to *C. amara*, but generally smaller, 10–50 cm. tall, with the stem hairy at least at the base. Lvs. thick,

usually hairy also on margin, with
10–16 leaflets. Cluster of 2–7 fls.; petals
smaller than in *C. amara*.
❀ Streamsides, damp pastures. To 1900
m. E. Alps. April–July.

C. raphanifolia *Pourr.* (**C. latifolia**
Vahl non Lej.). Perennial, 20–70 cm. tall.
Stem stout, hairless. Rhizome horizontal, long. Lvs. long-stalked, large,
thick, green. Lower stem-lvs. of 2–10
leaflets, decreasing in size from the very
large terminal one which is 3–7 cm.
wide. Petals 8–12 mm. long, lilac or
reddish violet, rarely white; anthers
yellow. Siliqua 1½–3 cm. long, 1–2 mm.
wide.
❀ Damp pastures, streamsides. To
2500 m. Pyrenees. May–July.

C. pratensis *L.* CUCKOO FLOWER, LADY'S
SMOCK. Perennial, to 55 cm. tall. Basal
lvs. in a rosette, long-stalked, with 2–14
oval to roundish leaflets, the terminal
one larger, with gland-tipped teeth on
margins. Stem-lvs. shorter-stalked, leaflets much narrower, the terminal
leaflet occasionally 3-toothed, all slightly
hairy. Petals lilac, pink or purplish,
rarely white. Sepals whitish tinged
with pink or violet. Anthers yellow.
Siliqua 25–40 mm. long, 1–1½ mm.
wide.
❀ Damp pastures, streamsides, woods.
To 2600 m. Alps; Apennines. Norway
to 1600 m. (Britain to 1100 m.) April–
July.   **198**

C. resedifolia *L.* Perennial, 5–15 cm.
tall, hairless. Lowest lvs. usually divided
into 3 leaflets, upper into 3–7 leaflets.
Petals white. Siliqua 12–22 mm. long,
1–1½ mm. wide.
❀ Damp and rocky places, gravels,
snow-beds, preferring granitic and
schistous soils. To 3500 m. Pyrenees;
Alps; Apennines. May–September. **983**

C. bellidifolia *L.* A low, tufted, hairless
perennial, making a rosette of thick,

long-spoon-shaped lvs. Fl. stems 1–8
cm. tall, with a few white fls; petals 3½–5
mm. long; siliqua 1–2½ cm. long, 1–1½
mm. wide, held erect.
  Ssp **bellidifolia**: stem-lvs. none or
1–3, on stalks longer than lf. blade.
Fls. 2–5 on 1–1½ mm. stalks. Silicula
purplish.
  Ssp. **alpina** (*Willd.*) *Jones* (**C. alpina**
Willd.), ALPINE BITTERCRESS (986):
stem-lvs. usually 2–3, with short or no
stalks. Fls. 3–8 on 2–3 mm. stalks.
Siliqua brown, not exceeding 1½ cm.
❀ Damp soil or meadows, gravels,
preferring acid soils. *Ssp. bellidifolia*:
Norway to 2070 m. *Ssp. alpina*: Pyrenees;
Alps; 1500–3000 m. July–August. **986**

DENTARIA *L.* (**Dentaria** (*L.*) *Benth.
& Hooker* when considered as a sub-
genus). TOOTHWORT. Characters as for
Cardamine, but root an underground
rhizome with scale-lvs. Besides the
species described the CORAL-ROOT, *D.
bulbifera* L., reaches 1600 m.

D. pentaphylla *L.* (**Cardamine pentaphylla** (*L.*) *Crantz*, **D. digitata** *Lam.*).
Perennial, 30–50 cm. tall. Rhizome
1½–2½ mm. thick, scale-lvs. 6–10 mm.
long, triangular, concave, divided
usually into 3. Lvs. of 3–5 broad,
toothed leaflets, not hairy except on
margins. Petals pale purple, pink or
white, 2 cm. long. Siliqua 2½–4 mm.
wide.
❀ Woody, rocky places. To 2200 m.
Pyrenees; Alps. May–July.   **194**

D. heptaphylla *Vill.* (**D. pinnata**
Lam., **Cardamine heptaphylla** (*Vill.*)
Schulz.). Like *D. pentaphylla*, but
rhizome 4–10 mm. thick, with sickle-
shaped 1–2 mm. scale-lvs. Lvs. of 3–5
rather narrow leaflets. Petals white,
pink or purplish, 1½–2 cm. long.
❀ Beech woods. To 1800 m. Pyrenees;
Alps; N. Apennines.

D. kitaibelii *Bech.* (**D. polyphylla** *W.*

& K., **Cardamine polyphylla** (*W. & K.*) *Schulz.*). Perennial, up to 55 cm. tall. Rhizome to 6 mm. thick, scale-lvs. concave. Lvs. divided into 2–6 pairs of leaflets which are toothed along the margins. Petals pale yellow, 1½–2 cm. long, twice length of stamens. Siliqua to 6½ cm. long, 2½–3 mm. wide.

❀ Woods. To 1660 (1900) m. Alps; Apennines. April–June. **196**

D. enneaphylla L. (**Cardamine enneaphylla** (*L.*) *Crantz*). Perennial, to 30 cm. tall. Rhizome to 6 mm. thick, with nodules (spherical swellings), and tiny scale-lvs. 1–2 mm. long. Lvs. up to 4 in a loose ring, with unevenly toothed leaflets. Fl. cluster usually pendulous. Petals pale yellow to white, 12–16 mm. long, scarcely longer than the stamens. Siliqua 4–7½ cm. long, 3½–4 mm. wide.

❀ Woods. To 2160 m. Alps; Apennines. April–July. **195**

ARABIS L. ROCK-CRESS. Annuals or perennials, almost always hairy. Lvs. undivided. Petals usually purple, pink or white; sepals sometimes slightly pouched on inner pair. Fruit a siliqua.

A. scopoliana *Boiss.* Perennial, to 10 cm. tall. Edges of lvs. hairy. Basal lvs. to 1¼ cm. long, oval, pointed, tapering towards lf. stalk. Stem-lvs. tapering at base, oblong. Petals white. Siliqua 6–10 mm. long, 2–2½ mm. wide, erect.

❀ Screes, rock crevices. To 2200 m. E. Alps. May–July. **995**

A. caerulea (*All.*) *Haenke.* BLUISH ROCK-CRESS. Perennial, 5–15 cm. tall, hairy or not. Basal lvs. oval, wider at top, tapering towards base, usually with 2–5 obvious teeth at the apex. Stem-lvs. 7–3. Cluster of 4–10 pale to purplish blue fls. Siliqua 1–3 cm. long, 2½–3 mm. wide, bluish when unripe.

❀ Damp rocky places, snow-beds, on limestone. To 3500 m. Alps; Apennines. July–August. **214**

A. pumila *Jacq.* (**A. nutans** *Lois.*, **A. stellulata** *Bert.*). DWARF ROCK-CRESS. Perennial, 5–18 cm. tall, lower part hairy. Basal lvs. narrowing at base towards the stalk, oval, sometimes with 1 or 2 small teeth, with branched hairs. Stem-lvs, up to 4, not stalked, rounded below. Cluster of up to 10 white fls. Siliqua 2–4 cm. long, 2 mm. wide.

❀ Damp places, rocks, gravels. To 2860 m. Alps; Apennines. June–July. **993**

A. alpina L. ALPINE ROCK-CRESS. Perennial, 6–40 cm. tall, forming many rosettes, with few, coarse, star-shaped hairs. Basal lvs. roundish-oval to oblong, narrowing to short stalk-like base, margin irregularly toothed. Stem-lvs. stalkless, oblong-oval, base clasping the stem, apex pointed, edge irregularly toothed. Fls. in dense cluster. Petals white; sepals with white edges, half length of the petals. Siliqua 1–6 cm. long, 1½–2 mm. wide.

❀ Damp rocky places, streamsides, steppe, preferring limestone. To 3000 m. Pyrenees; Alps; Apennines. Norway to 1980 m. (Britain: to 900 m. in Skye.) April–August. **994**

A. pedemontana *Boiss.* PIEDMONT ROCK-CRESS. Perennial, 15–30 cm., with few or no hairs. Basal lvs. stalked, as wide as long, oval or ivy-leaf-shaped, with a blunt tip. Stem-lvs. tapering towards the base and usually stalked. Petals white. Siliqua about 3 cm. long, 1–1½ mm. wide.

❀ Rocky places. Piedmont Alps. Rare. June–August. **992**

A. soyeri *Reut. & Heut.* Perennial, 15–50 cm. tall. Basal lvs. dark green, shining, toothed, oval, tapering towards base. Fls. 10–20, white. Siliqua 2½–5 cm. long, 1½–2 mm. wide.

Ssp. **soyeri**: stem slightly hairy; lvs.

224

thin, hairy on edges; stem lvs. more or less clasping.

Ssp. **jacquinii** *(Beck) Jones* (**A. bellidifolia** *Jacq.*, **A. jacquinii** *Beck*) (**991**): hairless; lvs. fleshy; stem-lvs. not clasping.

❋ Damp and marshy places, on calcareous soils. 1800–2800 m. *Ssp. soyeri:* Pyrenees. *Ssp. iacquinii:* Alps. June–August. **991**

AUBRIETA *Adans.* (commonly misspelt **Aubrietia** or **Aubretia**). **A. columnae** *Guss.* The alpine plant is *ssp.* **columnae**, a more or less tufted, matforming perennial with violet to purple fls.; inner sepals pouched. Siliqua 5–12 mm. long, 2–4½ mm. wide; seeds in 2 rows in each division. In *ssp. columnae* the stems are slender, lvs. paddle-shaped to oblong.

❋ Rocks, screes, woods. C. and S. Apennines. April–June. **215**

LUNARIA *L.* **L. rediviva** *L.* MOUNTAIN HONESTY. Perennial, 30–140 cm. tall, with stiffly hairy stem. Lower lvs. oval, pointed, coarse with irregularly toothed margin; roughly hairy, hairs flattened against surface; upper lvs. finely toothed; all lvs. long-stalked. Fls. large, violet to pale purple, fragrant. Inner sepals pouched slightly. Siliqua elliptical, 3½–9 cm. long, 1½–3½ cm. wide, seeds 7–10 mm. wide. The fruits of this plant are similar to those of of *L. annua L.*, known as 'Honesty', but are narrower.

❋ Moist shady places, woods, preferring calcareous soils. Occasionally cultivated. To 1400 m. Pyrenees; Alps. (Britain: introduced.) May–July. **199**

ALYSSOIDES *Mill.* **A. utriculata** *(L.) Med.* (**Vesicaria utriculata** *(L.) Lam.*). Perennial to 40 cm. with woody rootstock. Lvs. on non-flowering branches stalked, in dense rosettes, paddle-shaped to oblong, hairy; lvs. on flowering branches stalkless, lance-shaped, usually

hairless. Fls. yellow, with 2 cm. rounded petals; inner sepals pouched. Silicula about 1 cm. across, more or less spherical, with 4–8 seeds in each cell.

❋ Rocks, crevices, screes, preferring limestone. To 1500 m. Alps; Apennines. April–June. **197**

ALYSSUM *L.* Annuals to perennials, with branched or star-shaped hairs. Sepals not pouched. Petals yellow. Filaments of the long stamens usually winged. Fruit a silicula.

A. wulfenianum *Bernh.* Perennial, erect or spreading, to 20 cm. tall, white to grey-green. Lvs. in rosettes on nonflowering branches. Basal lvs. ovaloblong, blunt at tip, gradually tapering to stalk. Stem-lvs. round to lanceshaped, larger than lower lvs. Hairs starshaped with 10–20 rays. Petals not hairy. Fruiting spike long. Silicula inflated, slightly hairy, 6 mm. long, 3–4 mm. wide. Seeds 1–2 (rarely 6) in each cell.

❋ Dry rocky, stony places. S.E. Alps. June–August. **211**

A. montanum *L.* Perennial, erect or spreading, 5–25 cm. tall. Basal lvs. oblong to paddle-shaped, upper linear to narrow paddle-shaped, often whitish in alpine forms. Hairs star-shaped with up to 24 rays. Petals slightly notched at tip. Fruiting spike long. Silicula 3–5½ mm. across, inflated.

❋ Rocky, gravelly, sandy places. To 2500 m. Pyrenees; Alps; Apennines. May–July. **210**

A. alpestre *L.* Perennial, usually spreading, 10–30 cm. tall, with many nonflowering rosettes. Lvs. white (seldom grey-green), narrow-oval to oval paddleshaped. Silicula 2½–4½ mm. long, 2½–3½ mm. wide, elliptical, with white hairs.

❋ Rocks, meadows, sandy places. 1500–3100 m. Pyrenees; Alps. June–August.

A. serpyllifolium *Desf.* A variable plant sometimes regarded as a subspecies of

A. alpestre and similar to it, with 2 mm. fls. and round-topped, white-downy siliculae.
⚜ Rocks, meadows. To 3000 m. W. Alps. Rare. June–August.

DRABA *L.* WHITLOW-GRASS. Annual to perennial. Lvs. simple, sometimes toothed. Inner pair of sepals slightly or not pouched. Petals yellow or white. Filaments of stamens sometimes a little swollen at base. Fruit a silicula or siliqua. Seeds in 2 rows in each cell.

Besides the species described, the following rather local ones exist: *D. stylaris* Gay (*D. incana* Stev. *non* L.), 1500–2750 m. in C. Alps; *D. norica* Widd., 1850–1950 m. in E. Alps; *D. stellata* Jacq. (*D. saxatilis* Mert. & Koch), to 2500 m. in E. Alps; and *D. kotschyi* Stur in N.E. Alps. In Norway the following additional species exist: *D. incana* L., to 1450 m.; *D. daurica* DC., to 1600 m.; *D. norvegica* Gunn., to 1620 m.

D. aizoides *L.* YELLOW WHITLOW-GRASS. A tufted perennial 5–15 cm. tall, with much-branched stems, hairless, with a slender tap-root. Lvs. in dense rosettes, stiff, linear, narrowing towards each end, the midrib ending in a long white bristle at the top; edges of lvs. also fringed with bristles. Dead lvs. persisting. Fl. stem leafless, with 4–18 fls. 8–9 mm. across. Petals yellow, longer than sepals which are yellowish, and usually not pouched. Fruit a silicula, 6–12 mm. long, 2½–4 mm. wide, oval, flattened, narrowing above, held upright on stem. Seeds yellowish brown. A plant with considerable variation in minor characters, which are sometimes given varietal status.
⚜ Rocks, walls, preferring limestone. To 3600 m. Pyrenees; Alps; Apennines. (Britain: doubtfully native.) April–July. **206**

D. hoppeana *Reichb.* (**D. zahlbruckneri** *Host.*). A densely tufted perennial similar to *D. aizoides*, but 2–4 cm. tall. Lvs. very short, oval, with fringed margins. Petals yellow. Only 1–5 siliculae in fruiting head.
⚜ Rocky ridges, preferring limestone. 2200–3600 m. Pyrenees (Pic-du-Midi); Alps. July–August. **207**

D. sauteri *Hoppe.* Loosely tufted, with branched hairless stems covered with scale-like lf. bases which are yellowish and pressed to stem. Lvs. linear, rarely lance-like, fairly stiff, fringed with stiff hairs. Petals yellow. Silicula 4–6 mm. long, flat, usually hairless.
⚜ Open rocky or gravelly places, on limestone. 1900–2850 m. E. Alps (Styria). Very local. July–August. **208**

D. alpina *L.* ALPINE WHITLOW-GRASS. Perennial, densely tufted, with stems to 20 cm. Lvs. oval-lance-shaped, usually densely hairy, margins entire. Fls. in dense cluster. Petals bright yellow. Silicula hairless.
⚜ Rocky places. To 1650 m. Norway. July. **209**

D. ladina *Br.-Bl.* A tufted perennial to 5 cm. tall, slightly hairy. Lvs. entire, slightly hairy. Petals pale yellow, slightly downy. Silicula almost hairless, but with hairs on margins. This species is remarkable as it is related to an otherwise entirely Arctic group, of which *D. alpina* is a member, yet occurs, as an endemic, in the Alps.
⚜ Mountain rocks, preferring limestone. 2600–3090 m. Swiss Alps: Engadin. July–August.

D. nivalis *Lilj.* SNOWY WHITLOW-GRASS. Biennial or perennial. Fl. stems to 5 cm., often leafless. Basal lvs. roundish and wider in upper half, thickly covered in star-shaped hairs, giving the whole plant a distinctive pale bluish colour. Cluster of up to 9 fls. with very short

stalks. Petals creamy white. Silicula 4–9
mm. long, usually hairless.
❀ Rocky places. To 1920 m. Norway.
June.

D. carinthiaca *Hoppe*. A more or less
tufted perennial. Stems to 15 cm. tall,
hairless above. Basal lvs. lance-shaped,
with branched and star-shaped hairs;
hairs also on margins near the base of the
lf. Stem-lvs. up to 3. Cluster usually of
4–8 fls. Petals white. Silicula 3–8 mm.,
narrow, oblong, hairless.
❀ Rocks, screes, preferring limestone.
1500–3618 m. Pyrenees; Alps. June–
August. **989**

D. tomentosa *Clairv.* DOWNY WHITLOW-
GRASS. A loosely tufted perennial to 20
cm. tall, densely covered in star-shaped
hairs. Basal lvs. narrowly oval, wider in
upper half. Up to 3 stem-lvs. Petals
white. Silicula 6–14 mm. long, hairy,
oblong-oval, occasionally inflated when
ripe.
❀ Rocks, screes, preferring limestone.
1200–3475 m. Pyrenees; Alps. June–
August. **988**

D. dubia *Suter* (**D. frigida** *Saut.*). A
variable plant, like *D. tomentosa*, but not
so densely hairy; fl. stems practically
hairless.
❀ Rocks, screes. 1300–3200 m.
Pyrenees (uncommon); Alps. May–
July.

D. fladnizensis *Wulf.* (**D. wahlen-
bergii** *Hartm.*). Tufted, seldom taller
than 8 cm., completely hairless. Stem-
lvs. 0–2. Basal lvs. oblong-oval, hairless
except for margins, or thinly covered
with hairs. Up to 12 fls. in cluster.
Petals white. Silicula hairless, oval.
❀ Rocks, grassland, preferring acid
soils. 1600–3414 m. Pyrenees; Alps.
Norway to 2300 m. June–August. **990**

D. incana *L.* HOARY WHITLOW-GRASS.
Loosely tufted. Stems 7–35 cm. tall,
sometimes branched. Basal lvs. oblong

lance-shaped, tapering to a stalk, thickly
covered in star-shaped hairs, edges
hairy, occasionally toothed. Stem-lvs.
many, stalkless, oval, base rounded or
slightly clasping the stem. Petals white.
Silicula 7–9 mm. long, 2–2½ mm. wide,
oval or elliptic and twisted, with or
without hairs, held upright. Seeds
brown, numerous.
❀ Rocks, sunny positions, preferring
calcareous soils. 1000–2600 m. Pyrenees;
Alps. Norway to 1450 m. (Britain.)
May–July.

PETROCALLIS *R. Br.* This genus is
similar to *Draba*, but the lvs. are lobed, all
the hairs unbranched, and there are 2
seeds in each cell of the fruit.

P. pyrenaica (*L.*) *R. Br.* (**Draba
pyrenaica** *L.*). A tufted perennial with
dense rosettes of more or less greyish
lvs., 4–6 mm. long, wedge-shaped, with
3–5 lobes, stiff, with hairs on margins.
Stems to 3 cm., hairy. Cluster with few
fls. Petals pale lilac or pink, rarely white;
anthers yellow. Silicula roundish oval to
elliptic, hairless.
❀ Rocks, screes, preferring limestone.
1700–2900 (3400) m. Pyrenees; Alps,
mainly W.; Apennines. Local. June–
August. **224**

HUTCHINSIA *R. Br.* **H. alpina** (*L.*)
R. Br. (**Noccaea alpina** (*L.*) *Reichb.*).
CHAMOIS CRESS. A tufted perennial 2–10
cm. tall; basal lvs. deeply divided into
lobes or segments. Petals white, clawed.
Silicula lance-shaped to elliptic; seeds
1–2 in each cell.

Ssp. **alpina**: fl. stem 5–10 cm. tall,
slightly hairy; no stem-lvs.; basal lvs.
hairless, with 5–9 round to narrow
segments. Petals sharply narrowed into
a claw. Silicula 4–6 mm. long, 1½–2 mm.
wide, oval with pointed tip. Prefers
calcareous soils.

Ssp. **brevicaulis** (*Hoppe*) *Arcangeli*
(**996**): fl. stem to 5 cm. tall, hairless; lvs.
with 3–7 oval narrow segments, forming

tight rosettes. Silicula 3½–4 mm. long, 1–2 mm. wide, with blunt tip. Often on igneous or granitic soils as well as limestone.

✤ Rocks, screes. 1100–3415 m. *Ssp. alpina*: Pyrenees; Apennines. *Ssp. brevicaulis*: Swiss Alps. May–August. **996**

THLASPI *L.* PENNYCRESS. Annual or perennial. Stem-lvs. stalkless, practically clasping the stem. Hairs unbranched if present. Petals white or purplish. Sepals not pouched. Fruit a silicula. Seeds 1–8 in each cell.

T. stylosum (*Ten.*) *Mutel.* A dwarf tufted perennial 1–2½ (6) cm. tall. Basal lvs. 5–10 mm. long, rather fleshy, paddle-shaped to elliptic, stalked. Petals purplish. Anthers violet. Silicula with a broad wing. Sometimes referred to as a variety of *T. rotundifolium*, but quite distinct.

✤ Screes. To 2000 m. C. and S. Apennines. April–June. **223**

T. alpinum *Crantz.* ALPINE PENNYCRESS. A tufted, mat-forming perennial 10–15 cm. tall. Basal lvs. long-stalked, 1–2½ cm. long; stem-lvs. stalkless, clasping stems, hairless. Petals white, much longer than stamens. Anthers yellowish. Silicula narrowly triangular-rounded, about twice as long as wide, with wings to 5 mm. wide. Seeds 1–3 in each cell.

✤ Grassland, screes, rocky places, on acid soils. To 3000 m. Alps; Apennines. Local. June–August. **979**

T. rotundifolium (*L.*) *Gaud.* A loosely tuft-forming, hairless perennial with long, stout root and creeping stems. Lvs. oval, fleshy, occasionally lightly toothed. Fl. stems 5–10 (15) cm. tall, carrying roundish clusters of pink to purple, honey-scented fls. to 1 cm. across.

Ssp. **rotundifolium**, ROUND-LEAVED PENNYCRESS (**221**): basal lvs. more or less in a rosette, lowest ones with auricles (ear-like projections at base); fruiting head remaining compact. Silicula narrow-oval, rounded at tip, with distinct keel, and 1–3 seeds in each cell. Preferring limestone.

Ssp. **cenisium** *Rouy & Fouc.*: like *ssp. rotundifolium*, but silicula narrow, pointed at tip, on long stalks. Avoiding limestone.

Besides *ssp. cenisium* there are other variants local to certain areas, and preferring igneous or siliceous soils to limestone, such as *var. limosellifolium* Burn. and *var. corymbosum* (Gay) Gaud.

Ssp. **cepifolium** (*Wulf.*) *Rouy & Fouc.* (**222**): creeping stems long. Basal lvs. not in definite rosettes, without auricles, wavy-edged. Upper stem lvs. crowded. Fruiting head elongating to 3 cm. Silicula as in *ssp. rotundifolium*, but 4–6 seeds in each cell. Has been considered a separate species.   *

✤ Unstabilised screes, debris. To 2800 (3400) m. *Ssp. rotundifolium*: Alps; Apennines. *Ssp. cenisium*: Mt. Cenis. *Ssp. cepifolium*: S.E. Alps (Carinthia). May (*ssp. cenisium*). June–July. **221, 222**

AETHIONEMA *R. Br.* **A. saxatile** (*L.*) *R. Br.* Annual to perennial, often sprawling, stems to 30 cm. long, more or less branched. Lower lvs. oval to oblong, tip blunt; upper lvs. narrower with pointed tip. Petals white, purplish or lilac. Siliculae sometimes broader than long, with up to 8 seeds, in loose or dense clusters.

✤ Rocks, screes, preferring limestone. To 2300 m. Alps; Apennines. April–July. **219**

IBERIS *L.* CANDYTUFT. Annual to perennial. Hairs simple or absent. Fls. in flattish clusters. Sepals not pouched. Petals white, pinkish or purple, outer 2 larger than inner 2. Fruit a silicula. 1 seed in each cell, flat, rather large, sometimes winged.

I. sempervirens *L.* EVERGREEN CANDY-

TUFT. An evergreen, sprawling, hairless shrub 10–25 cm. tall. Lvs. thick, blunt-tipped, oblong-paddle-shaped, 2½–5 mm. across. Petals white. Silicula 6–7 mm. long, broadly winged from the bottom. ✤ Rocks, screes, crevices, preferring limestone. Often cultivated. 1000–2500 m. Pyrenees; Maritime Alps; Apuan Alps; Apennines. May–August. **218**

I. spathulata *Berg.* (**I. nana** *All.*, **I. carnosa** *Willd.*, **I. rotundifolia** *Lam.*, **I. cepeaefolia** *Pourr.*). Perennial, 3–10 cm. tall, more or less thickly hairy or hair-less. Erect stems unbranched, leafy to the top. Lower lvs. broadly paddle-shaped, fleshy; upper lvs. similar but narrower. Fls. in a dense cluster. Petals white, lilac-purple or purple. Silicula round-oval, with narrow wing. *Ssp.* **spathulata** (**217**): more or less downy; lvs. entire or with 1–2 lvs. at tip. *Ssp.* **nana** (*All.*) *Heywood* (**I. nana** *All.*): hairless; lvs. distinctly toothed. ✤ Rock crevices, gravels. 1500–2800 m. *Ssp. spathulata:* Pyrenees. *Ssp. nana:* Maritime Alps; Ligurian Apennines. June–August. **217**

I. aurosica *Chaix.* Perennial, 4–15 cm. tall. Lvs. fleshy, lower oblong-paddle-shaped, margin sometimes with 1–2 teeth at each side of tip. Fls. purple-lilac in a dense cluster. Silicula broadly oval, winged above. ✤ Rocks, gravels, preferring limestone. To 2600 m. W. Alps. July–August. **216**

BISCUTELLA *L.* **B. laevigata** *L.* BUCKLER MUSTARD. A very variable perennial to 50 cm. tall, generally hairy towards base. Basal lvs. oblong-paddle-shaped, more or less lobed or toothed,

hairy. Stem-lvs. stalkless, narrower. Fls. in clusters, loose to dense. Petals yellow. Sepals half length of petals, not pouched. Silicula flattened, divided down centre into 2 round halves, each containing 1 flattened seed. ✤ Grassland, rocky places, open woods. To 2600 m. E. Pyrenees; Alps; Apennines. (Britain: introduced, now a rare casual.) May–August. **220**

BRASSICA *L.* CABBAGE. **B. repanda** (*Willd.*) *DC.* (**Diplotaxis saxatilis** *DC.*). A very variable plant of which the alpine form is *ssp.* **repanda**. This is a rosette-forming perennial with dead lvs. persisting on the thick stem arising from a rootstock. Lvs. hairless, ½–4 cm. long, paddle-shaped or oval, with wavy, toothed margin, occasionally lobed. Fls. yellow, 2–12 in a small cluster on 2–10 cm. stem; petals up to 14 mm. long; siliqua 2–3 cm. long (occasionally to 6 cm.) by 3–3½ mm. wide, sharply narrowing into a seedless beak. ✤ Stony places, river gravels. 1500–2500 m. S.W. Alps. April–August. **1185**

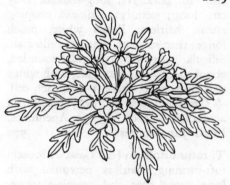

1185. *Brassica repanda ssp. repanda.*

RESEDACEAE—MIGNONETTE FAMILY

With spirally arranged lvs., and fls. in spikes (racemes). Fls. irregular, with 4–8 sepals and petals; stamens numerous, set on a disk. Fruit a capsule.

RESEDA *L.* MIGNONETTE. With the characters of the family and an oblong or ovoid capsule of one compartment, with numerous seeds.
R. glauca *L.* BLUISH MIGNONETTE. Perennial, forming erect clumps of slender 10–40 cm. stems arising from woody stock; lvs. linear, bluish, 1½–6 cm. long, often with 1 or 2 pairs of whitish teeth near base. Fls. in a loose spike, whitish, with 5 or 6 sepals and petals, latter up to ½ cm. long, upper petals 3-lobed.
✳ Rocks, screes, meadows, preferring limestone. 900–2500 m. E. and C. Pyrenees. July–August. **944**
R. lutea *L.* WILD MIGNONETTE. 30–75 (100) cm. tall, annual, biennial or perennial, with woody stock and deep tap-root, more or less branched, and ribbed, erect stem. Basal lvs. forming a rosette usually withered at fl. time; stem lvs. variously cut into 1–5 pairs of narrow lobes and a central more or less elliptical lobe. Fls. in a compressed, conical spike, yellow, 6 mm. across, sepals and petals usually 6, all petals 2- or 3-lobed.
✳ Waste and cultivated ground, fields, rocky places, preferring limestone. To 2000 m. Pyrenees; Alps; reaching greatest altitudes in Maritime Alps. (Britain.) June–September.

SESAMOIDES *Ortega* (ASTRO-CARPUS or ASTEROCARPUS *Necker*). **S. pygmaea** (*Scheele*) *O. Kuntze* (**Reseda sesamoides** L., **Astrocarpus sesamoides** (L.) *DC.*). With the characters of the family and a star-shaped fruit of 4–7, 1-seeded carpels. Perennial, with woody base and slender, sprawling stems 2–20 cm. long; fls. whitish, in spike, with 5–6 much-divided petals.
✳ Rocks, screes, meadows, preferring acid soils. 900–2000 m. Pyrenees; Auvergne; Cevennes. May–September. **943**

DROSERACEAE—SUNDEW FAMILY

Perennial herbaceous plants remarkable for their glandular-hairy lvs. which trap insects. Fls. in small spikes (cymes), with 4–8 parts.

DROSERA *L.* SUNDEW. Lvs. in rosettes, densely glandular, and fringed with long red glandular hairs resembling tentacles, each with a globule of sticky fluid at the tip. Insects alighting on these hairs are trapped by the stickiness, and the hairs then curve over the insect which is eventually digested. Fls. white.
D. rotundifolia *L.* COMMON SUNDEW. 6–10 (25) cm. tall. Lvs. round, spreading horizontally, with long stalks. Fls. 5 mm. across, usually 6-parted, in 2 rows, 6–10 on a seldom-branched stem.
✳ Acid wet heaths, moors, bogs, usually on peat or sphagnum. To 2000 m. Pyrenees; Alps. Norway to 1100 m. (Britain.) June–August. **997**

D. anglica *Huds.* (**D. longifolia** *L.* in part). LONG-LEAVED SUNDEW. 10–15 (30) cm. tall. Lvs. more or less erect, narrow-oblong, rounded, on long stalks. Fls. 5 mm. across, 5–8-parted, 3–6 on stem. ✤ Bogs, wet heaths, moors, usually on sphagnum. To 1900 m. Pyrenees; Alps. (Britain.) July–August. **998**

CRASSULACEAE—STONECROP FAMILY

Annuals or perennials, usually succulent, with lvs. usually undivided. Fls. typically in clusters (cymes); radially symmetrical, 3–32-parted, but usually 5-parted. Stamens either alternating with petals or twice as many; carpels separate, as many as petals; fruit various.

SEDUM *L.* STONECROP. Annuals or perennials with lvs. of various shapes. Fls. 3–10-parted, typically 5-parted, with both sexes present. Sepals rather fleshy, just jointed at base; petals usually separate; stamens usually twice as many as petals. Fruit a group of follicles.

Besides the species described, several others, mostly rather insignificant plants, are found above 1500 m. These include *S. anglicum* Huds., to 1800 m.; *S. annuum* L., to 2900 m.; *S. hirsutum* All., to 1800 m.; *S. hispanicum* L., to 2260 m.; *S. magellense* Ten., to 2150 m.; and *S. monregalense* Balb., to 1900 m. *S. annuum* L. and *S. villosum* L. are found in Scandinavia as well as Europe; the latter reaches 1150 m. in Britain.

Leaves flattened, at least 1 cm.
wide and long

S. telephium *L.* ORPINE, LIVELONG. A variable perennial, 15–80 cm. tall, seldom branched, with stout stem and 2–7 cm. lvs., varying from nearly round to lance-shaped; alternate, opposite or in whorls. Fls. 5-parted, up to 1 cm. across, in flattish terminal clusters.

Ssp. **telephium** (*ssp.* **purpureum** *Schultes* (*S. & K.*), **S. purpureum** *Koch*) (**226**): 25–60 cm. tall, with 5–8 cm., narrow-ovate, pointed irregularly toothed green lvs., and purplish red, lilac, or rarely white fls.

Ssp. **maximum** (*L.*) *Krock.* (S.

maximum (*L.*) *Hoffm.*): 30–90 cm. tall, with 4–10 cm., ovate to oblong, some times toothed, slightly bluish lvs., and greenish or yellowish-white, rarely purple fls. ✤ Woods, hedgerows, rocky places. Sometimes cultivated. To 1800 m. Pyrenees; Alps. (Britain.) June–September. **226**

S. anacampseros *L.* Perennial, with sprawling non-fl. shoots ending in leafy rosettes and 15–30 cm. erect fl. stems. Lvs. 12–25 mm. long, elliptic to ovate, blunt, bluish, alternate. Fls. usually 5-parted, occasionally 4-parted, 9 mm. across, bluish lilac outside, deep red inside, in crowded, rounded terminal clusters. ✤ Acid rocks. 1400–2500 (3000) m. Pyrenees; Alps; Apennines. Rare. July–August. **227**

Leaves narrow or rounded, small

S. reflexum *L.* (**S. rupestre** *L.* in part). ROCK STONECROP. A variable, often sub-divided species. Perennial, 20–40 cm. tall, with short non-fl. shoots tightly packed with rounded, linear lvs., spurred at base. Dead lvs. not persisting. Fls. 5–9-parted, 12–14 mm. across, rich or pale yellow (the latter sometimes called **S. albescens** *Haw.*), in loose heads. Sepals 2½–4½ mm. long, hairless. ✤ Rocky places, walls, banks. To 2000

m. Pyrenees; Alps. (Britain.) June–July.   231

S. forsteranum *Sm.* (S. elegans *Lej.*, S. rupestre *L.* in part). Similar to *S. reflexum*, but frailer, shorter, with lvs. flat on top and crowded on non-fl. shoots into cone-like rosettes, with dead lvs. persisting. ❋ Damp banks, sandy places, screes, on acid soils. To 2000 m. Pyrenees; Alps. Local. (Britain: naturalised.) June–July.

S. ochroleucum *Chaix* (S. rupestre *L.* in part). Resembling *S. reflexum*, but sepals 5–7 mm. long, glandular-hairy. *Ssp.* **ochroleucum**: fls. greenish to creamy, with 8–10 mm. petals. *Ssp.* **montanum** (*Perr. & Song.*) *Webb:* fls. bright yellow, with 7–8 mm. petals. ❋ Rocky places, walls, banks. To 2260 m. Pyrenees; Alps. *Ssp. montanum:* E. Pyrenees, S.W. Alps only. June–July.

S. acre *L.* WALL-PEPPER. A mat-forming perennial with short creeping stems and 2–15 cm., often branched fl. stems. Lvs. hot-tasting, 3–6 mm. long, usually triangular, elliptic in section, tight-packed especially on non-fl. stems. Fls. 2–4 together, 12 mm. across, bright yellow, with 5 pointed, lance-shaped, spreading petals. A variable plant: a specially dwarf form from higher altitudes has been named *var.* glaciale *Clar.* ❋ Rocks, rocky and sandy places, walls. To 2300 m. Pyrenees; Alps; Apennines; Norway to 1250 m. (Britain.) June–July.   229

S. sexangulare *L.* (S. mite *Gilib.*) is similar to *S. acre* and has been considered a subspecies, but has linear lvs. in 6 spiral rows, without peppery taste, and lemon-yellow fls. It reaches 2050 m. in Alps, Apennines.

S. alpestre *Vill.* ALPINE STONECROP. A dwarf perennial forming loose tufts 2–7

cm. tall, with flattish 4–6 mm. lvs., often streaked with red, crowded on the short non-fl. stems. Fls. 5-parted, 8 mm. across, dull yellow, several in small dense heads (cymes); fruits (follicles) dark red. ❋ Rocks, moraines, alluvial mud, snow-beds, usually on acid soils. To 3500 m. Pyrenees; Alps; N. Apennines. June–August.

S. album *L.* WHITE STONECROP. Perennial, bright green, forming large mats of short creeping stems and 5–18 cm. fl. stems. Lvs. alternate, 4–12 mm. long, more or less oblong, slightly flattened on top. Fls. 5-parted, white, sometimes pink-tinged on back, 6–9 mm. across, in a much-branched, flattish cluster (cyme) 2–5 cm. across. Fruit (follicles) pink. ❋ Rocky places, gravel, walls, roofs. To 2500 m. Pyrenees; Alps; Apennines. Norway to 1200 m. (Britain: probably introduced.) June–August.   228

S. dasyphyllum *L.* THICK-LEAVED STONECROP. A small tufted perennial 2–8 cm. tall, forming rounded mats. Lvs. 3–5 mm. long, alternate, ovoid, flattened on top, tight-packed, especially on non-fl. stems, greyish-pink, with a 'bloom' like hoar-frost. Fls. white, pink-tinged on back, 5–6-parted, 2–4 together, 6 mm. across. ❋ Rocks, walls, preferring acid soils. To 2500 m. Pyrenees; Alps; Apennines. (Britain: naturalised.) June–August.   1001

S. atratum *L.* DARK STONECROP. Annual, with erect 3–10 cm. stems. Lvs. 4–6 mm. long, alternate, oblong, tapering towards base. Fls. small, 5–6-parted, crowded in dense heads. *Ssp.* **atratum** (230): usually 3–6 cm. tall, unbranched, dark brownish red; fls. cream with red lines or flush, petals barely longer than sepals. *Ssp.* **carinthiacum** (*Hoppe ex Pacher*) *Webb:* to 10 cm., usually branched from base, greenish with red tinge; fls. pale greenish yellow, petals twice length of sepals.

⚜ Rocks, debris, screes, preferring limestone. 1000–3180 m. Pyrenees; Alps; Apennines. *Ssp. carinthiacum:* E. Alps only. June–August. **230**

RHODIOLA *L.* **R. rosea** *L.* **(Sedum rosea** or **roseum** (*L.*) *Scop.*, **S. rhodiola** *DC.*). ROSEROOT, MIDSUMMER-MEN. Resembling *Sedum telephium,* but fls. 4-parted, sexes on separate plants. 5–35 cm. tall, arising from a thick rhizome which is fragrant when cut. Lvs. flat, in outline rounded to narrow-oblong, usually toothed in upper part, bluish. Fls. in flattish clusters (cymes), petals usually dull yellow, sometimes reddish, often absent especially in females. Male fls. 6 mm. across, with prominent but useless carpels. Females with no stamens, and fruits (follicles) green, then reddish.

⚜ Rocks, screes, meadows, preferring acid soils. 900–3000 m. Pyrenees; Alps. Norway to 2280 m. (Britain to 1250 m.) May–August. **225**

MUCIZONIA (*DC.*) *A. Berger* **M. sedoides** (*DC.*) *Webb* **(Umbilicus sedoides** *DC.*, **Cotyledon sedoides** *DC.*, **Sedum candollei** *Hamet*). A tiny but pretty annual of uncertain affinities, forming dense tufts of 2–6 cm. stems. Lvs. small, ovoid, blunt, reddish like the slender stems. Fls. 5-parted, bell-shaped, 6–7 mm. long, pink, in small terminal heads.

⚜ Rocky places, screes, gravel, on acid soils. 2000–3000 m. C. and E. Pyrenees. June–August. **1000**

SEMPERVIVUM *L.* HOUSELEEK. Perennial herbaceous plants forming crowded rosettes, living for years but individual rosettes dying after flowering; usually reproducing also by stolons (runners). Fl. stem erect, with alternate lvs., bearing branched heads (scorpioid cymes); fls. 8–16-parted, of narrow-lance-shaped petals; stamens twice as many as petals. Fruit of carpels equalling petals in number.

Not only are some of the species naturally very variable but many also hybridise freely. The commonest hybrids are *S. × barbulatum* Schott (*S. arachnoideum* × *S. montanum*); *S. × fauconnettii* Reuter (*S. arachnoideum* × *S. tectorum*); and *S. × schottii* L. & S. (*S. montanum* × *S. tectorum*). Only the commonest synonyms are given: many species have been described under several names.

The group with 6-parted, bell-shaped fls. and fringed petals is now separated in the genus *Jovibarba* (*q.v.* p. 234).

Flowers yellow

S. wulfenii *Hoppe.* Rosettes 4–5 (9) cm. across, with inner lvs. incurving in bud-like manner, especially in winter; lvs. bluish or greyish green, usually reddish purple at the base, oblong-spoon-shaped, hairy at edges. Stolons long, thick, woody. Fl. stem 15–25 cm. tall; fls. pale yellow, with purple basal spot, 11–15-parted; petals 10 mm. long, 1–2 mm. wide; stamen filaments purple. The only yellow-fld. *Sempervivum* with smooth lvs. Praeger records a clump in the Bernina over 40 cm. across with more than 100 rosettes.

⚜ Rocks, rocky places, avoiding limestone. 1700–2700 m. C. Alps (local); E. Alps. July–August. **232**

S. grandiflorum *Haw.* (**S. gaudinii** *Christ*). Rosettes 5–10 (22) cm. across, flattish except in exposed positions, when it forms tight round balls. Lvs. dark green, usually brown-tipped, oblong, tapering to base, pointed at tip, finely hairy all over, with strong odour of resin and valerian. Stolons long, thick. Fl. stem 10–20 (30) cm. tall; fls. yellow, with purple basal spot, 12–14-parted; petals usually 1–2 cm. long,

2–3 mm. across, but fls. can be 6 cm. across, the largest of all sempervivums; stamen filaments purple.

✤ Rocks, walls, soil, roofs, avoiding limestone. 1250–2500 (3000) m. S.C. and S.W. Alps. Rather rare. July–October.
233

S. pittonii *Schott, Nym. & Kotschy.* Rosettes 2½–5 cm. across, dense, flattish. Lvs. greyish green, with dark red or purplish tip, narrow-lance-shaped, finely hairy. Stolons very short, so that tufts are tight-packed. Fl. stem 12–15 cm. tall; fls. pale greenish yellow, 9–12-parted; petals 13–14 mm. long, 1–2 mm. wide; stamen filaments pale.

✤ Serpentine rocks. Probably not above 1500 m. Styria: Murtal. Very local. July–August.
234

Flowers normally pink or red

S. arachnoideum *L.* COBWEB HOUSE-LEEK. A variable plant often forming extensive mats, always recognisable by the cobwebby mass of silvery hairs, which are, in fact, the much elongated tip hairs of the 7–12 mm., oblong to lance-shaped, hairy lvs. varying from red to pale or dark green, forming ½–2½ cm. rosettes. Fl. stem 4–12 cm. tall, with red-tipped stem lvs.; fls. rose red, 8–10-parted; petals 7–10 mm. long, 3 mm. wide, with purple central streak; stamen filaments purple.

The extreme forms of the many intermediates have been described as follows:

Ssp. **arachnoideum** (*ssp.* **doellianum** (*Lehm.*) *S. & K., var.* **glabrescens** *Willk.*): rosettes not over 1½ cm., rounded, hairs often few.

Ssp. **tomentosum** *Lehm. & Schnitts.*: rosettes ½–2½ cm. across, flattish, with plentiful hairs almost hiding the lvs.

The many hybrids of this species may usually be recognised by the 'spider web' normally being broken, not extending from outer to inner lvs., or by

just having a tuft of white hairs at the lf. tips.

✤ Rocks, screes, alluvial deposits, debris, walls, preferring acid soils. To 3090 m. Pyrenees; Alps; Apennines. *Ssp. arachnoideum* mainly E.; *ssp. tomentosum* mainly S.W. July–September. 240

S. montanum *L.* (including **S. frigidum** *Lam.*, **S. minimum** *Timb.*). A variable plant with rosettes 1½–3 (5) cm. across, fairly flat, dense; lvs. dull green, reversed lance-shaped, to 1 cm. long, downy on surfaces, with very short hairs on edges. Stolons short, slender. Fl. stem 5–10 (20) cm. tall, sometimes with as few as 2 dark red (rarely yellowish) fls., 11–13-parted; petals 12–20 mm. long, 2 mm. wide; stamen filaments pale. Three subspecies are recognised.

Ssp. **montanum** MOUNTAIN HOUSE-LEEK (**238**): rosettes not over 2 cm., entirely green.

Ssp. **burnatii** *Wettst.*: rosettes 2–8 (15) cm., entirely green; can be confused with *S. grandiflorum* out of fl., but lacks strong odour of that species.

Ssp. **stiriacum** *Wettst.* STYRIAN HOUSE-LEEK (**239**): rosettes (2) 4–5 cm., lvs. reddish at tip; fls. to 5 cm. across.

✤ Siliceous and primary rocks. 1500–2800 (3400) m. Pyrenees; Alps; N. Apennines. *Ssp. burnatii*: Pyrenees; Maritime Alps. *Ssp. stiriacum*: E. Austrian Alps only. July–August.
238, 239

S. dolomiticum *Facch.* DOLOMITES HOUSELEEK. Rosettes not unlike those of *S. montanum*, but denser, 2–4 cm. across, of more pointed lvs., which are bright green, brown-tipped, oblong lance-shaped, 1–1½ cm. long, lightly hairy, with pronounced bristles at tip. Stolons 2 cm. long, slender. Fl. stem 5–12 cm. tall, with 12–20 rose-pink fls., 10–14-parted; petals 1 cm. long, 2 mm. wide; stamen filaments hairless.

✤ Dolomitic and basaltic rocks. 1600–2500 m. E. Alps. Local. July–September. **236**

S. tectorum *L.* COMMON HOUSELEEK. A very variable plant, with rosettes usually 3–8 cm. across, lvs. dark or bluish green, occasionally pale green, sometimes flushed red or purple, 2–4 cm. long, 1–1½ cm. across, oblong-lance-shaped to obovate, with a long sharp point; very seldom hairy on surfaces, but sometimes with white hairs on edges, especially on the lvs. on fl. stems, the upper ones of which are distinctly hairy. Stolons thick, to 4 cm. long. Fl. stem 10–60 (100) cm. tall, with 40–100 dull pink or purplish fls., usually 13-parted; petals 10–12 mm. long, 2 mm. wide, downy beneath; stamen filaments purple.

At least 70 synonyms are recorded for this plant, which gives an idea of its variability, and it is also noted for hybridising freely, but it is basically easy to recognise by its wide lvs., almost always hairless on the surfaces, in a rosette open at the centre. One authority has subdivided the species into 40 varieties and forms, under the names *S. rupestre*, *S. calcareum* and *S. arvernense*, the latter described as hairy-lvd. in the young state. A more reasonable division appears to be into *ssp.* **alpinum** (*Gris. & Schenk*) *Wettst.*, with green, not bluish lvs. flushed red at the base; *ssp.* **schottii** (*Baker*) *Wettst.* (**S. glaucum** *Ten.*) (not to be confused with the hybrid *S.* × *schottii* mentioned on p. 232), with bluish, white-based lvs.; and **S. calcareum** *Jord.* (see below) with purple-tipped lvs.

✤ Rocks, debris, earth, grassy places. To 2800 m. Pyrenees; Alps. (*Ssp. alpinum* typically in Pyrenees and N. and C. Alps; *ssp. schottii* typically in S. and S.E. Alps). July–October. **235**

S. calcareum *Jord.* Often included under *S. tectorum*, but has bluish lvs. with distinct brownish purple tip; stem-lvs. distinctly clasping; petals narrower.

✤ Limestone rocks. To 1800 m. French Alps. July–September.

S. funckii *Braun.* Rosettes 2½–4 cm. across, dense, of bright green, sometimes purple-backed lvs., 1–1½ cm. long, obovate to reverse lance-shaped, pointed, finely hairy all over and with longer, translucent hairs on edges. Stolons 3–4 cm. long. Fl. stems to 20 cm. tall; fl.-head 3-branched, flattish, 6–8 cm. across; fls. purplish pink with dark central eye, 11–12-parted, 2–2½ cm. across; petals 1 cm. long, relatively broad, densely hairy on back and edges; stamen filaments purple. Reputed to be a triple hybrid, but apparently breeding true; also reputed to be introduced to its widely scattered stations, which seems improbable.

✤ Rocks. 1700–2200 m. Savoy Alps; doubtfully recorded from Switzerland; E. Alps to Styria. Very local. July–August. **237**

JOVIBARBA *Opiz* (**DIOPOGON** *Jord. & Fourr.*). Originally included under *Sempervivum*, similar in rosette but with quite distinct fls., which are usually 6 (5–7)-parted, bell-shaped, pale yellow or whitish, with keeled petals fringed with hairs. The fls. of each species are rather similar, and identification is best carried out from the rosettes and lvs.

J. allionii (*Jord. & Fourr.*) *Webb* (**Sempervivum allionii** (*Jord. & Fourr.*) *Nym.*, **S. hirtum** *auct.*, not *L.*). Rosettes 2–3 cm. across, rounded, closed in centre; lvs. pale yellowish green, occasionally tipped red or brown, 12–15 mm. long, oblong lance-shaped, pointed, shortly hairy. Stolons short or none, resulting in dense clusters. Fl. stem 10–15 cm. tall, fl. head of 2–3 branches. Fls. greenish white; petals 15 mm. long, markedly fringed.

❋ Rocks, debris. To 2000 m. S. Alps. July–September. **243**

J. arenaria (*Koch*) *Opiz* (**Sempervivum arenarium** *Koch*). Rosettes 2–3 cm. across, rounded, with incurving lance-shaped 8–15 mm. lvs., light green, often with small red-brown tip, sometimes flushed red, almost hairless. Stolons very short and slender. Fl. stem 7–12 cm. tall, fl. head dense, of 3 branches. Fls. numerous, greenish; petals 12–15 mm. long, hairy-fringed.
❋ Rocks, walls, gravelly places, avoiding limestone. To 1500 m. E. Alps August–September. **244**

J. hirta (*L.*) *Opiz* (**Sempervivum hirtum** *L.*). Rather variable. Rosettes 3–7 cm. across, open, with broad lance-shaped, 15–20 mm. lvs., green, rarely brown-tipped or flushed reddish, ciliate on edges but otherwise hairless. Stolons very short, thin and brittle, numerous. Fl. stems 10–20 cm. tall, fl. head dense,

sometimes convex, of 3 branches. Fls. yellowish white, 6-parted; petals 15–17 mm. long, fringed on edges and keel.
❋ Rocks, debris. To 1900 m. E. Alps. August–September. **241**

J. sobolifera (*Sims*) *Opiz* (**Sempervivum soboliferum** *L.*). HEN-AND-CHICKENS HOUSELEEK. Rosettes 1–3 cm. across, rounded but flattened, usually closed, forming dense tufts, with young plants produced very freely among the lvs. on very thin, brittle stolons, which elongate to surround the plant with offsets. Lvs. reverse lance-shaped, 1 cm. long, light green, often tipped red, ciliate on edges, otherwise hairless. Fl. stems 10–20 cm. tall, fl.-head dense. Fls. yellowish white, 6-parted; petals 15–17 mm. long, strongly fringed on edges and keel especially near tip.
❋ Sandy places, dry grassland, avoiding limestone. Probably seldom above 1500 m. C. and E. Alps (not France nor Switzerland). July–September. **242**

SAXIFRAGACEAE—SAXIFRAGE FAMILY

Herbaceous plants with simple but often deeply cut lvs., usually alternate or forming rosettes. Fls. 4–5-parted, without petals in *Chrysosplenium*; stamens alternating with petals or more often twice as many. Carpels 2, joined at base but usually separate above; fruit a capsule.

SAXIFRAGA L. SAXIFRAGE, ROCKFOIL. Herbaceous plants, sometimes with a woody base, mostly perennial. Fls. usually radially symmetrical, most often in clusters (cymes or panicles); petals present; stamens 10. Fls. occasionally replaced by reproductive buds. Lvs. sometimes with usually lime-secreting pits, sometimes white-encrusted round the margins in this way.
Many authors divide this large genus into sections and subsections. Although treatments vary considerably and several species do not fit perfectly into the

various schemes, the subdivision forms a useful subsidiary classification, especially valuable to the gardener. The sections and order used by A. Engler and E. Irmscher ('Das Pflanzenreich') are on the whole followed here. Species are perennial unless otherwise specified.
Some species are extremely variable and where this is so examples of the extremes have been given. Whether or not these deserve names as forms is debatable, except to the gardener.

Section *Boraphila* Engl. (*Micranthes* Haw.). Lvs. almost all basal in a sparse rosette, rather leathery; stem lvs. few or none. Fls. in spikes or clusters (panicles), white or pink, sometimes spotted (except in *S. hieracifolia*).

S. hieracifolia *W. & K.* HAWKWEED-LEAVED SAXIFRAGE. Arising from a single underground stem. Lvs. 3–7 cm. long, ovate-oblong, more or less toothed and variably hairy, with pronounced, thick stalk. Fl. stem 10–40 cm. tall, densely hairy, with 3–12 small, almost stalkless fls., greenish with purple-red flush, in a spike.
❀ Damp rocks, moraines, streamsides. 1100–2400 m. France: Auvergne (one locality); E. Alps. Norway to 2000 m. Very local. July–August. **246**

S. nivalis *L.* ALPINE SAXIFRAGE. A variable plant with branching rhizome. Lvs. 1½–5 cm. long, rounded to rhombic, with rounded or pointed teeth, hairy on edges, often reddish beneath, with broad stalk. Fl. stem 5–20 cm. tall, densely hairy; fls. 5 mm. across, white or pink, with erect sepals; often in a dense head, sometimes a looser cluster. Fruit beaked.
❀ Crevices of basaltic rocks. Norway to 2120 m. Very local. (Britain: montane.) July–August. **1007**

S. tenuis (*Wahl.*) *H. Sm.* SLENDER SAXIFRAGE. Similar to *S. nivalis*, but much smaller, 3–8 cm. tall, with beaks of fruit curved backwards like horns.
❀ Calcareous soils. To 1680 m. Norway. July.

S. stellaris *L.* STARRY SAXIFRAGE. A very variable plant, loosely or densely tufted, with short horizontal stem. Lvs. 1–5 cm. long, shining, ovate or straight-sided, tapering to base, or spoon-shaped, variously toothed, lightly hairy; rosette sometimes much elongated. Fl. stems 4–20 cm. tall, sometimes hairy, leafless, branching near top,

with small lf.-like bracts at the forks; fls. in a loose narrow cluster. Fls. small, with down-pointing sepals; petals lance-shaped, occasionally unequal (this has been called *ssp.* **engleri** *D.-T.*), white with 2 yellow spots.

The extremes of habit have been named *ssp.* **stellaris**, densely tufted, with hairy lvs.; and *ssp.* **alpigena** *Temesy*, loosely tufted, with creeping stems, and almost hairless lvs.
❀ Damp places, streamsides, marshes, usually on acid soils. To 3300 m. Pyrenees; Alps; N. Apennines. Norway to 1920 m. (Britain to 1300 m.) June–August. **1006**

S. foliolosa *R. Br.* LEAFY SAXIFRAGE. Very similar to *S. stellaris* and sometimes regarded as its *var.* or *ssp.* **comosa** *Retz.*, but has all but the terminal fl. replaced by clustered reddish bulbils.
❀ Damp places, streamsides. Norway to 1580 m. July–August.

S. clusii *L.* Not unlike a larger *S. stellaris*, but with more or less erect lvs. 6–15 cm. long, tapering towards a broad stalk, coarsely and irregularly toothed, and very hairy. Fl. stem 12–30 cm. tall, slender, branching from the middle or lower, with lf.-like bracts at the forks; fls. in a wide, loose cluster. Fls. small, with down-pointing sepals; petals always unequal, 2 short and 3 long, white with 2 yellow spots.
❀ Shady rocks, damp places, streamsides, on acid rocks. To 2600 m. Pyrenees. July–August. **1008**

Section *Robertsonia* Haw. (*Gymnopera* D. Don). With woody stock and short branches; lvs. all basal in permanent rosettes, spoon-shaped, leathery, uncut; stem-lvs. none. Fls. small, white or pink, sometimes spotted, in loose clusters.

S. umbrosa *L.* WOOD SAXIFRAGE. Forming a dense flat rosette of rather leathery, erect lvs., ovate-oblong, tapering to broad, flat, hairy stalk, with cartilaginous margin and broad, low, usually rounded teeth. Fl. stem 8–40 cm. tall, reddish, downy; fls. many in a loose cluster; sepals pointing downwards; petals white, red-spotted, with 1 yellow spot.

❀ Woods, preferring limestone. To 1830 m. C. and W. Pyrenees. (Britain: introduced.) June–July. **1010**

The familiar London Pride of gardens is a hybrid, *S. umbrosa* × *S. spathularis Brot.* The latter is an Iberian plant, similar to *S. umbrosa*, found also in Ireland where it reaches 1100 m.

S. hirsuta *L.* KIDNEY SAXIFRAGE. Forming a loose rosette; lvs. barely leathery, kidney-shaped, rounded or oblong, with usually rounded teeth, often hairy on both sides, often red below; stalk thin, typically hairy, 2–6 cm. long. Fl. stem 12–30 cm. tall, downy; fls. in a loose cluster, white, usually with a few pale red spots and 1 yellow spot; ovary pale pink.

The typical plant, *ssp.* **hirsuta**, has kidney-shaped, rounded lvs. heart-shaped at base, much shorter than stalk, with 17–25 teeth. *Ssp.* **paucicrenata** *(Gill.) Webb* has oblong-elliptic lvs. with short stalk, and 7–11 teeth.

❀ Shady rocks, streamsides. 1500–2500 m. C. and W. Pyrenees. *Ssp. paucicrenata:* W. Pyrenees only, on exposed limestone rocks and screes. (Britain: native in S.W. Ireland to 1000 m.; naturalised elsewhere.) May–July. **1012**

S. geum *L.* Now considered to be a hybrid between *S. umbrosa* and *S. hirsuta*, with lf. blade like that of *S. umbrosa*, lf. stalk like that of *S. hirsuta*.

❀ Shady rocks, streamsides. 1500–2500 m. C. and W. Pyrenees; naturalised elsewhere in W. and C. Europe. June–July.

S. cuneifolia *L.* Forming small, loose rosettes on radiating, creeping stems.

Lvs. rather fleshy, hairless, rounded spoon-shaped, barely toothed, tapering to broad, slightly hairy stalk. Fls. few in a small cluster, white.

❀ Woods, shady mossy rocks. To 2300 m. Pyrenees; Alps; N. Apennines. June–August. **1009**

Section Miscopetalum Haw. Similar to *Robertsonia*, but with lvs. on stem.

S. rotundifolia *L.* ROUND-LEAVED SAXIFRAGE. A variable plant with rhizome and short stem, and loose rosettes of rounded kidney-shaped, variously toothed, usually hairy lvs., with narrow cartilaginous border and long, thin, sometimes hairy stalk. Fl. stem 15–40 cm. tall, with a few lvs., branching near top into a narrow cluster of starry fls. Sepals erect; petals ½–1 cm. long, with distinct 'claw' at base, usually yellow-spotted near base and red-spotted nearer tip.

❀ Damp shady places. To 2500 m. Pyrenees; Alps; Apennines. June–October. **1011**

Section Tridactylites Haw. Annuals or biennials, forming rosettes of thin, uncut or 3-parted lvs.; fl. stems leafy. Fls. small, usually white.

S. tridactylites L. reaches 1550 m. in Valais, Switzerland, but does not exceed 1000 m. elsewhere.

S. adscendens *L.* (also spelt **ascendens**) (**S. tridactylites** (*L.*) *Engl. & Irmsch.* ssp. **adscendens** (*L.*) *A. Bly*, **S. controversa** *Sternb.*). Forming a neat rosette in the first year, of wedge-shaped 3–25 mm. lvs. usually with a few teeth near tip. Fl. stem to 25 cm. tall, with several lvs. resembling those of rosette. Fls. in more or less branched clusters, with short individual stems; calyx and capsule rather bell-shaped; petals 3–5 mm. long, notched, white or rarely yellow. *Ssp.* **adscendens** has

238

petals 2–2½ times length of sepals; *ssp.* **blavii** (*Engl.*) *Hayek,* petals 3 or more times length of sepals.

✤ Rocks, damp debris, pastures, preferring limestone. 1800–3480 m. Pyrenees; Alps. Norway to 1600 m. *Ssp. blavii:* Dinaric Alps and elsewhere in N.W. Yugoslavia. June–August. **1018**

S. petraea *L.* ROCK SAXIFRAGE. Lvs. of basal rosette semicircular to angular, deeply cut into toothed lobes. Fl. stem 10–20 cm. long, weak and often sprawling, with less deeply cut lvs. and many long stalks forming a loose, confused, leafy cluster. Fls. white; petals 8–10 mm. long, notched, occasionally unequal.

✤ Shady rocks, avoiding limestone. To 2000 m. S. Tyrol and S. of E. Alps. Very local. April–July. **1020**

Section Nephrophyllum Gaud. (*Saxifraga* auct.). Herbaceous plants, with perennial roots or overwintering by miniature bulbs or buds (bulbils); sometimes rosette-forming, but rosettes always producing fl. stalks, never sterile. Lvs. alternate, kidney-shaped to rounded, toothed or lobed, with long stalks; stem-lvs. present. Fls. white, if present.

S. arachnoidea *Sternb.* COBWEB SAXIFRAGE. A curiosity both in appearance and habitat. Tuft-forming with angular, very variable lvs., usually with 3–7 blunt lobes. Stems 10–30 cm. long, slender, sprawling. Fls. in small terminal clusters (cymes) on long footstalks; petals greenish white or dull yellow, petals 3 mm. long, barely longer than sepals. Entire plant covered with long, sticky hairs as if enveloped in cobwebs.

✤ Crevices of overhung cliffs, caverns, on limestone. To 1700 m. Italian Alps N.W. of Lake Garda. Extremely local. July–August.

S. granulata *L.* MEADOW SAXIFRAGE. A very variable plant, but not difficult

to recognise with its long-stalked, kidney-shaped, fleshy, usually blunt-toothed lvs., 2–4 cm. wide, with hairs at least on stalk. Basal lvs. in a rosette, arising from below ground level from a mass of brown bulbils by which the plant overwinters. Stem-lvs. few or none. Fl. stem 10–50 cm. tall, branching in upper half, with large white fls. in a loose cluster (cyme); petals 9–17 mm. long, 3–8 mm. wide.

✤ Grasslands, avoiding limestone. To 2170 m. Pyrenees (local); C. Alps (rare above 1500 m.); Apennines. (Britain.) March–July. **1186**

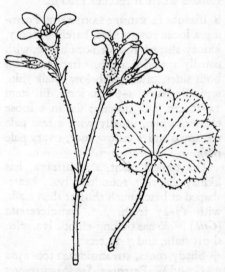

1186. *Saxifraga granulata.* Flower head and basal leaf.

S. rivularis *L.* BROOK SAXIFRAGE. Like a miniature *S. granulata,* with basal bulbils and several 2–8 cm. fl. stems, with 1–3 fls.

✤ Wet rocks. To 2150 m. Norway. (Britain: Scottish mountains to 1100 m.) July–August.

S. cernua *L.* DROOPING SAXIFRAGE. A slender plant 3–15 cm. tall with basal lvs. kidney-shaped, with 3–5 pointed lobes; lvs. 5–18 mm. long, stalk 2–3 times

longer, in a rosette. Stem-lvs. smaller, reducing to uncut, oblong to linear bracts in the axils of which are small red bulbils, often becoming more numerous and clustered near the top. Fls. frequently absent, or solitary at top of unbranched stem; white, with 8-13 mm. rounded oblong petals. Seeds almost never produced; the plant overwinters and reproduces by the bulbils.
❀ Rocky places, often in shade. 1800-2500 m. Alps. Norway to 2200 m. (Britain to 1300 m.) July.   **253**

Section Dactyloides Tausch. (*Sedoides* Gaud.). MOSSY SAXIFRAGES. Mat- or cushion-forming, with numerous individual sterile rosettes; lvs. usually cut into 3-5 (11) finger-like lobes; stem-lvs. few. Fls. white, yellow, pink or red. Typically montane plants.

Some species are very variable and confusion is worse confounded by hybridisation. *S. moschata* crosses very readily with many other species, notably *S. exarata* and *S. pubescens.*

S. tenella *Wulf.* Rosettes joined by leafy 5-10 cm. shoots, forming dense mats. Lvs. narrow awl-shaped, pointed, 1 cm. long, usually hairy at edges. Fl. stems 5-15 cm. tall, thin, hairless, with 2-8 creamy fls. Petals rounded, 2½ mm. long.
❀ Shady rocks, screes. To 2400 m. S.E. Alps. July–August.   **1013**

S. sedoides *L.* Forming a loose mat, leafy shoots sprawling. Lvs. 8-12 mm. long, narrow-spoon-shaped, pointed, tapering to broad stalk, usually hairy; undivided (*ssp.* **sedoides**) or some 3-lobed (*ssp.* **prenja** (*Beck*) *Hayek*). Fl. stems usually leafy, 2-4 cm. tall, with 1-2 yellow fls.; petals 2-3 mm. long, often purple-tipped, not exceeding sepals which are broader.
❀ Shady screes, snow-beds. To 3060

(4000) m. *Ssp.* **sedoides:** E. Pyrenees; E. Alps; Apennines. *Ssp.* **prenja:** N. Yugoslav mountains. June–September.   **1014**

S. aphylla *Sternb.* (S. stenopetala *Gaud.*). Resembling *S. sedoides,* but with mostly 3-lobed lvs. 1 cm. long, barely hairy; some forms from the E. Alps have uncut lvs. Petals pale yellow, linear, just exceeding the triangular sepals in length (2½ mm.), but much narrower.
❀ Screes, stony ground, snow-beds. (1000) 2000-3200 m. C. and E. Alps. July–September.   **248**

S. muscoides *All.* Making a dense, soft cushion of short, erect, tight-packed shoots. Lvs. linear-lance-shaped, 6 mm. long, downy; dead lvs. persisting and turning silvery. Fl. stems leafy, to 5 cm. tall, with 1-3 white or pale yellow fls; petals rounded, touching, 4 mm. long.
❀ Rocks, screes, usually avoiding limestone. (1800) 2200-4200 m. C. and E. Alps. June–August.   **1019**

S. facchinii *Koch.* Resembling *S. muscoides,* but forming smaller cushions; fl. stems barely emerging above lvs., often 1-flowered; petals only 2 mm. long, dull yellow usually flushed dull red.
❀ Rocks, screes, on limestone. 2000-3250 m. Italian Dolomites. Local. July.   **1017**

S. androsacea *L.* Forming loose, slightly elongated rosettes with a very short central stem, of 1-2 cm. sparsely hairy lvs.

Var. **integrifolia** *Ser.* (1021): lvs. narrowly spoon-shaped and round-ended.

Var. **tridentata** *Gaud.* (1022): lvs. with 3 pointed teeth.

These varieties have 1-3 fls. on 2-8 cm. stems. Specially compact forms have been named *var.* **uniflora** *Wulf.,* with 1-3 fls. on 2-8 cm. stems, and *var.*

pygmaea *Horn.* (*var.* **subacaulis** *Schultz*), with virtually stemless fls., but all gradations to these can be found. The fls. are in all cases white, with 5–7 mm. petals, rounded or notched, tapering to base.
❋ Snow-beds, fine damp debris. 1500–3550 m. E. Pyrenees; Alps. May–July.
1021, 1022

S. seguieri *Spreng.* A compact, tufted plant with densely hairy lvs. like those of *S. androsacea integrifolia*, and 1–3 dull yellow fls. with 3 mm., very narrow petals barely longer than sepals, on 1½–4 cm. stems.
❋ Snow-beds, fine damp debris. 2000–3700 m. C. and E. Alps. July–August.
247

S. italica *Webb* (*S. tridens Jan*). Very like *S. androsacea tridentata*, but more compact and densely tufted, with densely hairy lvs. and 2–4 cm. fl. stem. Fls. white, with 5–7 mm. petals.
❋ Debris. 2000–2500 m. Abruzzi. May–July.
1023

S. depressa *Sternb.* Resembling *S. androsacea tridentata*, but leafy shoots longer, to 6–8 cm. Lvs. 8–20 mm. long, 7–10 mm. broad, densely but shortly hairy, tapering from apex which has 3 (5) well-marked teeth, pointed or somewhat rounded. Fl. stems 5–10 cm. long, with 3–8 white fls., usually rather bell-shaped, with 4–5 mm. petals.
❋ Shady crevices, damp screes, usually on porphyritic volcanic formations. 2000–2850 m. Italian Dolomites. August.

S. presolanensis *Engl.* Like a much extended version of *S. androsacea integrifolia*, with long leafy stems, forming a deep, soft, tight-packed cushion, the whitish dead lvs. persisting. Lvs. 15 mm. long, pale green, densely hairy. Fl. stem 6–12 cm. tall, thin, weak, and sticky-downy, with 2–4 widely spaced greenish

yellow fls. with notched, almost oblong 3–4 mm. petals.
❋ Crevices in limestone rocks and cliffs in shade. 1750–2000 m. Bergamasque Alps, N. Italy. One locality. August.
1016

S. glabella *Bert.* Not unlike a weakly sprawling, extended *S. seguieri*, forming loose tufts; lvs. 8 mm. long, hairless, narrow spoon-shaped, blunt-ended. Fl. stems 3–10 cm. tall, with several small white fls. in a loose cluster; petals 2½ mm. long.
❋ Debris, preferring limestone. 1800–2500 m. E. Alps; Abruzzi. June–July.

S. pedemontana *All.* (*S. allionii Terr.*). PIEDMONT SAXIFRAGE. A species with distinct geographical races, having more or less erect, leafy shoots, forming dense cushions, with rather soft lvs., of wedge-shaped or semicircular outline, cut into 5–11 segments; dead lvs. usually persistent below. Fls. white, fairly large, in rather tight clusters; petals 4–14 mm. long, rather narrow.
Ssp. **pedemontana** (**1026**): lvs. fleshy to leathery, shallowly cut into segments twice as long as wide, tapering fan-shaped, broad-stalked, short-haired. Fl. stems 6–15 cm. tall; petals 11–14 mm. long.
Ssp. **prostii** (*Sternb.*) *Webb* (*S. ajugifolia L.*—now an ambiguous name): lvs. deeply cut into pointed segments varying from broad-triangular to linear, usually hairy. Fl. stems 3–7 cm. tall, with 1–3 fls.; petals 4–5 mm. long.
❋ Shaded rocks, snow-beds, icy streams, on acid soils. 1500–2800 m. *Ssp. pedemontana:* mainly S.W. Alps, just in C. Alps. *Ssp. prostii:* Pyrenees, Cevennes. June–August.
1026

S. praetermissa *Webb* (*S. ajugifolia auct. non L.*). A sprawling, mat-forming plant with leafy shoots, 3–6 cm. long, with dead lvs. persisting at base; lvs. 1½ cm. long, 1 cm. wide, sparsely hairy, rounded in outline, deeply cut into 3–5 oblong, pointed-tipped segments. Fl. stems erect, 6–12 cm. tall, arising from axils of leafy stems but themselves almost leafless; fls. 1–3, white; petals 4–5 mm. long, fairly broad.

✤ Damp screes, snow-beds. 1500–2000 (2500) m. Pyrenees. July–September.

1024

S. aquatica *Lap.* WATER SAXIFRAGE. With more or less erect leafy shoots 10–20 cm. long forming a large, loose cushion. Lvs. fleshy, glossy, to 4 cm. wide, with distinct stalk to 5 cm. long; semicircular in outline, deeply cut into many more or less triangular segments. Fl. stems upright, 25–60 cm. tall, very thick, with many stalkless lvs. and a tight narrow head of many white fls.; petals broad, 6–9 mm. long.

✤ Streamsides, damp places. 1500–2200 m. C. and E. Pyrenees. July–August.

1025

S. geranioides *L.* GERANIUM-LIKE SAXIFRAGE. A variable plant with woody base, short leafy stems ending in rosettes, and erect 7–20 cm. fl. stems. Lvs. 1½–3 cm. wide, roughly circular in outline, deeply cut into 9–27 narrow-triangular, pointed segments, very finely hairy. Lvs. on fl. stem few, with mainly deep-cut segments. Fls. in a compact head, some carried singly lower down stem; white, with 12 mm. petals.

Var. **palmata** (*Lap.*) *DC.* (1029) is smaller and silvery grey, with fl. stem not over 10 cm.

✤ Rocks, screes, avoiding limestone. To 2950 m. (*Var. palmata* always high, 2100–2950 m.) N. and C. Pyrenees (rare); E. Pyrenees. July–August. **1029**

S. corbariensis *Timb.* Similar to *S. geranioides* and sometimes considered a subspecies, with lvs. divided into 3 main lobes each cut into 4–11 segments. Fl. stem 6–25 cm. tall, with few lvs. cut

into 3 narrow lobes; petals 7–13 mm. long.

✤ Limestone rocks, screes. To 1500 m. E. Pyrenees, especially Spanish; Corbières. July–August.

S. hypnoides *L.* DOVEDALE MOSS. Forming loose mats of radiating, leafy, sprawling shoots to 15 cm. long, typically with spindle-shaped leafy bulbils in lf. axils, and ending in rosettes. Shoot-lvs. linear-lance-shaped, sometimes narrowly wedge-shaped and 3-lobed; rosette-lvs. with 3–7 narrow, distinctly sharp-pointed lobes. Fl. stem erect, 10–30 cm. tall, with upper stem-lvs. linear, uncut, and 3–7 white fls. in a small head; buds hanging; petals 7–10 mm. long. The British plant is *ssp.* **boreali-atlantica** *Engl. & Irmsch.*

✤ Rock-ledges, screes, stony grassy places. To 1300 m. Britain. Local. May–July. **1027**

S. groenlandica *L.* (now usually considered only a form, *var.* **uniflora** (*R.Br.*) *Engl.*, of the very variable, widespread, low-altitude **S. cespitosa** or **caespitosa** *L.*). TUFTED SAXIFRAGE. A neat cushion-forming plant 3–6 cm. tall, with hairless wedge-shaped lvs. divided into 3 blunt lobes; stem lvs. linear, few; fls. 1 (2), greenish white; petals 4–5 mm. long, twice as long as sepals. Stem, stem-lvs. and calyx with black glands.

✤ Rocks, debris. Jura to 1500 m. Norway to 2280 m. July. **1015**

S. cespitosa has lvs. 3–5-lobed, densely fine-haired, fls. 1–5. Britain to 1150 m.

S. pentadactylis *Lap.* Forming loose rounded cushions of leafy shoots with woody stems. Lvs. hairless, deeply cut into 3–5, grooved, linear lobes. Fl. stems 6–20 cm. tall, with few lvs., glandular but smooth, and few-fld. heads of small white fls.; petals 4 mm. long.

✤ Rocks, screes, avoiding limestone,

1880–2900 m. E. Pyrenees. July–
August. **1028**

S. pubescens *Pourr.* HAIRY SAXIFRAGE.
A very variable plant, sometimes with
large loose rosettes, sometimes densely
cushion-forming. Rosette-lvs. typically
deeply 5-lobed but varying from 3 to 9
lobes, with narrow strap-shaped segments; dark green, densely hairy. Stem-
lvs. usually similar. Fls. in loose clusters,
with petals rounded, touching or overlapping.

This species has been much subdivided, though it appears possible that
exposure has much to do with the habit
of the plant. Four forms are illustrated
to show the variation.

Ssp. **pubescens** (*ssp.* **pourretiana**
Engl. & Irmsch.) *forma* **elata** *Luiz*, the
typical form of this race (**1030**): loose,
with short leafy shoots and lvs. 1–2 cm.
long, with long narrow stalk and long,
deeply furrowed lobes; fl. stems 2–12
cm. tall; petals white, 4–6 mm. long,
twice as long as sepals.

Ssp. **pubescens** *forma* **cephalantha**
Luiz (**1031**): like foregoing, but more
compact in every way.

Ssp. **iratiana** (*F. Schultz*) *Engl. &
Irmsch. forma* **vulgaris** *Luiz*, the typical
form of this race (**1032**): always densely
tufted, forming long leafy shoots on
which the dead lvs. persist for years;
lvs. 4–10 mm. long, with broad, short
stalk, and short, lightly furrowed lobes.
Fl. stems 0–2 (6) cm. long; fls. in
smallish clusters; petals white, often
red-veined, more than twice as long as
sepals; calyx and anthers reddish.

Ssp. **iratiana** *forma* **polyantha** *Luiz*
(**1033**): like foregoing, but loosely multi-
flowered.

✤ Rocks, debris. To 2800 m. *Ssp.
pubescens:* E. Pyrenees. *Ssp. iratiana:*
always on exposed rocks: E. and C.
Pyrenees. June–August. **1030–1033**

S. exarata *Vill.* Not unlike *S. pubescens*

ssp. pubescens, forming a soft cushion,
with 4–15 mm. lvs. varying considerably in outline but typically 3- or 5-
lobed, usually densely hairy, with strap-
shaped, grooved lobes. The illustration
shows a rather loosely tufted form, but
condensed forms like those of *S.
pubescens* exist. Fl. stems 3–10 cm. tall,
with few, usually uncut lvs., and (1) 3–8
fls. in a loose cluster, with white or off-
white, occasionally pink, petals 4 mm.
long, 2 mm. wide, barely touching.
Several varieties have been named,
which differ in minor characters;
some forms are easily confused with *S.
moschata,* of which it has been considered a variety, and *S. exarata* and
'*S. iratiana*' of gardens are also frequently
confused.

✤ Rocks, stony places. To 2700 (3600)
m. Pyrenees (doubtful); Alps; Apuan
Alps; Apennines. June–August. **1034**

S. moschata *Wulf.* MUSKY SAXIFRAGE.
An almost infinitely variable species
with around 30 named variations.
Forming flattish, dense cushions of
numerous small leafy shoots. Lvs.
3–15 mm. long, 1–7 mm. wide, with or
without stalk, usually 3-lobed, sometimes entire or 5-lobed; segments
rounded, not grooved, usually with
short hairs. Fl. stems 1–7 cm. long, fls.
1–7, varying in colour, with 3–4 mm.
rounded petals, not touching.

The typical plant is *ssp.* **eumoschata**
Engl. & Irmsch. (*ssp.* **linifolia** *Br.-Bl.*),
with thin lvs., oblong petals, yellowish
to reddish or dark purple-red, seldom
white. Three forms of this are illustrated
to show the variation. (They are not
geographical races.)

Forma **compacta** *Mert. & Koch* (**249**):
a fairly dense plant with 3-lobed lvs.,
from the Dolomites.

Forma **pygmaea** (*Haw.*) *Engl.* (**250**): a
very compact form with densely over-
apping entire lvs., from the C. Pyrenees.

Forma lineata (*Sternb.*) *Engl. & Irmsch.* (**251**): with elongated lvs., from S. Tyrol, Dolomites.

The other race is *ssp.* **ampullacea** (*Ten.*) *Engl. & Irmsch.* (**252**): lvs. fleshy, uncut or with 3 rounded lobes; fls. 1–3, relatively large, petals obovate, always white.

❀ Rocks, debris, stony places. 1200–3400 (4000) m. Pyrenees; Alps; Yugoslav mountains; N. and C. Apennines. *Ssp. ampullacea:* Abruzzi only. July–August.   **249–252**

S. hariotii *Luiz & Soulié.* Resembling *S. moschata,* but lvs. 1–3-lobed, sometimes 1 small lobe and 1 big one, shining and almost hairless, lobes grooved, often pointed. Tufts loose to dense. Fl. stem 2–6 cm. tall; stem lvs. few, uncut to 3-lobed; fls. 1–4, petals cream or dull yellow.

❀ Rocks, debris, stony meadows, preferring limestone. 1600–2300 m. W. Pyrenees. July–August.   **1036**

S. nervosa *Lap.* (including **S. intricata** *Lap.*). Forming small loose cushions of dark green lvs., rough with very short, knobbly glands which also cover fl. stems and calyx. Lvs. of 3–5 strap-shaped grooved segments; aromatic (resin-like). Fl. stems 4–10 cm. long; fls. 3–12, with white, rounded, 4–5 mm. petals.

❀ Acid rocks. To 2600 m. C. Pyrenees. June–August.

Section **Trachyphyllum** Gaud. (*Hirculus* Tausch. in part). Small, branching, mat-forming plants with narrow uncut lvs., bristly on edges and at tip. Fls. white or yellow on more or less branched stems (in cymes).

S. aspera *L.* ROUGH SAXIFRAGE. Forming loose mats of long, sprawling, leafy shoots, with 3–8 mm. oblong lance-shaped lvs., held out from the stem,

with stiff bristly hairs on edges and at tip. Fl. stem 8–20 cm. tall, erect, with lvs. 1 (2) cm. long; fls. 2–5 in a loose cluster; petals 5–8 mm. long, often varying in size, rounded or pointed, usually rather pale yellow with brighter yellow near base, sometimes red-spotted.

❀ Rocks, stony places, usually avoiding limestone. To 2800 m. E. and C. Pyrenees; Alps; N. Apennines. July–August.   **269**

S. bryoides *L.* MOSS SAXIFRAGE. Similar to *S. aspera* and originally regarded as a subspecies, but with shoots shorter, 2–5 cm. long, forming dense mats, and with smaller, incurving lvs. Fls. solitary on 3–8 cm. stems with lvs. ½ cm. long.

❀ Rocks, debris, avoiding limestone. 2000–4000 m. Pyrenees; S. and E. Alps. July–August.   **268**

Section **Xanthizoon** Griseb. (*Hirculus* Tausch. in part). A section of one species only, as described below.

S. aizoides *L.* YELLOW MOUNTAIN SAXIFRAGE. With loosely sprawling 5–15 cm. leafy shoots and erect 15–25 cm. fl. stems. Lvs. 1–2½ cm. long, more or less oblong, sometimes lightly toothed and sometimes hairy in lower part. Fl. stems usually branching into a leafy cluster (cyme), with (1) 5–10 starry fls. Petals 3–6 mm. long, not touching, bright yellow or orange, often red-spotted, occasionally a striking dark red. The name *var.* **autumnalis** (*L.*) *Engl. & Irmsch.* has been applied to forms with larger and more toothed lvs. and larger fls., but it has no geographical significance.

❀ Damp stony places, shingles, streamsides. To 3150 m. Pyrenees; Alps; Apennines; Apuan Alps. Norway to 1700 m. (Britain to 1170 m.) June–September.   **245**

Section *Euaizoonia* (Schott.) Engl. EN-CRUSTED or SILVER SAXIFRAGES. Forming rosettes, the offsets often resulting in cushions or clumps, of lime-encrusted lvs., often strap- or spoon-shaped. Fls. white, usually spotted; occasionally pink or yellow, in clusters on long branching stems. Includes some of the largest species.

S. longifolia *Lap.* PYRENEAN SAXIFRAGE. Forming a single large, flat, regular, long-lived rosette which dies after flowering without making offsets (monocarpic). Lvs. many, 3-10 cm. long, 3-8 mm. wide, strap-shaped, sometimes slightly wavy, slightly broader at base, again broadening slightly near tip and then tapering to a blunt point; bluish, lime-encrusted at edges. Fl. stem 25-50 cm. tall, stout, branching almost from base to form a dense pyramidal spike (panicle) of many white fls. Petals 5-6 mm. long.
❈ Crevices in limestone cliffs, walls, rocks. 900-2400 m. Pyrenees. June-August. **256**

S. lingulata *Bell.* **(S. callosa** *Sm.***).** Forming large, rather untidy rosettes; flowering rosettes die afterwards, but short stolons carry young ones, so that clumps are formed. Fl. stem 15-35 cm. tall, with numerous white, often red-spotted fls. on reddish stalks in a long, narrow cluster (panicle) starting near the middle of the stem.

The name *S. callosa* is now botanically correct, but *S. lingulata* has been used here because of its familiarity to gardeners. The species is variable and modern botanists consider that its forms grade into each other too much to be separable; nevertheless sub-varieties have been distinguished and are well recognised by gardeners who have isolated them; they are described below as the various extremes of the species.

Var. **bellardii** *Sternb. sub-var.* **eubel-**

lardii *Engl. & Irmsch.* **(254):** the type, with 3-10 (23) cm. lvs., typically long and narrow, sometimes slightly wavy, broader at base, broadening gradually towards the tip, then tapering to a point; bluish, often reddish near base, lime-encrusted at edges.

Var. **bellardii** *sub-var.* **lantoscana** *(Boiss. & Reut.) Rouy & Camus* **(255):** lvs. only 2-4 cm. long, broadening at the base.

Var. **australis** *(Moric.) Engl.:* lvs. 2½-8 cm. long, tapering very slightly from tip to base, with no broadening at base.
❈ Limestone rocks, cliffs. To 2500 m. *Sub-var. eubellardii:* Cottian Alps; Maritime Alps; N. and C. Apennines. *Sub-var. lantoscana:* Maritime Alps; very local. *Var. australis:* Ligurian Alps; N. and C. Apennines. June-August.
254, 255

S. cochlearis *Reichb.* Sometimes regarded as a subspecies of *S. lingulata*, but with 1-4 cm. bluish, lime-encrusted lvs. which are spoon-shaped, the apex being distinctly rounded. Fl. stem 5-45 cm. tall, densely glandular-downy; fls. milk-white.
❈ Limestone rocks. To 1900 m. Maritime Alps; Ligurian Alps. Very local.
259

S. valdensis *DC.* Though superficially more like some of the *Kabschia* section (p. 246), this plant, in fact, resembles a small edition of *S. cochlearis*, forming a dense cushion of hard, columnar leafy shoots. The lvs., 8-11 mm. long and 1½-2 mm. broad, are lance-shaped, keeled, with a distinct point and translucent margin; they are reflexed from the middle to form small flat rosettes. Fl. stems 4-8 cm. tall, covered with black glands, with 3-8 relatively large fls. in a neat cluster (corymb); petals 9 mm. long.
❈ Crevices in limestone rocks. French

and Italian Alps. Very rare. To 2800 m. July–August. **1037, 1191**

S. crustata *Vest.* Forming dense rosettes, which elongate when flowering, of partly erect 1½–6 cm. bluish, lime-encrusted, strap-shaped lvs., broadening a little towards the lance-shaped tip and only very slightly at the base. Fl. stem 12–30 cm. tall, with a narrow, relatively few-fld. cluster (panicle) starting about halfway up the stem. Fls. white, sometimes pink-spotted, very rarely pink.
✣ Limestone rocks, stony places. To 2200 (2800) m. E. Alps. June–August. **258**

S. aizoon *Jacq.* (**S. paniculata** *Mill.*). LIVELONG SAXIFRAGE. A plant with innumerable minor variations, many important in gardens, forming dense tufts of neat rounded rosettes of usually bluish, usually lime-encrusted lvs., very variable in shape, normally 1–4 cm. long, with extremes of ½ and 6 cm., and typically tapering from a rounded or bluntly pointed tip, but sometimes almost strap-shaped; always with distinct, fine teeth. Fl. stem (4) 12–30 cm. tall, forming a small cluster usually in the upper third only. Fls. white to pale cream, very rarely pink, sometimes red-spotted.
The name *S. paniculata* is now botanically correct, but *S. aizoon* has been retained because of its familiarity, especially to gardeners.
✣ Rocks, stony places, stabilised screes. To 2700 (3415) m. Pyrenees; Alps; Apennines. May–August. **257**

S. hostii *Tausch.* Forming a large rosette of dark green, lightly lime-encrusted, 2–10 cm. lvs., often curving down towards the tip and with fine, rounded teeth. *Ssp.* **hostii** (*ssp.* **dolomitica** *Br.-Bl.*) has broad, blunt-edged lvs.; *ssp.* **rhaetica** (*Kern.*) *Br.-Bl.* has narrower lvs. tapering to a pointed tip. Fl. stem 25–60 cm. tall, with several quite large lvs. and a rather dense cluster on the upper part; fls. white, usually red-spotted.
✣ Rocks, debris. To 2500 m. *Ssp. hostii:* E. Alps (mainly S.). *Ssp. rhaetica:* C. Italian Alps. May–July. **260**

S. cotyledon *L.* PYRAMIDAL SAXIFRAGE. Forming large rosettes of green, finely toothed, broad 2–6 cm. lvs. with a point at the flattened tip. Fl. stem 15–50 (80) cm. tall, branching from near the base to form a large, many-fld., roughly pyramidal head. Fls. white, very occasionally thickly purple-spotted; petals 6–10 mm. long. Hybridises freely with *S. aizoon*.
✣ Damp crevices in rocks, avoiding limestone. 1500–2615 m. C. Pyrenees (very local); S. Alps. Norway to 1320 m. July–August. **262**

S. florulenta *Moretti.* Forming large rosettes of very many lvs.; very slow growing, with dead lvs. persisting at base of rosette, which dies after flowering (monocarpic). Lvs. 3–6 cm. long at maturity, dark green, cartilaginous and hairy at edges but not lime-encrusted. Fl. stem 15–30 cm. tall, extremely thick, reddish, leafy, with many flesh-pink fls., rather bell-shaped due to the round calyx, in a tapering spike. An almost mythical plant, which Farrer called 'The Ancient King'.
✣ Shady crevices in rocks and cliffs, on granite. 1950–3240 m. C. Maritime Alps. Very local. July–September. **261**

S. mutata *L.* Forming large, loose rosettes of broad, strap-shaped, blunt-ended, glossy, dark green lvs. with a well-marked translucent edge, pits which do not secrete lime, tiny teeth at the tip and a fringe of hairs at the base. Fl. stem 20–50 cm. tall, with several large lvs., forming a rather sparse, loose cluster of starry orange fls. with 5–8 mm. narrow petals.

✧ Damp stony places, on limestone. To 2200 m. Alps. June–August. **263**

Section Kabschia Engl. Small plants with usually narrow, rigid, often pointed lvs. in rosettes, forming large mats or tufts. Fls. white, yellow, pink or purple.

S. marginata *Sternb.* Forming a dense mass of leafy shoots, rosette-shaped to columnar. In the *ssp.* **eumarginata** *Engl. & Irmsch.*, found in our area, the lvs. are 5–12 mm. long, 3–5 mm. broad, blunt-ended, tapering, with translucent edges; and the fl. stem 7–10 cm. tall, carrying 2–8 large fls. with 8–11 mm. white or pale pink petals.
✧ Rocks, preferring limestone. To 2100 m. Abruzzi; S. Italian mountains.

S. caesia *L.* BLUE SAXIFRAGE. Forming dense cushions of leafy shoots each ending in small flat rosettes of metallic blue, lime-encrusted 3–6 mm. lvs. without translucent edge; these are oblong-spoon-shaped or narrowly elliptical, blunt-edged, and recurving from the base. Fl. stems 4–11 cm. tall, very slender, with 1–6 white fls.; petals 4–6 mm.
✧ Rocks, stony places, consolidated screes. To 3005 m. Pyrenees (very local); Alps; Apuan Alps; N. and C. Apennines. July–September. **1038, 1190**

S. squarrosa *Sieb.* Resembling *S. caesia*, but lvs. even more tightly packed, producing deeper, harder cushions; lvs. smaller, narrow-oblong, recurving from near the tip only. Intermediate forms between this and *S. caesia* can be found.
✧ Limestone rocks, stony places. 1200–2700 m. S.E. Alps. July–August. **1192**

S. vandellii *Sternb.* Forming a deep, hard cushion composed of numerous columnar, tufted shoots. Lvs. 8–11 mm. long, 1½–2 mm. wide, more or less erect, awl-shaped, pointed, keeled, green with translucent edge. Fl. stem 4–8 mm. tall, with 3–8 white fls. in a

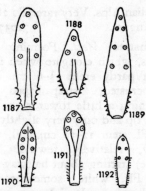

Individual leaves of Kabschia saxifrages, showing arrangement of pores and hairs. 1187. *Saxifraga diapensioides*. 1188. *S. tombeanensis.* 1189. *S. vandellii*. 1190. *S. caesia*. 1191. *S. valdensis* (for comparison). 1192. *S. squarrosa*. (Greatly enlarged.)

smallish cluster (corymb); petals 9 mm. long, 4 mm. wide.
✧ Crevices of limestone cliffs and rocks. To 2600 m. Italian Alps. Extremely local. June–July. **1035, 1189**

S. diapensioides *Bell.* Forming a stiff, thick cushion of many columnar, tufted shoots. Lvs. 4–6 mm. long, 1–1½ mm. wide, tightly overlapped; thick, oblong, blunt-ended, bluish with translucent edge. Fl. stem 3–7 cm. tall, downy, with 2–6 white fls.; petals 8 mm. long, 5 mm. wide.
✧ Rocks, preferring limestone. 1500–2900 m. S.W. Alps. July–August. **1187**

S. tombeanensis *Boiss.* Resembling *S. diapensioides*, but with shorter, lance-shaped, elliptical or angular lvs., with an incurving, pointed tip. Petals to 12 mm. long.
✧ Rocks, preferring limestone. To 2300 m. Italian Alps. Local: Brenta and Monte Baldo area. May–June. **1188**

S. burserana *L.* (spelt **S. burseriana** by most older authorities). Forming a dense mat of short leafy shoots, with lvs. 5–12 mm. long, 1½–2 mm. wide, narrow awl-shaped, tapering to a pointed tip,

bluish, with narrow translucent edge. Fl. stem 2–5 cm. tall, reddish, with a single large white fl.; petals 7–15 mm. long, 5–9 mm. broad.
✵ Rocks and screes, preferring limestone. To 2140 (2500) m. E. Alps. March–July. **266**

S. aretioides *Lap.* Forming a dense, solid cushion of many columnar, tufted shoots. Lvs. 5–7 mm. long, 1½–2 mm. wide, narrow-oblong, with a small point, slightly bluish, with translucent edge. Fl. stems 3–6 cm. long, with 3–5 (7) bright yellow fls.; petals toothed, 5–7 mm. long.
✵ Rocks. To 2300 m. Pyrenees. June–August. **267**

Section Engleria Sünd. Resembling the *Kabschia* group, but larger, with lime-encrusted lvs. and reddish fls. (also yellow but these not in our area).
S. media *Gouan.* Forming tight 1½–3½ cm. rosettes on woody shoots; lvs. standing out from the centre, 7–20 mm. long, bluish, narrow-oblong or reversed lance-shaped, with triangular point and marginal lime-pits. Fl. stem 10–18 cm. tall, with 6–12 mm. lvs. pink at base; fls. 6–15 in a narrow spike which is typically curved over until all fls. have opened; fls. pinkish purple, the rounded, 2½ mm. petals exceeded by the large, deep red, bell-shaped, densely hairy calyx.
✵ Rocks, preferring limestone. To 2510 m. C. and E. Pyrenees. June–August. **265**
S. porophylla *Bert. ssp.* **normalis** *Terr.* Very similar to *S. media*, but with flattish 1–2 cm. rosettes of bluish 8–11 mm. lvs. Fl. stem 5–8 cm. tall with shorter, also bicoloured lvs., and 6–12 pinkish purple fls. with 2–2½ mm., rather blunt-ended petals about as long as large, red, bell-shaped, densely hairy calyx.

✵ Rocks, preferring limestone. 1300–2500 m. N., C. and S. Apennines and S. Italian mountains. July–August. **264**

Section Porphyrion Tausch. The only group with usually opposite, uncut lvs. carrying lime-pits; lvs. sometimes apparently in rosettes at the end of the leafy stems. Creeping, mat-forming plants with pink, purple or red fls.
S. oppositifolia *L.* PURPLE SAXIFRAGE. A plant combining long creeping stems with short upright ones, forming loose mats or tighter cushions. Lvs. bluish-green or green, 2–6 mm. long, tightly packed in 4 rows, almost always opposite; oval, oblong or obovate, concave, ciliate on lower part (occasionally all round), with thickened tip carrying 1–5 lime-secreting pits; usually lime-encrusted. Fls. solitary on 1–2 cm. leafy stems, pink to rose, or deep purple, occasionally white; petals 5–15 mm. long, 2–7 mm. wide; stamen filaments shorter than petals; anthers bluish; sepals hairy on edges.
A very variable form, of which 4 extremes are illustrated. Each sub-species has many named varieties and sub-varieties; those in current use have been described, although modern botanists tend to discount the validity of these names, which are nevertheless valuable to the gardener.
Ssp. **euoppositifolia** *Engl. & Irmsch,* (270): the typical forms, *var.* **typica** *Vacc.* and *var.* **distans** *Ser.,* have lime-pits, and petals 5–12 (20) mm. long, tending to be lance-shaped; otherwise as described above.
Var. **typica** *Vacc.* sub-var. **grandiflora** *Griseb. & Schank.* (271): a large-fld form with rounded petals 1–2 cm. long.
Var. **distans** *Ser. sub-var.* **murithiana** *(Tiss.) Vacc.*: with gland-tipped hairs on calyx.
Var. **latina** *Terracc.*: similar to *var. typica,* but with 3 lime-pits.

Ssp. **blepharophylla** (*Kern.*) *Engl. & Irmsch.*: very compact, with rather spoon-shaped, blunt-ended 3–4 mm. lvs. carrying long hairs all round. Petals 5–8 mm. long, rounded, deep pink.

Ssp. **rudolphiana** (*Hornsch.*) *Engl. & Irmsch.* (**272**): an extremely compact form with very tight-packed 1½–2 mm. obovate lvs., with 1 lime-pit, triangular tip and very short hairs except at tip, forming little columnar shoots. Petals 5–7 mm. long, narrow, pointed or rounded, purplish.

Ssp. **speciosa** (*Dörfl. & Hayek*) *Engl. & Irmsch.* (**273**): lvs. slightly recurved, broad, 3½–5 mm. long, cartilaginous and hairless at tip, with 1 (3–5) lime-pits. Petals 7–10 mm. long, narrow and rounded, purple.

❀ Rocks, stony places, screes. To 3800 m. Pyrenees; Alps; Apennines. Norway to 2300 m. *Ssp. blepharophylla*: Austrian Alps only. *Var. latina*: Apennines only. *Ssp. rudolphiana*: E. Alps only. *Ssp. speciosa*: Abruzzi only. (Britain: *ssp. euoppositifolia*: to 1300 m.) May–August. **270–273**

S. retusa *Gouan.* Not unlike *S. oppositifolia*, but lvs. 2–4 mm. long, dark glossy green, oblong- to ovate-lanceolate, pointed, keeled and recurving from about the middle; hairy only at the base, with 3–5 lime-pits; somewhat lime-encrusted. Fl. stems to 5 cm. long, sparsely leafy, with 2–3 (1–5) reddish purple fls.; petals 4–5 mm. long, 2 mm. broad, ovate, with distinct narrow claw; stamen filaments purple, exceeding petals; anthers orange; sepals not hairy on edges.

Ssp. **retusa** (*var.* **baumgartenii** (*Schott.*) *Velen.*) (**274**): sepals quite hairless; fl. stalks 0–1½ cm. long, fls. 1–3.

Ssp. **augustana** (*Vacc.*) *Webb*: sepals densely downy; fl. stalks 2–5 cm. long, fls. 2–5.

❀ Rocks, debris, especially in exposed places. 2000–3000 (3600) m. E. and C. Pyrenees; Alps. *Ssp. retusa:* avoiding limestone, throughout range except for areas of S.W. Alps, but local. *Ssp. augustana:* preferring limestone: S.W. Alps. June–August. **274**

S. biflora *All.* With creeping or erect stems. Lvs. much less tightly packed than in two preceding species, 5–9 mm. long, 3–6 mm. broad, round to obovate, almost succulent, rather metallic-looking, with a single lime-pit but never lime-encrusted. Fls. 2–5 (9) in a terminal cluster; petals much separated, of an odd red or reddish purple, or off-white, centre often yellow; stamen filaments whitish, shorter than petals; anthers pink or orange, finally black; sepals downy and ciliate. The typical form has 5–6 mm. petals, lance-shaped or narrow-elliptical (**275**).

Var. **kochii** *Kitt.* (*ssp.* **macropetala** (*Kern.*) *Rouy & Camus*) (**276**): petals 6–9 mm. long, broad-elliptical.

❀ Screes, moraines, river shingle. 2000–3200 (4200) m. Alps. June–August. **275, 276**

CHRYSOSPLENIUM *L.* GOLDEN-LEAVED SAXIFRAGE. Herbaceous plants with small yellow fls., 4 (5)-parted; petals absent; with a nectar-secreting disk around the styles; stamens 8 (10). Fls. in leafy clusters (cymes).

C. alternifolium *L.* ALTERNATE-LEAVED GOLDEN SAXIFRAGE. Spreading by leaf-less runners; lvs. alternate, 1–2½ cm. long, on a long stalk; kidney-shaped, rounded-toothed. Fl. stems to 20 cm. tall; fls. 5–6 mm. across, in a small dense cluster, backed by bright greenish yellow bracts like the lvs.

❀ Damp shady places. To 2450 m. Pyrenees; Alps; N. Apennines. (Britain to 1000 m.) April–July. **1043**

C. oppositifolium *L.* OPPOSITE-LEAVED GOLDEN SAXIFRAGE. Spreading by leafy

rooting stems; lvs. opposite, 1–2 cm. long, rounded, barely toothed; otherwise similar to *C. alternifolium*, but not so robust, not exceeding 15 cm., with fls. only 4 mm. across.
ᛘ Damp shady places. To 1900 m. Pyrenees. (Britain to 1100 m.) April–July. **1042**

C. dubium *Gay*. Like *C. oppositifolium*, but with shorter lf. stalks and fls. only 1½–2 mm. across. Ripe fruit (capsule) asymmetrical and projecting from sepals, which is not the case with the other species.
ᛘ Damp shady places. To 2200 m. S. Italian mountains. Rare. April–June.

PARNASSIACEAE—GRASS OF PARNASSUS FAMILY

Resembling *Saxifragaceae* and sometimes included in that family, but with the special character of fringed, comb-like, nectar-secreting staminodes (sterile stamens) carried inside and opposite the petals, and about ⅓ their length.

PARNASSIA *L.* The only genus. **P. palustris** *L.* GRASS OF PARNASSUS. Herbaceous, 10–30 cm. tall, making tufts of long-stalked, heart-shaped lvs. 1–5 cm. long. Fl. stems with a single lf., clasping and about halfway up stem in *ssp.* **palustris** (1044); barely clasping and near base of stem, or entirely absent, in *ssp.* **obtusiflora** (*Rupr.*) *Webb*. Fls. solitary, white, 1–2 cm. across, 5-parted, with rounded, strongly veined petals.
ᛘ Grassy places, usually damp; moors. To 2500 m. *Ssp. obtusiflora:* Norway to 1700 m. (Britain to 850 m.) July–October. **1044**

GROSSULARIACEAE—GOOSEBERRY FAMILY

Resembling *Saxifragaceae* and sometimes included in that family, but deciduous shrubs with alternate, usually lobed lvs.

RIBES *L.* GOOSEBERRY, CURRANT. The only genus. Fls. in elongated clusters (racemes); small, 4–5-parted, with petals shorter than sepals, and a prominent, coloured 'receptacle' under the fls. Fruit, a juicy berry.
Besides the species described, *R. uva-crispa* *L.* (including *R. grossularia* *L.*), the WILD GOOSEBERRY, reaches 1800 m., and *R. nigrum*, the BLACK CURRANT, is sometimes naturalised in the Alps.

R. rubrum *L.* (including **R. sylvestre** (*Lam.*) *Mert. & Koch* = **R. vulgare** *Lam.*). RED CURRANT. 1–2 m. high. Lvs. around 6 cm. long, usually broader than long, with 3–5 rounded-triangular lobes with broad, rounded but pointed teeth. Lf. stalk as long as lf. Fls. greenish, 6–20 in a loose cluster, sideways-held or drooping, each with a bract half length of fl. stalk; calyx hairless; petals wedge-shaped, minute; receptacle flat; anthers separated by a distinct connecting band. Fr. 6–10 mm. across, red.
ᛘ Damp woods, hedges. To 2100 m. Alps. Local as a wild plant, sometimes naturalised. (Britain.) April–May. **1039**

R. schlechtendahlii *Lange*. NORTHERN RED CURRANT. Similar to *R. rubrum*, but receptacle cup-shaped, anthers adjoining. *

250

❧ Damp woods. To 1250 m. Norway. April–May; fruiting July–August.

R. petraeum *Wulf.* (not *Sm.*). ROCK RED CURRANT. 1½–2½ m. high. Lvs. to 15 cm. long, as broad as long, with 3–5 angular lobes with pointed teeth; lf. stalk longer than lf. Fls. pinkish red, bell-shaped, 20–35 in clusters more or less erect at first, then horizontal or drooping, each with downy bract as long as fl. stalk; calyx hairy; petals broadly wedge-shaped, half length of sepals. Fruit dark purple-red.

❧ Woods, streamsides, rocky places, preferring acid soils. To 2460 m. Pyrenees; Alps; N. and C. Apennines. April–June; fruiting August–September.   1040

R. alpinum. MOUNTAIN CURRANT. 1–3 m. high. Lvs. 3–5 cm. long, much longer than broad, deeply 3- or 5-lobed, straight or heart-shaped at base; lf. stalk shorter than lf. Fls. yellowish green, with minute petals; of different sexes though both apparently 2-sexed: males 4–6 mm. across, with flattish receptacle, 20–30 together; females 3–5 mm. across, with cup-shaped receptacle, 8–15 together. Bracts longer than densely glandular fl. stalks. Clusters always erect, even in fruit. Fruit 6–8 mm. across, red.

❧ Open woods, cliffs, rocky places, preferring limestone. To 1900 m. Pyrenees; Alps. April–May; fruiting August.   1041

ROSACEAE—ROSE FAMILY

A large family of trees, shrubs and herbaceous plants, with the lvs. almost always alternate, and usually with stipules (scale-like or lf.-like appendages at or near the base of the lf. stem): this distinguishes the family from *Ranunculaceae* with which it is possible to confuse it. Fls. regular, usually with both sexes present, with ovary below the petals and sepals, or with a ring-like structure (part of the receptacle) between segments and ovary. Sepals usually 5, usually overlapping; an exterior *epicalyx* may be present. Petals same in number as sepals, alternating with them, occasionally absent. Stamens varying in number, but usually numerous. Fruit of 1 or more sections, of various types, very seldom a capsule: this distinguishes the family from its nearest relations, *Saxifragaceae*, which always have capsular fruits.

Besides the plants described, the MEADOWSWEET, *Filipendula ulmaria* (L.) Maxim., reaches 1800 m.; the AGRIMONY, *Agrimonia eupatorium* L., 1800 m., and the similar *Aremonia agrimonioides* (L.) Neck., 1900 m. The HAWTHORNS, *Crataegus oxyacantha* L. and *C. monogyna* Jacq., reach 1665 m. and 1525 m. respectively in Valais, Switzerland.

ROSA L. ROSE. Shrubs with usually prickly stems and lvs. typically of several opposite leaflets, with stipules joined to base of lf. stalk. Fls. 4–5-parted, with many stamens. Fruit a hep or hip containing numerous seeds, red unless otherwise specified, and retaining the sepals at the end at least for a time; the heps are usually the easiest way of identifying the species.

Rather difficult to identify, especially as species are extremely variable and many hybrids exist. Nomenclature is confused and synonymy has been simplified here. Besides the species described, several others approach 1500 m. altitude.

R. cinnamomea L. CINNAMON or MAY ROSE. 30 cm. to 2 m. tall, with arching, purple-red or brownish stems and numerous hooked prickles. Lvs. often bluish or greyish, downy below, of 3–7 leaflets. Fls. 1–2, bright or pale pink, 4–6½ cm. across, barely scented or scentless. Sepals narrow, unlobed, erect on the small round hairless hep.   *
❀ Scrub, especially by streamsides. To 2200 m. C. Alps. Norway to 1250 m. Often cultivated and may naturalise. May–July.   **277**

R. pimpinellifolia L. (**R. spinosissima** L. in part). BURNET ROSE. A low bushy plant 10–40 (100) cm. tall, with many short straight prickles mingled with stiff bristles. Lvs. smooth, of 7–11 small leaflets. Fls. solitary, white or pale yellow, occasionally pink, 2–5 cm. across. Sepals small, reflexed on the roundish, purple-black hep.
❀ Dry places, rocks, dunes, sandy heaths. To 2000 m. Pyrenees; Alps; Apennines. May–August.   **278**

R. elliptica *Tausch.* 1–2 m. tall, with erect stems bearing hooked prickles. Lvs. downy on both sides, of 5–7 leaflets which are wedge-shaped at base. Fls. 1–3 together, white or pale pink, short-stalked, 2½–4½ cm. across, slightly scented. Sepals more or less lobed, erect to spreading on the roundish, hairless hep.
❀ Hedgerows, dry places. To 2000 m. Alps; Ligurian Alps. Local. (Britain: very rare.) June–September.   **279**

R. dumalis *Bechst.* (including **R. afzeliana** *Fr.*, **R. coriifolia** *Fr.*). A very variable plant 1–3 m. tall with arching stems and curved prickles. Lvs. hairless or slightly downy, often bluish, of 5–7 leaflets. Fls. 1–4 together, pink or white, short-stalked, 3–6 cm. across, scentless or apple-scented. Sepals more or less toothed, erect or nearly so on the round, hairless hep, falling when fruit ripens.

The name *R. coriifolia* Fr. is sometimes applied to the more hairy-lvd. forms of *R. dumalis*, and *R. afzeliana* Fr. to the hairless form.   *
❀ Scrub, stony places. To 2000 m. Alps; Apennines. (Britain.) June–July.   **280**

R. canina L. DOG ROSE. Very similar to *R. dumalis* and even more variable: an aggregate of which over 60 varieties and forms have been recognised in Britain alone. Prickles larger than in *R. dumalis*, fl. stalks longer (usually 1–2 cm.), fls. normally pink, sepals with few or no lobes, falling before the round to ellipsoid hep ripens.
❀ Scrub, thickets, hedgerows, grassy places. To 2200 m. Pyrenees; Alps; Apennines. (Britain.) June–July.

R. pendulina L. (**R. alpina** L.) ALPINE ROSE. 30 cm. to 2 m. tall, with fairly upright stems and straight prickles or more often none. Lvs. hairless, bright or yellowish green, of 7–11 leaflets. Fls. 1–3, bright or purplish pink, 3½–6½ cm. across. Sepals downy inside and at least as long as petals, erect on the smooth, usually pendant, rounded to flask-shaped hep.
❀ Woods, open places. To 2630 m. Pyrenees; Alps; Apennines. May–August.   **281**

R. abietina *Gren.* (sometimes considered an alpine subspecies of **R. obtusifolia** *Desv.*). An arching bush with large, slightly curved, brownish prickles. Lvs. barely downy, of 5–7 leaflets. Fls. in small clusters, pink or white, 4–5 cm. across. Sepals small, with small lobes, reflexed on the roundish, hairy hep, but soon falling.

♣ Hedgerows, scrub. To 2000 m. C. Alps; Apennines. May–August. **282**

R. glauca *Pourr., non Vill.* (**R. rubrifolia** *Vill.*). BLUE-LEAVED ROSE. 1–3 m. tall, with flexible, reddish stems covered in blue 'bloom', and hooked prickles. Lvs. hairless, dull or grey-blue, usually tinted red, of 5–7 narrow, pointed leaflets. Fls. in clusters of up to 20, 2½–5 cm. across, with small petals, bright or purplish pink, scentless; sepals narrow, smooth-edged, soon falling as round hep ripens.
♣ Stony places, edges of woods. To 2070 m. Pyrenees; Alps; N. Apennines. June–August. **283**

R. montana *Chaix.* MOUNTAIN ROSE. 1–4 m. tall, with arching bluish or purplish stems and straight or slightly hooked prickles. Lvs. usually hairless, deep green, often bluish or purple-tinged, normally of 7 blunt leaflets. Fls. solitary, pale pink, scentless, 3–5 cm. across. Sepals slightly lobed, erect on the narrow-oval, hairy hep.
♣ Rocks, screes. To 2000 m. Alps; Apennines. Rare and local. June–July. **284**

R. villosa *L.* APPLE ROSE. 50–150 cm. tall, with straight bluish stems and slender, straight prickles. Lvs. downy, bluish or greyish, thick and soft, of 7–9 (11) large leaflets. Fls. in small groups, 3–6 cm. across, bright pink to cerise, sometimes fragrant; sepals narrow, usually smooth-edged, with glandular hairs on the back, and becoming erect on the large, oval, hairy hep. The alpine plant is sometimes treated as *ssp.* **pomifera** (*Herr.*) *Crép.* (**R. pomifera** *Herr.*).
♣ Scrub, edges of woods. To 2000 (2500) m. Pyrenees; Alps; Apennines. (Britain.) May–July. **285**

R. tomentosa *Sm.* (**R. villosa** *var.* **tomentosa** *Hooker*). DOWNY ROSE. 1–2

m. tall, with arching pale green stems and curved or straight prickles. Lvs. usually densely downy, greyish, of 5–7 leaflets. Fls. 1–4 together, 3½–6 cm. across, pale pink or white, fragrant. Sepals long, narrowing at base, with pronounced paired lobes, erect, spreading or turned back on the ovoid, more or less hairy hep, but falling after fruit ripens.
♣ Rocky and sandy places, scrub, edges of woods. To 2000 m. Pyrenees; C. and E. Alps; N. Apennines. (Britain.) June–July.

R. rubiginosa *L.* (**R. eglanteria** *L.* in part). SWEET BRIAR. ½–3 m. tall, with erect stems and hooked prickles of different sizes, mingled with short bristles especially just below the fls.; whole plant with strong apple-like odour. Lvs. rather yellowish green, but may have brown or reddish tints; downy on the veins above, glandular below; of 5–7 (11) leaflets. Fls. 1–3 together, bright pink, 2½–5 cm. across, fragrant. Sepals lobed, erect or spreading on the round to ovoid, smooth to hairy hep, usually falling as fruit ripens.
♣ Scrub, dry and stony places. To 2100 m. Pyrenees (local); C. and S. Alps; Apennines. (Britain.) June–July. **286**

R. micrantha *Sm.* SMALL-FLOWERED ROSE. 1–3½ m. tall, with arching stems and hooked prickles. The whole plant has an apple-like odour. Lvs. green, shining on top, glandular below, of 5–7 leaflets. Fls. 1–4 together, on rather long stalks, 2½–4 cm. across, pale pink, rarely red or white, fragrant. Sepals lobed, reflexing on ovoid, rather flask-shaped, smooth or hairy hep, but falling early.
♣ Hedgerows, edges of woods. To 2200 m. Pyrenees; Alps; Apennines. (Britain.) May–July. **288**

R. sicula *Tratt.* A dwarf bush, usually 10–50 cm. tall, with straight or slightly

curved prickles. Lvs. dark green, sometimes bluish, with 5–7 small, rounded, often overlapping leaflets. Fls. usually solitary, short-stalked, 2–3 cm. across, pink. Sepals hardly lobed, erect on the small, ovoid, hairless hep.
✤ Dry and stony places. To 2000 m. Alps. June–July. **287**

R. seraphinii *Viv.* (also spelt **serafinii**). A busy plant similar to R. *sicula*, 30–100 cm. tall, with prickles of varied size, the largest hooked. Lvs. of 5–7 small, elliptical leaflets; fls. smoky pink, short-stalked, small. Sepals hardly lobed, spread out on the small, round, hairless hep. *
✤ Stony places. To 2000 m. Ligurian Alps; N. Apennines. June–August. **289**

RUBUS *L.* BRAMBLE. Shrubs or herbaceous plants with annual or biennial stems dying after fruiting. Fls. with 5 petals and sepals and many stamens. Fruit of many 1-seeded drupelets joined into a compound 'berry'. Besides the 4 species described, members of the blackberry group, R. *fruticosus* L., such as R. *hirtus* W. & K., may occasionally exceed 1500 m.

R. idaeus *L.* RASPBERRY. With erect slender stems 100–160 cm. tall, covered with thin, straight, reddish bristly prickles; suckering from the base. Lvs. with 3–5 (7) leaflets, green and lightly downy above, thickly downy below. Fls. small, 1–10 in dense clusters (cymes); petals white, as long as long-pointed sepals. Fruit red, occasionally pale yellow, opaque, of many drupelets.
✤ Woods, heaths. To 2350 (2610) m. Pyrenees; Alps; Apennines. Norway to 1330 m. (Britain to 850 m.) June–August. **1047**

R. saxatilis *L.* ROCK BRAMBLE. With annual, more or less erect 8–40 cm. fl. stems, and much longer, sprawling sterile stems, which root at the tips; stems downy, sometimes with small prickles. Lvs. 3-parted, green above, paler and downy below. Fls. very small, 2–8 in compact clusters (cymes); petals white, about as long as sepals. Fruit red, translucent, of 2–6 large, separate drupelets.
✤ Shady rocks, stony woods, scrub. To 2400 m. Pyrenees; Alps; Apennines. Norway to 1500 m. Uncommon. (Britain.) May–June. **1048**

R. arcticus *L.* ARCTIC BRAMBLE. Like a much smaller version of R. *saxatilis*, with smaller lvs., larger, solitary pink or red fls., and dark red fruit.
✤ Thickets, grassy places. To 1150 m. Norway. July.

R. chamaemorus *L.* CLOUDBERRY. With annual, erect 5–20 cm. stems without prickles, and creeping rhizomes. Male and female plants separate. Lvs. few, round in outline, to 8 cm. long, of 5–7 lightly indented, lightly toothed lobes, heart-shaped at base. Fls. solitary, white, 1½–2 cm. across, petals much longer than sepals. Fruit first red, finally orange, of a few large drupelets.
✤ Moors and bogs. To 1400 m. Norway. (Britain to 1250 m.) June–August. **1193**

1193. *Rubus chamaemorus*. Fruit and leaf.

FRAGARIA *L.* STRAWBERRY. Perennial herbaceous plants increasing by runners (aerial stolons). Fls. white, 5-parted, few together; epicalyx present. Fruit composed of the much enlarged fleshy receptacle in the surface of which achenes are embedded.

F. viridis *Duchesne*. (**F. collina** *Ehrh.*). 5–20 cm. tall, with very short stolons if any; lvs. of 3 leaflets rounded at base, downy below. Fl. stems little longer than lvs.; calyx closely surrounding the fruit, which is often red at the apex only, has no seeds at the base and is difficult to remove.
⚜ Meadows, woods, stony places. To 1850 m. Pyrenees; Alps. May–June. **292**

F. vesca *L.* WILD STRAWBERRY. 5–25 cm. tall. Similar to *F. viridis*, but leaflets wedge-shaped at base, fl. stems slightly exceeding lvs.; calyx reflexing from fruit, which is roundish to ovoid, always red, has seeds all over and comes away easily.
⚜ Scrub, woodland clearings. To 2400 m. Pyrenees; Alps. (Britain to 800 m.) May–June. **293**

F. moschata *Duchesne*. HAUTBOIS STRAW-BERRY. Like *F. vesca*, but stouter, 10–40 cm. tall, with fl. stems much exceeding lvs.; fruit purplish, often partly greenish, with no seeds at base, rather tapering.
⚜ Scrub, open woodland. Occasionally above 1600 m. Alps. (Britain: naturalised.) April–June.

GEUM *L.* Perennial herbaceous plants. Fls. usually 5–7-parted, with epicalyx and many stamens. Receptacle flat, carrying the separate dry achenes when ripe, on which the styles persist as feathery awns. The genus has been divided into *Geum* and *Sieversia* by some authors: in this treatment *Geum* has typically 5-parted fls. and styles jointed in S-shape, the upper part falling as the achenes ripen; in *Sieversia* the fls. are typically 6–7-parted and the styles are not jointed.

Besides the species described, the tall, small-flowered *G. urbanum* L. reaches 1860 m.

Section Sieversia

G. reptans *L.* (**Sieversia reptans** (*L.*) *R. Br.*). CREEPING AVENS. 10–20 cm. tall, with red runners (aerial stolons) 10–80 cm. long. Lvs. of several distinct leaflets of similar size, the terminal one little longer, lozenge-shaped, itself with 3 deep subdivisions. Fls. (3) 4 cm. across, bright yellow, solitary.
⚜ Moraines, debris, gravels, shaded rocks, preferring acid soils. 1450–3800 m. Alps. July–August. **294**

G. montanum *L.* (**Sieversia montana** (*L.*) *R. Br.*). ALPINE AVENS. 5–40 cm. tall, with stout stock. Lvs. of a series of opposed leaflets of varying sizes, terminating in one large lobe of several rounded, shallow subdivisions. Fls. 3 (4) cm. across, bright yellow, solitary.
⚜ Meadows, stony places, gravels, open woods, preferring acid soils. To 2800 m. Pyrenees; Alps; Apennines. July–August. **295**

Section Geum

G. pyrenaicum *Willd.* PYRENEAN AVENS. Very similar to *G. montanum*, 10–40 cm. tall, with woody stock, leaflets much smaller, upper lobe rounder, with less pronounced divisions; fls. occasionally more than one, and styles jointed near upper third.
⚜ Stony meadows. To 1800 m. Pyrenees. July–August. **296**

G. rivale *L.* WATER AVENS. 20–60 cm. tall, with short thick rhizome. Basal lvs. rather like those of *G. montanum*, upper lobe large, often deeply indented. Lower stem lvs. (illustrated) 3-lobed. Fls. few together, nodding on arching stalks, squarish bell-shaped, with red-dish brown triangular sepals and reddish yellow petals. Styles jointed near middle.
⚜ Streamsides, damp meadows and

woods. To 2100 (2400) m. Pyrenees; Alps. (Britain to 1050 m.) May–July. **302**

DRYAS *L.* **D. octopetala** *L.* MOUNTAIN AVENS. A creeping evergreen subshrub 2–15 cm. tall with oblong to ovate, rounded-toothed, ½–2 cm. lvs. like little oak lvs., dark green above, white-downy below. Fls. white, solitary, 2½–4 cm. across, 8 (7–10)-parted. Fruit of many achenes, on which the styles persist as feathery hairs. ✿ Rocks, meadows, preferring limestone. 1200–2500 m. Pyrenees; Alps; Apennines. Norway to 1830 m. (Britain to 1050 m.) May–August. **303**

POTENTILLA *L.* Perennial herbaceous plants unless otherwise stated; occasionally annuals or biennials, or small shrubs. Lvs. lobed or divided. Fls. solitary or in clusters (cymes), 5 (4)-parted; epicalyx present, of as many segments as sepals. Stamens 10–30. Style jointed at its base, not persisting on the achenes, which are grouped on a rounded or conical receptacle, spongy in *P. palustris*, otherwise dry.

Besides the species described, the following exceed 1500 m.: *P. anserina* L., the familiar SILVERWEED, reaches 2400 m.; *P. chrysantha* Trev., 1900 m.; *P. erecta* L. (Räusch.), the TORMENTIL, 2450 m., *P. micrantha* Ram., 1600 m. and *P. reptans* L., 1675 m.

P. palustris (*L.*) *Scop.* (**Comarum palustre** *L.*). MARSH CINQUEFOIL. A herbaceous plant 15–50 cm. tall, with creeping woody rootstock. Lower lvs. with long stalk and 5–7 leaflets 3–6 cm. long, coarsely toothed, whitish below, sometimes hairy. Fls. in a loose cluster, 5-parted, with 1–1½ cm. purplish sepals, a smaller, narrower epicalyx, and deep purple petals shorter than sepals. Stamens and styles also purple. ✿ Wet meadows, bogs, moors, preferring peaty soils. To 2100 m. Pyre-

nees (local); Alps. Norway to 1350 m. (Britain to 1000 m.) May–August. **300**

P. fruticosa *L.* SHRUBBY CINQUEFOIL. Deciduous shrub 20–100 cm. tall, with usually 5 leaflets 1–2 cm. long, not toothed, margins rolled in. Fls. 2–3 cm. across, in small terminal clusters, or solitary. Epicalyx green, of 5 narrow segments as long as the yellowish triangular sepals. Petals yellow, rounded. ✿ Rocks or rocky ledges, usually on basic soils. To 2550 m. Pyrenees; Maritime Alps; C. Alps. Extremely local. (Britain to 750 m.: local.) June–August. **297**

P. nitida *L.* PINK CINQUEFOIL. The only pink-fld. European potentilla, 2 (10) cm. tall, with silvery-haired lvs. of usually 3 leaflets which are toothed at the tip. Fls. 1–3, on short stalks, 2–2½ cm. across, pale to clear pink, occasionally white or deep rose-red. ✿ Rocks, screes, on limestone. 1200–3160 m. W. Alps; Dolomites; E. Alps; N. Apennines. Local. June–September. **311**

P. apennina *Ten.* 6–12 cm. tall, with lvs. of narrow leaflets toothed at the tip. Fls. few in tight clusters, with prominent cup-shaped epicalyx at least as long as sepals; petals white, narrow-spoon-shaped. ✿ Rocks, debris. 1600–2200 m. C. Apennines. July–August. **1051**

P. grammopetala *Moretti.* 10–30 cm. tall, with woody rootstock, and lvs. of 3 toothed leaflets covered in appressed hairs. Fl. stems much exceeding lvs. Fls. yellowish white, in clusters, with very narrow petals barely as long as hairy sepals and epicalyx, giving a starry effect. ✿ Sunny rocks, on gneiss. 1800–2100 (2500) m. Tessin; E. Graian Alps. July–August. **1054**

P. clusiana *Jacq.* 5–10 cm. tall, with short stock. Leaflets usually 5 hairy,

toothed at rather blunt tip. Fls. white or yellowish white, clustered, with narrow, hairy epicalyx segments almost as long as pointed sepals; petals broad, blunt-ended.
♣ Rocks, debris, on limestone or dolomite. 1200–2400 m. E. Alps. July–August. **1057**

P. caulescens L. With sprawling 10–30 cm. stems. Lvs. with 5–7 leaflets, each with 3–7 teeth at the tip. Fl. stems exceeding lvs. Fls. white, in clusters, with epicalyx and sepals about the same length; petals slightly longer than calyx and separated so that calyx lobes between are conspicuous; stamen filaments and achenes hairy.
♣ Rock crevices, on limestone. To 2400 m. Pyrenees; Alps; Apennines. Uncommon. July–August. **1055**

P. alchemilloides Lap. (now spelt **alchimilloides**). 10–30 cm. tall, with woody stock, on which dead lvs. persist. Lvs. of 5–7 thick, long, narrow leaflets, barely toothed, green and smooth above, silvery-downy below. Fls. white, clustered; epicalyx almost as long as sepals; petals twice as long, broad and lightly notched; stamens with smooth filaments.
♣ Rocks, screes. To 2200 m. Pyrenees. July–August. **1053**

P. valderia L. 20–50 cm. tall. Lvs. with 5–7 rather broad leaflets with many small teeth on the upper third; often silvery-downy below. Fls. white, clustered, with narrow epicalyx lobes longer than sepals, and small petals shorter than either. Stamen filaments and achenes hairy.
♣ Rocks, screes, grassy places, on acid soils. 1200–2400 m. Maritime Alps. Very rare. July–August. **1056**

P. nivalis Lap. (**P. lanata** Lam.). WOOLLY CINQUEFOIL. Resembling a smaller P. valderia, but with leaflets nearly as broad as long, with a few

teeth in the upper part. The whole 10–40 cm. plant is covered with silky hairs, but the stamen filaments are smooth.
♣ Rocks, screes, preferring limestone. 1500–2700 m. Pyrenees; W. Alps (rare); Maritime Alps (very rare). July–August. **1058**

P. rupestris L. ROCK CINQUEFOIL. 20–50 cm. tall, with thick, woody stock; plant downy. Basal lvs. up to 25 cm. long, silvery-downy at least below, with 3–7 toothed leaflets, smallest at base. Fls. white, 2 cm. across, several in loose clusters; epicalyx lobes narrow, much smaller than pointed sepals; petals a little longer than sepals.

A form called **P. macrocalyx** Huet du P. is shorter, with much larger fls., and silky calyx.
♣ Wooded and rocky slopes, rocks, preferring acid soils. P. macrocalyx on granite and schist. To 2200 m. Pyrenees; Alps; Apuan Alps; N. Apennines. P. macrocalyx: Pyrenees, Cevennes only. (P. rupestris: Britain: very rare.) June–August. **1052**

P. multifida L. 5–25 cm. tall, with lvs. green above, silvery-silky below, deeply divided into narrow strap-shaped lobes. Fls. yellow, small, in clusters, petals lightly notched, about as long as sepals and narrow epicalyx lobes.
♣ Meadows, rocks, preferring acid soils. 2200–3000 m. W. Alps. Very rare. July–August. **298**

P. nivea L. SNOWY CINQUEFOIL. 5–15 cm. tall, with thick stock on which old lvs. persist. Lvs. 3-lobed, snowy white with down below. Fls. yellow, solitary or in loose clusters, on stiff, white-downy stalks; epicalyx lobes very narrow, not as long as broad-triangular sepals; petals heart-shaped, notched, exceeding sepals.
♣ Rocks, debris, preferring limestone. 1600–2600 (3100) m. W. Alps

(very rare); E. Alps; N. Apennines. Norway to 1650 m. June–August. **307**

P. argentea *L.* (**P. tomentosa** *Gilib.*). HOARY CINQUEFOIL. A variable plant 15–50 cm. tall, with short thick stock. Basal lvs. of 5 narrow, wedge-shaped, unequal leaflets, sometimes deeply toothed, sometimes not, densely white-downy below. Fls. yellow, small (1 cm.), usually in clusters, with petals as long as the thickly downy calyx and epicalyx. ❧ Open woods, rocky and sandy places, on acid soils. To 1950 (2150) m. Pyrenees; Alps; Apennines. (Britain.) June–August. **299**

P. grandiflora *L.* LARGE-FLOWERED CINQUEFOIL. 15–40 cm. tall, the stems and fl. stalks bearing hairs standing out at right angles. Lvs. 3-lobed, wedge-shaped at base, silky below. Fls. golden yellow, 1½–3 cm. across, 2–5 together; epicalyx and sepals similar in size, much shorter than the broad, heart-shaped, notched petals. Styles much longer than the carpels. ❧ Meadows, rocky places, on acid soils. To 3100 m. E. Pyrenees; Alps. Uncommon. June–August. **306**

P. delphinensis *G. & G.* DAUPHINÉ CINQUEFOIL. 30–50 cm. tall, the stout, straight stems and fl. stalks bearing hairs at an angle to the stem. Basal lvs. usually of 5 leaflets. Stipules not fused to stem (differentiates it from *P. pyrenaica*). Fls. yellow, 2½–3 cm. across, with narrow epicalyx lobes, oval, pointed sepals, and blunt-ended petals twice as long as sepals. ❧ Rocky places, meadows, on limestone. 1500–2800 m. Savoy and Dauphiné Alps. Rare. July–August. **304**

P. pyrenaica *Ram.* A variable plant 10–40 cm. tall with stems curving at the base, resembling *P. delphinensis*, but with stipules joined to the stalks for most of their length.

❧ Rocky places, meadows. 1200–2300 m. Pyrenees. July–August.

P. aurea *L.* (**P. halleri** *Ser.*). GOLDEN CINQUEFOIL. 5–20 cm. tall, with sterile shoots carrying brown scaly remains of old stipules. Lvs. 5-lobed, with an edging of silvery hairs, toothed, the apical tooth very much smaller than its neighbours. Fl. stems longer than lvs.; fls. in loose clusters, bright yellow, often orange or deeper yellow in the centre, 1½–2 cm. across, with very broad notched petals, a third longer than the silvery-downy sepals and epicalyx segments. ❧ Meadows, rocks, open woods, preferring acid soils. To 2850 (3260) m. Pyrenees; Alps; Apennines. June–September. **309**

P. crantzii (*Crantz*) *Beck.* (**P. alpestris** *auct.*, **P. verna** *L.* in part). ALPINE CINQUEFOIL. A variable plant 5–20 cm. tall, similar to *P. aurea*, but without hairs edging lvs., and all teeth of lf. lobes of similar size. Stems, epicalyx and calyx hairy. Fls. golden yellow, occasionally orange-spotted in centre, 1½–2½ cm. across. ❧ Rocks, gravels, stony places. To 3000 (3600) m. Pyrenees; Alps; Apennines. Norway to 2100 m. (Britain to 1110 m.) June–August. **305**

P. tabernaemontani *Asch.* (**P. verna** *L.* in part). SPRING CINQUEFOIL. A mat-forming plant with rooting sterile shoots not carrying brown scales, and 5–20 cm. fl. stems barely exceeding lvs. which have 5 lobes, the apical tooth of each smaller than its neighbours. Fls. in loose clusters, on silky-haired stems, yellow, 1–1½ cm. across; petals notched, longer than sepals which are longer than blunt epicalyx segments. ❧ Meadows, sunny slopes. To 3000 m. Pyrenees; Alps. Rare above 1500 m. (Britain: local.) March–August. **310**

P. cinerea *Chaix* (**P. verna** *L.* in part).

A variable plant, in its montane form usually only 5–10 cm. tall. Lvs. 3–5-lobed, toothed, sometimes almost hairless, sometimes with star-shaped hairs, or (more commonly in lowland forms) with white down of starry hairs on both surfaces. Fls. yellow, 1½–2 cm. across, in small clusters on erect stems; epicalyx lobes blunt and narrower than pointed sepals; petals 1½–2 times length of sepals.

❀ Rocks, meadows, open woods. To 1600 m. W. Alps. May–July.   312

It is possible to confuse this plant and *P. tabernaemontani*, but it has starry hairs while the latter has straight ones. Some older floras call this plant *P. subacaulis* L., but this name now refers to a purely Asiatic species.

P. frigida *Vill.* (**P. glacialis** *Hall*). A low, congested plant 2 (8) cm. tall, entirely downy and slightly sticky-glandular. Lvs. silky-downy on both sides, 3-lobed, each lobe with 3–5 deep, rounded teeth on each margin. Fls. pale yellow, small, seldom opening fully, the sepals longer than petals.

❀ Rocks, exposed crests, on acid soils. 2000–3700 m. Pyrenees; Alps. July–August.   308

P. dubia (*Crantz*) *Zimm.* (**P. minima** *Hall*). DWARF CINQUEFOIL. Like a small but less congested version of *P. frigida*, with lvs. downy only on the veins, lobes only 6–7 mm. long with 2–4 teeth on each side. Petals a little longer than sepals.

❀ Damp grass, screes, snow-patches, on limestone. 1100–3160 m. Pyrenees; Alps. July–August.

SIBBALDIA *L.* **S. procumbens** *L.* (**Potentilla sibbaldii** *Hall f.*). A downy, tufted perennial 2–4 cm. tall, rarely more, with branched, woody rootstock. Lvs. bluish, often purplish below, 3-lobed, each ½–2 cm. lobe wedge-shaped abruptly cut off at tip

which carries 3 teeth, the central one shorter than the others. Fls. few, 5 mm. across, in a dense cluster; epicalyx segments narrow, shorter than green or purplish sepals; petals small and yellow, or none.

❀ Damp rocky or grassy places, screes, snow-patches. 2000–3000 (3350) m. Pyrenees; Alps; C. Apennines. Norway to 2130 m. (Britain to 1300 m.) July–August.   1059

ALCHEMILLA *L.* (also spelt **ALCHIMILLA**). LADY'S MANTLE. Perennials with lvs. more or less deeply lobed. Fls. small, green, 4-parted, many in clusters (cymes); epicalyx present but petals absent. A confusing group, the species often variable, and in any case often very similar.

A. pentaphyllea *L.* With prostrate stems, rooting at the nodes. Lvs. small, hairless, divided almost to centre into 5 wedge-shaped, deeply toothed lobes. Fls. in 1 or 2 whorls on 3–15 cm. stems.

❀ Gravels, snow-beds, on acid soils. 1850–2900 (3100) m. Alps. July–August.   1068

A. alpina *L.* ALPINE LADY'S MANTLE. A variable species often divided into subspecies of which *ssp.* **subsericea** (*Reut.*) *Cam.* is illustrated. 10–30 cm. tall, with stoloniferous rootstock and lvs. divided to the centre into 5–7 finely toothed lobes, silvery-silky at least on underside. Fls. in small round heads, sometimes spaced apart on stem, which is slightly to much longer than lvs. Sepals erect after flowering.   *

❀ Meadows, open woods, stony places, on acid soils. To 2600 (3000) m. Pyrenees; Alps; Apennines. (Britain to 1300 m.) June–August.   1061

A. hoppeana (*Reichb.*) *D.T.* (**A. conjuncta** (*Bab.*) *D.T.*). 10–30 cm. tall, without stolons. Lvs. divided into 7–9 toothed lobes, joined together near the

base, and edged with silvery hairs. Subspecies have been named in which the
lobes vary in shape from quite narrow
and neatly separate to broad and joined
up to halfway. Such are *ssp.* **asterophylla**
(*Tausch*) *Bus.* (1062), in which the lobes
are narrow, divided almost to base, and
radiate mainly in a semicircle; and *ssp.*
conjuncta *Bab.* (1063), in which they
are broad, joined for up to one third
and radiate in a circle. The teeth also
vary in size, and extend farther down
the lf. than in *A. alpina.* Fls. and fl.
stem as in *A. alpina.*   *
✤ Meadows, gravels, stony places, on
limestone. To 2600 m. Alps; Apennines. (Britain: very rare.) June–
August.   **1062, 1063**

A. glaberrima *Schm.* A variable species:
several subspecies have been named.
15–25 cm. tall, quite hairless, with
slender stems and transparent lvs.
divided more or less deeply into 7
coarsely toothed lobes. Calyx and epicalyx prominent, spread out after
flowering.   *
✤ Meadows, stony places, snow-beds.
To 3150 m. Pyrenees; Alps; Ligurian
Alps. June–September.

A. splendens *Christ.* 10–30 cm. tall,
with lvs. slightly silky below, divided
to near the centre into 7–11 rounded,
toothed lobes. Fls. on stiff, slender
stalks, in small, separate clusters.
✤ Meadows, edges of woods. 1300–
2100 m. Pyrenees; Alps. July.   **1067**

A. hybrida *L.* (*A. pubescens Lam.*).
5–15 cm. tall; stems weak, covered in
long fine hairs. Lvs. thick, 7–9-lobed,
variable in size but often relatively small,
varying greatly in extent of teeth.   *
✤ Meadows. To 3100 m. Pyrenees;
Alps; Apennines. May–October. **1064**

A. vulgaris *L.* This name can now be
considered only as an aggregate. The
basic characteristics of the group are as
follows:

5–45 cm. tall, varying in degree of
hairiness; rootstock woody, very thick.
Lvs. rounded or kidney-shaped in
outline, more or less deeply lobed, but
not more than halfway, into (5) 7–11
broad, toothed lobes, the teeth always
bearing a tuft of hairs. Fls. in small,
dense or loose clusters.
The following alpine species belong
to this group; most have been considered previously as subspecies.
✤ All grow in damp meadows, open
woods, rock ledges, gravels. Some forms
exist in the Apennines, but distribution
is uncertain. June–September.

A. glabra *Neyg.* (**A. vulgaris** *ssp.*
alpestris (*Schmidt*) *Camus*). 10–40 cm.
tall, with slender, sparsely hairy stems.
Lvs. kidney-shaped, with hairs only on
the tips of the veins, of 7–11 broad,
usually round, fairly shallow lobes. Fls.
in loose clusters.
✤ To 2400 m. Pyrenees; Alps. (Britain
to 1300 m.)   **1060**

A. palmata *Gilib.* (**A. silvestris**
Schm.). Like *A. glabra*, but lvs. downy on
undersides, stems very hairy.   *
✤ To 3100 m. C. and E. Alps; Apennines.

A. coriacea *Bus.* Like *A. glabra*, but
entirely hairless.
✤ To 2800 m. W. Alps.

A. inconcinna *Bus.* Like *A. coriacea*,
but lobes more angular.
✤ To 2500 m. W. and C. Alps.

A. semisecta *Bus.* Lf. lobes cut to $\frac{2}{5}$ or
$\frac{2}{3}$, more or less hairy below.
✤ To 2500 m. W. Alps.

A. wichurae (*Bus.*) *Stef.* A small plant
with the gap between the lowest lobes
on each side entirely closed, and resembling in outline those of *A. splendens.*
✤ To 1650 m. Norway. (Britain to 1000
m.: very local.)

260

A. glaucescens *Wallr.* A small plant, resembling *A. wichurae*, but even smaller, and densely covered in silky hairs.
❀ To 1650 m. Norway. (Britain.)

A. murbeckiana *Bus.* (**A. acutidens** *Bus.* in part). Lvs. barely hairy, with pronounced lobes and fairly prominent gap between basal pair.
❀ To 2000 m. Alps. Norway to 1400 m. **1066**

A. glomerulans *Bus.* A handsome plant with particularly large, downy lvs.
❀ To 1500 m. Norway. (Britain to 1000 m.) **1065**

SANGUISORBA *L.* **S. officinalis** *L.* (**Poterium officinale** (*L.*) *Gray*). GREAT BURNET. A thick-stocked perennial 30–100 cm. tall, with large lower lvs. of 3–7 pairs of opposed, toothed, oblong leaflets, increasing in size towards tip. Fl. stems branched. Fls. in a dense oblong head, 1–2 cm. long, dark blood-red; individually tiny, with 4 sepals, 4 projecting stamens, and neither epicalyx nor petals.

A 3–10 cm. unbranched montane form has been named *var.* **montana** (*Jord.*) *Cav. & St. Lag.*, but its small stature may be due only to exposure and habitat.
❀ Damp meadows, woods. To 2300 m. Pyrenees; Alps; Apennines. (Britain.) June–October. **301**

The similar but smaller *Poterium sanguisorba* L. (*S. minor* Scop.), the SALAD BURNET native to Britain, may reach 2200 m. It has round lf. lobes and round heads of greenish or purplish fls.

ARUNCUS *L.* **A. vulgaris** *Raf.* (**A. silvester** *Kost.*, **Spiraea aruncus** *L.*). GOATSBEARD. An impressive perennial ½–2 m. tall, arising from a thick woody stock. Lvs. up to 1 m. long, twice or three times divided into oval, pointed, double-toothed, stalked lobes up to 14

cm. long and 7 cm. wide. Fls. small, white, bell-shaped, very numerous, forming narrow, close-packed spikes in branching heads. Seeds poisonous.
❀ Damp shady places in humus beds or stone-falls, preferring acid soils. To 1700 m. Pyrenees; Alps; Apennines. May–August. **1049**

SPIRAEA *L.* **S. decumbens** *Koch* (**S. lancifolia** *Hoffm.*). To 1 m. tall. Plant white-downy (*ssp.* **tomentosa** *Poech.*) or hairless (*ssp.* **decumbens**). Lvs. alternate. ovate-wedge-shaped or lance-shaped, toothed in upper part only. Fls. small, white, in rounded heads (corymbs).
❀ Calcareous debris. Seldom reaching alpine levels. S.E. Alps. May–July (September). **1050**

COTONEASTER *Med.* Shrubs or small trees with undivided lvs., deciduous in alpine species. Fls. small, borne singly or in clusters, the petals, sepals and numerous stamens on a large fleshy receptacle becoming a mealy-fleshed berry-like fruit with 2–5 stones.

C. nebrodensis *Koch* (**C. tomentosa** (*Ait.*) *Lindl.*). 1–2 m. tall, with erect trunk and relatively few branches. Lvs. egg-shaped, 4–6 cm. long, 2–3½ cm. wide, downy on top, white- or grey-woolly below. Fls. pink, 4–12 in small erect clusters (corymbs). Fruit brick-red.
❀ Rocks, cliffs, stony places. To 2400 m. Pyrenees; Alps; Apennines. April–May. **290**

C. integerrimus *Med.* (**C. vulgaris** *Lindl.*). (15) 50 cm. to 1 (2) m. tall, bushy. Lvs. rounded to elliptic, 1½–4 cm. long, green and hairless above, grey-woolly below. Fls. pink, 1–4 in clusters (cymes). Fruit purplish red.
❀ Rocks, stony places, open woods. To 2760 m. Pyrenees; Alps; Apennines.

Norway to 1400 m. (Britain: one locality.) April–June. **291**

PYRUS *L.* (also spelt **PIRUS**). PEAR.
P. amygdaliformis *Vill.* A spiny deciduous tree 2–6 m. tall, with long-ovate lvs., 5–8 cm. long, 2 cm. wide, thick and leathery, white-cottony below. Fls. large, white, long-stalked in clusters (corymbs). Fruit round, brown-ish, tapering slightly into the stalk, the calyx remaining prominent.
✧ Hillsides, stony places. To 1700 m. S. Alps. April–May. **320**
The WILD PEAR, *P. communis* L., original of the cultivated pears, occasionally reaches 1600 m., and the CRAB APPLE, *Malus sylvestris* Mill., 1580 m.

SORBUS *L.* Deciduous trees or shrubs. Fls. in large compound clusters (corymbs). Petals white or pink; sepals triangular; stamens 15–25. Fruit round, berry-like, with 1–2 seeds in each cell.

S. aucuparia *L.* (**Pyrus aucuparia** (*L.*) *Ehrh.*). MOUNTAIN ASH, ROWAN. A slender, round-topped tree to 15 (20) m. tall, with pinnate lvs. of 6–7 (4–9) pairs of toothed leaflets, dark green above, more or less whitish below, downy at first. Fls. off-white, many in a dense cluster with downy stems. Fruit scarlet, round, 6–9 mm. across. The deciduous tree reaching the highest altitude in the Alps.
✧ Woods, scrub, rocky slopes. To 2400 m. Pyrenees; Alps; Apennines. Norway to 1500 m. (Britain to 1070 m.) May–June. **314**

S. aria (*L.*) *Crantz.* WHITEBEAM. Large shrub or wide-crowned tree to 15 (25) m. tall, with very variable lvs., more or less oval or elliptic, toothed, 5–12 cm. long, 1–2½ times longer than broad, green above, markedly white-woolly below. Fls. off-white or pinkish, many in a broad cluster with woolly stems.

Fruit round or oblong, scarlet or orange-red, 8–15 mm. long.
✧ Rocks, stony places, dry woods, often on chalk. To 1675 (2155) m. Pyrenees; Alps; Apennines. (Britain.) May–June. **316**

S. austriaca *Hedl.* (**S. anglica** *Hedl.*, **S. mougeotii** *S.-W. & Godr.*). Large shrub or tree to 20 m. Not unlike *S. aria*, but with lvs. 1⅓–1¾ times longer than broad, with prominent upward-pointing lobes, cut up to ¼ way to mid-rib, toothed, white-downy below. Fls. pinkish, in clusters of varying size. Fruit round, dark red, 7–12 mm. across.
✧ Cliffs, stony places, preferring limestone. To 1980 m. Pyrenees; Alps; Apennines. (Britain: very local.) May. **315**

S. chamaemespilus (*L.*) *Crantz.* FALSE MEDLAR. A bush or small tree 1–3 m. tall. Lvs. lance-shaped, lightly toothed, sometimes greyish below. Fls. pink, with strap-shaped, erect petals, in small clusters. Fruit round to oval, scarlet to brownish red, 10–13 mm. long.
✧ Cliffs, stony places, open woods. To 2450 m. Pyrenees; Alps; Apennines. May–July. **317**

PRUNUS *L.* Trees or shrubs, deciduous in alpine species, with undivided lvs., also stipules. Fls. showy with flat or concave receptacle, 5 petals and sepals, and about 20 stamens. Fruit fleshy, with a large, hard, 1-seeded stone'.

The CHERRY, *P. cerasus* L., is wild to 1600 m. and cultivated to 1800 m., and the PLUM, *P. domestica* L., is cultivated to 1650 m. and spontaneous to 1980 m. The SLOE, *P. spinosa* L., sometimes reaches 1600 m.

P. padus *L.* BIRD CHERRY. A tree 3–15 m. tall with brown, peeling bark which is strong-smelling (the French call it STINKING WOOD). Lvs. 5–10 cm. long on 1-2 cm. stalks, more or less elliptic, pointed, with small sharp teeth. Fls. with lvs., white, 1-2 cm. across, 10-40 in a long spike (raceme) which may be more or less erect or drooping. Fruit black, round to ovoid, 6-8 mm. long. ❀ Woods, moors. To 2200 m. Pyrenees; Alps. Norway to 1265 m. (Britain.) May. **318**

P. mahaleb *L.* ST. LUCIE'S CHERRY. A shrub or small tree 1-4 (12) m. tall, with broad, oval, pointed, toothed lvs., developing after fls. Fls. white, 1-1½ cm. across, 4-8 in small clusters Fruit black, bitter, the size of a pea, carried in upright clusters. ❀ Woods, rocks, hillsides, preferring limestone. To 1700 m. S. Alps. Sometimes cultivated. April–May.

P. avium *L.* GEAN, WILD CHERRY. Tree 5-25 m. tall, with open crown, and red-brown peeling bark. Lvs. developing after fls., elliptic, 6-15 cm. long, on 5 cm. stalk, rounded-toothed, slightly downy below. Fls. white, 1½-3 cm. across, 2-6 in stemless clusters (umbels). Fruit (cherry) round, 1 cm. across, pale or dark red, sweet or acid.

❀ Woods. To 1700 m. Pyrenees; Alps. Often cultivated. (Britain.) April–May.

P. brigantina *Vill.* (also spelt **brigantiaca**). MARMOT PLUM. A bush or small tree 2-5 m. tall. Lvs. developing after fls. oval, heart-shaped at base, pointed, toothed. Fls. white, 1½-2 cm. across, 2-5 in stemless clusters. Fruit like a glossy yellow plum 3-4 cm. long, with greenish, acid flesh. Stone like that of an apricot.

❀ Hillsides, stone-falls, woods, scrub. 1400-1700 m. W. Alps. Uncommon. April–May. **319**

AMELANCHIER *Med.* **A. ovalis** *Med.* (**A. rotundifolia** (*Lam.*) *Koch.*, **A. vulgaris** *Moench.*). A deciduous shrub 1-2 m. tall, with stalked, rounded-oval, 2-4 cm., finely toothed, uncut lvs., cottony below when young. Fls. white, in short erect clusters, with 5 long, narrow petals on an urn-shaped receptacle which becomes a 1 cm. round, blue-black, sweet fruit.

❀ Rock crevices, rocky slopes, open woods, usually on limestone. Pyrenees; Alps; Apennines. To 2400 m. April–June. **1046**

LEGUMINOSAE—PEA FAMILY

Herbaceous or shrubby plants, sometimes small trees, with or without spines. Lvs. sometimes simple, or more usually of numerous, typically opposite leaflets, occasionally with a terminal tendril. Fls. with 5 petals: a large often upright central one, the *standard*, one on each side, the *wings*, and the 2 lower, more or less joined at the base, forming the *keel*. Sepals usually 5, more or less united into a tube. Stamens 10, either all joined together or 9 joined and one free. Fruit a pod. Seeds often large.

Besides the genera described the following plants reach alpine levels: the MELILOTS, *Melilotus albus* Medic., 1850 m.; *M. altissimum* Thuill., 2000 m., and *M. officinalis* (L.) Medic., 2000 m., usually naturalised; and the BLADDER SENNA, *Colutea arborescens* L., 1600 m. The edible PEA, *Pisum sativum* L., is cultivated to 2125 m.

LABURNUM *Medic.* Shrubs or small trees with smooth bark. Lvs. of 3 leaflets. Fls. yellow, in loose hanging clusters. Stamens all united into a tube, anthers free. Seeds many, poisonous.

L. anagyroides *Medic.* (**Cytisus laburnum** *L.*, **L. vulgare** *Griseb.*). GOLDEN RAIN. Small tree or bush to 7 m. Lf. stalks 5–8 cm. long with 4–8 cm. oblong-oval leaflets, the lower surface densely hairy, giving a paler green appearance. Pendulous fls. in drooping clusters 10–20 cm. long, each about 2 cm. long; stems also hairy. Pods green, becoming dark brown, 3–5 cm. long, hairy, swelling over the seeds, remaining on the tree throughout the winter.
⚘ Often cultivated, but also found in waste places, woodland clearings, sunny hillsides, cliffs, preferring limestone. To 2000 m. S. Alps. (Britain: introduced.) April–May. **321**

L. alpinum (*Mill.*) *Bercht. & Presl.* (**Cytisus alpinus** *Mill.*, **Cytisus angustifolius** *Moench.*). ALPINE LABURNUM. 3–5 m. tall. Similar to *L. anagyroides*, but smaller; lvs., pods and stems not hairy; fls. much smaller, scented, in smaller, slenderer clusters. Leaflets more rounded. Pods have a slight wing running down the join of the two halves.
⚘ Woods, stony places. To 1900 m. Alps; N. Apennines. May–June.

ERINACEA (*Clus.*) *Adanson.* **E. anthyllis** *Link.* (**E. pungens** *Boiss.*). HEDGEHOG BROOM. A spiny shrub or undershrub 10–30 cm. tall with opposite lvs. and branches. The lvs. fall early, leaving the spines which give the plant a hedgehog-like appearance. The young branches are silky-white. Fls. pale mauve to violet-blue. Calyx a swollen bladder-like tube with 5 short teeth. Pod 2 cm. long, covered in silky hairs.
⚘ Rocks, dry meadows, preferring limestone. To 2000 m. E. Pyrenees. Extremely rare. May–June. **331**

SAROTHAMNUS *Wimm.* **S. purgans**

Godr. (**Cytisus purgans** *Benth.*). PYRENEAN BROOM. A dense bluish green sub-shrub 30–60 cm. tall. Lvs. few, undivided, alternate. Fls. yellow, in short clusters at ends of stems, small, scented; standard petal large, upright, keel curved. Stamens all joined. Style long, curved in a spiral. Calyx with 5 tiny teeth forming 2 lips. Pod and calyx hairy. Pod discharging seeds explosively by its two halves twisting. *
⚘ Screes and waste places, on granitic and volcanic soils. To 1900 m. Pyrenees. Rare. May–July. **330, 1195**
S. scoparius (L.) Wimm. ex Koch (*Cytisus scoparius* Link.), the COMMON BROOM, may reach 1600–1700 m. *

Sarothamnus, Cytisus and *Genista* have been the subject of much botanical study, being separated on minute differences. Some species will be found under one or other name in some floras. *Sarothamnus* has now been re-submerged in *Cytisus* (according to *Flora Europaea*). The many recent changes are listed in the Appendix.

CYTISUS *L.* **C. hirsutus** *L.* HAIRY BROOM. A sub-shrub 30–80 cm. tall. Lvs. alternate, of 3 leaflets. Fls. 1–3 in axils of lvs. never terminal, usually on previous season's growth. Standard

1194. *Cytisus hirsutus.* Flowers and pods.

petal yellow with brown marks. Calyx tubular, much longer than wide. No bracts below calyx. Young stems, lvs. and pods all bristly-hairy. Extremely variable in growth habit and degree of hairiness.

❋ Copses, grassy hillsides. To 1900 m. Pyrenees; Alps; Apennines. April–June.
1194

C. sessilifolius L. may reach 1600–1700 m., 2300 m. in Italy.

For remarks on relationship with *Sarothamnus* and *Genista*, see under *Sarothamnus*.

GENISTA L. Shrubs, sometimes spiny, stem sometimes creeping. Lvs. usually undivided, sometimes of 3 leaflets. Fls. yellow. Stamens all fused, but anthers alternately long and short. Style curved. Calyx 2-lipped. Pod not twisting when ripe.

For remarks on relationship with *Sarothamnus* and *Cytisus*, see under *Sarothamnus*.

Leaves undivided; plants not spiny

G. tinctoria L. DYER'S GREENWEED. A spineless shrub 30–70 cm. tall. Stems slender, young ones slightly hairy. Lvs. stalkless or shortly stalked. Lvs. oblong-lance-shaped, to 30 cm. long, with hairy edges. Fls. hairless, in lf. axils, at ends of main branches. Pod hairless, flat, narrowing at each end, 2½–3 cm. long.

❋ Woods, clearings, meadows. To 1800 m. Pyrenees; Alps. (Britain.) April–August.
328, 1196

G. cinerea DC. A whitish, spineless sub-shrub, 40–90 (200) cm. tall, with long arching branches. Old stems leafless. Lvs. small, rather remote. Fls. in loose upright clusters all along branches. Petals hairy. Pod hairy, with 2–5 greenish seeds.

❋ Rocky hillsides, wood edges. To 1900 m. E. Pyrenees; W. Alps. April–July.
329

G. pilosa L. HAIRY GREENWEED. A sprawling, spineless shrub, 10–40 cm. tall. Stems stoutish, very branched, greyish. Lvs. 3–5 mm. long, slightly stalked, oval, blunt-tipped, hairless above, hairy below. Fls. hairy, 1 cm. long, on small side branches in lf. axils. Stems densely hairy. Pods densely hairy, 1½–2¼ cm. long, swelling over seeds, round at base, pointed at top.

❋ Woods, heaths, stony places. To 1400 (1950) m. Alps; Apennines. (Britain.) April–October.

Leaves undivided; plants spiny

G. germanica L. (Cytisus germanicus *Vis*.). A spiny shrub, leafless at base, 30–60 cm. tall with spines in lf. axils. Lvs. elliptical, hairy on edges. Fls. in loose upright clusters, hairy. Standard petal much shorter than keel. Pod short, about ½ cm. long.

❋ Copses, scanty grassland, heaths. To 2300 m. E. Pyrenees; Alps; Apennines. May–September.
327, 1199

1195. *Sarothamnus purgans*. 1196. *Genista tinctoria*. 1197. *Genistella sagittalis*. 1198. *G.s. ssp. delphinensis*. 1199. *Genista germanica*. Pods.

G. hispanica L. SPANISH GORSE. Similar to *G. germanica*, but more spiny, and smaller, 10–25 cm. tall, forming dense hummocks. Fls. in a short terminal head. Lvs. undivided, more or less stalkless, bristly-hairy. Pod almost hairless. *Ssp.* **occidentalis** *Ry*. is a geographical race 100–120 cm. tall with very short hairs and very large spines, fls. and pods twice as large as in *G. hispanica*.

❋ Dry hillsides, stony places, rocks,

cliffs. To 1500 m. C. and E. Pyrenees. *Ssp. occidentalis:* W. Pyrenees (rare). April–September. **326**

Leaves of 3 leaflets

G. radiata *Scop.* (Cytisanthus radiatus *Lang.*, Cytisus radiatus (*L.*) *Lang.*). A very bushy sub-shrub 10–50 cm. tall, not spiny. Lvs. mainly of 3 linear leaflets. Fls. in heads of up to 7. Standard petal hairy. Pod ½ cm. long, oval.
✢ Woods, thickets, rocks, preferring limestone. To 2200 m. Alps (less rare to E.); Apennines. May–July. **325**

G. glabrescens *Briq.* (Cytisus emeriflorus *Reichb.*). A shrub 30–60 cm. tall with rather gnarled stems and old wood. Lvs. alternate, leaflets oblong, blunttipped. Fls. 1–3, not clustered. *
✢ Thickets, stony grassland. To 1840 m. S. Alps. Local. June.

CYTISANTHUS (*DC.*) *Gams.* **C. horridus** (*Vahl.*) *Gams.* (Genista horrida *DC.*). A very spiny shrub 20–40 cm. tall. Lvs. and stems opposite, leaflets mainly 3. Fls. 1–2 at ends of stems. Calyx tube short; 1 bract below calyx. Pods silky-hairy, long and narrow (1½–3 cm. × ½ cm.), seeds 1–4. *
✢ Dry meadows, stony places, preferring limestone soils. To 1800 m. C. Pyrenees. Rare. June–September. Differs from *Genista* in minor characters. **324**

GENISTELLA (*Tourn.*) *Moench.* Differs from *Genista* in being smaller and having flattened, winged stems.

G. sagittalis (*L.*) *Gams.* (Genista sagittalis *L.*) (**322, 1197**): bushy, 10–30 cm. tall, with creeping stem. Lvs. simple, stalkless, hairy. Fls. yellow, numerous, in clusters on top of stems. Standard petal not hairy. Sepals silky-hairy. *
Ssp. **delphinensis** (*Verl.*) P.F. (Genista delphinensis *Verl.*) (**323, 1198**): a smaller, neater plant with prostrate, silky-hairy stem growing in

a zigzag. Fls. small, in groups of 2–3, sometimes in lf. axils. Standard petal hairy.
✢ Woods, hillsides, preferring limestone. To 1960 m. Alps; Apennines. *Ssp. delphinensis:* Pyrenees: 1300–1700 m. May–July. **322, 323, 1197, 1198**

ONONIS *L.* RESTHARROW. Small shrubs or herbaceous plants, sometimes spiny. Lvs. of 3 leaflets, occasionally only 1. Fls. in lf. axils, pink or yellow.

O. rotundifolia *L.* ROUND-LEAVED RESTHARROW. A sub-shrub with woody base and herbaceous stems, 30–50 cm. tall, with glandular hairs, not spiny. Leaflets large, round, toothed; lf. stalks long. Fls. large, pink, 2–3 on a long stem.
✢ Woods, stony places, normally on limestone. To 1900 m. Pyrenees; Alps; Abruzzi. Uncommon. May–August. **332**

O. fruticosa *L.* is a handsome 30–100 cm. shrublet rather similar to *O. rotundifolia* but with much narrower, saw-toothed leaflets, which reaches 1600 m. in one or two places in the Pyrenees and Alps.

O. cenisia *L.* MT. CENIS RESTHARROW. Sub-shrubby, not spiny, often matforming with 5–25 cm. stems. Lvs. with short stalks or none, hairless, small and toothed at edges. Fls. solitary on long stalks, pink and white striped. Pods slightly glandular.
✢ Meadows, screes, on limestone. To 1750 (2300) m. Pyrenees; W. Alps; Apennines. Uncommon. June–September. **333**

O. aragonensis *L.* A straggling, untidy sub-shrub, 15–25 cm. tall, with yellow fls. in a long cluster. Leaflets round, toothed, hairless.
✢ Rocks and meadows. To 2500 m. Pyrenees. Extremely rare. June–July. **1069**

O. natrix *L.* A very sticky, much-branched sub-shrub 20–50 cm. tall.

Leaflets oblong. Fls. large, yellow streaked with red, in lf. axils. Petals twice as long as calyx, in a short cluster. Pods oblong-linear, hanging.

⚜ Dry waste places, on limestone. To 2100 m. S. Alps. May–July. **1200**

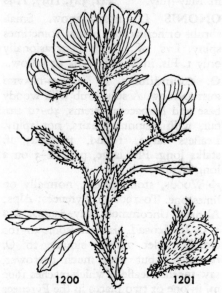

1200. *Ononis natrix.* Flowers and pod.
1201. *O. spinosa.* Pod only.

O. spinosa *L.* (**O. campestris** *Koch*). RESTHARROW. A variable perennial with upright or sprawling 30–60 cm. stems, usually spiny. Leaflets narrowly oval, toothed, hairy and more or less glandular. Fls. pink, 1–1½ cm. long, stalks to ½ cm. Pod round-oval, just longer than calyx, with 1–4 seeds.

⚜ Meadows, dry hillsides, waste places, preferring calcareous, clay soils. To 1800 m. Pyrenees; Alps; Apennines. (Britain.) April–September. **1201**

MEDICAGO *L.* **M. suffruticosa** *Ram.* A sprawling plant with woody base and 10–40 cm. herbaceous stems, more or less downy. Lvs. of 3 leaflets with toothed edges. Fls. yellow, small, 2–6 in a short cluster. Pods twisted into about 2–3 spirals, with many seeds.

⚜ Waste places, rocks. To 2300 m Pyrenees. July–August. **1081**

M. lupulina L., the BLACK MEDICK, reaches 2300 m.

TRIFOLIUM *L.* CLOVER, TREFOIL. Perennials unless otherwise specified; usually sprawling. Lvs. of 3 leaflets, often with toothed edges. Fls. stalkless or with short stalk, usually in dense heads, red, yellow, pink or white, with nectar. Upper stamen free, others united. Pod small, 1–6-seeded, more or less covered by calyx, and sometimes covered by standard petal which often remains after pod has formed.

Besides the species described, the following reach alpine levels: *T. alpestre* L., 2310 m.; *T. aureum* Pollich, 1800 m.; *T. campestre* Schreb., 1715 m.; *T. hybridum* L., 2150 m.; *T. ochroleucon* Huds.. 1800 m.; *T. resupinaton* L., 1700 m. *T. saxatile.* All. is a true alpine reaching 3100 m.: it is an insignificant pink-fld. plant.

T. badium *Schreb.* BROWN CLOVER. A sprawling, creeping plant with upright 10–20 cm. stems. Lvs. with longish stems, more or less opposite. Fls. yellow, turning brown, in a roundish head on long stalk.

⚜ Meadows, damp stony places, preferring limestone. 1400–2800 (3100) m. Pyrenees; Alps; Apennines. July–August. **336**

T. spadiceum *L.* Very similar to *T. badium*, but grows to 20–40 cm. The heads of fls. are more conical in shape, twice as long as wide, yellow turning deep brown.

⚜ Meadows, peaty places, on acid soils. To 2200 m. Pyrenees; Alps; C. Apennines (rare). June–August. **337**

T. repens *L.* WHITE or DUTCH CLOVER. A hairless, creeping plant to 50 cm. Leaflets 1–2 cm. long, rounded-oval, sometimes with a whitish angled line across the lower part. Fls. with very

short stalks grouped in oblong heads on stems in lf. axils. Each fl. hangs down when mature. Petals white or pink, turning brown. Calyx white with green veins. Pod oblong, up to ½ cm. long, with 3–6 seeds. Standard petal twice length of calyx and folded over pod.
❀ Meadows, heaths. To 2750 m. Pyrenees; Alps; Apennines. (Britain.) May–October. **1070**

T. thalii *Vill.* A sprawling, hairless plant, 5–15 cm. tall; stems growing straight from rootstock, creeping stems rooting. Lvs. with 4–10 cm. stem; leaflets oval, with 7–10 pairs of veins. Fls. white or red, in longish oval clusters on long stems. Petals 1–1½ times as long as calyx which is whitish when mature.
❀ Meadows, stony places, on alluvial or calcareous soils. To 3090 m. Pyrenees; Alps; Apennines. July–August. **1071**

T. pallescens *Schreb.* Shrubby at base, 5–20 cm. tall, similar to *T. thalii*, but creeping stems not rooting. Fls. yellowish white. Leaflets with 10–20 pairs of veins.
❀ Meadows, stony places, screes, gravels, on acid soils. To 2700 (3100) m. Pyrenees; Alps; C. Apennines. July–September. **1074**

T. montanum *L.* MOUNTAIN CLOVER. Shrubby at base, 15–50 cm. tall. Leaflets oval to lance-shaped, hairy on lower surface, hairless above. Fls. white, in heads 2 cm. long, 1–1½ cm. wide. Teeth of calyx equal in length.
❀ Open woods, meadows, preferring poor calcareous soils. To 2560 m. Pyrenees; Alps; Apennines. May–July. **1072**

T. alpinum *L.* ALPINE CLOVER. 5–20 cm. tall. Lvs. long-stalked; leaflets narrow lance-shaped, 1–5 cm. long. Fls. large, about 2 cm. long, 3–12 in a head, rose-pink or purplish (seldom

yellowish white), scented. Lower tooth of calyx much longer than others.
❀ Meadows, stony places, on acid soils. To 3100 m. Pyrenees; Alps; N. Apennines. June–August. **339**

T. incarnatum *L.* CRIMSON CLOVER. A spectacular, upright annual or biennial to 50 cm. tall. Leaflets broadly oval, 1½–8 cm. long, lf. stems to 8 cm. Fls. stalkless, each 1 cm. long, in dense terminal, oval or cylindrical heads 4–5 cm. long, crimson (rarely white). Pod 3 mm. long, 1-seeded.
❀ Fields, waste places, preferring acid soils. Widely cultivated, occasionally naturalised. To 1500 m. Pyrenees; Alps; Apennines. (Britain: introduced, now cultivated and practically naturalised.) May–July. **338**

T. pratense *L.* RED CLOVER. An upright or sprawling, more or less densely hairy plant, with a central rosette and side stems, to 60 cm. tall. Lvs. opposite. Leaflets broad, oval or squarish oval, 1–3 cm. long, with smooth or slightly toothed margins, often with a whitish spot at base. Fl.-heads terminal, roundish to oval, 3 cm. long. Fls. to 1½ cm. long, pink-purple or whitish. Pod opening by means of the top talling off.
The alpine plant is usually *var.* **frigidum** *Gaud.* (= **T. nivale** *Sieb.*), the ALPINE RED CLOVER (**1073**), which is usually low, reaching 30 cm. exceptionally, and with larger fl.-heads.
❀ Pastures, fields, waste places. Often cultivated. To 2700 m. *Var. frigidum* from 1800–3150 m. Pyrenees; Alps; Apennines. (Britain.) May. **1073**

T. noricum *Wulf.* Perennial to 15 cm. Lvs. with longish, hairy stems. Leaflets oval, 1½ cm. long, about ½ cm. wide, edges hairy. Fls. in spherical heads on stout hairy stems, white. Calyx with 5 long points above tube, very hairy.
❀ Meadows, on limestone. 1600–2600 m. E. Alps; Apennines. July–August.

T. medium *L.* MEADOW or ZIGZAG CLOVER. 20–50 cm. tall; more or less hairy. Lvs. with fairly long stems. Leaflets oval, up to 5 cm. long. Fls. in a globular head, bright purplish red, rarely white, on a fairly short stem. Calyx hairless.

❁ Woods, poor grassland, vineyards, preferring clay and chalky soils. To 2125 m. Pyrenees; Alps. May–July.   **335**

T. rubens *L.* (**Lagopus glaber** *Bernh.*). RED TREFOIL. 25–60 cm. tall, with creeping rootstock, hairless. Leaflets oval, about 5 cm. long, 1½ cm. wide. Fls. in long oval heads, 6 cm. by 3 cm., purple-red. Calyx with long fine points.

❁ Woods, stony places, preferring limestone. To 2050 m. Pyrenees; Alps; Apennines. June–August.   **334**

ANTHYLLIS *L.* Herbaceous plants or shrubs; lvs. with many opposite leaflets, lower ones sometimes with only a terminal leaflet. Fls. in heads, red or yellow, surrounded at the base of the head by a whorl of small bracts (involucre). Calyx tube swollen. Pod enclosed in tube, with 1–3 seeds.

A. montana *L.* MOUNTAIN KIDNEY-VETCH. Shrubby at base, 10–30 cm. tall, very hairy. Lvs. with up to 13 pairs of oval, linear leaflets, all nearly equal in size. Fls. red or purplish red, in round head at top of stem.

❁ Rocks, stony places, meadows, preferring limestone. To 2400 m. Pyrenees; Alps; Apennines. June–July.   **341**

A. vulneraria *L.* COMMON KIDNEY-VETCH, LADY'S FINGERS. A variable biennial or perennial, upright or sprawling, to 60 cm. The type, *ssp.* **vulneraria** (**342**) has lvs. to 14 cm. long. Leaflets of lower lvs. elliptic, the terminal one largest; upper lvs. with narrow-oblong leaflets all usually the same size. Lvs. hairless above, short-haired below. Fls. cream to yellow, or red (*var.*

purpurascens *Shutt.*), in roundish flattened heads about 4 cm. across, which are usually in pairs, occasionally solitary. Calyx 1 cm. long, more or less woolly, pinched in at the top. Pod 3 mm. long, semicircular, flattened, hairless, with 1 seed.

Ssp. **vulnerarioides** (*All.*) *Arcang.* (**343**): a small plant 5–10 cm. tall, with lvs. hairy on both sides; fls. dark yellow with touches of red.

Ssp. **alpestris** (*Heg.*) *Asch. & Graebn.* (**344**), ALPINE KIDNEY-VETCH: basal lvs. of 1 leaflet; calyx 1½ cm.; fls. yellow.

Ssp. **coccinea** *L.* (*ssp.* **dillenii** *Schultes, var.* **spruneri** *Boiss.*, **A. rubra** *Gouan*), RED KIDNEY-VETCH (**345**): lvs. with up to 5 pairs of leaflets with the terminal one the largest, hairless above, hairy below. Fls. in roundish heads on stout stems, all hairy, bright red.   *

❁ Dry meadows, stony places, preferring limestone. To 3000 m. *Ssp. vulneraria:* Pyrenees; Alps; Apennines. Norway to 1350 m. (Britain.) *Ssp. vulnerarioides:* Pyrenees, Alps; 2200–2800 m. *Ssp. alpestris* and *ssp. rubra:* Alps; Apennines; to 3000 m. May–August.   **342–345**

LOTUS *L.* **L. alpinus** (*DC.*) *Schleich.* (**L. corniculatus** *L. var.* **alpinus** *Ser.*). ALPINE BIRDSFOOT TREFOIL. The alpine form of the familiar 'Eggs and Bacon' or 'Fingers and Toes': a hairless 3–5 cm. perennial with lvs. of 5 leaflets 3–10 mm. long, and tiny brown stipules. Fls. 3–6 in a head, 1½ cm. long, yellow freely marked with red; calyx triangular, 5-toothed. Pod to 3 cm. long.

❁ 2000–3100 m. Pyrenees; Alps; Apuan Alps; C. Apennines. Norway to 1350 m.: *L. corniculatus.* (Britain: *L. corniculatus.*) May–August.   **340**

TETRAGONOLOBUS *Scop.* **T. maritimus** (*L.*) *Roth.* (**T. siliquosus** *Roth.*, **Lotus siliquosus** *L.*). WINGED PEA. Similar in habit to *Lotus alpinus,* but

lvs. of 3 leaflets, large green stipules, and fls. larger, 2½–3 cm. long, sulphur-yellow to yellow-orange, solitary on long stems. Pod 2½–5 cm. long with 4 wings. Stems and calyx hairy.
✳ Damp meadows, marshes, mineralised soils. To 1800 m. Pyrenees; Alps. (Britain: naturalised: very local.) May–July. **346**
ASTRAGALUS L. A confusing, complex group. Herbs or shrubs, perennial unless otherwise specified. Lvs. of many leaflets. Fls. in loose clusters on long stems, purplish, blue, mauve, yellow or white. Keel of fls. blunt-ended, and thus differing from *Oxytropis* (p. 271) in which the keel is pointed (1202), although some authorities combine the two genera. Pods 2-celled.
Besides the species described, *A. glcyphyllos* L. and *A. onobrychis* L. may exceed 1900 m.

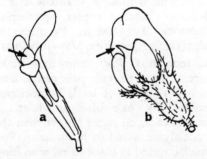

1202a. Flower of typical *Astragalus* showing rounded keel. 1202b. Flower of typical *Oxytropis* showing pointed keel.

A. exscapus L. (**A. syphilitica** *Moench*). A tufted, very hairy plant 2–10 cm. tall, with stalks of fls. and lvs. clustered on rootstock. Lvs. of 10–15 pairs of leaflets, elliptic or lance-shaped. Fls. bright yellow, large, stalks much shorter than lvs. Pod hairy.
✳ Meadows, open woods, preferring limestone. To 2200 m. S. Alps. Very local. May–July. **350, 1203**
A. depressus L. (**A. helminthocarpos**

Vill.). Rather similar to *A. exscapus*, but 5–10 cm. tall, with bristly hairs. Lvs. of 8–12 pairs of leaflets, hairless above, bluish and silky-hairy below. Fls. white, sometimes whitish yellow, sometimes with dark blue markings on keel. Stalk nil or very short. Pod 1½–2½ cm. long, less than ½ cm. wide, hairless at the tip.
✳ Sunbaked limestone rocks. To 2700 m. Pyrenees; Alps; Apennines. Rare. May–July. **1204**
A. australis *Lam.* (**Phaca australis** *Ledeb.*). 5–30 cm. tall, hairless. Lvs. of 4–8 pairs of leaflets. Fls. white, rarely purple, sometimes with violet markings on standard or at tip of keel. Edge of wing petals cut into two points. Pod pendant, hairless.
✳ Stony places, meadows, preferring siliceous soils. 1800–3120 m. Pyrenees; Alps; Apennines. May–July. **357, 1205**
A. oroboides *Horn.* (**Phaca oroboides** *DC.*). To 30 cm. tall, with slender creeping stems which are leafless. Lvs. of 5–9 pairs of elliptic leaflets, stalks rather short. Fls. in a loose head on longer stalks, violet. Sepals hairy. Pod egg-shaped with persistent hooked style, hairy. *
✳ Meadows. 1900–2500 m. E. Alps. Local. July–August. **1207**
A. alpinus L. (**Phaca minima** *All.*, **P. astragalina** *DC.*). ALPINE MILKVETCH. A slender 8–20 cm. plant with soft white hairs. Lvs. with 7–12 pairs of leaflets. Fls. variegated white, blue and violet: often the standard bluish, wings white, and keel violet at top. Standard as long as the keel. Pod to 1 cm. long, with short adpressed brown or black hairs.
✳ Rocks, stony places, meadows, preferring acid soils. 1900–3100 m. Pyrenees; Alps. Norway to 1600 m. (Britain.) July–August. **356, 1206**
A. danicus *Retz.* (**A. hypoglottis** *auct.* not *L.*). PURPLE MILKVETCH. Very

similar to *A. alpinus* in general appearance, but sturdier, 5–35 cm. tall. Fls. blue-purple, sometimes yellowish at base. Calyx with flattened black and white hairs. Pod ½–1½ cm. long, with long persistent style and crisp white hairs; 2 seeds.

❧ Meadows, preferring limestone. 1800–2400 m. S.W. Alps. (Britain.) May–July. **353, 1208**

A. frigidus (*L.*) *A. Gray* (**Phaca frigida** *L.*). 15–40 cm. tall, with unbranched, hairless stems. Lvs. of 4–17 pairs of large, oval, pointed, blue-green, hairless leaflets. Fls. whitish yellow. Pods brown, a little swollen, 2½ cm. long to ½ cm. wide.

❧ Meadows, stony places, preferring limestone. 1700–2800 m. Pyrenees; Alps. Rare. July–August. **352**

A. penduliflorus *Lam.* (**Phaca alpina** *Jacq.*). MOUNTAIN LENTIL. 20–50 cm. tall. Stem branched, very hairy. Lvs. with 7–12 pairs of bright green hairy leaflets. Fls. bright yellow. Pod very swollen, 2–3 cm. long, 1 cm. wide.

❧ Screes, meadows, woods. 1400–2400 m. Pyrenees; Alps. Rare. July–August. **359, 1209**

A. alopecuroides *L.* A striking plant 50–100 cm. tall, with whitish hairs, rather resembling a bushy lupin. Lvs. with 20–40 pairs of narrowly oval leaflets. Fls. in a large ovoid head, yellow. Pod much shorter than the sepals.

❧ Woods, meadows. 1200–1600 m. W. Alps. May–August. **1075**

A. cicer *L.* (**A. microphyllus** *Schubl. et Mart.*, *non L.*, **Astragaloides cicera** *Moench*). WILD LENTIL. A straggling, hairy plant 30–80 cm. tall. Lvs. with 8–12 pairs of rather small elliptic to oblong leaflets. Fls. pale yellow, in globular heads. Pod swollen, almost globular, rough, hairy, very short, 1½ cm. long, ½–1 cm. wide.

❧ Meadows, scrub. To 1800 m. E. Pyrenees; Alps. Rare. June–July.

1077, 1210

A. purpureus *Lam.* (**A. glaux** *Vill.*, *non L.*, **A. hypoglottis** *L. var.* **purpureus** *Fiori et Paol.*) PURPLE VETCH. 10–30 cm. tall, greyish green. Lvs. with 6–10 pairs of oval-oblong leaflets. Fls. large, bright purple. Calyx with teeth shorter than the tube, and covered in black hairs. Pod very hairy, 1–1½ cm. long, ½ cm. wide with long persistent style.

❧ Stony places, copses, preferring limestone. To 1800 m. Pyrenees; S. Alps (rare); Apennines. May–July. **1211**

A. leontinus *Wulf.* TYROLEAN MILK-VETCH. 5–20 cm. tall; pale green. Lvs. with 6–10 pairs of oval, blunt-tipped leaflets. Fls. pale blue or violet, in round heads, on stems longer than the lvs. Calyx covered in black hairs. Pod small, covered in black hairs, with long persistent style. **1212**

❧ Meadows, stony places, preferring

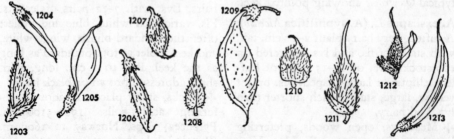

Pods of *Astragalus* species. 1203. *A. exscapus.* 1204. *A. depressus.* 1205. *A. australis.* 1206. *A. alpinus.* 1207. *A. oroboides.* 1208. *A. danicus.* 1209. *A. penduliflorus.* 1210. *A. cicer.* 1211. *A. purpureus.* 1212. *A. leontinus.* 1213. *A. monspessulanus.*

limestone. To 2650 m. Alps. July–August. **355, 1212**
The very similar *A. vesicarius* L. reaches 2000 m. in the Abruzzi.

A. monspessulanus L. FALSE VETCH. A tufted plant, 10–20 cm. tall. Lvs. hairless, of 10–20 pairs of leaflets. Fls. 2–2½ cm. long, reddish purple, in loose heads on stems equalling or slightly longer than the lvs. Calyx with teeth as long as the tube. Pod hairless, curved up and back.
❋ Meadows, damp stony, gravelly places, preferring limestone. To 2600 m. Pyrenees; Alps; Apennines. April–August. **354, 1213**

A. sempervirens *Lam*. (**A. aristatus** *L'Herit*). MOUNTAIN TRAGACANTH. A bushy, grey-hairy plant 10–40 cm. tall. Lvs. of 12–20 pairs of leaflets with a terminal point instead of a leaflet. Old lf. stalks persisting, spine-like. Fls. off-white or marked with lilac. Stalks much shorter than lvs., and in lf. axils. Sepals hairy, teeth as long as the tube. Pod hairy.
❋ Gravelly, stony places, on limestone. To 2740 m. Pyrenees; S.W. Alps; Apennines. May–August. **351**
The similar *A. siculus* Biv., which has very long hairs on calyx, is found to 2400 m. on Mt. Etna. *

OXYTROPIS *DC*. A confusing group, like *Astragalus* (p. 269), and by some authorities included in that genus, but differing in the keel of the fls. ending in a small point, not blunt (**1202**). Alpine species herbaceous perennials; lvs. of many leaflets; fls. in loose clusters on long stems, purplish, blue, mauve, yellow or white. Pods 2-celled.

O. jacquinii *Bunge* (**O. montana** *DC.*, **Astragalus montanus** *L.*, **Phaca montana** *Crantz*). MOUNTAIN MILKVETCH. A straggling plant 5–15 cm. tall, sometimes hairy. Lvs. with 6–17 pairs of oval, blunt-tipped, grey-hairy leaflets.

Fls. at right angles to stem, violet-blue to purple or purplish pink, deepening with age; sepals hairy. Pod swollen, carried on a small stalk inside sepal tube, equalling the tube or longer.
❋ Stony places, meadows, moraines, on limestone. 1500–2930 m. Pyrenees; Alps; C. Apennines. July–August. **358, 1214**

O. lapponica *Gray*. (**Astragalus lapponicus** *Gray*, **Phaca lapponica** *Wahl.*). Very similar to *A. montanus*; hairy, 10–30 cm. tall. Lvs. of 8–14 pairs of leaflets. Fls. violet-blue, teeth of sepals much longer than tube. Fls. and pods pendant. Pod stalk much shorter than tube of sepals. Pod very hairy.
❋ Stony places, screes, meadows, gravels, on acid soils. 1800–3050 m. Alps. Rare. July–August. **349, 1215**

O. triflora *Hoppe ex Sturm*. (**Astragalus triflorus** (*H. ex St.*) *Gams.*, **O. gaudini** *Bunge*). A sprawling plant 3–15 cm. tall, very silky-hairy. Stems and foliage with a reddish tinge. Lvs. of 7–20 pairs leaflets. Fls. violet, usually in heads of 3–15 on longish stem. Pod on stalk half length of tube.
❋ Stony places, meadows. 1800–3100 m. Alps; Apennines. Rare. July–August. **348, 1217**

O. pilosa *DC*. (**Astragalus pilosus** *L.*). WOOLLY MILKVETCH. A sprawling

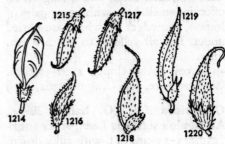

Pods of *Oxytropis* species. 1214. *O. jacquinii*. 1215. *O. lapponica*. 1216. *O. pilosa*. 1217. *O. triflora*. 1218. *O. campestris*. 1219. *O. foetida*. 1220. *O. sericea*.

plant 15–30 cm. tall, covered with very long soft hairs. Lvs. with 9–13 leaflets. Fls. clear yellow, small, in a many-flowered globular head. Sepals very hairy, teeth at least as long as the tube. Pod on very short stalk inside tube, upright on stem.

✻ Stony and gravelly places. To 2600 m. Alps; Apennines. Uncommon. June–August. **360, 1216**

O. campestris L. (**Astragalus campestris** (L.) *DC.*, **Phaca campestris** *Wald.*). MEADOW MILKVETCH 10–20 cm. tall, more or less downy. Lvs. with 10–15 pairs of large leaflets. Fls. long, yellowish white, rarely marked with violet. Pod without stalk.

✻ Pastures, rocks, screes, preferring acid soils. 3000 m. Pyrenees; Alps; C. Apennines. (Britain.) July–September. **361, 1218**

O. alpinus *Ten.* Very similar to *O. campestris*, and now considered only a subspecies: plant covered in silvery silky hairs, with black hairs on inflorescence.

✻ Pastures, rocks, screes. To 3000 m. Piedmont Alps. July–September.

O. foetida *DC.* (**Astragalus foetidus** *Vill.*, **A. halleri** *All.*, **Phaca viscosa** *Clairv.*). STINKING MILKVETCH. Similar to *A. campestris*, 10–20 cm. tall, but covered with glandular hairs, and giving off an offensive smell. Lvs. with 10–25 pairs of leaflets, the edges of which are curled under. Fls. all yellow, to about 2 cm. long. *

✻ Screes, grassy slopes. 1800–3000 m. W. Alps. Rare. July–August. **362, 1219**

O. sericea *Sim.* (**O. halleri** *Bunge.*, **Astragalus sericeus** *Lam.*) SILKY MILKVETCH. 5–15 cm. tall, with silky down. Lvs. with 8 or more pairs of leaflets. Fls. violet, rarely yellowish, in an oval head. Pod without stalk.

✻ Dry meadows, stony places, prefer-

ring acid soils. 1500–2940 m. Pyrenees; Alps. Rare. June–August. **347, 1220**

CORONILLA L. Herbaceous plants or shrubs with fls. in umbels in lf. axils. Calyx shortly bell-shaped with almost equal teeth. Pod swollen into joints over the individual seeds.

Besides the species described, the herbaceous *C. varia* L., with white, pink and violet fls., and *C. minima* L., with yellow fls., may reach 1800 m.

C. emerus L. FALSE SENNA. A handsome shrub 1–2 m. tall with green twigs. Lvs. light green, with 3 pairs of heart-shaped leaflets and a terminal one, 1–2 cm. long, ½–1 cm. broad. Fls. 2–4 on slender stalks, 2 cm. long, golden yellow, standard often striped red. Pods 5–10 cm. long, thin, barely swollen over the seeds.

✻ Stony places, edges of woods. To 1800 m. Alps. Often escaped. April–May. **1221**

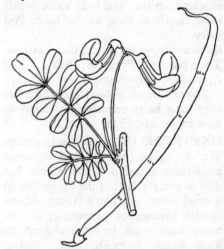

1221. *Coronilla emerus*. Flowers and pod.

C. vaginalis *Lam.* A herbaceous plant 10–25 cm. tall. Lvs. with 3–7 pairs of oval leaflets, rather thick, blue-green, sometimes with whitish margins. Lf. stalks emerging from a sheath made by the stipules. Fls. yellow, 5–15 in a loose head. Pod long, swollen over seed, 6-sided.

✤ Stony places, preferring limestone. To 2230 m. Alps; Apennines (very local). June–August. **363, 1222**

1222. *Coronilla vaginalis.* Pod.

HIPPOCREPIS *L.* **H. comosa** *L.* HORSESHOE VETCH. An almost hairless perennial 5–40 cm. tall, resembling *Coronilla vaginalis*, but differing by the lvs. with 4–5 pairs of oval to oblong leaflets. Fls. yellow in heads of 5–8. Pod about 3 cm. long, flattened, segments horse-shoe shaped, giving a twisted appearance.

✤ Stony places, meadows. To 2800 m. Pyrenees (uncommon); Alps; Apennines. (Britain.) April–June. **365**

HEDYSARUM *L.* **H. hedysaroides** (*L.*) *Schinz & Thell.* (**H. obscurum** *L.*) ALPINE SAINFOIN. A striking herbaceous perennial, 10–25 cm. tall, hairless. Lvs. with 5–9 pairs of leaflets, under-surface blue-green. Fls. purplish-red, pendant, in a long spike. Pod hairless, pendant, with slight wing down edge, and constricted at intervals forming joints.

A tall white-fld. form often found in the W. Alps and Maritime Alps has been named **H. boutignyanum** *d'Alleiz.*

✤ Pastures, stony places, screes. To 2800 m. Pyrenees; Alps. Local. July– **364, 1223**

1223. *Hedysarum hedysaroides.* Pod.

ONOBRYCHIS *Scop.* SAINFOIN. Alpine species herbaceous perennials, with many leaflets; stipules scale-like. Fls. in a long spike; with short wings, keel at least as long as standard; upper stamen separate from rest. Pod short, not

jointed, abruptly cut off, with tubercles, sometimes spiny, 1–2-seeded.

O. montana (*Pers.*) *Lam. & DC.* (**O. viciifolia** *Scop.* ssp. **montana** (*Pers.*) *Gam.*). MOUNTAIN SAINFOIN. 10–20 cm. tall, clear green, slightly hairy. Lvs. with 5–8 pairs of oval or narrow-oblong leaflets. Fls. deep red, numerous in a dense more or less conical head. Stem stout, longer than lvs. Calyx teeth much longer than tube, which is often woolly. Pod up to 1 cm. long, hairy, narrow, with swellings on lower edge, 1-seeded.

✤ Stony places, pastures. 1400–2500 m. Pyrenees; Alps; Apennines. (*O. viciifolia* in Britain.) July. **366**

O. saxatilis (*L.*) *Lam.* ROCK SAINFOIN. 10–30 cm. tall, white-downy, the lvs. and fl. stalks arising close to the rootstock. Lvs. with 6–14 pairs of narrow-elliptic leaflets. Fls. numerous, close-packed in a long spike, yellowish white with red veins. Pod with tubercles but no spines.

✤ Rocks, stony places, gravels, meadows. To 1800 m. E. Pyrenees; W. Alps. June–August. **1076**

VICIA *L.* VETCH. Alpine species herbaceous perennials, climbing or sprawling. Lvs. with many leaflets, but usually with a terminal tendril, single or branched, instead of a leaflet. Fls. in loose clusters in lf. axils, violet, bluish or white with blue markings. Pod flattened, 2-celled, with several seeds.

Besides the species described, *V. hirsuta* (*L.*) Gray and *V. tetrasperma* (*L.*) Moench may reach 1650–1750 m. *V. faba* L., the BROAD BEAN, is cultivated to 2125 m., and *V. sativa* L., the COMMON VETCH, to 2000 (2400) m.

V. argentea *Lap.* SILVERY VETCH. 10–30 cm. tall, with silvery hairs. Lvs. of 4–10 pairs of oblong leaflets and a terminal leaflet. Fls. 2–2½ cm. long, whitish with violet markings, keel with purple edge, 4–10 on stem, all growing to one side.

✤ Stony places, meadows, screes, preferring acid soils. 1600–2300 m. Pyrenees. Very rare. July–August.
1079, 1224

Calyces of *Vicia* species. 1224. *V. argentea.* 1225. *V. sylvatica.* 1226. *V. cracca.* 1227. *V. pyrenaica.* 1228. *V. sepium.*

V. sylvatica *L.* WOOD VETCH. A trailing, hairless plant, 60–130 cm. long. Lvs. with 6–10 pairs of leaflets and a much-branched terminal tendril. Fls. white with violet veins, drooping in clusters of up to 18. Pod oblong, $2\frac{1}{2}$–3 cm. long, pointed at both ends, hairless, few-seeded, black when ripe.

✤ Woods, especially of beeches and conifers. To 2200 m. Alps; S. Apennines. Uncommon. (Britain.) June–August.
1080, 1225

V. cracca *L.* TUFTED VETCH. A variable, scrambling, usually hairy plant, 60–200 cm. long. Lvs. with 10–40 pairs of narrow-elliptic leaflets and branched tendrils. Fls. pale blue or violet, drooping, to $1\frac{1}{2}$ cm. long, numerous in a long, loose, rather narrow cluster. Pod to 2 cm. long, hairless, 2–6-seeded.

✤ Fields, clearings, hedgerows, edges of woods. To 2230 m. Pyrenees; Alps; Apennines. (Britain.) June–August.
372, 1226

V. onobrychioides *L.* 50–120 cm. tall. Similar to *V. cracca*, but more spectacular, with 2 cm. violet or deep blue fls, 6–12 in a loose 1-sided cluster on very long stem. Stipules toothed; leaflets 12-16 pairs, narrow strap-shaped, blunt.

✤ Fields, dry places. To 1900 m. Pyrenees; Maritime Alps. May–August.

V. pyrenaica *Pourr.* PYRENEAN VETCH. A usually hairless plant, 10–30 cm. tall. Lower lvs. without tendrils and of 1–2 pairs of leaflets, upper lvs. with short tendrils and 4–6 pairs of leaflets. Fls. large, violet-purple, solitary.

✤ Pastures. 1400–2500 m. Pyrenees (rare); French Alps. June–August.
371, 1227

V. sepium *L.* BUSH VETCH. A very variable plant, 30–50 cm. tall. Lvs. with 5–10 pairs of oval, blunt tipped leaflets and branched tendrils. Fls. dirty violet with purple stripes, rather small, 1–$1\frac{1}{2}$ cm. Pods hairless, black when ripe, 6–10-seeded.

✤ Fields, hedgerows, scrub. To 2130 (2416) m. Pyrenees; Alps; Apennines. (Britain.) April–October. **1078, 1228**

LATHYRUS *L.* Similar to *Vicia*, but stems winged or angled, and leaflets fewer. Perennial unless specified.

L. vernus (*L.*) *Bernh.* SPRING VETCHLING. 20–40 cm. tall. Lvs. of 2–4 pairs leaflets, which are green, shiny and end in a terminal point. Fls. 3–8, large, $1\frac{1}{2}$–2 cm. long, pendant, reddish violet turning blue. Pod hairless.

✤ Woods, particularly on limestone. To 1900 m. Pyrenees; Alps; Apennines. April–June. **367**

L. montanus *Bernh.* (**L. macrorrhizus** *Wimm.*, **Orobus tuberosus** *L.*). BITTER VETCH. Upright, hairless, 15–40 cm. tall. Stems winged. Lvs. with 2–4 pairs of narrow-oblong to oval leaflets. Fls. bright crimson turning greenish blue, in heads of 2–6; stems hairless. Pod 3–4 cm. long, hairless, 4–6-seeded.

✤ Woods, pastures, heaths, preferring acid soils. To 2190 m. Pyrenees; Alps; Apennines. (Britain.) April–June.

L. luteus (*L.*) *Peterm.* YELLOW PEA. A usually erect plant, 20–60 cm. tall, with unbranched stems. Lvs. with 2–6 pairs of large, elliptic, lance-shaped pointed leaflets, 3–7 cm. long, clear green, with terminal point (sometimes absent) or leaflet. Fls. large, $1\frac{1}{2}$–$2\frac{1}{2}$ cm. long, yellow to dark yellow, in heads of 3–12.

Modern authorities use the name **L. laevigatus** (*L.*) *Pers.* for this plant. ❧ Forests, fields, preferring calcareous soils. To 2300 m. Pyrenees; Alps; Apennines. June. **368**

L. pratensis *L.* MEADOW VETCHLING. A scrambling, finely hairy plant, 30–120 cm. long. Stem sharply angled. Leaflets in one pair with a tendril. Fls. yellow, 1½–2 cm. long, 5–12 in a cluster on stem longer than lvs. Pod 2½–3½ cm. long, hairless or finely hairy, flattened, with 5–10 smooth seeds. ❧ Meadows, hedges, sides of woods. To 2130 m. Pyrenees; Alps. Norway to 800 m. (Britain.) June–July. **370**

L. aphaca *L.* YELLOW VETCHLING. A hairless, scrambling annual to 100 cm. long. Lvs. reduced to unbranched tendrils in mature plants, and replaced by oval spear-shaped stipules. Fls. solitary, yellow, 1–1½ cm. long, usually upright. Calyx teeth nearly as long as petals. Pod 2–3 cm. long, shaped rather like a sickle, 6–8-seeded. ❧ Fields, waste places, usually on limestone. To 1800 m. Pyrenees; Alps. (Britain.) June–August. **1082**

L. heterophyllus *L.* WOOD PEA. A sturdy, blue-green plant 1½–3 m. tall. Lower lvs. with 1 pair of 4–10 cm. leaflets, upper ones usually 2 pairs; with branched tendrils. Fls. pink, fairly large, in heads of 4–8. Pod swollen. Sometimes treated as a subspecies of the narrower-lvd. *L. sylvestris* (*L.*) P.F. ❧ Woods, damp places, hedgerows, preferring limestone. To 1900 m. Pyrenees (very rare); Alps. July–August. **369**

OXALIDACEAE—SORREL FAMILY

Fls. 5-parted with 10 stamens inserted near base of (3)5-celled ovary; styles (3)5. Related to *Geraniaceae*, but ovary beakless.

OXALIS *L.* **O. acetosella** *L.* WOOD SORREL. The only species reaching alpine levels. A perennial 5–15 cm. tall, with thick creeping rhizome, and 3-parted bright green lvs. with leaflets wedge-shaped at base, heart-shaped at apex, acid-tasting. Fls. solitary, white with lilac veins or, seldom, altogether pink, lilac or purple, 2–3 cm. across, petals 3–4 times longer than sepals. Fruit an explosive capsule, usually following the summer production of insignificant (cleistogamic) fls. ❧ Woods, shady rocks, in humus of moss. To 2120 m. Pyrenees; Alps; Apennines. (Britain to 1250 m.) April–July (showy fls.). **1045**

GERANIACEAE—GERANIUM FAMILY

Alpine species herbaceous, perennials unless otherwise specified, with usually alternate, lobed or dissected lvs.; stipules usually present. Fls. with both sexes present, radially or only vertically symmetrical, 5-parted, with 10 stamens. Ovary with a long 'beak', carrying the stigmas, which persists when the fruit, a capsule, ripens, the beak then often breaking into sections.

GERANIUM *L.* CRANESBILL. Lvs. hand-shaped or cut into segments radiating from a central point. Fls. usually in pairs, radially symmetrical. Beak of fruit usually rolling up from the base on ripening, to release the seeds in the capsule.

Besides those described, the following rather insignificant species reach alpine levels: *G. bohemicum* L. to 1900 m.; *G. columbinum* L., 1500 m.; *G. dissectum* L., 1500 m.; *G. lucidum* L., 1600 m.; *G. pusillum* Burm., 2000 m.; *G. rotundifolium* L., 1600 m.

G. cinereum L. ASHY CRANESBILL.
A low, thick-stocked plant 8–15 cm. tall,
covered in greyish hairs. Lvs. divided
almost to centre into 5–7 segments,
each 3-lobed at apex. Fls. in pairs,
reddish to pale mauve with darker
veins, to 3 cm. across; petals rounded.
✤ Meadows, rocks. 1500–2400 m. W.
and C. Pyrenees; C. and S. Apennines.
Uncommon. July–August. **376**

G. argenteum L. SILVERY CRANESBILL.
A low, thick-stocked plant 7–12 cm.
tall, covered in silvery hairs. Lvs. cut
almost to the centre into 5–7 segments,
themselves divided into 3 narrow, strap-
shaped lobes. Fls. in pairs, pale rose-
pink, 3 cm. across; petals wedge-
shaped, notched.
✤ Meadows, rock crevices, screes,
1690–2200 m. Alps; Apuan Alps; N.
Apennines. Rare. July–August. **377**

G. sanguineum L. BLOODY CRANESBILL.
With stout creeping rhizome, and 10–40
cm. sprawling to erect stems, swollen
at the nodes, with many long hairs. Lvs.
white-hairy, deeply cut into 5–7 segments each divided into 2 or 3 narrow
lobes, themselves often further divided.
Fls. solitary or occasionally in pairs, on
long stems, bright magenta pink,
occasionally pink or white, 1½–4 cm.
across; petals notched.
✤ Dry hillsides, hedgerows, open
woods, preferring calcareous soils. To
1900 m. Pyrenees; Alps. (Britain.)
June–September. **378**

G. sylvaticum L. CROW FLOWER (373).
30–80 cm. tall, with stout rhizome;
plant downy-glandular in upper part.
Lvs. 7–12 cm. across, deeply cut into
5–7 segments jaggedly cut into small
toothed lobes. Fls. in pairs, bowl-
shaped, blue-violet, 2½–3 cm. across;
petals rounded. A form with smaller,
pink, red-veined fls. has been named
G. lemanianum *Briq.*
  Ssp. **rivulare** (*Vill.*) *Rouy* (sometimes

treated as a species under the name **G.
rivulare** L. or **G. aconitifolium**
L'Herit.) (1087): 15–40 cm. tall, with
slender rhizome and stems. Lvs. cut
almost to centre into 5 segments themselves deeply and jaggedly subdivided.
Fls. up to 12 together, bowl-shaped,
white with pink veins, 2–3 cm. across.
✤ Meadows, woods, stony places,
scrub, usually on acid soils. Pyrenees;
Alps; Apennines. Norway to 1750 m.
Ssp. rivulare: Alps, 1400–2400 m.: rare.
G. lemanianum: Savoy at 2000 m.: very
rare. (The species in Britain to 1100 m.)
June–August. **373, 1087**

G. pratense L. MEADOW CRANESBILL.
30–60 cm. tall, with stout rhizome.
Similar to *G. sylvaticum* but fl. stalks bend
downwards after flowering, becoming
erect again in fruit. Fls. in pairs, bowl-
shaped, violet-blue to sky-blue, 3–4 cm.
across; petals rounded.
✤ Meadows, ditches, streamsides, preferring calcareous soils. To 1900 m.
Pyrenees; Alps (rare); N. Apennines.
(Britain.) June–September. **375**

G. macrorrhizum L. ROCK CRANESBILL.
10–30 cm. tall, with long, thick,
straggling rhizome. Lvs. aromatic, to
10 cm. across, downy, deeply cut into
5–7 segments with toothed lobes. Fls.
in pairs on stout stalks, grouped into a
close cluster, 2½ cm. across, pink to
blood-red or carmine, with prominent
2 cm. stamens which surround the beak
of the fruit.
✤ Rocks, stony places, especially in
shade, on limestone. To 2500 m.
Maritime Alps (very rare); S. and S.E.
Alps; Apennines. (Britain: naturalised.)
July–August. **374**

G. phaeum L. MOURNING WIDOW or
DUSKY CRANESBILL. 30–60 cm. tall, with
stout rhizome. Stems hairy, glandular
near top of plant. Lvs. to 12 cm. across,
often dark-blotched, cut into 5–7 deep,
often uneven segments which are lobed

near the apex. Fls. in pairs on long stalks, forming a loose head, flattish, to 2 cm. across; petals broad and rounded. Colour varying from blackish purple to dark violet or reddish brown, occasionally pinkish, sometimes whitish or mauve in the centre.
❋ Damp meadows, open woods. To 2400 m. Pyrenees; Alps; Apennines. (Britain: naturalised.) May–August. 380

G. palustre *L.* MARSH CRANESBILL. 20–50 cm. tall, with thick rootstock. Lvs. to 12 cm. across, cut ¾ to centre into about 5 large, irregular, toothed segments. Fls. to 3 cm. across, carmine-red or purplish red; stalks reflexed as fruit ripens.
❋ Damp meadows. To 1500 m. Pyrenees (rare); Alps. June–August. 381

G. divaricatum *Ehrh.* Annual, with sprawling 25–60 cm. stems with swollen, angled joints; plant velvety-glandular. Lvs. divided almost to centre into 5 segments which are irregularly lobed; segments of upper lvs. often asymmetrical. Fls. in small clusters, pink, the petals barely as long as the pointed 5 mm. sepals. Fruit downy.
❋ Woods, hedgerows, stony places. To 2000 m. C. and E. Pyrenees; Alps. May–August. 1085

G. pyrenaicum *Burm.* (**G. perenne** *Huds.*). PYRENEAN or MOUNTAIN CRANESBILL. 25–60 cm. tall; stems hairy, glandular. Lvs. hairy on both sides, cut nearly to centre into 5–9 wedge-shaped segments, with 3–5 irregular, rounded lobes at the apex. Fls. purplish pink, cup-shaped, 1½–2 cm. across, in pairs forming a loose cluster (cyme); petals deeply notched. Fl. stalks bending over after flowering, then recurving near base so that fruit is erect.
❋ Meadows, open woods, waste places. To 1900 (2230) m. Pyrenees; Alps; Apennines. (Britain.) May–October. 379

G. nodosum *L.* 20–50 cm. tall, with horizontal rhizome. Stems markedly swollen at joints, sometimes hairy. Lvs. cut ¾ to centre into 3–5 irregularly toothed segments. Fls. 3 cm. across, pink or lilac with violet veins; petals notched.
❋ Open woods. To 1600 m. Pyrenees; Alps; Apennines. (Britain: introduced and occasionally naturalised.) May–September. 1083

G. molle *L.* DOVESFOOT CRANESBILL. Annual or biennial, 10–40 cm. tall, branching from the base; plant covered in long soft white hairs. Lvs. round or kidney-shaped, cut up to halfway into 5–9 often uneven, wedge-shaped segments close to each other, with 3 short lobes at apex. Fls. bright pink-purple, ½–1 cm. across, with deeply notched petals, in pairs forming clusters.
❋ Dry grassland, waste places, fields, paths. To 2000 m. Pyrenees; Alps. (Britain.) April–September. 1084

G. robertianum *L.* HERB ROBERT. Annual or biennial, 10–30 (50) cm. tall. A fragile plant, often tinged red, and with a pungent smell; rather sprawling, and often hairy in lower parts. Lvs. cut to centre into 3–5 stalked segments, themselves cut into opposed, toothed lobes. Fls. bright pink, 1–1½ cm. across, with rounded petals and orange or purple anthers.
❋ Walls, stony places, clearings. To 2000 m. Pyrenees; Alps. (Britain to 750 m.) May–September. 1086

ERODIUM *L'Herit.* STORKSBILL. Lvs. usually of many more or less opposed lobes. Fls. solitary, in pairs, or clustered, radially symmetrical or slightly irregular (vertically symmetrical) Stamens 10, but those opposite the petals without anthers. Beak of fruit twisting spirally on ripening, and becoming detached with the seeds attached to them within the capsule walls at the base.

E. cicutarium *(L.)* *L'Herit.* COMMON STORKSBILL. A variable annual or biennial to 60 cm. tall, usually branching, with lvs. 2–20 cm. long irregularly divided into segments on either side of midrib, themselves coarsely lobed. Fls. 1 cm. across, bright rose-purple, often with a dark spot at the base of the upper petals, sometimes slightly irregular; 3–7 (2–9) in radiating clusters (umbels). Fruit with 2–4 cm. beak.
⚘ Fields, sandy places, dry meadows. To 2100 m. Pyrenees; Alps; Apennines. (Britain.) June–September. **1088**

E. manescavi *Coss.* 20–40 cm. tall, with woody rootstock and large lvs. cut to midrib into more or less opposed, irregularly lobed segments; hairy. Fls. 2–4 cm. across, bright carmine-pink with rounded petals, in radiating clusters (umbels), each umbel emerging from a 'cup' formed of pointed stipule joined together. Fruit with 6–8 cm. beak.
⚘ Meadows. To 2300 m. C. and W. Pyrenees. July–August. **385**

E. alpinum *(Burm.)* *L'Herit.* (**E. apenninum** *Ten.*). ALPINE STORKSBILL. 10–30 cm. tall, with woody, scaly rhizome and lvs. cut not quite to midrib into more or less opposed, rather narrow, irregularly lobed segments; hairy. Fls. to 2 cm. across, purplish violet, with rounded or slightly truncated petals, in radiating clusters (umbels) emerging from a group of small triangular, separate stipules. Fruit with 2–5 cm. beak.
⚘ Stony places. N. and C. Apennines. July–August. **382**

E. petraeum *(Gouan.)* *Willd.* ROCK STORKSBILL. A tufted, stemless, hairy, strong-smelling plant 5–15 cm. tall. Lvs. fern-like, of small, neatly lobed, opposed segments. Fls. usually regular, 2–3½ cm. across, of slightly truncated pink petals, veined with purple.
Several rather similar subspecies have been distinguished, as follows:
Ssp. **petraeum** (384): fls. 2–2½ cm. across, bright pink; lvs. velvety, flat, with strap-shaped secondary lobes.
Ssp. **crispum** *Lap.*: fls. 2–2½ cm. across, slightly irregular, pale pink with dark blotch on upper petals; lvs. grey-downy, with short, oval, curled lobes.
Ssp. **rodiei** *Br.-Bl.*: fls. to 3½ cm. across, pink; lvs. hairless on midrib, shortly hairy on the thread-like lobes. *
Ssp. **lucidum** (Lap.) Webb & Chater: plant hairless and shining, barely smelling; fls. white with pinkish veins.
⚘ Rocks, stony places, on limestone. To 1700 (2300) m. *Sspp. petraeum, crispum, lucidum:* Pyrenees. *Ssp. rodiei:* Maritime Alps: very rare. May–June. **384**

E. macradenum *L'Herit.* (**E. glandulosum** *Willd.*). Sometimes considered a form of *E. petraeum* and certainly similar, but distinctive and usually smaller. A tufted, stemless, hairy, strong-smelling plant 3–6 (15) cm. tall with long, scaly, woody stock. Lvs. as in *E. petraeum.* Fls. slightly irregular, 1½–2 cm. across, with rounded petals, pale violet with darker veins. The upper petals with large violet blotch; sepals pointed, half length of petals. *
⚘ Schistous or granitic rocks. To 2300 m. Pyrenees. Rare. June–August. **383**

LINACEAE—FLAX FAMILY

Lvs. usually alternate, uncut. Fls. usually in clusters (cymes or racemes), occasionally solitary, with both sexes present. Fls. usually 5-parted, with persistent, overlapping sepals and often fleeting petals, twisted in the bud.

Stamens usually as many as sepals. Fruit a large capsule which splits into segments.

LINUM L. FLAX. Herbaceous plants with narrow usually stalkless lvs. on which the midrib is prominent and the veins, if visible, parallel. Fls. in clusters (cymes), 5-parted, with clawed petals, 5 stamens and 5 tooth-like false stamens (staminodes) between. Fruit of 10 segments.

Besides the species mentioned the small-flowered white, British, PURGING FLAX, L. *catharticum* L., reaches 2373 m. L. *salsoloides* Lam. and L. *tenuifolium* L. may attain 1500 m.

L. flavum L. YELLOW FLAX. Perennial, 20–55 cm. tall, with lance-shaped, pointed lvs. Fls. golden yellow, 2½–4 cm. across, in a small cluster, tightly grouped especially in var. **capitatum** *Kit.*

✲ Sunny slopes. Occasionally reaching alpine levels. E. Alps. *Var. capitatum:* Apennines. June–July. **386**

L. viscosum L. STICKY FLAX. Perennial, 30–60 cm. tall; lvs. velvety, oval lance-shaped, with 3–5 veins. Upper lvs., bracts and sepals sticky-hairy; fl. stalks with long hairs; fls. pink with violet, occasionally white or blue veins, 2½–4 cm. across, petals rounded, truncated.

✲ Meadows, clearings. To 1900 m. Pyrenees; Maritime Alps; S.E. Alps. May–July. **387**

L. alpinum *Jacq.* ALPINE FLAX. Perennial, 10–30 (50) cm. tall, hairless, with lance-shaped, 1-veined lvs. 1–2 mm. wide. Fls. sky-blue, 1½–3½ cm. across. Subspecies have been named which vary in size and stoutness of stems, which are sometimes erect and sometimes sprawling at base, and vary in number of fls., but all are basically similar in general appearance. *

✲ Grassy and stony places, on limestone. To 2280 m. Pyrenees; Alps; Apuan Alps; Apennines. (The related L. *perenne ssp. anglicum* (Mill.) Ock. = L. *anglicum* Mill. in Britain.) May–August. **388**

L. usitatissimum L. FLAX. Annual, 30–100 cm. tall, with erect, branching stems, lance-shaped lvs. 2–3 cm. long, 2–4 mm. broad, sometimes stalked, and blue fls. up to 3 cm. across.

✲ Meadows. To 1800 m. C. and E. Alps. Often cultivated for linen and linseed. July–August. **389**

POLYGALACEAE—MILKWORT FAMILY

Alpine representatives herbaceous perennials or small shrubs. Lvs. usually alternate, undivided. Fls. with both sexes present, more or less symmetrical in vertical plane only (zygomorphic). Sepals 5; petals 3–5, joined to the tube made by the 8 stamens. Fruit a capsule.

POLYGALA L. MILKWORT. The only genus represented in the Alps. Fls. with 2 inner petal-like sepals, sometimes outspread, much larger than outer 3; petals 3, consisting of an upper pair united with the lower one, which is ⌐urved. forming a keel, and is usually

cut into small strap-shaped segments at the end.

Apart from the shrubby P. *chamae-buxus*, the species are superficially very similar, and nomenclature has been confused.

P. *vayredae* Costa, a delicate shrublet,

only reaches 700 m. in the E. Spanish Pyrenees.

P. chamaebuxus L. BOX-LEAVED or SHRUBBY MILKWORT. A low, much-branched shrublet 5–10 (30) cm. tall, with shining pointed-oval lvs. Fls. 1–3 together, 1½–2 cm. across, the sepals forming prominent 'wings', petals forming a tube, lower petal uncut at end. Sepals usually white and petals lemon yellow, the latter reddening at the tip after the fl. is fertilised; sepals sometimes buff-yellow, pink or carmine. The latter forms, which can be quite spectacular, have been given a number of varietal names which seem justified only horticulturally, e.g. var. *rhodoptera* Ball., and '*atropurpurea*' of gardens.
✼ Woods, rocks, preferring limestone. To 2480 m. E. Pyrenees (very rare); Alps; N. and C. Apennines. (March–)July–September. **394**

P. comosa *Schkuhr.* TUFTED MILKWORT. A plant with several vars. of which the usual alpine form is var. **pedemontana** *Perr. & Song.* (391). It has numerous 7–15 (30) cm. stems arising from a woody stock, and narrow-lance-shaped lvs. Fls. many in a spike, each with 3 narrow bracts 2–3 times longer than fl. stalks, giving the spike a whiskery look. Fls. 6–7 mm. long (bigger than in the species), blue, violet-purple or rose-red.
✼ Dry meadows, hillsides, open woods, on limestone. The species to 1500 m.; var. *pedemontana* to 2200 m. Alps. Very local. May–August. **391**

P. nicaeensis *Risso.* Similar to P. *comosa*, but with lvs. narrower, more widely spaced, fls. 6–10 mm. long, blue, pink or white, with short 'whiskers' in a long, usually loose spike.
✼ Meadows, stony places, open woods. To 1500 (1700) m. Alps. April–July.

P. alpestris *Reichb.* MOUNTAIN MILK-WORT. 7–15 cm. tall, with slender stems and thick stock. Lvs. lance-shaped, becoming larger from base upwards, the topmost often hiding the base of the spike of 4 mm. blue fls.
✼ Meadows, preferring limestone. To 2700 m. Pyrenees; Alps; Apennines. June–July. **390**

P. vulgaris L. COMMON MILKWORT. A variable plant of which the *var.* pseud-alpestris *Gren.* is found at alpine levels. This is up to 10 cm. tall, with upper lvs. smaller than lower ones; and a short, dense, head-like spike of blue, pink or white fls. 6–8 mm. long; bracts very short and thin.
✼ Meadows, scrub, hillsides, on acid soils. 1500–2200 m. Alps; Apennines. (The species in Britain.) May–July.

P. amara L. (**P. amarella** *Crantz*; including **P. austriaca** *Crantz*). BITTER MILKWORT. A rosette-forming plant, the growths forming a tight tuft, each basal rosette giving rise to one (5) 15–20 cm. fl. stem. Lvs. 1½–3½ cm. long, 6–10 mm. wide, broadest near tip, tapering to base. Fls. only 2–5 mm. long, pink, purplish pink or blue, sometimes white, many in a loose spike. Plant bitter-tasting.
✼ Damp meadows, mineralised marshes, preferring limestone. To 2600 m. Alps. Norway to 1080 m. (Britain: rare.) April–July. **392**

P. alpina (*DC.*) *Stendal.* ALPINE MILK-WORT. A more or less prostrate plant forming small tufts, with woody 2–10 cm. stems leafless between the small lf. rosettes which terminate in leafy shoots, the fl. stems emerging at the base of the rosettes. Fls. small, clear blue.
✼ Meadows, preferring limestone. 1500–3000 m. Pyrenees; S. Alps. Rare. July–August. **393**

EUPHORBIACEAE—SPURGE FAMILY

Alpine representatives herbaceous plants with alternate lvs. Fls. in a compound head, the sexes separate, with floral segments 3 or absent.

Mercurialis perennis L., the DOG'S MERCURY, with minute green fls. in spikes, has floral segments. This insignificant plant reaches 1800 m. in the Alps and 1100 m. in Britain. The similar *M. ovata* Sternb. & H. reaches 1880 m. in the Alps.

EUPHORBIA *L.* SPURGE. Annuals or perennials with poisonous milky juice. Fls. small: several male and 1 female are grouped in a cup-shaped organ (cyathium) resembling a perianth, around which 4–5 small teeth alternate with the same number of broader glands. Fls. usually greenish; fl.-heads (cymes) with lf.-like bracts below fls. and often at junctions of paired stems.

These plants need detailed study for identification and only two striking species are described. Besides these the annuals *E. helioscopia* L. and *E. peplus* L. reach 1700–1800 m., and the following perennials up to a maximum of 2000 m.: *E. amygdaloides* L., *E. chamaebuxus* Bern., *E duclis* L., *E. hyberna* (or *hibernica*) L., *E. valliniana* Belli and *E. verrucosa* Jacq.

E. cyparissias *L.* CYPRESS SPURGE. Perennial, with erect 15–50 cm. stems arising from horizontal stock in a dense cluster. Lvs. long and narrow, clustered tightly, especially on non-fl. stems, bright green or yellowish, turning red in autumn. Fls. yellow, in a flattish head. ⚘ Dry meadows, waste and stony places. To 2650 m. Pyrenees; Alps; Apennines. (Britain: doubtfully native.) April–July. **96**

E. myrsinites *L.* BLUE SPURGE. Perennial, with 20–50 cm. prostrate stems radiating from central stock; lvs. diamond-shaped, bluish. Fls. yellow, turning red, in large flat heads. ⚘ Stony places. To 2260 m. Apennines. May–August. **97**

CALLITRICHACEAE

A family of aquatic plants of which a few species of *Callitriche* are found above 1500m., notably *C. palustris* L. which reaches 2630 m. and is found in stagnant ponds in the Pyrenees, Alps and Appenines.

The submerged lvs. are usually narrow strap-shaped, the floating ones spoon-shaped or oval, often forming rosettes. In *C. palustris* almost all lvs. are spoon-shaped, and the plant is 10–30 cm. long. The fls. are small, with sexes separate, without perianth.

BUXACEAE—BOX FAMILY

BUXUS sempervirens *L.*, the BOX, reaches 1600 m. in more southerly parts of the mountains, and is an important component of sub-alpine woodland in the Spanish Pyrenees, Italian Alps and Apennines. **924**

AQUIFOLIACEAE—HOLLY FAMILY

ILEX aquifolium *L.*, the COMMON HOLLY, reaches 2000 m. in the Pyrenees, 1500 m. in Valais, Switzerland, and is subalpine elsewhere.

CELASTRACEAE—SPINDLE FAMILY

EUONYMUS europaeus *L.*, the COMMON SPINDLE-TREE, a British native, reaches 1600 m. in the Maritime Alps and is subalpine elsewhere.

E. latifolius *Mill.*, the ALPINE SPINDLE-TREE, with rather broader lvs., reaches 1600 m. in the E. Pyrenees, Provence and W. Alps, and 1500 m. in N. Tyrol.

ACERACEAE—MAPLE FAMILY

ACER opalus *Mill.*, a tree of 8–20 m., with 5 cm., 5-lobed lvs., is found up to 1900 m. in the Pyrenees and S.W. Alps.
928
A. campestre L., the FIELD MAPLE, reaches 1500 m.; *A. platanoides* L., the NORWAY MAPLE, 1620 m.; and *A. pseudoplatanus* L., the SYCAMORE, 1980 m.

RHAMNACEAE—BUCKTHORN FAMILY

RHAMNUS *L.* The only alpine genus. Trees or shrubs with undivided lvs. and small, greenish, usually 4-parted fls., the petals small and attached to the mouth of the tubular calyx. Stamens 4; style divided; fruit bitter, 2–4-seeded.

Besides the two species described, *R. catharticus* L., the PURGING BUCKTHORN common in Britain, may reach 1500 m.

R. alpinus *L.* ALPINE BUCKTHORN. An erect shrub 1–3½ m. tall; branches seldom contorted. Lvs. 7–13 cm. long, alternate, blunt-oval, with (7) 10–20 pairs of straight veins. Fruit bluish black.
✣ Open woods, streamsides, stony places, on limestone. To 1700 (2150) m. Pyrenees; Alps; Apennines. May–June.
922
R. pumilus *L.* DWARF BUCKTHORN. A shrublet with contorted 5–20 cm.

branches hugging the rock or stones. Lvs. 3–6 cm. long, alternate, blunt-oval, finely toothed, with 5–7 (4–9) pairs of prominent, curved veins. Buds downy. Fruit bluish black.
✣ Rocks, cliffs, screes, on limestone. 1100–3050 m. Pyrenees; Alps; Apennines. May–August.
923

TILIACEAE—LIME FAMILY

Tilia cordata *Mill.*, the SMALL-LEAVED LIME, reaches 1500 m.
T. platyphyllos *Scop.* (*T. grandifolia Ehrh.*), the LARGE-LEAVED LIME, with 15–28 cm. lvs., white-downy below, reaches 1800 m. in the Pyrenees and Alps.
927
Both are British natives.

MALVACEAE—MALLOW FAMILY

Alpine representatives herbaceous, annual or perennial, with an erect or sprawling stem. Lvs. spirally arranged, divided or lobed. Fls. in clusters, with

5 (rarely 3) sepals, and often an epicalyx of additional sepal-like segments outside the calyx. Petals 5, separate. Stamens many, with filaments joined into tube. Fruit a group of one-seeded nutlets, one style to each nutlet.

MALVA *L.* MALLOW. Basal lvs. larger and less deeply divided than stem lvs. Fls. purple, rose or white; sepals 5, joined. Epicalyx of 3 separate segments.

M. moschata *L.* MUSK MALLOW. Perennial, 30–80 cm., with sparse simple hairs. Basal lvs. long-stalked, 5–8 cm. across, kidney-shaped, lobes touching at margins. Stem-lvs. shorter-stalked, more deeply divided into slender segments. Fls. 3–6 cm. across, usually singly in lf.-axils, forming a loose terminal cluster, rose-pink, rarely white, petals about 3 times length of calyx. Nutlets blackish when ripe, hairy on back.
✲ Pastures, hedgebanks, meadows. Seldom above 1500 m. Pyrenees; Alps; Apennines. (Britain.) May–September.
400

M. alcea *L.* Similar to *M. moschata*, but hairs are star-shaped, and nutlets completely hairless.
✲ Woods, hedgebanks, meadows, preferring calcareous soils. To 2000 m. (Britain: casual.) June–September.

M. sylvestris *L.* COMMON MALLOW. Perennial, 40–90 cm., erect or sprawling, hairs sparse and spreading. Basal lvs. 5–10 cm. across, roundish, shallow-lobed, slightly folded, long-stalked. Stem-lvs. with 5–7 deep lobes. Fls. 2½–4 cm. across, petals purple-rose with darker stripes, 2–4 times as long as sepals, deeply notched at tip. Nutlets brownish-green when ripe.
✲ Meadows, paths, waste places. To 1820 m. Pyrenees; Alps. (Britain.) May–September.

M. neglecta *Wallr.* (*M. rotundifolia auct.*). DWARF MALLOW. Usually annual, sometimes perennial, sprawling or with erect central 15–60 cm. stem, densely downy, hairs star-shaped. Lvs. long-stalked, 4–7 cm. across, with 5–7 shallow, toothed lobes. Fls. 2–2½ cm. across, pale lilac or whitish with mauve veins, 2–3 times length of calyx. Nutlets brownish green when ripe.
✲ Waste places, paths, fields. To 1900 (2300) m. Pyrenees; Alps; Apennines. (Britain.) May–September.
401

ALTHAEA *L.* Resembles *Malva*, but has an epicalyx of 6–9 segments joined together to form a cup.

A. hirsuta *L.* HAIRY MALLOW. Annual or biennial, with coarsely hairy, slender 8–60 cm. stems. Lower lvs. 2–4 cm. across, with more or less 5 blunt lobes, long-stalked. Upper lvs. with 3–5 deep lobes. Fls. about 2½ cm. across, singly in lf.-axils and in a terminal cluster, with slender stalks longer than lvs.; petals pale pink-purple, becoming bluish, longer than the sepals. Nutlets dark brownish green.
✲ Waste places, field edges, wood margins, paths. To 1500 m. Pyrenees; Alps. (Britain: doubtfully native.) May–August.
1229

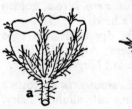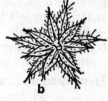

1229. *Althaea hirsuta.* Flower: a, side view; b, bottom view, to show epicalyx.

GUTTIFERAE (HYPERICACEAE)—ST. JOHN'S WORT FAMILY

Alpine representatives perennial. Lvs. opposite, simple, often with gland-dots. Fls. usually in branched heads, sometimes solitary. Sepals and petals usually 5. Stamens numerous, often joined into bundles.

HYPERICUM L. ST. JOHN'S WORT. Usually erect plants. Lvs. stalkless or nearly so. Fls. yellow. Styles 3 or 5. Fruit a capsule, or rarely a berry. Besides the species described *H. hirsutum* L. and *H. hyssopifolium* Vill. reach 1600 m., and the prostrate *H. humifusum* L., a plant of wet places, reaches 1800 m. in one or two areas.

H. maculatum *Crantz* (**H. dubium** *Leers*, **H. quadrangulum** *auct.*). IMPERFORATE ST. JOHN'S WORT. 20–60 cm. tall, hairless, root rhizomatous. Stems 4-sided. Lvs. 1–2 cm. long, stalkless with few or no glandular dots. Fls. 2 cm. across, golden yellow, several in a head; sepals glandular, $\frac{1}{3}$–$\frac{1}{4}$ length of petals. Fruit 3-celled.
✤ Damp fields, wood edges, streamsides. To 2650 m. Pyrenees; Alps; Apennines. Norway to 1260 m. (Britain.) June–September. **396**

H. perforatum L. COMMON ST. JOHN'S WORT. 30–100 cm. tall, woody at base, hairless, root rhizomatous. Lvs. 1–2 cm. long, stalkless, with many translucent glandular dots. Fls. 2 cm. across, golden yellow, many in a head.
✤ Woods, scrub, dry fields. To 2000 (2400) m. Pyrenees; Alps; N. and C. Apennines. (Britain.) May–September.

H. montanum L. MOUNTAIN ST. JOHN'S WORT. 40–80 cm. tall, slightly hairy. Lvs. 3–5 cm. long, stalkless, with a marginal row of black glands beneath. Fl.-head dense, with numerous fragrant, pale yellow fls. 1–1$\frac{1}{2}$ cm. across; sepals $\frac{1}{2}$–$\frac{1}{3}$ length of petals, glandular-toothed,

joined at base. Stamens joined into 3 bundles. Fruit one-celled.
✤ Woods, fields, riverbanks, on calcareous or gravelly soils. To 1900 m. Pyrenees; Alps. (Britain.) June–September. **395**

H. nummularium L. With slender 10–30 cm. sprawling to erect stems. Lvs. roundish, without glandular dots. Fls. large, 2–3 cm. across, yellow, 3 or 4 times length of sepals.
✤ Limestone rocks. To 2500 m. Pyrenees; Maritime Alps (rare); Savoy Alps (rare). June–September. **399**

H. richeri *Vill.* ALPINE ST. JOHN'S WORT. 15–40 cm. tall, with robust, hairless stem. Lvs. oval with glandular dots, stalkless. Fls. bright yellow, 2–3 cm. across; sepals with fringed margins; fruit barely longer than sepals.
✤ Screes, meadows, woods, usually on limestone. 1150–2450 m. Alps; N. and C. Apennines. Uncommon. June–September. **398**

H. burseri *Spach.* (**H. maculatum** *Reichb. non Crantz*). Similar to *H. richeri* and sometimes considered a subspecies, but lvs. with bright green undersurface, and fruit twice as long as sepals which are persistent.
✤ Screes, meadows, woods. 1100–2400 m. Pyrenees (local). June–August.

H. coris L. YELLOW CORIS. 15–40 cm, tall, sometimes sprawling. Lvs. linear, in whorls of 3–4, with glandular dots, margins rolled in. Fls. bright yellow, about 2 cm. across; stamens in 3 bundles. Capsule ⅓ longer than sepals. Waste places, rocky hillsides. To 2000 m. Maritime Alps and Provence Alps (rare); Alps (more common eastwards); N. and C. Apennines (rare). May–July. **397**

TAMARICACEAE—TAMARIX FAMILY

Shrubs with slender branches and minute alternate lvs. Fls. very small, in slender, catkin-like spikes.

MYRICARIA *Desv.* **M. germanica** (*L.*) *Desv.* A shrub to 2 m. tall, with bluish lvs. and pale pink fls. in many lateral spikes on each erect stem. A characteristic plant of stony streams and river-banks, also on paths and railway tracks. To 2350 m. Pyrenees; Alps; N. and C. Apennines. May–August. **926**

CISTACEAE—ROCKROSE FAMILY

Shrubby or herbaceous plants; lvs. usually opposite, simple, sometimes with stipules (small lf.-like objects at base of lf.-stalks). Fls. solitary or clustered. Petals 5 (seldom 3 or absent), usually lasting only one day; sepals 5 or 3; stamens many; style with 3 or 5 stigmas. Fruit a capsule.

HELIANTHEMUM *Mill.* SUN ROSE, ROCKROSE. Fls. in a cluster; petals 5; sepals 5, outer 2 usually smaller than inner 3. Some of the species are very similar and nomenclature is confused.

H. oelandicum *DC. ssp.* **italicum** (*L.*) *F. Q. & Rothm.* (**H. italicum** (*L.*) *Pers. ssp.* **alpestre** (*Jacq.*) *Beger*). 3–12 cm. tall; lvs. oval to obovate, bright green, hairy on both surfaces, without stipules. The flowerless stems form a dense tuft. Fls. yellow; petals twice as long as white-hairy sepals. Dry meadows, stony places, preferring limestone. 1600–2900 m. Pyrenees; Alps; Apennines. May–September. **404**

H. canum (*L.*) *Baumg.* HOARY ROCKROSE. An erect or sprawling undershrub to 20 cm. tall. Lvs. to 2 cm. long, round or oval, with pointed tip; shortstalked, green, hairless or slightly hairy above, densely grey- or white-hairy below, *without stipules* (figure is in error). Fls. 1–1½ cm. across, bright yellow up to 10 in loose clusters; the 3 inner sepals are twice as large as other 2. Dry meadows, stony places, on limestone. To 1650 m. Pyrenees; Alps (only above 1500 m. in Swiss Jura); Apennines. (Britain.) May–July. **409**

H. lunulatum *Lam. ex DC.* 10–20 cm. tall, with sprawling branches, old ones sometimes leafless and appearing almost prickly. Lvs. elliptic, green, slightly hairy, often with fringe of hairs on margins, usually without stipules. Petals yellow, with a central orange mark. Sepals slightly hairy. Rocks, stony places. To 1600 m. French and Italian Maritime Alps. Extremely local. June–August. **403**

H. apenninum (*L.*) *Mill.* (**H. polifolium** *Mill.*, **H. pulverulentum** *Lam. & DC.*). WHITE ROCKROSE. An undershrub 5–30 cm. tall, sprawling or erect, branches often rooting. Lvs. ½–2 cm. long, densely grey-hairy, margins rolled under; stipules long, narrow, with a fine sharp point. Fls. about 2 cm.

286

across, 1–12 in loose clusters, usually white, with yellow basal blotch. Sepals densely grey-hairy. (402a)

A form with pink flowers, often cultivated, has been named *var.* **roseum** *Gross.* (402b)

✿ Stony and grassy places, clearings, on limestone. To 1800 m. Pyrenees; Alps; Apennines. *Var. roseum:* Pyrenees, especially on Spanish side. May–July.

402

H. hirtum (*L.*) *Pers.* 10–20 cm. tall, grey-white, with lvs. to 1 in. long, hairy on both sides, margins rolled under; stipules always much longer than lf.-stalk. Fls. 2 cm. across, several in a loose cluster, each in the axil of a bract. Petals usually yellow, seldom white, orange or pink, much longer than sepals. Sepals hairy, twice as long as capsule.

✿ Scrub, grassy slopes. To 1800 m. Pyrenees (rare); Dauphiné. June–July.

405

H. nummularium (*L.*) *Mill.* (**H.**

vulgare *Gaertn.,* **H. chamaecistus** *Mill.,* **H. ovatum** (*Viv.*) *Duval.*). COMMON ROCKROSE. Under-shrub to 30 cm. tall, erect or sprawling, branches often rooting; has thick woody stock and vertical tap-root. Lvs. ½–2 cm. long, green above, densely white-hairy below; lower lvs. oval, remainder oblong with short stalks. Fls. 2 cm. or more across, 1–12 in loose clusters, bright yellow, rarely cream, white, pink or orange, occasionally with small orange spot at base of petals.

406

A species of confused nomenclature, often much subdivided. Two of the more interesting forms are:

Ssp. **grandiflorum** (*Lam. & DC.*) *Schinz & Thell.* (407): lvs. to 3 cm. long and fls. to 3 cm. across.

Ssp. **tomentosum** (*Scop.*) *Schinz & Thell.* (408): white-woolly lvs. and 3 cm. fls., pink or at least spotted pink in centre.

✿ Dry meadows, clearings, preferring limestone. To 2820 m. Pyrenees; Alps; Apennines. (The species in Britain.) June–September. 406, 407, 408

VIOLACEAE—PANSY AND VIOLET FAMILY

Alpine representatives herbaceous, mainly perennial. Petals and sepals 5, stamens 5, alternating with petals, with short filaments. Fruit a capsule.

VIOLA *L.* Lvs. alternate, with stipules (appendages, sometimes lf.-like). Fls. solitary, seldom 2; symmetrical in vertical plane only (zygomorphic) with 2 upper pairs of petals and 1 lower, central one, which is spurred. Sepals elongated into appendages. Capsule 3-valved, many-seeded. Many species hybridise readily and most are very variable in any case. White forms may occur, especially with blue-fld. species. A rough division into 'pansies' and 'violets' can be made, but it is not an

exact one. Species are perennial unless otherwise specified.

Pansies: Side petals usually close to upper pair or overlapping them

V. tricolor *L.* HEARTSEASE. An extremely variable species, usually divided into several subspecies. Annual or occasionally perennial, 10–20 cm. tall, usually much branched, with thin, scarcely creeping root and 15–45 cm. sprawling stems. Lvs. very variable, lowest usually oval, upper becoming

oblong; stipules usually deeply lobed.
Fl. stalks 2–8 cm. long, several on each
stem. Fls. 1½–2½ cm. deep, yellow,
blue-violet or occasionally pink, or
combinations of these. Spur to twice
length of sepal appendages.
❧ Cultivated and waste ground, grassland, usually on acid and neutral soils.
To 2700 m. Pyrenees; Alps; Apennines.
Norway to 1080 m. (Britain.) April–
October. 410

V. lutea *Huds.* MOUNTAIN PANSY. A
variable species, usually divided into
subspecies. 7–20 cm. tall, with slender
creeping rhizome. Lower lvs. oval,
upper becoming oblong, with a few
short stiff hairs, at least on margins and
undersurface veins. Stipules deeply
lobed. Fl. stalks 5–9 cm. long, fls. 2–3½
cm. deep, bright yellow, blue-violet,
reddish violet or combinations of these;
base of lower petal usually yellow, but
fl. sometimes entirely violet. Spur 2–3
times length of sepal appendages.
❧ Grassland, rock ledges, on acid soils.
To 2000 m. Pyrenees; Alps. (Britain to
1100 m.) May–July. 412

V. dubyana *Burnet* (**V. declinata** *Gaud.*).
With sprawling, partly erect stems 2–20
(30) cm. long. Lower lvs. egg-shaped to
circular, toothed; upper lvs. much
narrower. Stipules short, deeply cut into
narrow sections. Fls. 2–2½ cm. deep,
usually violet, the lower petal with pale
yellow throat and deep violet lines.
Sepal appendages rounded, 3–5 mm.
long; spur rather thin, straight.
❧ Dry meadows, rocky places. Alps. To
2100 m. May–July. 411

V. calcarata *L.* LONG-SPURRED PANSY.
3–10 cm. tall, with fragile creeping
stems. Lvs. ovate, short-stalked, often
forming a rosette arising from a stout
stock. Stipules deeply cut into 3–5 narrow segments. Fls. large, 2–4 cm. deep,
usually violet, but in a great range of
shades, sometimes pink or yellow,

rarely white or parti-coloured; petals
varying greatly in shape (see illustrations). Spur long, equalling sepals. *
❧ Meadows, screes. 1000–2400 (3100)
m. Alps; Apennines (*var. eugeniae* Parl.).
April–October. 413

V. zoysii *Wulf.* (also spelt **zoisii**).
DINARIC PANSY. Very similar to *V.
calcarata* and is now regarded as a
geographical ssp. only. Fls. usually
yellow, sometimes lilac or parti-
coloured. *
❧ Meadows, screes. 1800–2200 m. S. E.
Alps; Yugoslavia. May–June.

V. nummulariifolia *All.* 3–8 cm. tall,
with thin underground root and fragile
stems. Lvs. round, inverted heart-
shaped, on long stalks. Stipules short,
lance-shaped. Fls. small, violet. Spur
slightly longer than appendages.
❧ Rocky, damp places. 1800–2900 m.
French and Italian Maritime Alps. Very
rare. August–September. 417

V. cenisia *L.* MT. CENIS PANSY. 3–15 cm.
tall, with spreading stem. Lower lvs.
broadly oval to round; upper lvs.
larger, longer than wide. Stipules very
similar to lvs., but lobed at the base.
Fls. 2–2½ cm. deep, violet or lilac.
Several geographical races exist,
which many authors treat as species.
These include **V. comollia** *Mess.*, with
entire stipules; **V. diversifolia** (*Ging.*)
Beck., greyish, with deeply divided
fan-shaped stipules, and making tight
rosettes with 2 cm. fl.-stalks; **V. valderia**
All., greyish, with stipules deeply
divided into 2–7 unequal lobes, and
making loose rosettes with 2–8 cm.
fl. stalks; and **V. magellensis** *Porta &
Rigo*, with extremely small lvs.
❧ Meadows, screes, stony places. 950–
2900 m. *V. cenisia:* W. Alps. *V. comollia:*
Lombard Alps. *V. diversifolia:* Pyrenees;
Maritime Alps (rare). *V. magellensis:*
Central Apennines. *V. valderia:* French

and Italian Maritime Alps (very rare). June–September. **418**

V. alpina *Jacq.* ALPINE PANSY. 4–8 cm. tall, tufted, with stout rootstock, not creeping. Lvs. all basal, ovate or heart-shaped, glossy. Stipules lance-shaped, entire, sometimes toothed, joined to the lf.-stalk to ½ their length. Fl. stalks 2–5 (10) cm. long. Fls. 1½–3 cm. deep, with well separated petals, violet, lower petal with gold throat and darker lines. Sepals lance-shaped, appendages broad and short; spur 3–4 mm. long.
❀ Meadows, rocky places, on limestone. 1600–2200 m. E. Alps. June–July. **415**

V. cornuta *L.* HORNED PANSY. 5–30 cm. tall. Lvs. narrow-ovate; stipules triangular-oval and markedly toothed. At once recognisable by its very long spur, about 6 times longer than appendages, and at least equalling the petals. Fls. large, fragrant, blue or blue-violet, throat of lower petal white.
❀ Meadows, clearings, rocky places. To 2500 m. Pyrenees; Savoy (naturalised); Apennines. June–August. **416**

V. heterophylla *Bert.* 10–20 cm. tall. Lower lvs. short, rounded oval, upper linear lance-shaped. Upper stipules divided into toothed segments, lower not divided. Fls. yellow; spur slightly longer than sepals, much shorter than petals. The alpine form is *ssp.* **cavallieri** *Becker.* *
❀ Meadows. To 2150 m. Mt. Cenis; Maritime Alps; Apennines. Very rare. July–August.

Violets: Side petals usually closer to the lower petal than the upper pair

V. biflora. YELLOW WOOD VIOLET. 5–10 cm. tall, fragile. Lvs. kidney-shaped, broader than long. Fls. usually 2 on each stem, small, golden yellow with brown lines; spur straight, short.
❀ Rock clefts, damp stony, shady places, woods. To 3000 m. Pyrenees;

Alps; Apennines. Norway to 1500 m. May–August. **422**

V. palustris *L.* BOG VIOLET. 3–8 cm. tall, with slender creeping rhizome. Lvs. 3–4, 1–4 cm. long, usually broader than long. Stipules ovate. Fls. 10–15 mm. deep, pale lilac (occasionally white) with darker veins; spur longer than appendages of oval sepals.
❀ Bogs, fens, marshes, wet heaths. 1200–2600 m. Pyrenees; Alps; Apuan Alps; N. Apennines. Norway to 1750 m. (Britain to 1300 m.) April–July. **421**

V. mirabilis *L.* A rosette-forming plant with thick stock, at first only 5–8 cm. tall but elongating to 20–30 cm. in fruit. It has blue-lilac or pale blue, very fragrant fls. 1½–2 cm. deep early in the season, with rather narrow, widely separated petals and 6–7 mm. greenish-white spur, which are followed by small fls. without petals which produce the seeds. These fls. consist of 5 sepals surrounding the swollen ovary surmounted by a hooked stigma. As the season proceeds the rounded to heart-shaped lvs. become up to 6 cm. across and their stalks elongate as do the fl. stalks. Stipules 1–2 cm. long, broad lance-shaped.
❀ Woods, clearings. To 1820 m. Alps. Norway to 1260 m. April–June.

V. pinnata *L.* FINGER-LEAVED VIOLET. 4–12 cm. tall, with all stems arising from top of stock. Lvs. deeply divided into a fan-shape with equal lobes. Fls. violet, blue, rarely white, the two upper petals streaked. Sepals oval, with pointed tips. Spur much longer than appendages.
❀ Rocky places, screes, meadows, preferring limestone. To 2300 (3000) m. Alps. Rare. June–August. **420**

V. riviniana *Reichb.* COMMON VIOLET. 2–20 cm. tall, elongating when fruiting, forming non-flowering rosettes. Lvs. rounded, ½–8 cm. long; stipules short,

finely fringed. Fls. on axillary branches; fls. 14–22 mm. deep, petals usually overlapping, blue-violet, lower petal often with whitish throat and darker area with dark veins. Spur pale blue, or whitish, rarely yellowish, thick, notched at tip. Sepals with large squarish appendages.
❀ Woods, hedgerows, heaths, usually in dry places. To 1800 (2300) m. Pyrenees; Alps; Apennines. (Britain to 1110 m.) April–June. **424**

V. canina L. DOG VIOLET. A very variable species, often divided into subspecies, with sprawling 2–30 cm. stems, elongating in fruit, arising from a short, creeping rhizome. Rather similar to *V. riviniana,* but not forming rosettes. Lvs. ½–8 cm. long, more or less triangular; stipules lance-shaped, sometimes toothed or fringed. Fls. 7–20 mm. deep, blue; spur yellowish, thick, straight, 5–6 mm. long, at least twice length of large sepal appendage.
❀ Open woods, heaths, marshes, on acid soils. To 2500 m. Pyrenees; Alps. Norway to 1250 m. (Britain.) April–July.

V. rupestris *Schmidt.* (**V. arenaria** *DC.*). TEESDALE VIOLET. A small tufted perennial, usually hairy, 2–4 cm. tall, elongating in fruit, arising from a thick, non-creeping stock. Lvs. heart-shaped, ½–2 cm. long. Fls. on axillary branches, pale blue-violet; spur paler, thick, furrowed, twice as long as sepal appendages.
❀ Meadows, gravel, heaths, preferring dry, calcareous places. To 3080 m. Pyrenees; Alps; Apennines. Norway to 1000 m. (Britain.) March–July. **425**

V. hirta L. HAIRY VIOLET. 8–12 cm. tall, downy, elongating in fruit, with short, thick, non-creeping rhizome. Lvs. light green, truncated or heart-shaped at base; stalks with many long spreading hairs. Stipules lance-shaped. Fls. 1½ cm. deep, blue-violet, rarely white, or white streaked with pink or violet.
❀ Pastures, open woods, preferring calcareous soils. To 2000 m. Pyrenees; Alps. (Britain.) March–June. **419**

V. thomasiana *Perr. & Song.* Sometimes considered a subspecies of **V. ambigua** *W. & K.,* itself similar to *V. hirta,* and with resemblances both to it and *V. collina.* 5–10 cm. tall, forming tufts arising from a branched woody rhizome. Lvs. more or less heart-shaped; stipules with fringes about half as long as breadth of stipules. Fls. 1½ cm. deep, fragrant, light violet, with thin, pointed spur 3–4 mm. long. Sepals small.
❀ Meadows, heaths, rocky places, on acid soils. To 2300 m. Alps. April–September. **423**

V. collina *Bess.* HILL VIOLET. 8–20 cm. tall, with spreading underground stem. Lvs. reversed heart-shaped; stipules with fringes as long as breadth of stipules. Fls. small, fragrant, pale violet; spur paler, short, pointed. Sepals fringed with hairs.
❀ Woods, preferring calcareous soils. To 2000 (2300) m. Pyrenees; Alps. March–April. **427**

V. pyrenaica *Ram.* PYRENEAN VIOLET. 8–10 cm. tall, slightly hairy, yellowish green. Lvs. reversed heart-shaped, lower lvs. sometimes wider than long. Stipules with long fringes. Fls. blue-violet, with large white patch on lower petal, 1–2 cm. deep, strongly scented. Sepals oval.
❀ Rocky places, open woods, meadows, preferring limestone. To 2250 m. Pyrenees; Alps. March–July. **426**

THYMELAEACEAE—DAPHNE FAMILY

Alpine species all shrubby. Lvs. alternate. Fls. more or less trumpet-shaped, consisting of a tubular receptacle terminating in 4 equal sepals. Stamens 8, near the top of the receptacle.

THYMELAEA *Endl.* (**PASSERINA** *auct.*). Alpine species small twisted shrubs, with lvs. clustered at ends of branches, and tiny yellow fls. among them. Fruit a nutlet.

T. calycina *Meiss.* 10–20 cm. tall. Lvs. 1 cm. long, 1–2 mm. wide, pointed, horny, with edges rolled inwards, and no prominent vein. Fls. 3–4 mm. long, downy, with blunt lobes as long as tube. ☘ Stony places. To 2500 m. W. and C. Pyrenees. June–September. **435**

T. nivalis *Ram.* 10–20 cm. tall. Lvs. 1 cm. long, 1–2 mm. wide, strap-shaped, blunt-ended, grey-downy when young, without vein. Fl. 6–10 mm. long, hairless with angular lobes. Sometimes considered a subspecies of *T. tinctoria* Huds.
☘ Stony places. 1800–2500 m. W. and C. Pyrenees. Rare. June–July.

T. dioica *All.* 10–30 cm. tall. Lvs. narrow spoon-shaped, with prominent central vein; 1 cm. long, 1–2 mm. wide. Fl. 6–10 mm. long, hairless, with angular lobes much shorter than tube; yellow, turning purple with age.
☘ Limestone rocks. To 2000 m. Pyrenees; S. French Alps (rare); Italian Maritime Alps (local). May–June. **436**

DAPHNE *L.* MEZEREON. Shrubs with alternate or whorled lvs., fls. in clusters (racemes or umbels), fragrant, usually showy and coloured. Fruit a berry-like drupe.

Flowers yellow-green

D. laureola *L.* SPURGE LAUREL. An erect shrub 50–100 cm. tall. Lvs. ever-green, thick, shining, dark green, 5–12 cm. long, clustered at ends of branches. Fls. 8–12 mm. long, yellow-green, honey-scented, among and below lvs. Fruit black.

Ssp. **phillippii** *G. & G.* is a more or less prostrate plant with leafy stems and 3 mm. fls.
☘ Woods and clearings. *Ssp. phillippii*: rocky hillsides. To 1600 m. Pyrenees; Cevennes. (The species in Britain.) February–April. **433**

Flowers pink

D. mezereum *L.* MEZEREON. An erect shrub 30–100 (250) cm. tall. Lvs. deciduous, thin, bright green, clustered at ends of branches. Fls. mauve, pink or reddish, occasionally white, strongly scented, actually in small clusters but giving the appearance of a continuous cylindrical spike, opening before lvs. appear. Fruit orange turning red; yellow in white-fld. forms.
☘ Woods, pastures, usually on lime-stone. To 2580 m. Pyrenees; Alps; Apennines. Norway to 1250 m. (Britain: rare.) February–July. **428**

D. cneorum *L.* GARLAND FLOWER. A prostrate or straggling bush to 50 cm. tall, with downy stems, often prostrate. Lvs. evergreen, more or less spoon-shaped, 1–2 cm. long, 3–5 mm. wide, hairless. Fls. bright pink, fairly fragrant, with downy tube, short-stemmed in clusters of 6–8. Fruit yellow.
Var. **verloti** *Meissn.* has lvs. longer and narrower, fls. virtually stalkless.
☘ Pastures, stony places, on limestone. To 2150 m. Pyrenees; E. Alps; N.

Apennines. Local. *Var. verloti:* Savoy, Maritime Alps: very rare. April–August.

D. striata *Tratt.* A prostrate or straggling bush 10–50 cm. tall, with hairless stems suckering underground for long distances. Lvs. evergreen, strap-shaped, 2–3 cm. long, in down-pointing clusters at ends of stems. Fls. carmine or reddish purple, occasionally white, very fragrant, with smooth striated tube, stemless, in terminal heads of 8–12. Fruit yellow, orange, finally red. ✤ Woods, pastures, rocks, on limestone and also crystalline rocks. To 2860 m. French Alps (very rare); E. Swiss Alps; E. Alps. May–August. **429**

D. petraea *Ley.* (**D. rupestris** *Facc.*). ROCK MEZEREON. A small shrub forming an 8–15 cm. tuft of gnarled, hairy twigs. Lvs. evergreen, leathery, to 12 mm. long, 2–3 mm. wide, lance-shaped or more often long wedge-shaped with rounded tip. Fls. rich glistening pink, hairy on tube, up to 1 cm. across lobes, usually in fours at ends of stems. ✤ Limestone cliffs. To 2000 m. Confined to a small area near Lake Garda, N. Italy. June–July. **432**

Flowers white

D. alpina *L.* ALPINE MEZEREON. A twisted bush 20–50 cm. tall, with soft, thin lvs. 2–3 cm. long, 1 cm. wide. Fls. white, fragrant, with downy tube, in clusters of 4–7. Fruit red. ✤ Rocks, stony places. To 2000 m. Pyrenees; Alps; Apennines. Local. April–June. **430**

D. blagayana *Frey.* 10–25 cm. tall, with long sprawling, rooting stems. Lvs. spoon-shaped, smooth, 3–4 cm. long. Fls. white or cream, fragrant, with downy tube, 2 cm. long, in terminal clusters of up to 30. ✤ Meadows, scrub, rocky places. To 1200 m. E. Alps. Rare. April–May. **434**

ELAEAGNACEAE

HIPPOPHAË *L.* **H. rhamnoides** *L.* SEA BUCKTHORN. The only alpine species. A shrub 1–3 m. tall, sometimes more, spreading by suckers, with occasional spines. Lvs. narrow-lance-shaped, to 8 cm. long, covered with silvery scales at least on underside. Fls. minute, appearing before the lvs., males and females on different plants. Fruit round, pale orange, 6–8 mm. across, grouped along the stems on short stalks. ✤ Sandy places, riversides. To 1900 m. Alps. March. (Fruits in September.) **313**

ONAGRACEAE (OENOTHERACEAE)—EVENING PRIMROSE FAMILY

Annuals or perennials with undivided lvs. Fls. solitary in lf.-axils or in spikes (racemes); both sexes normally present; often with a long 'calyx-tube'. Sepals and petals 2 or 4 in alpine species. Fruit a capsule, arising from an ovary below the floral parts, with a single stigma.

EPILOBIUM *L.* WILLOWHERB. Alpine species herbaceous, with the lower lvs. opposite or in alternate-facing opposite pairs, or in whorls of 3–4; upper lvs. usually spirally arranged. Fls. typically erect, solitary or in clusters, radially symmetrical, 4-parted, with a very short 'calyx-tube'. Petals often 2-lobed.

Fruit a long capsule containing hairy-plumed seeds.

Apart from *E. fleischeri*, the numerous alpine species are botanically confused, very similar, rather insignificant and hybridise freely; only two are described as examples. Several species reach 1500–1600 m.; those that exceed this level are *E. alsinifolium* Vill., to 2900 m.; *E. collinum* Gmel., to 2300 m.; *E. duriaei* Gay, to 2500 m.; *E. montanum* L., to 2600 m.; *E. nutans* Schmidt, to 2450 m.; *E. palustre* L., to 2300 m.; *E. parviflorum* Schreb., to 1700 m.

E. fleischeri *Hochst.* ALPINE WILLOW-HERB. A rather sprawling perennial with 20–40 cm. stems arising from a thick rootstock and suckering underground stems. Lvs. thick, stiff, narrow lance-shaped, lightly toothed. Fls. bright pink, about 2½ cm. across, in short terminal clusters mingled with lvs., the 4 spoon-shaped petals and 4 strap-shaped sepals alternating; style thick, half length of stamens.

✿ Gravels, moraines, watersides, preferring acid soils. To 2700 m. Alps. July–September. **95**

The similar *E. dodonaei* Vill., a taller, erect plant with larger lvs. and style as long as stamens, reaches 1500 m.

E. angustifolium L. **(Chamaenerion angustifolium** (L.) *Scop.*). ROSEBAY WILLOWHERB, FIREWEED. An erect perennial 50–120 cm. tall arising from a creeping rootstock, with 5–15 cm. thin, narrow lance-shaped lvs. tapering at each end, all spirally arranged. Fls. many in a long, dense spike (raceme), held horizontally, 2–3 cm. across on 1–1½ cm. stalks; petals deep pink, upper part wider than lower, sepals purple; style

longer than stamens. Capsule to 8 cm. long.

✿ Clearings, waste ground, damp sandy places. To 2530 m. Pyrenees; Alps; Apennines. Norway to 1450 m. (Britain to 1000 m.) June–September. **94**

E. trigonum *Schrank* **(E. alpestre** (*Jacq.*) *Krock.*). An erect perennial 30–100 cm. tall, with hollow stems carrying 3–4 lines of hairs; lvs. in whorls of 3 (4), lance-shaped, rounded at base, toothed, stalkless. Fls. pink, 1–1½ cm. across, on long 'calyx-tube'.

✿ Damp rocks, open woods. To 2400 m. Pyrenees; Alps. July–August. **1003**

E. alpinum L. **(E. anagallidifolium** *Lam.*). Perennial, 2–20 cm. tall, forming a tuft of slender 4-sided stems arising from one rootstock; lvs. opposite, lance-shaped, lightly toothed. Fls. pink, 4–5 mm. across; capsules at first inclined, then erect.

✿ Streams, marshes, on acid soils. To 3000 m. Pyrenees; Alps; N. Apennines. Norway to 1750 m. (Britain to 1300 m.) June–September. **1004**

CIRCAEA L. **C. alpina** L. ALPINE ENCHANTER'S NIGHTSHADE. Perennial, with tuberous rootstock, 5–30 cm. tall, sometimes sprawling. Lvs. 2–6 cm. long; thin, shining above; triangular, pointed, heart-shaped at base, with large, distant teeth. Fls. in a cluster at the end of a stalk that elongates markedly as the fruit ripens. Fls. very small, with 2 sepals and 2 petals, followed by bristly 1–1½ mm. fruits.

✿ Damp woods, on rotting timber, by streamsides, stony places, preferring acid soils. To 2150 m. Pyrenees; Alps; Apennines. (N. Britain.) June–August. **1002**

UMBELLIFERAE—COW PARSLEY FAMILY

Alpine species annual or perennial herbaceous plants with furrowed stems, the centres spongy or hollow. Lvs. alternate, usually greatly divided, the bases of their stalks forming a sheath around the main stem. Fls. typically in an umbrella-like cluster (umbel) which usually consists of one ring of 'spokes' bearing subsidiary umbels; there is often a whorl (involucre) of lf.-like appendages (bracts) at the base of the umbels. The umbels are sometimes compressed and even stalkless, with minute fls. in the centre of a large, showy involucre (*Bupleurum, Astrantia, Hacquetia*), or the fls. may be carried in round or oblong heads (*Eryngium*).

Fls. with 5 petals, sometimes very unequal; calyx with 5 small unequal teeth, or sometimes absent. Stamens 5, alternating with petals, styles 2. Sexes sometimes separate, sometimes together. Fruit of 2 dry carpels with a single seed in each.

Many species are extremely similar and have been placed at different times in several genera, though synonyms have been largely omitted in this treatment. Identification is often difficult with the cow-parsley-like species, and ripe seeds are very often essential for correct naming. Owing to this problem only a selection of the more prominent and interesting species of the latter type has been described here, without reference to many others which exceed 1500 m. altitude.

Flowers with short or no stalks, compressed into centre of a prominent involucre

HACQUETIA *Necker.* **H. epipactis** *DC.* (**Dondia epipactis** *Spreng.*). A hairless perennial with 5–10 cm., long-stalked, bright green lvs. deeply cut into 5 or more toothed segments. Fl. stem 10–25 cm. tall. Fls. yellow, tiny, in centre of green, spreading involucre of 5–6 bracts.

✿ Open woods, scrub. To 1500 m. E. Alps. April–May. **440**

ASTRANTIA *L.* MASTERWORT. Herbaceous perennials with deeply lobed lvs. Fls. white or pinkish, with projecting stamens, in compressed, short-stalked umbels; involucre of many bracts, sometimes coloured.

A. major *L.* GREAT MASTERWORT, MOUNTAIN SANICLE, BLACK HELLEBORE.

30–100 cm. tall. Lvs. 8–15 cm. across, long-stalked with 3–7 coarsely toothed lobes. Bracts numerous, 1–2 cm. long, sometimes slightly toothed at tip, green and purple above, whitish below. Fls. greenish white or pinkish; umbel convex, 1–5 cm. across. Fruit 6–8 mm. long.

Several subspecies have been named, based on different proportions and degree of toothing on bracts.

✿ Meadows, woods, preferring calcareous soils. To 2000 m. Pyrenees; Alps; Apennines. (Britain: introduced.) June–September. **441**

A. minor *L.* LESSER MASTERWORT. A slender plant 15–40 cm. tall. Lvs. divided into 5–9 toothed, narrow lobes. Umbels about 1 cm. across, bracts 1–2 cm. long, sometimes red-flushed.

✤ Meadows, stony places, woods, preferring acid soils. To 2700 m. Pyrenees; Alps; Apennines. July–August. **442**

A. carniolica *Wulf.* CARNIC MASTERWORT. A slender plant 15–20 cm. tall with fl. stalks of very varying length. Lvs. cut to centre into 5 oblong, toothed lobes Fls. white, exceeding the 10–12 bracts 5–10 mm. long.

✤ Meadows, scrub, woods, preferring calcareous soils. To 1600 (2100) m. S.E. Alps. July–August.

A. bavarica *Schultz.* BAVARIAN MASTERWORT. Resembling *A. carniolica,* but 20–50 cm. tall, with few umbels; lvs. cut to centre into 5 wedge-shaped lobes; bracts 10–15, white, exceeding the fls.

✤ Meadows, scrub, woods, on limestone. To 2300 m. E. Alps.

With compound umbels, the secondary ones often surrounded by a prominent involucre of broad bracts

BUPLEURUM L. HARES-EAR. Annuals or (alpine species) perennials; hairless. Lvs. undivided. Fls. small, yellow or purplish, few to many, in loose compound umbels, often with unequal stalks. Calyx without teeth. Fruit with prominent ridges.

B. longifolium L. A pale green plant 15–100 cm. tall. Stem hollow and leafy. Lower lvs. long-stalked, oval to round, 15–20 cm. long, 5–6 cm. wide, with 1 main vein. Upper lvs. stalkless, with pronounced basal lobes, clasping the stem. Umbels of 5–12 rays; secondary umbels of about 20 fls., surrounded by 5–8 yellowish, separate, elliptic bracts.

✤ Open woods, meadows, stony places. To 2000 m. Alps. Rare. July–August. **1089**

B. angulosum L. 10–50 cm. tall. Lower lvs. very long and narrow, stalked, with 1 main vein; stem leafy;

upper lvs. broader, finally just clasping the stem. Umbels of 3–6 rays; secondary umbels surrounded by 5–6 yellowish green, separate, broad, rounded bracts.

✤ Rocks, stony places. 1500–2300 m. Pyrenees. July–August. **1090**

B. stellatum L. STARRY HARES-EAR. 10–40 cm. tall. Lvs. long and narrow, stalkless, with 1 main vein, forming grass-like tufts; stem seldom leafy, except for 1 lf. which sheaths stem. Umbels of 3–6 rays, lower involucre of 2–5 long lf.-like bracts; secondary umbels surrounded by 5–10 short, broad, pointed bracts, joined together in a cup-shape.

✤ Rocks, meadows, scrub, on acid soils. 1000–2650 m. Alps. Rare. July–August. **1091**

B. petraeum L. (**B. graminifolium** *Vahl.*). ROCK HARES-EAR. 20–30 cm. tall. Lvs. long and narrow, stalkless, with 3 distinct veins, forming grass-like tufts; stem usually leafless. Umbels of 5–10 rays, lower involucre of 3–5 narrow, unequal, pointed bracts; secondary umbels surrounded by 5–7 yellowish, separate, oval to lance-shaped bracts.

✤ Rocks, stony places, screes, preferring limestone. 1300–2300 (3000) m. Alps. Uncommon. July–August. **1092**

B. ranunculoides L. 5–60 cm. tall. Lvs. linear to oval, broadest near base, with 3 distinct veins; upper lvs. pointed-oval, clasping the stem; stem leafy. Umbels of 4–10 unequal, loosely radiating rays; secondary umbels of 5–6 oval to elliptic, yellowish, separate bracts, barely exceeding the fls.

✤ Meadows, rocky places, preferring limestone. 1000–2600 (3000) m. Pyrenees; Alps; Apennines. July–August. **1093**

Flowers in dense heads

ERYNGIUM L. Stiff, spiny perennials, often whitish or bluish. Lvs. usually deeply cut and toothed, sometimes entire. Fls. small, in dense globular or elliptic heads, with a whorl of stiff, leafy, spiny bracts at the base.

E. spinalba *Vill.* SILVER ERYNGO. A sturdy, whitish, very spiny plant 20–40 cm. tall. Lower lvs. deeply cut, spiny, with long stalks. Upper lvs. similar, but smaller and stalkless. Fls. white, in oval heads 4–5 cm. long. Involucre of 9–20 upright, spiny-lobed bracts.
✤ Rocks, screes, preferring limestone. 1400–1700 m. W. Alps. Rare. June–July. **437**

E. alpinum *L.* ALPINE ERYNGO, QUEEN OF THE ALPS. 30–60 cm. tall, bluish green, with long-stalked, undivided lower lvs. 25 cm. long, 20 cm. wide, with toothed edge and small spines. Fls. blue on egg-shaped head 3–5 cm. long. Involucre of 10–20 radiating, supple, bright violet-blue bracts with numerous spines.
✤ Meadows, stony places, preferring limestone. 1000–2500 m. Alps. Uncommon. Often cultivated. July–September. **439**

E. bourgatii *Gouan.* PYRENEAN ERYNGO. Robust, 20–40 cm. tall, bluish. Lower lvs. with subsidiary divisions and white patterning on veins, and long stalks; upper lvs. stalkless, similarly divided; all very spiny. Fls. blue, in dense round head. Involucre of 10–12 narrow, pointed bracts.
✤ Stony places, meadows. 1000–2000 m. Pyrenees. July–August. **438**

Flowers in distinctly stalked, usually compound umbels without pronounced secondary involucre

CHAEROPHYLLUM *L.* **C. hirsutum** *L.* HAIRY CHERVIL. A hairy, darkish green perennial 30–120 cm. tall. Lvs. divided into 3 main sections of wedge-shaped segments. Fls. white to pink, petals edged with minute hairs, in loose umbels. Involucral bracts of secondary umbels radiating or pointing downwards. A variable plant with several subspecies, some of which have more fern-like lvs. than that illustrated.
✤ Damp meadows, woods, shady banks. To 2480 m. Alps; Apennines. July–August. **443**

MYRRHIS *Mill.* **M. odorata** *(L.) Scop.* SWEET CICELY. A stout, densely hairy perennial 60–120 cm. tall, strongly aromatic, with hollow stems. Lvs. large, 30 cm. long, divided, fern-like, lobes coarsely toothed, paler green below. Fls. white, with unequal petals, in terminal umbels, 1–5 cm. across. Fruit 2–2½ cm. long, narrow-elliptic, strongly ridged, grouped in upright clusters.
✤ Woods, stony, grassy, humid places, preferring calcareous soils. Sometimes cultivated. To 2000 m. Pyrenees; Alps; Apennines. (Britain: probably native.) June–August. **1105**

MOLOPOSPERMUM *Koch.* **M. peloponnesiacum** *(L.) Koch.* (**M. cicutarium** *DC.*). A hairless perennial 80–200 cm. tall with an unpleasant smell. Lvs. deeply divided. Fls. white, umbels in loose clusters with an involucre of 6–9 small bracts. Fruit ovoid, 1 cm. long, 7 mm. broad.
✤ Stony places, hillsides, undergrowth, preferring acid soils. Rare. To 2000 m. Pyrenees; Alps. May–August. **1106**

PLEUROSPERMUM *Hoffm.* **P. austriacum** *(L.) Hoffm.* A large hairless perennial, 80–150 cm. tall, sometimes more, with hollow stems. Lvs. stalked, divided into 3 main segments of rather strap-shaped lobes. Umbels 15–30 cm. across, of 20–40 rays. Fls. white. Fruit yellow, 1 cm. long, ½ cm. or more across.
✤ Humid stony places, open woods, preferring calcareous soils. To 2000 m. Alps. June–September.

CARUM *L.* **C. carvi** *L.* CARAWAY. A hairless biennial, branched, upright, 25–60 cm. tall. Stem hollow, furrowed.

Lvs. linear-oblong to slightly triangular, deeply divided into linear to oval lobes. Umbels 2-4 cm. across, somewhat irregular, bracts 1-4 or usually none. Fls. white, outer ones of each umbel larger than the inner ones. Fruit oblong, just under ½ cm. long, aromatic when crushed: seeds used as flavouring. ❧ Meadows, waste places. To 2200 m. Pyrenees; Alps; Apennines. (Britain: naturalised rarely in waste places.) May–July. **1108**

PIMPINELLA *L.* Perennials with divided lvs. and compound umbels, bracts few or none. Fls. white or pinkish. Fruit oblong or oval, flattened along sides.

P. major *L.* (**P. magna** *L.*). GREATER BURNET SAXIFRAGE. Robust, upright, virtually hairless, 50-120 cm. tall. Stem brittle, deeply furrowed, sometimes reddish towards base. Lvs. deeply divided, lobes of basal lvs. opposite, oval, toothed, with short stalks. Upper lvs. stalkless, sometimes with 3 lobes, topmost stem lvs. quite small, sometimes with short stalk which sheaths the stem. Umbels flat-topped, 3-6 cm. across. Fls. white or pinkish or occasionally reddish (*var.* **rubra** (Hoppe) F. & B.). ❧ Stony places, meadows, hedgebanks, wood margins. To 2300 m. Pyrenees; Alps; Apennines. (Britain.) May–July. **444**

P. saxifraga *L.* BURNET SAXIFRAGE. Similar to *P. major*, but more slender and softly hairy, 30-100 cm. tall. Stem tough, slightly furrowed, rough. Lvs. not so divided, extremely variable in shape. Topmost stem lvs. either absent or very small, sheathing stalks, sometimes purplish. Umbels flat-topped, 2-5 cm. across. Fls. white. ❧ Dry grassy, stony places, preferring calcareous soils. To 2400 m. Pyrenees; Alps; Apennines. Norway to 1050 m. (Britain.) July–October.

ATHAMANTA *L.* **A. cretensis** *L.* Perennial, 15-30 cm. tall, hairy. Lvs. deeply divided, lobes narrow strap-shaped, stalkless. Umbel of 6-15 unequal rays. Involucre of narrow-oblong, pointed bracts. Fls. white. Fruit up to 1 cm. long, 2 mm. wide. ❧ Rocky places, screes, preferring limestone. To 2700 m. Alps; Apennines. June–August. **1110**

MEUM *Mill.* **M. athamanticum** *Jacq.* SPIGNEL, MEU, BALDMONEY. A tufted, hairless perennial, 20-60 cm. tall, very aromatic. Stems striped, hollow. Lvs. nearly all basal, greatly divided, segments very slender, stalked. Bases of old stalks remaining, forming a coarse fibrous crown to the rootstock. Umbels 3-6 cm. across, of 6-15 rays. Bracts linear, 0-8. Fls. white. ❧ Meadows. To 2500 (2800) m. Pyrenees; Alps; Apennines. (Britain.) June–October. **1109**

LIGUSTICUM *L.* LOVAGE. Hairless perennials with divided, stalked lvs. Umbels compound, bracts none to many. Fls. white to pink or purplish red. Fruit oblong or egg-shaped with prominent ridges.

L. mutellinoides (*Crantz*) *Vill.* (**L. simplex** *Vill.*, **Gaya simplex** *Gaud.*). 5-25 cm. tall but usually low-growing, with lvs. all basal, deeply divided into linear or narrow-oblong lobes. Remains of old lvs. surrounding the thick rootstock. Umbel of 10-15 short-stalked, 1-3 cm., small umbels. Fls. pinkish or greenish white. Calyx with distinct teeth. Involucre of 5-10 forked bracts with white edges, at least as long as umbel stalks. ❧ Stony, grassy places, exposed crests, preferring acid soils. Uncommon. 1900-3350 m. Alps. July–August. **446**

L. mutellina (*L.*) *Crantz* (**Meum mutellina** *Gaertn.*). Similar to *L. mutellinoides*, but taller—10-60 cm.; with

1–5 involucral bracts which rapidly fall; calyx minute. Stem robust, ridged. Lvs. large, very much divided, variously shaped but lobes more or less linear. Fls. white to deep pink and pinkish purple. Umbel of 10–15 small umbels.

⚘ Open woods, damp meadows. To 3020 m. Alps. July–August. 1095

L. ferulaceum *All.* A much-branched plant 30–60 cm. tall, with very stout stem and pronounced sheaths to stem lvs., carrying a dense head of 15–30 white-fld. umbels on almost equal stalks. Calyx 5-toothed. Bracts cut into narrow segments and edged with white.

⚘ Rocks, screes, on limestone. 1500–2100 m. W. Alps (rare); Apennines. June–July. 1107

XATARTIA or **XATARDIA** *Meissn.* **X. scaber** *Meissn.* A very sturdy, thick, robust perennial, 10–25 cm. tall. Lvs. deeply divided into short, wide lobes, stems widening and thickening to encircle stem and other lf. bases, giving plant a very bulky appearance. Main umbels rounded, dense, on slightly hairy, unequal stems which become thickened towards the base. Involucre of about 5 slightly linear bracts. Fls. greenish yellow.

⚘ Screes, on acid formations. 1600–2300 m. E. Pyrenees. Rare. August–September. 1096

ENDRESSIA *J. Gay.* **E. pyrenaica** *Gay.* A hairless perennial, 5–70 cm. tall. Stem hollow, angled. Lvs. all basal, divided into long, narrow, wedge-shaped lobes; lf. stalks becoming thicker at base. Umbels compound, semicircular in section. Fls. white. Fruit oval.

⚘ Fields, meadows. 900–2200 m. E. Pyrenees. August–September. 1094

ANGELICA *L.* Tall perennials. Lvs. divided into large segments. Umbels compound. Bracts few or absent. Fls. greenish, white or pink. Fruit oval, with 2 wide wings on each side.

A. sylvestris *L.* WILD ANGELICA, JACK-JUMP-ABOUT. Robust, to 2 m. or more tall. Stem hollow, greenish purple, ridged, hairy towards base. Lower lvs. large, 30–60 cm. long, divided into three main lobes of paired segments, lower ones stalked. Main lf. stalks with deep channel on upper face, widening and sheathing stem. Upper lvs. smaller, divided, some reduced to swollen sheaths which sometimes enclose the fl. buds. Umbels 3–15 cm. across, of 20–40 small umbels. Fls. white or pink. Fruit ½ cm. long, wings dry, stiff, tissue-like.

⚘ Clearings, stony places, shady pastures. To 1780 m. Pyrenees; Alps. Norway to 1200 m. (Britain.) July–September. 1097

A. razulii *Gouan.* (also spelt **razulsi** or **razoulsii**). A smaller edition of *A. sylvestris*, and sometimes considered its *var. elatior* Wahl., 50–100 cm. tall. Lf. segments much narrower; no stem-lvs. Umbels of 25–40 small secondary umbels. Fls. white to pinkish. Fruit slightly longer than wide, again with dry wings.

⚘ Fields. To 1800 m. Pyrenees. June–August. 1098

A. archangelica *L.* (**Archangelica officinalis** *Hoffm.*). ANGELICA. Only at alpine levels in *ssp.* **norvegica** (*Rupr.*) *Nordh.* Very similar to *A. sylvestris*, but stems are all green. Lf. segments fewer, more rounded and more toothed, sometimes extending down lf. stalk. Umbels more globular, of 20–40 small umbels. Fls. greenish white to green. Fruit wings corky. Plant aromatic.

⚘ River-banks, waste places. Often cultivated for use as a confection. To 1600 m. Norway. (Britain: naturalised.) July–August. 1099

PEUCEDANUM *L.* **P. ostruthium** (*L.*) *Koch.* MASTERWORT. An erect, downy perennial 30–100 cm. tall, with thick, irregular, horizontal rootstock. Stem hollow, ridged. Lvs. divided into few rounded segments, often irregularly lobed, downy beneath. One or two stem-lvs., divided, with stalks widening and sheathing stems. Umbels 5–10 cm. across of 20–50 small umbels; no bracts. Fls. white or pinkish. Fruit up to ½ cm. long, slightly longer than wide.

❧ Fields, stony places, streams. Sometimes cultivated for medicinal purposes. 1400–2790 m. Pyrenees; Alps; Apennines. (Britain: naturalised.) June–August. 1111

HERACLEUM *L.* Annuals, biennials or perennials of great size. Lvs. divided into broad segments. Umbels compound. Fls. white, petals sometimes unequal. Fruit round to oval-oblong, flattened, with broad wings.

H. sphondylium *L.* cow parsnip, hogweed, keck. A variable, erect biennial 50–200 cm. tall, robust. Stems ridged, hollow, with down-pointing hairs. Lvs. 15–60 cm. long, hairy on both sides, stalks thickening and sheathing stem at base. Segments stalked, very variable in shape, rounded with toothed edges. Fls. white or pinkish, in rather flattened umbels 5–15 cm. across, of 7–20 small umbels. Bracts few or none. Fruit almost round, whitish.

❧ Meadows, damp woods, paths. To 2500 m. Pyrenees; Alps; Apennines. (Britain.) June–September. 1100

H. austriacum *L.* Similar to *H. sphondylium*, but only 10–60 cm. tall; stem slightly furrowed. Lvs. of 3–9 more regularly rounded, less irregular, lightly toothed segments. Fls. white. Fruit ½–1 cm. long.

❧ Fields, scrub. 1000–2110 m. E. Alps. July–September. 1101

LASERPITIUM *L.* Perennials with lvs. of triangular outline, deeply divided, and large umbels of 10–50 secondary umbels. Involucre of numerous bracts. Fls. white to pink. Fruit with 8 large wings.

L. siler *L.* **(Siler montanum** *Crantz*). SERMOUNTAIN. Hairless, 30–100 cm. tall, blue-green. Lf. segments narrow-elliptical, not toothed, 2–7 cm. long, ½–2½ cm. wide. Involucral bracts spread out. Rays long. Fls. white. Fruits ½–1 cm. or more long, strong smelling.

❧ Open woods, stony places, preferring limestone. To 2000 (2400) m. Pyrenees; Alps. July–August. **445**

L. latifolium *L.* Hairless, 60–150 cm. tall, slightly bluish. Lvs. stalked, divided into rounded, undivided toothed segments which are also stalked. Umbels large, of 30–50 stalked secondary umbels. Involucre of numerous bracts. Fls. white. Fruit bristly, wings crisp and wavy.

❧ Open woods, rocks, dry places, preferring limestone. To 2000 m. Pyrenees; Alps; Apennines. July–August. 1102

L. gallicum *L.* Hairless or nearly so, 30–100 cm. tall. Lvs. large, stalked, divided into 3–6 variable, stalked segments which are again divided into pointed lobes, shining dark green. Fls. white to pink.

❧ Dry and stony places, preferring limestone. Uncommon. To 2000 m. Pyrenees; Alps. June–July. 1103

L. halleri *Crantz* **(L. panax** *Gouan*). More or less hairy, 15–60 cm. tall, with robust, slightly ridged stem. Lvs. almost all basal, divided into stalked, opposite segments themselves subdivided into fern-like lobes. Umbel large, of 20–50 secondary umbels. Fls. white. Fruit large, up to 1 cm. long, hairless.

❧ Dry slopes, clearings, on granite. To 2710 m. Alps. July–August. 1104

CORNACEAE—DOGWOOD FAMILY

Trees, shrubs or occasionally herbaceous plants with undivided lvs., fls. clustered, small, 4-parted, with ovary below a fleshy disk and giving rise to a fleshy fruit (drupe).

Cornus sanguinea L., the COMMON DOGWOOD, a shrub with dark red twigs, white fls. and black fruit, reaches 1550 m.,

Cornus mas L., the CORNELIAN CHERRY, a tree with very early yellow fls. in small round clusters, and red fruit, reaches 1530 m.

CHAMAEPERICLYMENUM *Hill.* **C. suecicum** (L.) *Asch. & Graebn.* (**Cornus suecica** L.). DWARF CORNEL. A perennial herbaceous plant 6–20 cm. tall, with erect, sometimes shortly branched stems, often carpeting the ground for large areas. Lvs. paired, 1–3 cm. long, ovate to elliptic, stalkless, green and downy above, bluish and hair-less below. Fls. very small, dark brownish purple, short-stalked, 8–25 in a small head surrounded by 4 white lf.-like 5–8 mm. bracts, giving the impression of a single fl. Fruit red, berry-like, clustered.

☙ Moors, typically under heather or bilberry. To 1200 m. Norway. (Britain to 1000 m.: very local.) June–August. 925

PYROLACEAE—WINTERGREEN FAMILY

Evergreen perennial herbaceous plants with creeping rhizome; some species probably partly saprophytic (living on decayed vegetable matter): typical plants of pine woods. Fls. regular, 5-parted, with small calyx and separate petals, 1 stigma, and ovary within petals; fruit capsular.

PYROLA *L.* (also spelt **PIROLA**). WINTERGREEN. Stems with alternate lvs., often reduced to a loose rosette; fls. carried all round the fl. stem in a loose spike (raceme). Fls. without disk scented.

P. minor *L.* SMALL WINTERGREEN. Stems very short or lvs. all basal, ovate or oval, wavy, pale green, 2½–4 cm. long with 2½–3 cm. stalk always shorter than blade. Fl. ste m 7–30 cm. tall, with 6 mm. wide, pinkish, rounded fls. fairly close together. Style straight, 1–2 mm. long, shorter than stamens.

☙ Dry woods, scrub, moors, rock ledges. To 2700 m. Pyrenees; Alps; Apennines. Norway to 1620 m. (Britain to 1200 m.) June–August. 1116

P. media *Sw.* INTERMEDIATE WINTER-GREEN. Lvs. all basal, round or oval, slightly wavy, dark green, 3–5 cm. long with 2½–5½ cm. stalk at least as long as blade. Fl. stem 15–30 cm. tall, with 1 cm. wide, white, pink-flushed, rounded fls. in rather loose spike. Style straight, 5 mm. long, longer than stamens.

☙ Damp woods, mossy places, moors. To 2200 m. Alps; Apuan Alps; N. Apennines. (Britain.) June–August. 1117

P. rotundifolia *L.* ROUND-LEAVED WINTERGREEN. Lvs. all basal, round or oval, slightly wavy, dark green, shining

$2\frac{1}{2}$–$5\frac{1}{2}$ cm. long with 3–7 cm. stalk longer than blade. Fl. stem 10–40 cm. tall, with 12 mm., pure white, cup-shaped fls. in rather loose spike. Style reddish, curved, projecting beyond petals and stamens.

❧ Damp woods, scrub, marshes, rock ledges, preferring limestone. To 2280 m. Pyrenees; Alps; N. Apennines. (Britain.) June–September. **1118**

P. norvegica *Knaben.* NORTHERN WINTERGREEN. Similar to *P. rotundifolia*, with round to round-oval lvs. on which veins form a network round margins (which they do not in *P. rotundifolia*). Style whitish, long and markedly curved; lower part of calyx with a white 'collar'.

❧ Birch woods, willow scrub, damp moors, rock ledges, preferring limestone. To 1430 m. Norway. July–August. **1115**

P. chlorantha *Sw.* GREENISH WINTERGREEN. Lvs. all basal, rounded to oval, $1\frac{1}{2}$–2 cm. long with 2–$2\frac{1}{2}$ cm. stalk longer than blade. Fl. stem 5–30 cm. tall, with 8–10 mm. yellowish green, cup-shaped fls. in rather loose spike. Style curved, projecting beyond petals and stamens.

❧ Dry open woods, grassy places. To 2200 m. Pyrenees; Alps. June–August. **1114**

ORTHILIA *Raf.* (**RAMISCHIA** *Garcke*). **O. secunda** (*L.*) *House* (**R. secunda** (*L.*) *Garcke*, **Pyrola secunda** *L.*). NODDING WINTERGREEN. Similar in habit to *Pyrola*, but fls. all on one side of the stem, and containing a disk bearing 10 small glands. Rhizome up to 1 m. long, carrying stems 2–10 cm. long with pointed, ovate, lightly toothed, pale green lvs. 2–4 cm. long with 1 cm. stalks. Fls. 5 mm. wide, rounded, greenish

white, with straight style projecting beyond petals.

❧ Woods, damp rock ledges, usually on limestone or gypsum. To 2200 m. Pyrenees; Alps; Apennines. (Britain.) July–August. **1112**

MONESES *Salisb.* **M. uniflora** (*L.*) *Gray* (**Pyrola uniflora** *L.*). ONE-FLOWERED WINTERGREEN. Resembling *Pyrola* in habit, but with opposite lvs., which are 1–$2\frac{1}{2}$ cm. long, rounded, lightly toothed, light green, on stalk shorter than blade. Fl. stem 5–15 (28) cm. tall with solitary, white, fragrant $1\frac{1}{2}$–2 cm. flat fl. with straight, projecting stigma.

❧ Moss and humus in damp woods. To 2100 m. Pyrenees; Alps; Apennines. (Britain: very local.) May–August. **1113**

MONOTROPACEAE— BIRDSNEST FAMILY

Similar to *Pyrolaceae* and originally included in that family, but differing in being entirely saprophytic (living on decaying matter) and hence completely yellowish or white.

MONOTROPA *L.* **M. hypopitys** *L.* YELLOW BIRDSNEST, DUTCHMANS PIPE. With unbranched stems 8–30 cm. tall, yellowish to ivory-white, waxy, covered especially near base with $\frac{1}{2}$–1 cm. scale-like lvs. Fls. of same colour, scented, 1–$1\frac{1}{2}$ cm. long, tubular bell-shaped, up to 11 in a short, tight spike (raceme) which forms a crook shape as fls. start opening, gradually straightening till stem is erect in fruit.

❧ Beech and pine woods. To 1800 m. Pyrenees; Alps. (Britain.) June–September. **1119**

ERICACEAE—HEATHER FAMILY

Shrubs with undivided lvs., evergreen unless otherwise specified. Fls. with both sexes present, usually regular, with 4–6 (3–7) divisions. Calyx typically small, persisting in fruit; corolla usually tubular, bell- or funnel-shaped, petals sometimes separate, fixed on to the edge of a fleshy disk. Stamens usually twice as many as corolla lobes, not attached to corolla. Style 1. Fruit a capsule, berry or drupe. Mostly lime-hating plants.

RHODODENDRON *L.* European alpine species are shrubs with alternate short-stalked lvs., and 5-parted fls. in terminal clusters (racemes), Corolla funnel-shaped, very slightly irregular. Stamens 5 or 10. Fruit a capsule.

R. ferrugineum *L.* ALPENROSE. A rounded, hairless shrub 20–100 cm. tall with rounded-oblong lvs. 3–5 cm. long, 1–2 cm. broad, dark green and shining above, rusty-coloured with glandular scales below. Calyx lobes very short, with blunt-oval lobes; fls. pale to rich pink, 1½ cm. long.
✣ Meadows, stony places, rocks, open woods, preferring acid soils, but also on limestone formations. To 3200 m. Pyrenees; Alps; N. Apennines. May–August. **447**

R. hirsutum *L.* HAIRY ALPENROSE. An erect shrub 20–100 cm. tall, with downy hairs on young stems, fl. stalks and calyx; lvs. bright green on both sides, with a few reddish glands below, toothed and hairy on edges. Calyx lobes narrow, pointed. Fls. pink, about 13 mm. long.
✣ Meadows, stony places, open woods, on limestone. To 2600 m. C. and E. Alps (very rare in Savoy). May–July. **448**

R. lapponicum (*L.*) *Wahl.* LAPLAND RHODODENDRON. A gnarled, usually prostrate bush 5–10 cm. tall. Lvs. elliptic, dark green, leathery, covered with rusty-coloured hairs below. Fls. mauve-pink, to 1 cm. long.
✣ Heaths, dry exposed ridges, gravels, on calcareous soils. To 1320 m. Norway. June–July. **449**

RHODOTHAMNUS *Reichb.* **R. chamaecistus** (*L.*) *Reichb.* (**Rhododendron chamaecistus** *L.*). DWARF ALPENROSE. The only species. A shrub to 40 cm. tall, with leathery lvs. 8–10 mm. long and 2–4 mm. wide, elliptic, hairy on edges, bright green on both sides. Fls. pink, 1–3 together, flattish, with separate petals; 10 stamens and single style prominent. Fruit a capsule.
✣ Stony places, on limestone. To 2400 m. E. Alps. May–July. **450**

LOISELEURIA *Desv.* **L. procumbens** (*L.*) *Desv.* (**Azalea procumbens** *L.*). CREEPING AZALEA. The only species. An entirely prostrate shrub forming an intricate mat of 10–30 cm. branches carrying close-packed, oval to oblong, leathery 3–8 mm. lvs. Fls. 1–5 together, bell-shaped, 5-lobed, pink, 4–5 mm. long. Fruit a capsule.
✣ Dry meadows and heaths, rocks, almost always on acid soils. 1500–3000 m. Pyrenees; Alps. Norway to 1920 m. (N. Britain to 1300 m.) May–July. **451**

PHYLLODOCE *Salisb.* **P. caerulea** (*L.*) *Bab.* BLUE MOUNTAIN HEATH. A heath-like bush 10–20 (40) cm. tall. Lvs. alternate, strap-shaped, leathery, with a hairy furrow below. 5–9 mm. long, close-packed on erect branches. Fls. 2–6, with reddish, glandular stalks and calyx, and 7–8 mm. bluish purple corolla, oval-pitcher-shaped, 5-toothed at mouth. Fruit a capsule.

❀ Rocky moors, bilberry heaths, gravels. 2000–2600 m. C. Pyrenees: one locality. Norway to 1850 m.: abundant. (Britain: one locality.) June–August.

462

ANDROMEDA *L.* **A. polifolia** *L.* (**Rhododendron polifolium** *Scop.*). MARSH ANDROMEDA. A hairless shrub 10–40 cm. tall, with creeping rhizome and thin erect stems. Lvs. alternate, strap-shaped to narrow-elliptic, $1\frac{1}{2}$–$3\frac{1}{2}$ cm. long, dark green above, bluish below, with inrolled margins. Fls. 2–8 together, nodding on curved stalks 2–4 times length of 5–7 mm. pink corolla, flat-pitcher-shaped, 5-toothed at mouth. Fruit a capsule.

❀ Sphagnum bogs, wet heaths. To 2000 m. Pyrenees; Alps. Norway to 1150 m. (Britain.) June–August. **463**

CASSIOPE *Don.* **C. tetragona** (*L.*) *Don.* The only alpine species. A shrub 10–30 cm. tall, the erect stems covered with hard, scale-like, overlapping lvs. in 4 ranks. Fls. solitary in lf.-axils, bell-shaped; white with 5 pinkish lobes, stalks and calyx red; or yellowish white with stalks and sepals yellowish green; fragrant. Fruit a capsule.

❀ Heaths; often the dominant plant, especially on N.-facing slopes. To 1647 m. Norway. July. **464**

HARRIMANELLA *Coville.* **H. hypnoides** *Coville* (**Cassiope hypnoides** (*L.*) *Don*, **Andromeda hypnoides** *L.*). Very similar to *Cassiope* but altogether smaller: a prostrate under-shrub 5 cm. tall, forming a spreading mat of thin, upright branches with crowded $\frac{1}{8}$ in. linear, spreading lvs. Fls. solitary, terminal, rounded-bell-shaped, white with pink lobes, stalks and calyx red. *

❀ Snow-beds, especially in places which dry out in summer, on acid and mineral-ised soils. To 1870 m. Norway. July–August.

ARCTOSTAPHYLOS *Adans.* **A. uva-ursi** (*L.*) *Spreng.* BEARBERRY. A prostrate shrub with 50–200 cm. branches rooting and forming mats, with reversed-oval to elliptic lvs., wedge-shaped at base, dark green above, paler below, with netted veins. Fls. up to 12 in small dense clusters (racemes), rounded-bell-shaped, white, pink-tinged, 4–6 mm. long, on 3–4 mm. stalks. Fruit a red, glossy, round, 6–8 mm. drupe. Resembles *Vaccinium vitis-idaea*, but its lvs. are not inrolled nor spotted below.

❀ Open woods, scrub, stony places, moors. To 2780 m. Pyrenees; Alps; Apennines. Norway to 1840 m. (Britain to 1000 m.) June–September. **456**

ARCTOUS (*Gray*) *Nied.* **A. alpinus** (*L.*) *Nied.* (**Arctostaphylos alpinus** (*L.*) *Spreng*). BLACK BEARBERRY. Similar to *Arctostaphylos uva-ursi*, but deciduous; a prostrate, much-branched shrub with lvs. lightly toothed and hairy on edges, wrinkled, 1–$2\frac{1}{2}$ cm. long, bright green on both sides; old lvs. turning red in autumn, often persisting withered. Fls. 2–5 together, white, greenish inside, round-pitcher-shaped, 4 mm. long; fruit a glossy, round, 6–10 mm. drupe, first green, then red, black when ripe.*

❀ Open woods, scrub, stony places, moors. 1900–2660 m. Pyrenees; Alps (rare). Norway to 1625 m. (N. Britain to 1000 m.: very local.) May–July. **457**

VACCINIUM *L.* WHORTLEBERRY. Evergreen or deciduous shrubs with alternate lvs. Fls. 4- or 5-parted, with 8 or 10 stamens. Ovary below calyx and corolla (inferior), thus differing from *Arctostaphylos*, *Arctous* and the rest of the family, resulting in a berry on which the calyx lobes persist at the free end.

V. vitis-idaea *L.* COWBERRY, RED WHORTLEBERRY, MOUNTAIN CRANBERRY. An evergreen shrub 10–30 (80) cm. tall, with creeping rhizome and much-branched curving stems. Lvs. more or less in 2 ranks, 1–3 cm. long, thick, leathery, dark green and shining above, paler and dotted with dark glands below, margins somewhat inrolled. Fls. 3–6 in a dense, rather drooping cluster (raceme), 6 mm. long, white tinged pink, bell-shaped with recurving lobes about ⅓ length of tube. Fruit red, round, acid, edible.
❀ Dry open woods, meadows, heaths, bogs. To 3040 m. Pyrenees; Alps; N. Apennines. Norway to 1800 m. (Britain to 1150 m.) May–August. **460**

V. myrtillus *L.* BILBERRY, WHORTLE-BERRY, HUCKLEBERRY. A hairless, deciduous shrub 20–60 cm. tall, with creeping rhizome and erect branched stems; twigs green, angular. Lvs. 1–3 cm. long, pointed-oval, toothed, bright pale green, with netted veins. Fls. 1–2 in lf.-axils, 4–6 mm. long, greenish pink, rounded-pitcher-shaped with very short reflexed lobes. Fruit black with blue 'bloom', round, 8 mm. across, sweet, edible.
❀ Open woods, scrub, heaths, moors. To 2840 m. Pyrenees; Alps; N. and C. Apennines. Norway to 1700 m. (Britain to 1100 m.) April–June. **461**

V. uliginosum *L.* BOG WHORTLEBERRY. A deciduous shrub 30–50 (80) cm. tall, often slightly downy, with creeping rhizome and spreading, branched stems; twigs brownish or greyish. Lvs. 1–2½ cm. long, oval, blue-green, with netted veins. Fls. 1–4 in lf.-axils, 4 mm. long, pale pink, shortly bell-shaped, with very small reflexed lobes. Fruit black with blue 'bloom', sweet, edible but not recommended.
❀ Wet woods, bogs, moors. To 3100 m.: usually lower. Pyrenees; Alps;

N. Apennines. Norway to 1730 m. (Britain to 1150 m.) May–June. **459**

V. oxycoccus *L.* (**Oxycoccus quadripetala** *Gilib.*, **O. palustris** *Pers.*). CRANBERRY. An evergreen, prostrate sub-shrub with slender 20–80 cm. stems. Lvs. alternate, widely spaced, 4–8 mm. long, oval or oval-oblong, dark green above, bluish below, margins inrolled. Fls. 1–4 together on 1½–4 cm. stalks; corolla pink, cut into 4 narrow, pointed, almost separate 5–6 mm. lobes; stamens and style forming a projecting column. Fruit 6–8 mm. across, round or pear-shaped, red or brownish, edible. *
❀ Sphagnum bogs, wet heaths. To 2000 m. Alps. Local. (Britain: local.) May–August. **458**

CALLUNA *Salisb.* **C. vulgaris** (*L.*) *Huds.* (**Erica vulgaris** *L.*). LING, HEATHER. The only species. A bushy shrub 20–60 (120) cm. tall with branched, intertwined stems. Lvs. 1–3 mm. long, linear, stalkless, distant on main stems, arranged very closely in 4 ranks on the many short axillary shoots. Fls. in a 3–15 cm. long leafy spike; 4-parted, with deeply lobed calyx of the same pink-purple colour as the smaller, bell-shaped corolla. Stamens 8. Fruit a capsule.
❀ Moors, wet heaths, open woods, on acid soils; often the dominant plant. To 2720 m. Pyrenees; Alps; Apennines. Norway to 1350 m. (Britain.) July–October. **455**

ERICA *L.* Evergreen shrubs with narrow undivided lvs. in whorls. Fls. 4-parted; calyx deeply lobed, not petal-like as in *Calluna*; corolla pitcher- or bell-shaped or tubular, with short lobes. Stamens 8. Fruit a capsule.

Besides the species described *E. cinerea* *L.*, the BELL HEATHER, reaches 1550 m. in the Pyrenees and Alps.

E. carnea *L.* SPRING HEATH. A bushy shrub 15–60 cm. tall with sprawling

304

stems and 7 mm. pointed, linear lvs. usually in whorls of 4. Fls. in dense terminal clusters, often all facing the same way, cylindrical, bright or flesh pink, the dark purple anthers projecting.

❋ Open woods, stony places, on limestone, flowering as the snow melts. To 2650 m. Alps, more common eastwards; N. and C. Apennines. March–June.
452

E. tetralix L. CROSS-LEAVED HEATH. A loose shrub 30–60 (80) cm. tall, with branched stems; twigs downy. Lvs. linear, 2–4 mm. long, margins inrolled so that lower surface is hidden, in whorls of 4. Fls. 4–12 in rounded terminal clusters, which are nodding at first, erect in fruit; rose pink, oval pitcher-shaped, 6–7 mm. long. Calyx edged with long wavy hairs.

❋ Bogs, wet heaths, damp pastures. To 2200 m. C. and W. Pyrenees; Alps. (Britain.) June–October.
453

E. vagans L. CORNISH HEATH. A loose, hairless shrub 30–80 (100) cm. tall, with branched stems. Lvs. linear, bright green, margins inrolled, 7–10 mm. long. Fls. forming a long, dense, 8–16 cm. spike, leafy and often ending in lvs. Fls. lilac-pink, bell-shaped, 3–4 mm. long, with erect lobes, the deep purple stamens projecting; calyx not fringed.

❋ Woods, heaths, dry hillsides, preferring acid soils; often dominant. To 1800 m. Pyrenees; W. Alps (rare). (Britain.) May–August.
454

EMPETRACEAE— CROWBERRY FAMILY

EMPETRUM L. The only European genus. Low heath-like evergreen shrubs with small, alternate, undivided lvs. and

fls. 1–3 in axils, with 2 whorls of 3 similar segments (perianth), 3 stamens; fruit a juicy drupe.

E. nigrum L. CROWBERRY. A sprawling shrub with long, thin, 15–45 cm. stems rooting around the central tuft. Young twigs reddish. Lvs. dark green, 4–6 mm. long, narrow-oblong. Fls. pinkish or purplish, 1–2 mm. across, the sexes on different plants. Fruit 5 mm., rounded, black.

❋ Moors, bogs, damp stony places, on acid soils; sometimes dominant. To 3040 m. Pyrenees (rare); Alps; N. Apennines. (Britain.) May–June. **465**

E. hermaphroditum Hag. MOUNTAIN CROWBERRY. Similar to *E. nigrum* and originally included in that species, but fls. with both sexes present, the stamens often persisting around the fruit, and stems more erect, not rooting around the tuft; young twigs greenish.

❋ Moors; often dominant. To 3040 m. Alps. Norway to 1700 m. (Britain to 1100 m.) May–June.

DIAPENSIACEAE

DIAPENSIA L. **D. lapponica** L. The only European species. At first sight resembling an *Androsace*, but in fact a cushion-forming evergreen sub-shrub 2–5 cm. tall, with deep taproot, thin woody stems and dense rosettes of 5–10 mm. leathery, narrow-spoon-shaped lvs. Fls. on 1–3 cm. stalks with 1 bract near middle, white, 5-parted, with 5 mm. calyx lobes and 1 cm. rounded corolla lobes; stamens 5, fixed to corolla and alternating with its lobes; style 1, stigma 3-lobed.

❋ Exposed ridges. To 1600 m. Norway. (Britain: one locality.) May–July. **507**

PRIMULACEAE—PRIMROSE FAMILY

Almost always herbaceous plants, perennial or occasionally annual. Fls. radially symmetrical, with both sexes present, usually 5-parted, corolla salver-shaped (with lobes at right-angles to a tube), or bell- or funnel-shaped. Stamens fixed on the corolla tube; style 1; stamens near top of tube and stigma low down, or vice versa. Ovary above the calyx. Fruit a capsule.

PRIMULA *L.* PRIMROSE. Perennials, with lvs. all basal in a rosette, and fls. on erect stems, in clusters (umbels in our species), occasionally solitary; bracts present at base of clusters. Calyx 5-toothed; corolla funnel- or salver-shaped, with 5 lobes, which are usually truncated or notched, occasionally 2-lobed.

Many authorities divide the genus into groups, and this arrangement has been followed here as it somewhat simplifies identification. The genus is difficult owing to natural variation and free hybridisation (there are innumerable selected garden forms), and also because many of the species have had the same name given them by different authorities, with corresponding confusion. *Primula vulgaris* Huds., the COMMON PRIMROSE, reaches 1500 m. in the Tessin.

Flowers yellow

P. elatior (*L.*) *Hill*, or *Schreb.* OXLIP. With short, thick rootstock. Lvs. 10–20 cm. long, wrinkled, ovate, irregularly toothed, downy, with long, winged stalk. Fl. stem 10–30 cm. tall, downy, with up to 20 pale yellow fls. with orange-marked throat, 1½–2½ cm. across, flattish, on 1 cm. stalks, in a 1-sided, rather nodding cluster. Calyx 15 mm. long, 4–5 mm. wide, tapering to base, with 4 mm. lance-shaped teeth.

Ssp. **elatior** (**484**): lvs. greyish below; stalk distinct.

Ssp. **intricata** (*G. & G.*) *Lüdi*: lvs. green below, downy above; blade tapering into stalk.

✤ Woods, hedgerows, meadows. To 2645 m. Pyrenees; Alps; Apennines. (Britain: local.) March–August.　**484**

P. veris *L.* (**P. officinalis** (*L.*) *Hill*). COWSLIP. With short, thick rhizome. Lvs. 5–15 cm. long, wrinkled, ovate, toothed, downy, with long stalk. Fl. stem 10–30 cm. tall, downy, with up to 30 deep yellow fls. on short stalks in a nodding cluster. Fls. with orange spots by throat, and 1–1½ (2) cm. notched lobes forming a cup-shape. Calyx 12–15 mm. long, 6–8 mm. broad, with 2–3 mm. teeth.

Ssp. **veris** (**485**): lvs. barely hairy, with distinct winged stalk; calyx shorter than corolla tube; fls. to 1½ cm. across.

Ssp. **canescens** (*Opiz*) *Hayek*: lvs. covered below with long woolly hairs, and gradually tapering into stalk; calyx bell-shaped, longer than corolla tube; fls. to 2 cm. across. Seldom alpine.

Ssp. **columnae** (*Ten.*) *Lüdi* (**P. suaveolens** *Berk.*): lvs. covered below with long, whitish, woolly hairs; stalk often without wings; calyx shorter than corolla tube; fls. 2 cm. across.

✤ Meadows, open woods. To 2200 m. Pyrenees; Alps; Apennines. (Britain.) April–May.　**485**

P. auricula *L.* BEARS-EAR. Lvs. 5–12 cm. long, smooth, fleshy, sometimes shining, sometimes mealy, with a cartilaginous edge bearing dark glands, more or less toothed. Fls. yellow, 1½–2½ cm. across, with mealy-white throat, 2–10 (25) on a hairless 5–25 cm. stem, usually fragrant.

A variable plant of which numerous variations have been named and cultivated. The two extreme wild forms have been called:

Ssp. **bauhinii** (*Beck*) *Lüdi* (**486**): lvs. oval-oblong, tapering into stalk, white-edged; lvs., calyx and fl. stalks mealy; fls. sulphur-yellow.

Ssp. **balbisii** (*Lehm.*) *Wid.* (*ssp.* **ciliata** (*Moretti*) *Lüdi*): lvs. round, with distinct stalk, edged with hairs; plant not mealy; fls. bright yellow, scentless.

✹ Rock crevices, occasionally in grassy or marshy places, on limestone. To 2900 m. Alps; Apennines. May–July. **486**

P. auricula interbreeds very freely with *P. hirsuta All.* (p. 480) and forms a range of variable hybrids known collectively as *P.* × *pubescens Jacq.*, many of which have been stabilised, or further developed, in cultivation.

Flowers pink to purple; leaves fleshy; bracts short and broad; calyx short

P. marginata *Curtis*. With shrubby rhizome up to 20 cm. long. Lvs. 2–10 cm. long, deeply toothed, young lvs. and at least edges of old ones mealy-white, as are the bracts, fl. stalks and calyx. Fls. on 5–12 cm. stems, 2–20, whitish, pink to violet, 18–28 mm. across, with notched lobes; stalks much longer than the bracts.

✹ Rock crevices, debris. 1000–2600 (3300) m.,W. Alps. Local. June–July. **468**

P. carniolica *Jacq.* Lvs. bright green, 3–15 cm. long, smooth, slightly waved, sometimes lightly toothed, with a thin cartilaginous edge, narrowing into stalk. Fls. on 8–25 cm. stems, 3–12 (20), rose pink to pale lilac, eye mealy-white; somewhat bell-shaped, with notched petals and 6–10 mm. tube much longer than calyx; stalks to 2 cm. long.

✹ Woods, scrub, shady places, sometimes in grass. To 2000 m. E. Julian Alps. Local. April–June. **469**

P. viscosa *All.* (**P. hirsuta** *Vill.*). Lvs. pale green, 5–8 (18) cm. long, 1–5 cm. broad, rather limp, usually toothed, narrowing into stalk; edged with hairs, covered with colourless sticky glands, pungent smelling. Fls. on sticky 5–18 cm. stem, often numerous, blue-purple to reddish violet, with mealy throat of same colour, in a rather one-sided cluster. Calyx 3–5 cm. long, narrow-bell-shaped, divided to middle into triangular lobes. Corolla funnel-shaped, 15 mm. across, with tube longer than calyx.

There are numerous variations, notably in lf. size. *Flora Europaea* now applies the old name *P. latifolia* Lap. to this species; as *var. latifolia* it used to refer to forms with particularly broad, deeply toothed lvs. The rare, Central Alpine *P. graveolens Heg. & Heer*, again regarded previously as a form, with narrow lvs., is now considered another synonym.

✹ Crevices of acid rocks. 1800–3050 m. Pyrenees; Alps. June–July. **467**

Flowers pink to purple: leaves leathery, un-toothed, with cartilaginous edge: bracts long and narrow: calyx long

P. spectabilis *Tratt.* (**P. calycina** *Reichb.*, **P. glaucescens** *Reichb.*, **P. integrifolia** *Tausch.*, etc.). Lvs. bright glossy green, 3–9 cm. long, 1–4 cm. broad, gland-pitted on upper surface, stiff, with broad cartilaginous edge; more or less oblong, tending to curl backwards. Fls. on 2–16 cm. stem, 1–7, rose-red, with flat corolla 2–3 cm. across, petals sometimes wavy, giving a frilled appearance. Calyx tubular-bell-shaped, 8–11 mm. long, lightly cut into purplish lobes; shorter than corolla tube.

Not to be confused with the true *P. integrifolia* (see p. 308).

✿ Shady limestone rocks, stony places. To 2500 m. S.E. Alps. May–August.

473

P. glaucescens *Moretti* (**P. calycina** *Duby*). Lvs. blue-green, 3–10 cm. long, stiff, smooth, with broad cartilaginous edge, lance-shaped, tending to curl inwards. Fls. on 5–15 cm. stem, 2–7, pink, lilac or purple, 2–3 cm. across, the lobes rather funnel-shaped. Calyx tubular, 7–20 mm. long, lobed to middle at least.

Ssp. **calycina** (*Duby*) *Pax* (472): a stout plant tending to reach the larger measurements given above, with fls. 2½–3 cm. across.

Ssp. **langobarda** (*Porta*) *Wid.*: a smaller plant with fls. 2 cm. across, calyx 7–9 cm. long.

✿ Shady crevices in limestone rocks, stony meadows. To 2400 m. C. and S.E. Alps. *Ssp. langobarda*: Judicarian and Bergamasque Alps only. May–July. **472**

P. wulfeniana *Schott.* (**P. calycina** *Reichb.* in part, **P. integrifolia** *var.* **uniflora** *Schott.*, **P. spectabilis** *Josch*, **P. carniolica** *Wulf.* in part, **P. clusiana** *E. Wein.*). Rather like a smaller, more brilliant version of *P. glaucescens*, with closely tufted habit; lvs. deep blue-green, shining, 2–5 cm. long, ½–1 cm. wide, with membranous edge; young lvs. tending to curl inwards. Fls. on sometimes reddish and slightly mealy 1–5 cm. stem, 1–3, bright pink or mauve-pink, white-throated; 2½–3 cm. across. Calyx tubular, 7–9 mm. long, lobed to about ¼, and constricted below lobes.

✿ Shady rocks, rocky ridges, meadows. 1200–2130 m. E. and Julian Alps. May–July. **466**

P. clusiana *Tausch.* (**P. integrifolia** *L.* in part, **P. spectabilis** *Mert. & Koch*). Lvs. medium green, glossy, 1½–9 cm. long, 1–3 cm. broad, stiff, with narrow,

hairy, cartilaginous edge. Fls. on 2–11 cm. stem, 1–2 (6), rose pink or lilac, whitish in centre, 2½–3 cm. across; lobes deeply cleft. Calyx bell-shaped, 10–14 mm. long, lobed nearly to middle.

✿ Grassy and stony places, on limestone. To 2200 m. N.E. Austrian Alps. May–July. **470**

Flowers pink to purple; leaves fleshy, often toothed, with reddish or brownish glandular hairs; bracts short, usually scale-like

P. pedemontana *Thomas.* PIEDMONT PRIMROSE. Lvs. 2–10 cm. long, 1–3 cm. wide, tapering to stalk, usually irregularly toothed, smooth and shining but occasionally lightly glandular; edges densely covered with short red glands. Fls. on 4–12 cm. glandular stem, (1) 2–10, bright pink, white-throated, 2–2½ cm. across. Calyx tubular-bell-shaped, 4–6 mm. long, barely lobed, glandular.

✿ Acid rocks. 1400–3000 m. W. Alps. Very local. June–July. **482**

P. apennina *Widmer.* Lvs. 2½–6½ cm. long, ¾–2½ cm. broad, usually tapering into stalk, usually with a few teeth at tip; covered with yellowish brown glands. Fls. on 2½–9 cm. stem, 1–8, pale to rose-pink, with white throat. Calyx 4–6½ mm. long, lobed to ¼–½ its length, glandular.

✿ Rocks. N. Apennines. Very rare. May–August.

P. daonensis *Leyb.* (**P. oenensis** *Thom.*). Lvs. ½–6 cm. long, ½–2 cm. wide, very sticky and densely covered with red glands; tapering into fairly long stalk, lightly toothed near tip. Fls. on stem to 8 cm. tall, usually exceeding the lvs., 1–7, rose-pink with white throat. Calyx tubular-bell-shaped, lobed to middle, densely glandular.

✿ Stony places, occasionally on rocks. 1600–2800 m. Rhaetian Alps (S.W.

308

Switzerland, S.E. Tyrol, Dolomites).
Very local. June.   477

P. villosa *Jacq.* (**P. hirsuta** *Reichb.*, **P. commutata** *Schott.*). SHAGGY PRIMROSE. Lvs. 3–17 cm. long, 1–4 cm. broad, very sticky and densely covered with red glands; tapering more or less suddenly into a thin stalk, usually lightly toothed from middle to tip. Fls. on glandular 3–15 cm. stem, well exceeding the lvs., 1–12, rose-pink or lilac, with glandular white throat, 2–3 cm. across. Calyx broadly bell-shaped, 4–6 mm. long, usually divided into shallow lobes, glandular. Bracts green or scale-like. *
The name *forma* cottia (*Wid.*) *Lüdi* (**P. cottia** *Wid.*) has been given to a barely distinguishable geographical race.
✤ Limestone rocks. 1500–2200 m. E. Alps. *Forma cottia:* Cottian Alps. April–June.   483

P. hirsuta *All.* (**P. rubra** *Gmel.*, **P. viscosa** *Vill.*, etc.). RED ALPINE PRIMROSE. Lvs. 3–6 (15) cm. long, 1–2 (4) cm. broad, very sticky, densely covered with yellow or sometimes reddish glands; rhomboidal to wedge-shaped, tapering suddenly into stalk, coarsely toothed. Fls. on glandular 2–7 (13) cm. stem, usually barely exceeding lvs., 1–3 (6), rose-pink, lilac or white, often with white throat and tube, 1½–2½ cm. across. Calyx broad bell-shaped, 3–7 mm. long, deeply toothed.
A variable plant with many named forms. Often confused with *P. viscosa* All. in gardens, but differs in its spreading fl. cluster of rose-shaded fls. on short stem, while *P. viscosa* has a 1-sided cluster of bluish-toned fls. on stem longer than the lvs.
✤ Damp rocks and cliffs, screes, meadows, on granite. To 3600 m. Pyrenees; Alps. April–July.   480
The frequent, variable hybrids with *P. auricula* are known as *P. x pubescens* Jacq. (see p. 306).

Flowers pink to purple; leaves fleshy, often toothed, with colourless glandular hairs; bracts long and narrow

P. integrifolia *L.* (**P. incisa** *Lam.*). Lvs. 1–3½ cm. long, ½–1 cm. broad, slightly sticky, hairy on edges, barely stalked, bright green. Fls. on glandular, often reddish 2–6 cm. stem, 1–3, rose-pink or lilac, 1¾–2½ cm. across; lobes often deeply notched. Calyx tubular-bell-shaped, 6–9 mm. long, shortly lobed, glandular. Bracts green or reddish.
✤ Wet places on limestone and schist. 1900–2700 (3500) m. Pyrenees; French Alps (very rare); C. Alps. May–August.   478

P. tyrolensis (or **tirolensis**) *Schott.* (**P. allionii** *Hausm.*). DOLOMITES PRIMROSE. Lvs. 1–3 cm. long, 1–5 cm. broad, rounded, with very short, thin stalk, finely toothed, glossy, glandular, unpleasant-smelling when crushed, bright green. Fls. on glandular ½–2 cm. stem, 1 or sometimes 2, lilac-pink or pink with white throat, 1½–2½ cm. across, lobes deeply notched. Calyx open—bell-shaped, lobed to middle, glandular. Bracts green.
✤ Dolomitic rocks. 1000–2300 m. Dolomites. Very local. May–June. 479

P. allionii *Lois.* (**P. glutinosa** *All.*). Lvs. 1–4½ cm. long, ½–1 cm. broad, thick, very sticky, covered with glands, sometimes toothed, narrowing into stalk, greyish green. Fls. virtually stemless, 1–2 (7), rose-pink or purplish, occasionally white, with white or pale pink throat, ½–2 cm. across. Calyx bell-shaped, 4–6 mm. long, lobed to middle, glandular. Bracts scaly.
✤ Limestone cliffs, in crevices and under sunless overhangs. 700–1900 m. Maritime and Ligurian Alps. Extremely local. March–May.   481

Flowers blue-violet; leaves fleshy, sticky, hairless; bracts broad

P. glutinosa *Wulf.* STICKY PRIMROSE. Lvs. 2–6 cm. long, 3–7 mm. wide, stiff, erect, smooth, dotted with sticky glands, rounded-toothed, deep green. Fls. on stem to 7 cm. tall, 1–7, violet-blue, fragrant, rather bell-shaped, 12–18 mm. across, lobes deeply notched. Calyx 5–8 mm. long, lobed to centre. Bracts broad, overlapping, purplish brown, tending to conceal calyx. ❧ Granitic rock ledges, meadows. 1800–3250 m. C. and E. Alps. June–August. **475**

Flowers pink to purple; leaves hairless, mealy below; bracts sac-shaped at base

P. farinosa L. BIRDSEYE PRIMROSE. Lvs. 1–5 (8) cm. long, ½–2 cm. broad, rather spoon-shaped, round-toothed, smooth above, with white or yellow meal below. Fls. pale or deep rose-pink, occasionally white, on 2–15 (25) cm. stem which is mealy in early stages, numerous in compact clusters, with well separated, notched, oblong lobes. Calyx tubular, 3–4 mm. long, toothed. *Var.* **hornemanniana** *Lehm.* is recorded as having no meal, and *var.* **acaulis** *Ahlq.* as having very short stems. ❧ Marshes, damp meadows, usually on acid soils. To 2900 m. Pyrenees; Alps. (N. Britain.) May–August. **474**

P. scandinavica *Bruun.* NORTHERN PRIMROSE. Very like *P. farinosa*, with white meal below lvs.; fl. stem 5–10 cm. with 2–10 purple-pink fls. Calyx lobed to middle. ❧ Moist grassy places, rock ledges. To 1500 m. Norway. June–July.

P. scotica *Hook.* is similar to *P. scandinavica* and *P. farinosa* and has been considered a subspecies of the latter: the only endemic British primula, it is usually annual or biennial, has lvs.

broader than those of *P. farinosa*, fl. stem seldom over 10 cm. tall, fl. stalks not lengthening in fruit, corolla tube 7–10 mm. as against 5–6 mm. in *P. farinosa*, fls. light purple. (Scotland: not high.)

P. stricta *Hornem.* A smaller version of *P. scandinavica*, with narrow, distinctly stalked lvs. without meal, 18–25 cm. very slender stem, and 2–4 (8) pale lilac fls. 5–8 mm. across. Calyx mealy. ❧ Damp meadows, streamsides, rock ledges. To 1120 m. Norway. Rare in S. June–July.

P. halleri *Gmel.* (**P. longiflora** *All.*). LONG-FLOWERED PRIMROSE. Lvs. 2–7 cm. long, ½–3 cm. wide, sometimes lightly toothed, pale green. Fls. on strong 10–30 cm. stem, with many fls. in a cluster that appears loose due to the elongated fl. tubes, 2–3 cm. long, which much exceed the tubular 7–14 mm., shortly lobed calyx. Fls. 2 cm. across, pink, lilac or violet, with yellow throat. ❧ Damp meadows, stony places, on both limestone and acid soils. 1000–2900 m. Alps. Rare in W. June–July. **476**

Flowers pink; leaves fleshy, truncated, toothed at apex; bracts long and narrow

P. minima L. LEAST PRIMROSE. Lvs. ½–3 cm. long, 3–8 mm. broad, shining, stiff, wedge-shaped, with sharp teeth at the truncated apex. Fls. on stem only 2–8 mm. long, almost always shorter than lvs., 1–2 together, rose-pink to magenta, occasionally white, 1½–3 cm. across, with lobes deeply divided into a Y shape. Calyx 6–9 mm. long, lobed to about ¼. ❧ Rock ledges, grassy places, on both limestone and granite. (1200) 2000–3000 m. E. Alps, especially Dolomites. June–July. **471**

VITALIANA *Sesl.* **V. primuliflora** *Bert.* (**Douglasia vitaliana** (*L.*) *Pax*, **Gregoria vitaliana** *Duby*, **Aretia vita-**

liana *Lodd.*, **Primula vitaliana** *L.*, **Androsace vitaliana** *Reichb.*). Botanists cannot make up their minds what to call this, the only European species. A prostrate plant 2–3 cm. tall, forming loose mats or tufts; stems with rosettes of 5 mm. linear, green or grey-green lvs. at the ends. Fls. almost stemless in lf.-axils, 1–5 together, about 1 cm. across, 5-lobed, yellow, turning green when dried, never opening fully, with long tube exceeding the tubular, deeply lobed calyx. Several ssp. are recognised.
⚜ Stony places, short grass, stabilised screes, on acid soils. 1700–3100 (3440) m. Pyrenees; Alps (very local in E.); Abruzzi. Local. May–July. **508**

ANDROSACE *L.* ROCK JASMINE. Small herbaceous perennials or rarely annuals forming dense rosettes or elongated lf. tufts, sometimes closely packed into cushions which may reach 15 cm. across. Fls. white or pink, less than 1 cm. across, either solitary in lf.-axils or in small clusters (umbels) on a leafless stem. Calyx barely longer than corolla tube which is swollen and pinched in at the throat.

The genus has been divided into groups and this subdivision has been retained here, although it is sometimes considered that the first two groups (*Aretia* and *Chamaejasme*) merge into each other. Most of the *Aretia* section form dense cushions but some of the drawings show separate lf.-tufts: it is difficult otherwise to indicate lf. shape.

Hybrids may occur where species grow together.

Section Aretia: Rosettes usually packed into cushions or tufts, with flowers solitary, sometimes stemless

A. helvetica (*L.*) *Gaud.* Lvs. densely covered with unbranched hairs, grey-green, 3 mm. long, 1 mm. wide; rosettes building up into columns, forming very dense, hard, rather irregular cushions 2–4 cm. high. Sepals bristly, pointed. Corolla white with yellow throat, 4–6 mm. across, lobes rounded; 1 fl. to each rosette, almost stemless.
⚜ Rocky ridges, crevices, screes, usually on limestone. 1900–3500 m. Alps. May–August. **491**

A. vandellii (*Turra*) *Chiovenda*. (*A. imbricata Lam.*, **A. multiflora** *Vand.* not *Lam.*, **Aretia argentea** *Gaertn.*). Lvs. densely covered with starry hairs, silvery white, 3–6 mm. long, 1 mm. wide; rosettes building up into columns, forming dense rounded cushions 1½–4 cm. high. Sepals with starry hairs, blunt. Corolla white with yellow throat, 4 mm. across; lobes rounded; several fls. to each rosette, almost stalkless, stalks lengthening in fruit.
⚜ Granitic and other basic rocks, cliffs, often under overhangs. 2000–3100 (3500) m. Pyrenees; Alps. More common to E., but always local. June–August. **496**

A. pubescens *DC.* Lvs. with long unbranched hairs, ashy green, 7 mm. long, 1½ mm. wide, long-spoon-shaped, blunt-ended; rosettes forming irregular, rounded tufts 2–6 cm. high. Sepals pointed. Corolla nestling in centre of rosettes on short stalk, white, 4 (8) mm. across; lobes rounded; usually 1 fl. to each rosette.
⚜ Rocks and cliffs, screes, on all formations. 2000–3100 (3850) m. Pyrenees; Alps, E. to Gross Glockner. Always local. June–July. **494**

A. hirtella *Duf.* (*A. pubescens var.* **hirtella** *G. & G.*, **A. cylindrica** *var.* **hirtella** *Ktze.*). Like a miniature version of *A. pubescens* with rather more open rosettes; lvs. 5–6 mm. long, 2 mm. wide, white-downy with branched hairs, columns forming dense, neat, flattish domes 2–4 cm. high. Fls. white or palest pink, on short stalks, 3–4 mm.

across, lobes rounded or truncated; 1 fl. to each rosette.
⚘ Rocks, cliffs. Around 2000 m. W.C. Pyrenees. Very rare. June–July. **493**

A. cylindrica *DC.* (**A. pubescens** *var.* **cylindrica** *G. & G.*). Lvs. downy with unbranched hairs, 5–6 mm. long, 1 mm. wide, grey-green, building up into cylindrical or conical columns with old lvs. persisting, the numerous close-packed columns forming domed clumps 3–6 cm. high. Fls. white or pinkish, 4–6 mm. across, on distinct, thin stalks, lobes rounded; up to 3 fls. to each rosette.
⚘ Limestone rocks, cliffs. 2000–3400 m. C. Pyrenees. Very rare. July–August. **495**

A. pyrenaica *Lam.* Lvs. covered with unbranched hairs, 3 mm. long, 1 mm. wide, keeled and arched, dark green, building up into cylindrical columns with old lvs. persisting, forming humped cushions 3–6 cm. high. Fls. white with yellow throat, 4–5 mm. across; lobes rounded, rather narrow; calyx surrounded by 2–3 bracts; stalk very short; usually 1 fl. to each minute rosette.
⚘ Rock crevices, screes, on granite. 1900–3000 m. E. and C. Pyrenees. Local. June–October. **497**

A. mathildae *Lev.* With large rosettes of lvs. 1–1½ cm. long, 1½ mm. broad, pointed, fleshy, smooth, glossy. Fls. white, 4–5 mm. across, lobes rounded, on distinct, downy stalk, 1 to each rosette.
⚘ Rock crevices. 2800 m. Abruzzi. Very local. July–August. **499**

A. ciliata *DC.* (**A. pubescens** *var.* **ciliata** *G. & G.*). With large rosettes of flat, widely spaced lvs. 7 mm. long, 1–2 mm. wide, tapered to both ends, hairless except on edges, old lvs. not persisting at all. Rosettes forming loose mats 3–6 cm. tall, with much-divided branches Fls. rose-pink with yellow throat, 5–8 mm. across, lobes rounded, on often curving slightly hairy stalks, 1–2 to each rosette.
⚘ Rocks, stony places. 2800–3400 m. C. Pyrenees. Very rare. July–August. **502**

A. wulfeniana *Sieb.* With pointed, just hairy, bright green lvs. tapering to both ends, 4 mm. long, 1½ mm. broad, old lvs. persisting; forming loose tufts. Fls. reddish pink, 8 mm. across, on distinct stalks, lobes truncated, slightly notched; calyx triangular, downy; 1–2 fls. to each rosette.
⚘ Sandstone and shaly cliffs, rocks. 2000–2600 m. E. Alps (Tauern and Carnic Alps). Very local. June–July. **503**

A. brevis *Heg.* (**A. charpentieri** *Heer.*). With blunt, densely downy spoon-shaped lvs. 3–5 mm. long, 1–1½ mm. wide, old lvs. persisting, forming loose mats or tufts of many short-branched shoots (occasionally forming long columns as in illustration). Fls. rose-pink, 5–8 mm. across, with rounded or truncated lobes; calyx bell-shaped, downy; 1 (2) fls. to each rosette.
⚘ Rock crevices, avoiding limestone. 1700–2600 m. S.C. Alps. Extremely local. June–July. **498**

A. hausmannii *Leyb.* Lvs. 5–10 mm. long, 1 mm. broad, long-spoon-shaped, tending to recurve, downy with silvery spoon-shaped hairs, forming rounded cushions. Fls. white to pale pink, 4–5 mm. across, stalkless, with rounded lobes; calyx shortly bell-shaped; 1 fl. to each rosette.
⚘ Rock crevices on limestone. (1500) 1900–3170 m. E. Alps (mainly Dolomites). Local. July–August. **501**

A. alpina (*L.*) *Lam.* (**A. glacialis** *Hoppe*) (**492**). Lvs. 5 (2–8) mm. long, 1½ mm. broad, rather fleshy, pointed or blunt, covered with short star-shaped hairs; old lvs. not persisting. Rosettes forming small 2–6 cm. high cushions which often form extensive mats up to 30 cm. across. Fls. white, pink-flushed, or pink, with gold throat, 5 mm. across, almost stemless; 1 to each rosette.

Var. **tirolensis** *Wettst.* (500): lvs. 2–4 mm. long, 1 mm. broad, rounded, with branched hairs, forming rounded clusters at the end of long stems forming a loose tuft. Fls. red, 4 mm. across. *

✤ Stabilised screes, debris, occasionally on rocks, on granite and volcanic outcrops, usually on ridges. 1870–4043 m. Alps. *Var. tirolensis:* Gschmitztal, N. Tyrol: one locality at 3050 m. July–August.   **492, 500**

Section Chamaejasme: Rosettes distinct, joined by distinct stems or runners; flowers in clusters (umbels)

A. carnea L. A variable plant forming short tufts of close-packed rosettes with lvs. 1–1½ cm. long, 1–2 mm. wide, linear or awl-shaped, pointed, sometimes slightly hairy, bright green. Fls. on 2–8 (15) cm. stems, 1–6, pink or occasionally white, with yellow throat, 5–9 mm. across.   **504**

Several localized varieties or ssp. have been named, as follows*:

Var. **brigantina** or **brigantiaca** *Jord. & Fourr.*: lvs. with spreading hairs, sometimes toothed, with recurved tips. Fl. stem to 12 cm., fls. small, pink.

Var. **halleri** L. (*var.* **rosea** *Jord. & Fourr.*): forming a loose clump of rosettes with lvs. 2–2½ cm. long, hairless, with recurved tips. Fl. stems short, fls. large, clear pink.

Var. **laggeri** *Huet.* (505): forming fairly dense tufts with lvs. to ½ cm. long, blunt-tipped, radiating, not recurved, hairless. Fl. stems only 3–4 cm. long, fls. large, few, rose-pink.

Var. **puberula** *Jord. & Fourr.*: forming small tufts with lvs. covered in

short greyish down. Fl. stems short, fls. few, medium-sized, pink.

✤ Damp screes, debris, short turf, on acid soils. 1400–3100 m. Pyrenees; Alps. Local. *Var. brigantina:* W. Alps. *Var. halleri:* Cevennes. *Var. laggeri:* C. and E. Pyrenees. *Var. puberula:* C. Alps. July–August.   **504, 505**

A. villosa L. Forming small tufts of rounded rosettes, lvs. and fl. stems covered in long silvery silky hairs. Lvs. 5 mm. long. Fl. stem 3 (10) cm. tall with numerous small fls. in tight clusters, white with yellow centre turning pink, 6–10 cm. across, fragrant. Bracts longer than fl. stalks.

✤ Limestone rocks, turf. 1200–3000 m. Pyrenees; Alps; Apennines. June–July.   **506**

A. chamaejasme (*Wulf.*) *Host.* Rosettes well spaced, flattish, of lvs. ½–1 cm. long, 2–3 mm. broad, with long, white silky hairs on edges. Fl. stems also hairy, 3–6 (12) cm. tall, with 2–8 fls. 7–10 mm. across, on distinct stalks, white flushing pink with age, with yellow eye. Bracts barely as long as stalks.

✤ Rocks, turf, on limestone and acid soils. To 3000 m. Pyrenees (one locality); Alps. June–July.   **514**

A. obtusifolia *All.* Rosettes in loose tufts, of blunt-ended, spoon-shaped lvs. usually 1–1½ cm. long, 2–5 mm. broad, with a few star-shaped hairs on edge. Fl. stems 4–6 (10) cm. tall, with several short-stalked fls. 7–9 mm. across, whitish. Bracts about as long as stalks.

✤ Dry turf, on acid soils. 1600–3400 m. Alps; N. Apennines. June–August. **511**

A. lactea L. Mat-forming, with underground runners joining the rosettes of 1–1½ cm. linear, almost hairless lvs. Fl. stems 2–6 (16) cm. tall, with 1–6 fls., to 1 cm. across, with notched lobes, milk-white with yellow eye, on 2½–5 cm. stalks much longer than bracts.

✿ Rocks, screes, turf. To 2400 m. Alps, more common to E. May–August. **509**

Section Andraspis: Annuals or biennials with solitary rosettes of toothed leaves; flowers in umbels

A. septentrionalis *L.* Annual or biennial, lightly downy. Rosette of 1–1½ cm. long, lance-shaped, lightly toothed, downy lvs. Fl. stems 5–15 (30) cm. tall, with 5–30 stiff, erect stalks bearing 5 mm. white or slightly reddish fls.
✿ Dry meadows, sandy places. To 2200 m. W. Alps. Rare. Norway to 1030 m. May–July. **512**

A. chaixii *G. & G.* (**A. lactiflora** *Pall.*). Similar to *A. septentrionalis* and sometimes considered a subspecies, but barely or not downy, with 5–20 mm. fl. stems carrying 4–10 very unequal stalks, often radiating sideways, bearing 8 mm. pink or white fls.
✿ Open woods, turf, rocks. To 1800 m. W. and Maritime Alps. Rare. April–July. **513**

A. maxima *L.* Annual. Lvs. broad, distinctly stalked, toothed. Unmistakable with its large green calyxes surrounding the tiny white or pink fls. carried in radiating clusters above 1 cm. bracts on thick 5–10 (15) cm. stems.
✿ Fields, waste places, on poor soils. To 1600 m. Pyrenees; Alps; Abruzzi. April–May. **510**

CORTUSA *L.* **C. matthioli** *L.* (**Androsace primuloides** *Moench*, **Primula matthioli** *Richt.*). ALPINE BELLS. The only alpine or European species. A perennial with large, dark green, lobed, irregularly toothed, crinkled lvs. of rounded outline, hairy below, on hairy stalks radiating from rootstock. Fl. stem hairy, 10–40 cm. tall, with 3–12 hanging bell-shaped rosy purple 5-parted 1 cm. fls. in a cluster (umbel) on very unequal stalks. Fruit a capsule.
✿ Damp copses, often among alders,

ravines, wet rocks, preferring limestone. 1100–2200 m. Alps. Always local, less rare to E. June–July. **487**

SOLDANELLA *L.* SNOWBELL. Small herbaceous plants with lvs. all basal, rounded, on long stalks; fls. also on long stalks, solitary or few in a cluster, more or less nodding, with a bell- or funnel-shaped corolla cut more or less deeply into a fringe of narrow segments. Fruit a narrow, erect capsule.
Soldanellas often flower through the snow as it melts. Hybrids occasionally occur.

S. pusilla *Baumg.* DWARF SNOWBELL. Lvs. rounded or kidney-shaped, usually heart-shaped at base, 5–8 (10) mm. across, young lvs. sparsely hairy. Fl. stem 4–9 cm. tall with 1 nodding or pendulous 1–1½ cm. rosy violet, narrow bell-shaped fl. fringed to ¼–⅛ of its length.
✿ Snow-patches, moist soil, on acid formations. 1200–3100 m. Alps; N.W. Apennines (local). May–August. **517**

S. minima *Hoppe.* LEAST SNOWBELL. Resembling *S. pusilla* but smaller, lvs. rounded, 6 (10) mm. across, slightly longer than broad, with very short stalks; young lvs. and their stalks hairy. Fl. stem 4–9 cm. tall with 1 pendulous, whitish-lilac, narrow bell-shaped fl. (rarely 2), fringed to ¼–⅓ of its length.*
✿ Turf, damp soil, on limestone. To 2500 m. S.E. Alps, Abruzzi. May–July. **515**

S. austriaca *Vierh.* AUSTRIAN SNOWBELL. Sometimes considered a subspecies of *S. minima*, but lvs. at least as broad as long, with very small hairs on the longer lf. stalks, and fringe radiating more around the whitish bell.
✿ Turf, damp soil, on limestone. To 2500 m. N.E. Alps. May–July. **518**

S. alpina *L.* ALPINE SNOWBELL. Lvs. kidney-shaped, heart-shaped at base, thick and leathery, 1½–3½ cm. across, young lvs. and stalks hairy; stalks often long. Fl. stem 5–15 cm. tall with 2–3, rarely 1, violet-blue (occasionally white), 8–13 mm. funnel-shaped fls. fringed at least ½ their length, more or less nodding.

✻ Damp meadows and stony places, preferring limestone. To 3000 m. C. and E. Pyrenees; Alps; Apennines. April–August.　　　　　　　　　　**516**

S. montana *Willd.* MOUNTAIN TASSEL-FLOWER. Lvs. rounded, with deep basal sinus, lightly toothed, 2½–7 cm. across, young lvs. and stalks more or less hairy. Fl. stems 10–20 cm. tall, with 3–6 violet-blue (occasionally white) 10–17 mm. funnel-shaped fls. fringed ½ to ⅖ of their length, usually facing outwards.

Ssp. **villosa** (*Darracq*) *Lüdi*: lvs. with markedly inrolled edges, distinctly hairy (hairs to 1 mm. long); fls. fringed to ⅖, segments reflexed; calyx lobes 3-veined.

Ssp. **eumontana** (*Willd.*) *Lüdi* and *ssp.* **hungarica** (*Simk.*) *Lüdi*: less hairy (hairs 0·5 and 0·2 mm. long respectively); fls. fringed beyond ½, calyx lobes 1-veined.

✻ Clearings, often under conifers, on humus, sometimes on wet moors. To 1700 m. *Ssp. villosa:* W. Pyrenees: very rare. *Ssp. eumontana:* N.E. Alps. *Ssp. hungarica:* E. Alps. May–July.　　**519**

CYCLAMEN *L.* **C. europaeum** *L.* (**C. purpurascens** *Mill.*). SOWBREAD. With long-stalked, leathery, dark green, often silver-patterned lvs., purple-red underneath, rounded-oval, heart-shaped at base, arising from a flattened tuber. Fl. stems 5–15 cm. tall, leafless, each with a single 1½ cm. pink to carmine,

fragrant fl. with 5 reflexed, pointed segments. Capsule carried to the ground by the stem coiling downwards.

The name *C. purpurascens* Mill. is now botanically correct, but *C. europaeum* has been retained because it is so much more familiar.

✻ Stony woods, scrub, preferring limestone. To 1800 m. Alps, more common to E. June–October.　　　　　　**489**

LYSIMACHIA *L.* **L. nemorum** *L.* YELLOW PIMPERNEL. A more or less creeping herbaceous perennial with stems up to 40 cm. long, bearing opposite 2–4 cm. rather diamond-shaped lvs. rounded at base, and solitary, bright yellow 12 mm. fls. in the axils, on thin stalks often longer than the lvs. Corolla with 5 flat lobes.

✻ Damp woods, occasionally wet meadows, avoiding limestone. To 1800 m. Pyrenees; Alps. (Britain.) May–July.　　　　　　　　　　**490**

The familiar CREEPING JENNY, *L. nummularia* L., with rounded lvs. and larger fls., reaches 1500 m. (1700 m. in Valais).

TRIENTALIS *L.* **T. europaea** *L.* CHICKWEED WINTERGREEN. A perennial, arising from a creeping rootstock bearing tubercles, with slender erect 10–25 cm. stems bearing a whorl of 5–6 stiff, glossy, lance-shaped lvs. near the top, and sometimes small alternate lvs. below. Fls. erect, 1–2 (4), white, 2½–5 cm. across, on long slender stalks, with usually 7 flat lobes.

✻ Damp pine woods, mossy places in meadows and moors, on acid soils. To 2000 m. Alps: extremely local. Norway to 1580 m. (Britain to 1160 m.) June–July.　　　　　　　　　　**488**

PLUMBAGINACEAE—THRIFT FAMILY

Alpine species perennial herbaceous plants. Fls. radially symmetrical, 5-parted, with persistent, papery, tubular-based calyx and 5 almost separate petals. Stamens and styles 5; ovary within the petals; fruit dry.

ARMERIA *Willd.* (**STATICE** (*Tourn.*) *L.*) THRIFT. Perennials with branching, woody stock and basal rosettes of long, very narrow, undivided lvs. Fls. numerous, packed into hemispherical heads on leafless stems, with a tubular sheath enveloping the upper part, the head surrounded by papery bracts. Calyx funnel-shaped at base, ribbed, spreading, papery and pleated above. Petals persistent, like calyx. Spp. difficult to distinguish.

A. arenaria *Ehel* (**A. plantaginea** *Willd.*, **S. plantaginea** *All.*). PLANTAIN-LEAVED THRIFT. Lvs. 6–12 cm. long, 3–8 mm. broad, with 3–7 veins, lance-shaped, tapering to both ends but broadest near tip, usually hairless. Fl. stem 20–60 cm. tall, with head about 2 cm. across; sheath 4–10 cm. long; fls. pink or carmine. Calyx with points at least as long as tube.   *
The *var.* **leucantha** *Boiss.* is recorded as having bluish lvs., white fls. and early summer flowering only.
★ Sandy and stony meadows, preferring acid soils. To 2800 m. Pyrenees; Alps. May–September. **557**

A. montana *Willd.* (**A. alliacea** (*Cav.*) *Hoffm.*, **S. montana** *Mill.*).   *
MOUNTAIN THRIFT. Lvs. 3–8 (15) cm. long, 1–4 mm. broad, with 1–3 veins, linear. Fl. stem 10–25 cm. tall, with head 2–2½ cm. across; sheath 2–3 cm. long; fls. pink to carmine or purplish red. Calyx with points shorter than tube.
★ Screes, damp meadows. 1400–3100 m. Pyrenees; Alps; Apennines. July–August. **558**

A. halleri *Wallr.* (**S. muelleri** *Huet du P.*). Now considered a subspecies of the common SEA PINK, *A. maritima Willd.* (*S. armeria L.*). Lvs. 5–10 cm. long, 1–2 mm. broad, with 1 vein, linear. Fl. stem slender, 10–30 cm. tall, with head 2 cm. across; sheath 2½ cm. long; fls. bright pink.
★ Dry meadows, gravels. 1800–2900 m. E. Pyrenees. Rare. June–August.

A. alpina *Willd.* Now also considered a ssp. of *A. maritima Willd.* Lvs. 3–8 cm. long, 2–4 mm. broad. Fl. stem to 25 (30) cm. tall, with fl. head 2–3 cm. across. Fls. deep pink, red or purplish, occasionally white. Bracts pointed.
★ Rocky places. 1600–3000 m. Pyrenees; Alps; Julian Alps. July–August.

OLEACEAE—OLIVE FAMILY
Fraxinus excelsior *L.*, the COMMON ASH, reaches 1630 m. in a few places. **F. ornus** *L.*, the MANNA ASH, with its arresting white flower plumes, attains 1500 m. in the S. Tyrol.

GENTIANACEAE—GENTIAN FAMILY

Herbaceous annuals or perennials with undivided, typically stalkless lvs., opposite on stems, basal ones sometimes in rosettes. Fls. solitary or in clusters, 4- or 5-parted, regular, with overlapping calyx lobes or occasionally irregular teeth; corolla with stamens fixed to it, alternating with its lobes. Style 1. Ovary within corolla; fruit a capsule.

SWERTIA *L.* **S. perennis** *L.* Perennial, 20–60 cm. tall, with elliptic lvs. 1–4 cm. long, the lower stalked, upper almost clasping the 4-angled, winged stem. Fls. in regularly branching clusters (panicles), 5-parted, with narrow, pointed sepals visable between the almost separate, reflexing 1–1½ cm. petals. These are light blue to dark violet-red, occasionally yellowish green, black-dotted, with 2 dark violet hair-fringed nectaries at their base.

⚜ Marshes, boggy meadows. To 2500 m. Pyrenees; Alps; N. Apennines. Uncommon. July–October.   **520**

LOMATOGONIUM *A. Br.* **(PLEU-ROGYNE** or **PLEUROGYNA** *Eschsch.*). **L. carinthiacum** *(Wulf.)* *Reichb.* **(Pleurogyne carinthiaca** *Griseb.*, **Pleurogyna carinthiaca** *G. Don.*). Annual, with oval lvs. Fls. solitary on occasionally branching 4-angled 2–13 cm. stems; light blue, saucer-shaped, 1–2½ cm. across, with broad petals and narrower sepals almost as long visible between them.

⚜ Meadows, grassy stream-banks. 1400–2700 m. C. and E. Alps. Very local: most concentrated in Tauern area. August-October.   **521**

GENTIANA *L.* GENTIAN. Usually perennial (unless otherwise specified). Calyx more or less tubular, with teeth usually joined by a membrane forming the upper part of the tube, and some-times minute (**1230**). Corolla funnel-shaped to tubular with more or less spreading lobes, between which are teeth or smaller lobes (plicae). Stigmas 2. Capsule often very large.

The genus falls into several fairly well-defined groups which provide identification features.

The genus *Gentianella* is sometimes submerged in *Gentiana*, but the latest botanical thinking treats it separately.

A number of rearrangements of *Genti-*

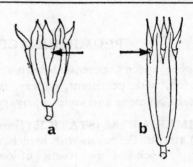

a   b

1230. Typical calyx membranes of *Gentiana*: a, *G. angustifolia*; b, *G. verna*.

ana have been made in *Flora Europaea* which have been mentioned briefly in the text.

With 4–6 cm. solitary, funnel-shaped, 5-lobed blue flowers on short central stem; basal leaves in rosette. (Originally lumped under the name G. acaulis L.)

G. clusii *Perr. & Song.* TRUMPET GENTIAN. 4–8 cm. tall (abnormally to 20 cm.). Lvs. stiffly leathery, shiny, 3–4 cm. long, sometimes wavy, elliptic to elliptic lance-shaped, much longer than broad, with cartilaginous point. Calyx bell-shaped, with long, straight-sided, narrow-pointed lobes at least equal to tube, held close to the corolla; mem-branes absent. Corolla deep sky-blue, lighter blue and spotted green inside; occasionally paler or even white.

⚜ Poor grassland, stony places, rocks, usually on limestone. 1200–2760 m. C. and E. Alps; Apuan Alps; N. Apen-nines. April–August.   **525**

G. angustifolia *Vill.* (including **G. occidentalis** *Jak.*). NARROW-LEAVED GENTIAN. 5–10 cm. tall. Lvs. soft, to 5 cm. long, narrow lance-shaped, taper-ing to base, broadest near tip, 3–5 times longer than broad, blunt-tipped. Calyx bell-shaped, with lobes shorter than half length of tube, contracted near base, sharp-pointed, standing away from corolla; membranes narrow-triangular.

Corolla deep sky-blue, green-spotted inside.

G. occidentalis Jak. is a large-fld., long-lvd. relation from the Pyrenees only, usually unspotted.

⚜ Turf, stony places, on limestone. 1200–2500 (3000) m. Pyrenees; S.W. Alps, Jura. May–August. **526**

G. kochiana *Perr & Song.* (**G. exisa** *Koch.*, **G. latifolia** *Jak.*). TRUMPET GENTIAN. 5–10 cm. tall. Lvs. soft, 4–15 cm. long, elliptic-oval, blunt-ended, 2–3 times longer than broad. Calyx bell-shaped, with lobes half length of tube, contracted at base, standing away from corolla; membranes broadly triangular. Corolla very deep blue, green-spotted inside, occasionally white, pink, purplish or particoloured.

Linnaeus' old name **G. acaulis** has, according to *Flora Europaea*, been re-accepted for this species.

⚜ Dry meadows, stony places, bogs, on acid soils, including clay. 1400–3000 m. Pyrenees; Alps; Apennines; Apuan Alps. June–August. **527**

G. alpina *Vill.* SOUTHERN GENTIAN. A tufted plant rather like a small version of *G. kochiana*, with lvs. 1½–3 cm. long, elliptic-oval, a little less broad than long. Fl. stem 0–1 cm., fl. about 4 cm. long. Calyx bell-shaped, with lobes less than half length of tube, ovate-triangular, widely separated; membranes minute. Corolla broad–funnel-shaped, deep sky-blue, darker in throat and green-spotted; lobes more prominent than in other trumpet species, and tending to recurve.

⚜ Meadows, on acid soils. 2000–2800 m. C. Pyrenees; S. and S.W. Alps. June–August. **523**

With 3–4 cm. usually solitary trumpet flowers as in acaulis *group, but stems not central*

G. froelichii *Jan.* KARAWANKEN GENTIAN. Very similar to *acaulis* type, but upper pair of stem lvs. immediately below fl. Forms tufts of narrow lance-shaped lvs. 5–10 cm. tall, occasionally 2-fld. Calyx tubular, lobes nearly as long as tube, long, narrow and pointed, widely spaced. Corolla mid-blue, often white at base, never spotted within, lobes ovate, pointed.

⚜ Screes, short turf, on limestone. 1400–2400 m. the E. Austrian Alps; Karawanken. July–September. **524**

With 1–3 trumpet flowers 2–3½ cm. long, 5-lobed, on leafy stem

G. frigida *Haenke.* STYRIAN GENTIAN. More or less densely tufted, often with elongated, leafy stem 5–10 (15) cm. tall, with strap-shaped lvs. to 8 cm. long, ½ cm. broad. Fls. terminal, 1–3. Calyx tubular, lobes shorter than tube, long, narrow and sharp-pointed. Corolla tubular-bell-shaped, with short, blunt lobes, yellowish with blue flush and stripes, spotted inside.

⚜ Meadows, rocks, on limestone. 2000–2420 m. Styrian Alps. Very local. July–September. **522**

With several or numerous trumpet-shaped, 5-lobed flowers on tall stems; leaves widest towards base

G. asclepiadea *L.* WILLOW GENTIAN. 20–50 (100) cm. tall, with opposite, stalkless lvs. 3–8 cm. long, 2–5 cm. broad, and groups of 1–3 fls. in lf.-axils on either side up the stem. Fls. 3½–5½ cm. long, deep blue with paler bands, rarely white.

⚜ Woods, damp meadows, stony places, on limestone. To 2200 m. Alps; N. Apennines. August–October. **545**

G. pneumonanthe *L.* MARSH GENTIAN. Usually elongated, sometimes small and tufted, 10–50 cm. tall, with scale-like basal lvs. and linear-lance-shaped stem-lvs. 1½–4 cm. long, to 8 mm. wide, with only 1 vein and inrolled edges. Fls. 1–7, on short stalks, terminal and in lf.-axils. Corolla sky-blue with green lines and broad, rounded, upturned lobes.

⚜ Marshy meadows, bogs, heaths. To

1500 m. Pyrenees; Alps. (Britain: very local.) July–October. **546**

Flowers usually solitary, small, long-tubed, with 5 (4) spreading lobes and intermediate teeth

(i) G. verna *group: Basal leaves in rosettes, always longer than stem-leaves*

G. verna L. SPRING GENTIAN. With basal rosettes forming tufts of elliptic lance-shaped lvs. 3 cm. long, 2–3 times as long as broad, and 3–12 cm. stems with 1–3 pairs of lvs. Calyx narrow, with 1–2 mm. wings on the angles, and narrow triangular teeth. Corolla normally brilliant blue but occasionally white, pale blue, pinkish, or reddish purple, often with white throat, 18–30 mm. across, lobes oval, teeth bifid; tube twice length of calyx.
✵ Meadows, heaths, marshes, rocks, on both limestone and primary formations. To 2570 (3550) m. Pyrenees; Alps; Abruzzi. (Britain: N. England to 800 m.; W. Ireland; very local.) March–August. **528**

G. tergestina *Beck* (**G. angulosa** *Reichb.* in part, not of *Bieb.*). KARST GENTIAN. Forming loose mats of open rosettes; lvs. narrow-lance-shaped, 1–6 cm. long, 4 times longer than broad. Stems 3–12 cm. tall with 1–3 pairs of stem-lvs; fls. occasionally 2. Calyx somewhat inflated, with 2–8 mm. wings on angles, and triangular teeth. Corolla sky-blue, 18–25 mm. across, lobes ovate; tube nearly twice length of calyx.
Flora Europaea now regards this sp. as a ssp. of *G. verna* confined to the Eastern and Italian mountains.
✵ Dry turf, on limestone. To 2000 m. Pyrenees; S. Alps; Apennines. April–June. **531**
The plant now known as *G. angulosa* Bieb., with much swollen, broad-winged calyx, is not found in Europe.

G. brachyphylla *Vill.* SHORT-LEAVED GENTIAN. Forming mats of small, compact rosettes; lvs. bluish, thick, diamond-shaped, 1 cm. long and ½ cm. broad. Stems 3–6 cm. tall, with 1 pair of lvs. Calyx very slender, not winged, with long narrow teeth. Corolla bright pale blue, 13–22 mm. across, lobes narrow-oval; tube twice length of calyx.
✵ Turf, debris, alluvial soil, on acid formations. 1800–3100 (4100) m. Pyrenees; Alps. July–August. **529**

G. orbicularis *Schur.* (**G. favrati** *Ritt.*). ROUND-LEAVED GENTIAN. Making tufts ½–3 cm. high of small rosettes; lvs. bluish green, often almost circular, to 1 cm. long, lightly edged with projections (papillae). Fl. stem 3–6 cm. tall, much lengthening in seed, with 1–2 pairs of lvs. Calyx tubular, 1–2 cm. long, with triangular lobes up to ½ cm. long. Corolla deep intense blue, 18–25 mm. across, with rounded lobes broader than long.
Flora Europaea now regards this sp. as a ssp. of *G. brachyphylla*.
✵ Turf, dry places, on limestone. 2000–2800 m. Pyrenees; Alps. August–September. **530**

G. pumila *Vill.* (**G. imbricata** *Willd., non Froel.*). SMALL GENTIAN. A tufted plant to 5 cm. tall with rosettes of narrow lvs. to 1½ cm. long, 4 times longer than broad. Fl. stem 4 (12) cm. tall, with 1–3 pairs of lvs. Calyx slender, tubular, 8–15 mm. long, often violet-tinged, angled but not winged, with narrowly triangular lobes 6–7 mm. long held slightly away from corolla tube. Corolla sapphire blue, 15–20 mm. across, with triangular-pointed lobes. (*G. rostani* is similar in lvs., but does not form rosettes.)
✵ Damp meadows, on limestone. 1600–2800 m. Pyrenees; S.E. Alps; N. Apennines; Abruzzi. June–August. **536**

(ii) G. bavarica *group: Leaves not in basal rosettes, all about the same size*

G. bavarica L. (including **G. imbricata**

Schleich.). BAVARIAN GENTIAN (534). Forming mats ½–2 cm. tall of shoots covered with overlapping, rather yellow-green, rounded to spoon-shaped lvs. 10–15 mm. long, about twice as long as wide. Fl. stems 4–12 cm. tall, with 3–4 close-spaced pairs of similar lvs. Calyx bell-shaped, angled, very slightly or not winged, often violet-tinged, 10–16 mm. long, with narrow triangular teeth. Corolla tube about twice as long (to 2½ cm.); corolla dark blue, rarely violet or white, 16–20 mm. across, with blunt lobes longer than broad.

Var. **subacaulis** *Schlieh.* (**G. imbricata** *Schleich., non Froel.*, **G. rotundifolia** *Hoppe*) DWARF BAVARIAN GENTIAN (**535**); a very compact form with short or no fl. stalk and overlapping, almost circular lvs. Calyx tending to be conical, lobes pressed close to corolla tube. Intermediate forms between this and *G. bavarica* can be found but the compact variety retains its habit in cultivation.

✤ Wet meadows, boggy places, moors. 1300–3620 m. *Var. subacaulis:* over 2400 m. Alps; Abruzzi. July–September.

534, 535

G. terglouensis *Hacq.* (**G. imbricata** *Froel., non Schleich., non Willd.*) TRIGLAV GENTIAN. A very compact, tufted plant ½–2 cm. tall, like a miniature version of *G. verna*, except that it does not form rosettes, with tightly overlapping, pointed, rough-edged lvs. 3–5 mm. long, 2–4 mm. broad. Fl. stem 3–6 mm. long. Calyx tubular to conical, with short triangular teeth, angled but not winged, ⅓ to ½ length of corolla tube. Corolla 18–24 mm. across, sky-blue, with slightly pointed, irregularly nicked, elliptic lobes.

✤ Meadows, usually on limestone. 1900–2700 m. Ssp. *terglouensis:* S.E. Alps. Ssp. *schleicheri:* Maritime Alps to W. Swiss Alps. July–August. **532**

1231. Gentiana rostani.

G. rostani *Reut.* A narrow-leaved version of *G. bavarica*, rather like *G. pumila*, but not making rosettes; to 3 cm. tall, with bright green, fleshy, pointed lvs. ½–2½ cm. long, 4 times longer than broad. Fl. stems 3–14 cm. tall, with 2–4 well-spaced pairs of similar lvs. Calyx conical, angled but not winged, with long, very narrow triangular lobes held well away from corolla tube which is twice as long. Corolla rather small, with long narrow lobes. *

✤ Damp meadows, marshes. (1600) 2400–2900 m. Pyrenees; S.W. and S.C. Alps. Very rare. July–August. **1231**

G. pyrenaica *L.* PYRENEAN GENTIAN. 3–10 cm. tall; with pointed elliptic, overlapping lvs., and deep violet-blue fls. unmistakable in having the intermediate corolla lobes almost as large as the main ones.

✤ Damp meadows, boggy places. 1200–2800 m. C. and E. Pyrenees. June–September. **533**

Annuals with small starry flowers and relatively large calyx

G. utriculosa *L.* BLADDER GENTIAN. 8–25 cm. tall, with slender, erect, branching stems, a basal rosette and stem pairs of pointed, elliptic 6–10 mm. lvs. Fls. usually several, with oval calyx 10–20 mm. long, strongly winged, expanding to 8–12 mm. wide in fruit. Corolla 12–18 mm. across, brilliant blue. ✤ Damp and boggy meadows, stony places, heaths. To 2490 m. Alps; Apennines. May–August. **538**

G. nivalis L. SNOW GENTIAN. 1–15 cm. tall, with slender, erect, branching stems, and a basal rosette and stem pairs of narrow oval 2–5 cm. lvs. Fls. usually several, with tubular 10–15 mm. calyx, angled but not winged. Corolla 8 (12) mm. across, brilliant deep blue, with small pointed lobes giving a starry effect. ✤ Meadows, marshes, heaths, gravels, rock ledges. 1650–3100 m. Pyrenees; Alps; N. Apennines. Norway to 1880 m. (Britain: Scottish mountains to 1100 m.) June–August. **537**

Tall, stout plants with broad, deeply veined leaves and large yellow or purplish, starry or bell-shaped flowers clustered terminally and in upper axils

G. lutea L. GREAT YELLOW GENTIAN. ½–2 m. tall, with very stout, hollow stem. Lvs. rather bluish, to 30 cm. long and 15 cm. broad. Fls. 3–10 in each cluster; corolla starry, cut almost to the base into narrow golden-yellow lobes. (Differs from *Veratrum* in the unfld. state by having lvs. opposite, not alternate, and hairless, not downy below). *
✤ Pastures, marshes, waste and stony places. To 2500 m. Pyrenees; Alps; Apennines. June–August. **543**

G. burseri *Lap.* 30–60 (100) cm. tall. Lvs. to 25 cm. long. Fls. numerous in each cluster. Calyx papery, split to the base, with several teeth on one side. Corolla yellow, sometimes spotted, narrow-bell-shaped, with 5–7 triangular, pointed lobes.
Ssp. **burseri** (540): membranes between corolla lobes small, triangular; fls. pale yellow, unspotted.

Ssp. **villarsii** *Ronn.*: membranes truncated; fls. deep. yellow, heavily brown-spotted.
✤ Woods, meadows. 1500–2700 m. *Ssp.* *burseri*: Pyrenees. *Ssp. villarsii*: W. Alps. July–August. **540**

G. punctata L. SPOTTED GENTIAN. 20–60 cm. tall. Lvs. pointed elliptic, to 10 cm. long. Fls. mostly terminal and also around upper pair of lvs. Calyx not split, or split to one-third, with 2–8 very unequal pointed lobes. Corolla yellow, maroon-spotted, wide bell-shaped, with very short, blunt or pointed membranes between the 5–8 blunt, rounded lobes.
✤ Meadows, stony places, open woods. 1100–3050 m. Alps. Local. July–September. **539**

G. purpurea L. PURPLE GENTIAN. 20–60 cm. tall. Lvs. to 20 cm. long. Fls. mostly terminal, but often also clustered around upper lf. pair. Calyx papery, split to base, with small unequal teeth. Corolla purplish red or coppery, paler within, spotted, green-striped on tube, honey-scented; wide-bell-shaped, with short, truncated membranes between the 5–8 blunt lobes which are broadest at the middle.
✤ Meadows, open woods. (1000) 1600–2750 m. Alps; Apuan Alps; N. Apennines. Norway to 1100 m. July–October. **542**

G. pannonica *Scop.* BROWN or HUNGARIAN GENTIAN. 15–60 cm. tall. Lvs. to 20 cm. long, becoming lance-shaped towards top of stem. Fls. several in each cluster. Calyx not split, bell-shaped, with 5–8 unequal, outward-curving lobes. Corolla brownish purple, darker spotted, wide-bell-shaped, with short, small, blunt membranes between the 5–7 broad, elliptic lobes.
✤ Meadows, heaths, debris, scrub. To 2275 m. E. Alps. Local. July–September. **541**

Flowers 4-parted (not fringed)

G. cruciata L. CROSS GENTIAN. More or less erect, with 10–40 cm., very leafy, thick stems in tufts emerging from a basal rosette. Lvs. oval-lance-shaped, shining, to 10 cm. long, 1–2 cm. wide, in opposite pairs (decussate), joined at base. Fls. dull blue or greenish outside, sky-blue inside, stalkless, clustered terminally and in lf.-axils, tubular 2–2½, cm. long, with 4 erect lobes.
❀ Dry meadows, stony places, woods. Alps; Apennines. To 2050 m. July–October. **544**

G. prostrata *Haenke*. CREEPING GENTIAN. Annual, with more or less prostrate stems 2–5 cm. long, carrying opposite spoon-shaped lvs. 8 mm. long, 4 mm. broad, and terminating in single fls. Corolla steely blue, with 11–20 mm. tube, 4 spreading, pointed 4–5 mm. lobes and subsidiary teeth almost as large; calyx long and narrow, tubular, with triangular lobes and narrow triangular membrane.
❀ Short turf, stony places. (1600) 2200–2720 m. Swiss and E. Alps. Very rare. July–August. **547**

GENTIANELLA *Moench*. Annuals or biennials (exceptionally perennial), often with symmetrical branching; fls. 4- or 5-parted, with nectaries forming a fringe at the throat or (*G. ciliata*) fringed on edges of corolla lobes. Calyx membrane absent; corolla lobes without teeth (plicae) between them.

Despite these fairly clear distinctions from *Gentiana*, several species with fringes were still not always named *Gentianella* until quite recently. However, botanists have now placed all the fringed species under this name, but either name may well be found especially in older floras. Although *Gentianella crispata*, *G. austriaca*, *G. ramosa*, *G aspera*, *G. anisodonta* and *G. engadinensis* might well be considered merely as local variations of *G. germanica*, I have inclu-ded them since they are treated as distinct by some European authorities.

Flowers 4-parted, fringed on edges of corolla lobes

Gentianella ciliata (*L.*) *Borkh* (**Gentiana ciliata** *L*). FRINGED GENTIAN. Biennial or rarely perennial, 7–25 cm. tall, with angular, sometimes branched stems and narrow pointed lvs. Fls. solitary, terminal, 4–5 cm. across, brilliant blue, with 4 broad, fringed lobes.
❀ Dry meadows, stony places, woods, on limestone. To 2500 m. Pyrenees; Alps; Apennines. August–November. **548**

Unbranched annuals with 4- or 5-parted flowers fringed at the throat

Gentianella tenella (*Rott.*) *Börn:* (**Gentiana tenella** *Rott.*, **G. borealis** *Bunge*). SLENDER GENTIAN. 3–10 cm. tall, with very slender fl. stems arising from a loose rosette, with 1 pair of stem-lvs. in lower part. Fls. solitary, terminal, 4-parted, pale blue, 4–6 mm. across, with oval calyx.
❀ Damp pastures, grassy screes, gravels, preferring acid soils. 1500–3190 m. Pyrenees; Alps. Norway to 1400 m. July–September. **549**

Gentianella nana (*Wulf.*) Pritchard (**Gentiana nana** *Wulf.*) DWARF GENTIAN. 2–5 cm. tall, with a tuft of lvs. at base, sometimes 1 pair of lvs. on fl. stem. Fls. solitary, terminal, usually 5-parted, with short bell-shaped calyx and small, bell-shaped, pale violet-blue fls.
❀ Moraines, debris. 2200–2800 m. E. Austrian Alps. Very local. July–September. **550**

Erect annuals or biennials, often with symmetrical branching; flowers 4- or 5-parted, fringed at throat

A difficult group with several variable species, some of which appear to merge into each other.

Gentianella campestris (*L.*) *Börn.* (**Gentiana campestris** *L.*; including **G. hypericifolia** *Murb.* and **G. baltica** *auct.*). FIELD GENTIAN. Annual or biennial. 10–30 cm. tall, sometimes branched. Fls. 4-parted. Calyx with two outer sepals much larger than inner pair which they partly conceal. Corolla tube at least as long as calyx; corolla bluish-lilac, occasionally white, 1½–2½ (3) cm. across.
⚘ Meadows, clearings, occasionally bogs. To 2750 m. Pyrenees; Alps; Apennines. Norway to 1375 m. (Britain to 850 m.) July–October. **551**

Gentianella germanica (*Willd.*) *H. Smith* (**Gentiana germanica** *Willd.*). Usually biennial. 7–35 (2–50) cm. tall, usually branched above the middle. Basal rosette of spoon-shaped lvs., usually disappearing the first autumn. Stem-lvs. 1–2½ cm. long, ovate to ovate-lance–shaped. Fls. 5-parted. Calyx teeth long-triangular, more or less equal. Corolla 2–3½ cm. across, tube at least as long as calyx, lavender-blue to violet, occasionally white.
A plant varying from low and much-branched to tall and hardly branched, with internodes between lvs. varying in proportion to size of lvs. and fls. Several subspecies have been named, including *ssp.* **solstitialis** (*Wettst.*) *Voll.*, which flowers from May to July; the others only start flowering in July or August.
⚘ Meadows, marshes, waste places, preferring chalk and limestone. To 2700 m. Alps. (Britain: very local.) May–October. **552**

Gentianella austriaca (*Kern*) *J. Holub* resembles some forms of *G. germanica*, but has lance-shaped, pointed lvs.: S.E. Alps to 2000 m.

Gentianella crispata (*Vis.*) *J. Holub* (**Gentiana crispata** *Vis.*) Very similar to *G. germanica*, but has crisped or wavy

edges to the broad calyx lobes, and twisted corolla lobes.
⚘ Meadows. To 2150 m. S. Apennines. July–October. **553**

Gentianella amarella (*L.*) *H. Smith* (**Gentiana amarella** *L.*, **G. axillaris** (*F. W. Schmidt*) *Reichb.*). FELWORT. Biennial in alpine form; often purple-tinged. 5–30 (3–50) cm. tall, forming a narrow column with short several-fld. branches almost erect around the main stem. Basal rosette of lance- to strap-shaped lvs., disappearing the first autumn; second-year basal lvs. spoon-shaped, stem lvs. 1–2 cm. long, ovate to narrow lance-shaped, pointed. Fls. 4- or 5-parted, even on same plant. Calyx teeth long and narrow-triangular. Corolla 1–2 cm. long, up to twice length of calyx, reddish violet, occasionally white or yellow, 14–22 mm. across.
⚘ Meadows, moors, sandy places. To 1750 m. Alps. Norway to 1200 m. (Britain.) June–October. **554**

Gentianella ramosa (*Hegets.*) *J. Holub* (**Gentiana ramosa** *Hegets.*, **G. murbeckii** *Wettst.*). BRANCHED GENTIAN. Biennial. A low, tufted ,very much branched plant 1–15 cm. tall. Lvs. oval to oval lance-shaped, blunt. Fls. 5-parted. Calyx cut to about ¾ into very long narrow teeth separated by rounded gaps. Corolla ½–2 cm. long, slightly exceeding calyx, starry with long narrow lobes, pale lilac to whitish.
⚘ Dry meadows on acid soils. 1700–3100 m. E. and S.C. Alps (Valais and Piedmont to Tyrol). July–October.

Gentianella aspera (*Hegets. & Heer*) *Dostál ex Skalický, Chrtek & Gill* (**Gentiana aspera** *Hegets. & Heer*) Biennial. 4–20 cm. tall, branching, rather congested. Lvs. broad lance-shaped, lower ones tending to clasp stem. Fls 5-parted. Calyx with 2 lobes slightly larger than other 3, ciliate on edges and central vein, edges not rolled outwards (see

G. anisodonta). Corolla tubular, to 4 cm. long, with long pointed reflexed lobes, violet, lilac or occasionally white.
⚜ Damp meadows. To 2500 m. C. and E. Alps. May–September.
Gentianella anisodonta (*Borb.*) *A. & D. Löve* (**Gentiana anisodonta** *Borb.*) Biennial or rarely annual. 5–30 (80) cm. tall, usually branched from near base. Basal lvs. spoon-shaped, stem-lvs. lance-shaped. Fls. 5-parted. In the alpine *var.* **calycina** *Koch.* the calyx has triangular lobes, 2 being much broader than the other 3, ciliate on edges only, which are strongly rolled outwards. Corolla 2–3 cm. long, bell-shaped, slightly constricted at throat, blue-violet.
⚜ Meadows, on acid soils. To 2540 m. C., E. and S. Alps; Abruzzi; S. Apennines. May–October.

Gentianella engadinensis (*Wettst.*) *J. Holub* (**Gentiana engadinensis** (*Wettst.*) *Br.-Bl. & Sam.*) Similar to *G. anisodonta*, 3–15 cm. tall, calyx similar, corolla 1½–2 cm. long, dark reddish violet, rarely bluish or white.
⚜ Meadows, on limestone. 1800–2800 m. E. Swiss Alps; W. Tyrol. Very local. June–September.

MENYANTHACEAE— BOGBEAN FAMILY

Similar to *Gentianaceae* and by older authorities included in that family, but aquatic or bog plants with lvs. typically alternate.

MENYANTHES *L.* **M. trifoliata** *L.*

BOGBEAN, BUCKBEAN. The only species. A plant of wet places and ponds to 4 m. deep, with creeping rootstock; lvs. and fls. raised above the water. Lvs. 3-parted, of elliptical 3–7 cm. leaflets, on 7–20 cm. stems, sheathing at the base. Fl. stem 12–30 cm. tall, with 10–20 short-stalked, 5-parted fls. to 10 cm. across, the corolla heavily fringed, pink outside, whitish within, falling quickly. Fruit a large rounded capsule.
⚜ Ponds, flooded meadows, bogs, ditches, fens. To 1800 (2400) m. Pyrenees (rare); Alps; Apennines. Norway to 1150 m. (Britain to 1000 m.) May–August.   **1005**

ASCLEPIADACEAE— MILKWEED FAMILY

VINCETOXICUM *T. Walter* (**CYNANCHUM** *L.*) **V. hirundinaria** *Medic.* (**V. officinale** *Moench*, **C. vincetoxicum** (*L.*) *Pers.*). SWALLOW-WORT. The only alpine member of a mainly tropical family. An erect perennial 30–80 (120) cm. tall, with opposite, ovate-lance-shaped lvs., and fls. in small stalked clusters in lf.-axils. Fls. 5–15 mm. across, white, greenish or yellowish, but purplish in bud; calyx lobed; corolla with short tube and spreading lobes; stamens 5, fused into a tube enveloping the ovary; styles 2. Fruit of pod-like follicles, usually paired, 5–7 cm. long, opening to release seeds with plume of silky hairs. Poisonous.
⚜ Woods, scrub, waste and stony places. To 1800 m. Pyrenees; Alps. May–August.   **556**

CONVOLVULACEAE—BINDWEED FAMILY
(including CUSCUTACEAE)

Annuals or perennials, usually climbing, parasitic in Cuscuta. Fls. typically 5-parted, sometimes 4-parted. Calyx of separate sepals, or lobed; corolla funnel- or bell-shaped. Stamens 5, fixed at bottom of corolla tube. Style 1, stigmas 2. Fruit a 2-celled capsule.

CONVOLVULUS *L.* **C. arvensis** *L.*
FIELD BINDWEED. A twining or scrambling perennial with slender stems to 75
cm. long, and stout rhizome to 2 m.
long. Lvs. 2–5 cm. long, arrow- or
halberd-shaped, on distinct stalk. Fls.
1–3 together, to 2 cm. long, stalked.
Calyx of 4 mm. almost separate lobes;

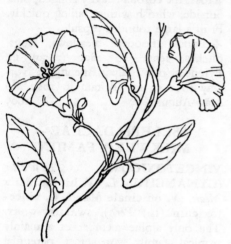

1232. Convolvulus arvensis.

corolla broad funnel-shaped, to 3 cm.
across, white or pink. A serious weed.
❧ Fields, hedgerows, grassy places. To
2000 m. Pyrenees; Alps. (Britain.) May–
October.   1232

CUSCUTA *L.* DODDER. Parasitic annuals with small scale-like colourless
lvs. on slender twining stems, fixing
themselves to host plants by suckers.
Fls. in small round clusters on the
stems; occasionally 4-parted, with lobed
calyx and bell- or urn-shaped, lobed
corolla. Sometimes placed in the family
Cuscutaceae.

C. epithymum *L.* COMMON DODDER.
Stems reddish, very slender ($\frac{1}{10}$ mm.).
Fls. pinkish, fragrant, stalkless, in dense

5–10 mm. heads. Calyx open-bell-
shaped, cut to $\frac{3}{4}$ of its length into triangular lobes; corolla tube closed by
scales at the base.
❧ On many plants, notably *Trifolium* as
illustrated. To 2200 m. Pyrenees; Alps;
Apennines. (Britain.) June–September.
                                            559

C. europaea *L.* LARGE DODDER. Similar
to *C. epithymum*, but larger, with 1 mm.
wide, often reddish stems to 1 m. long.
Fls. pink in 10–15 mm. clusters; briefly
stalked, to 2 mm. across; calyx lobes
blunt; corolla with very small scales
not closing the throat.
❧ On many plants, including *Umbelliferae, Galium,* nettles, hop, and *Vincetoxicum* (illustrated). To 2000 m.
Pyrenees; Alps. (Britain: rare.) June–
September.   560

POLEMONIACEAE

POLEMONIUM *L.* **P. caeruleum** *L.*
JACOB'S LADDER. The only alpine member of the family in Europe. Perennial,
20–50 (120) cm. tall, with alternate,
10–40 cm., pinnate lvs. of 6–12 pairs of
narrow pointed leaflets and a terminal
one. Fls. numerous in clusters
(corymbs), blue or white, 2–3 cm.
across. Calyx bell-shaped with 5 pointed
lobes, corolla with short tube, expanding into 5 broad, triangular lobes.
Stamens 5, projecting. Ovary within
calyx; fruit a capsule.
❧ Damp meadows and woods, streamsides. Often naturalised. To 2300 m.
C. Pyrenees; Alps. Uncommon. (Britain:
N. England; escaped elsewhere.) May–
August.   555

BORAGINACEAE—BORAGE FAMILY

Alpine members herbaceous, often rough or bristly. Lvs. almost always alternate and uncut. Fls. typically carried in scorpioid cymes, namely curving, one-sided spike-like clusters well shown in forget-me-nots. Fls. usually symmetrical radially, sometimes only in vertical plane. Calyx of 5 teeth or lobes. Corolla 5-lobed, funnel- or bell-shaped, or with lobes at right angles to tube; throat often closed by scales or hairs. Stamens 5, fixed to the corolla and alternating with its lobes. Ovary within calyx, divided into 4 deep lobes in the centre of which stands the single style; fruit of 4 nutlets.

A family with many rather similar plants; in many genera the species seem to grade into each other and nomenclature is correspondingly confused.

Besides the plants described the insignificant MADWORT, *Asperugo procumbens* L., reaches 2565 m. (1000 m. in Norway); the BORAGE, *Borago officinalis* L., reaches 1700–1800 m. in a few places; and the COMFREYS *Symphytum officinale* L. and *S. tuberosum* L. occasionally exceed 1500 m.

MYOSOTIS L. FORGET-ME-NOT, SCORPION GRASS. Annuals or perennials, more or less covered with soft hairs, shorter than width of basal lvs.; fls. in scorpioid cymes. Corolla with tube and radiating lobes; throat closed by 5 notched scales. Fls. blue in alpine species, often pink in bud. Fruit smooth and shining.

Besides the species described, several others reach around 2000 m. *M. scorpioides* L., a plant of wet places, and *M. arvensis* (L.) Hill, have fls. 4–5 mm. across. *M. collina* Hoffm. and *M. micrantha* Pallas have minute fls.

M. alpestris *Schmidt* (including M. pyrenaica *Pourr.*). ALPINE FORGET-ME-NOT. 3–20 cm. tall, with horizontal rootstock, varying from a leafy cushion to an erect plant with leafy stems, covered with spreading downy hairs. Lvs. oblong-lance-shaped, lower ones stalked. Fls. in compact cymes; individual fl. stalks not exceeding calyx, which has narrow teeth ½–¾ length of tube. Corolla 6–10 mm. across, vivid blue, with flat, rounded lobes. Fls. often scented.

This plant has been considered a subspecies of *M. sylvatica*, into which it appears to grade. The plant called **M. rupicola** *Smith*, of tight cushion habit, is only an extreme alpine form, grading into the mat-forming, 12 cm. Pyrenean *M. alpina Lap.*

✳ Damp woods, meadows. 1500–2800 (3090) m. Pyrenees; Alps; Apennines. (Britain: northern mountains, 800–1300 m.) April–September. **565**

M. sylvatica *Hoffm.* WOOD FORGET-ME-NOT. The 'type' plant of the preceding, into which it grades; taller, 15–45 cm. high, with spoon-shaped lvs., long loose cymes, and fl. stalks 1½–2 times length of calyx.

✳ Damp woods. To 2000 m. Pyrenees; Alps; Apennines. (Britain.) April–September.

ERITRICHIUM *Schrad.* E. nanum (*All.*) *Schrad.* (E. **terglouiense** D.T. & Sarth., **Myosotis nana** *All.*). KING OF THE ALPS. Like a dwarf forget-me-not, forming dense leafy cushions 3–10 cm. across, 1½–3 (8) cm. tall. Lvs. 4–10 mm. long and 1½–3 mm. broad, densely covered in long silky hairs at least as long as lvs. are broad, and with bristles on the margins. Fls. pale to brilliant azure blue, rarely white, 1–5 in compact scorpioid cymes, often barely exceeding the lvs.

❀ Rocks, screes, debris, usually on primary (acid) and volcanic formations but apparently occasionally on dolomite and limestone. 2000–3620 m. Alps. Very local. July–August.   568

(Hegi suggests that *Eritrichium nanum* grows on acid soils in the W. and C. Alps and on dolomite and limestone in in the S.E. Alps.)

LAPPULA *Gilib.* **L. myosotis** *Moench.* **(L. echinata** *Gilib.,* **Echinospermum lappula** *Lehm.*). Annual, with erect 10–50 cm. stems branched in upper quarter. Fls. 2–4 mm. across, sky-blue. The plant is a curiosity for its egg-shaped fruit, 3–4 mm. long, which carry 2 rows of broad bristles on the edges and together form a mitre-like erection in the centre of the long, strap-shaped calyx lobes.   *

❀ Dry slopes, vineyards, waste places. To 2500 m. Pyrenees; Alps; Apennines. June–July (September).   562

L. deflexa (*Lehm.*) *Garcke* is a more branching annual or perennial with pendulous fruit carrying 1 row of hooked bristles on the edges, which reaches 2300 m. (1200 m. in Norway.)

CYNOGLOSSUM *L.* Annuals or biennials; bristly or silky-haired. Corolla funnel-shaped, with large scales closing the opening of the long tube. Nutlets covered with hooked or barbed bristles.

C. officinale *L.* HOUNDS-TONGUE. An erect biennial 30–90 cm. tall, softly grey-downy. Basal lvs. to 30 cm. long, more or less lance-shaped, stalked; upper lvs. stalkless; all covered in silky, flattened hairs. Fls. 1 cm. across, dark red-purple, mouse-smelling, on 1 cm. stalks; cymes often branched, loose,

lengthening to 10–25 cm. in fruit. Nutlets 5–6 mm. across, flattish, with short barbed bristles.

❀ Dry and stony places, grass. To 2400 m. Pyrenees; Alps; Apennines. (Britain.) May–August.   561

C. nebrodense *Guss.*, sometimes considered a subspecies of *C. officinale*, with smaller fls. and thick bristles on nutlets, reaches 2150 m. in the C. and S. Apennines.

C. magellense *Ten.* (**C. apenninum** *L.*). 60–120 cm. tall, with stout, erect, branching stem, softly grey-downy. Fls. in dense, close-packed cymes, 12–15 mm. across, purplish blue.

❀ Meadows, woods. To 2080 m. Apennines. May–August.

LITHOSPERMUM *L.* **L. gastonis** *Benth.* An erect perennial 10–30 cm. tall, with large ovate-lance-shaped lvs. 4–8 cm. long, 2–3 cm. broad, increasing in size up the stem, covered in short, rigid, appressed hairs. Fls. purple to blue, with white base, in congested heads partly hidden by the upper lvs. Stamens fixed near base of corolla.   *

❀ Wooded slopes, grassed rocks, debris. To 2000 m. W. French Pyrenees. Rare. July–August.   564

L. officinale *L.*, the GROMWELL, with its curious shining white fruit, reaches 1570 m. (2300 m. in one locality), and the equally insignificant *L. arvense* *L.* reaches 2300 m.

MOLTKIA *Lehm.* **M. suffruticosa** (*L.*) *B. & H.* (**Lithospermum suffruticosum** *Kern.*). A sub-shrub with horizontal woody stock and erect herbaceous stems 10–30 cm. tall. Basal lvs. long and narrow, upper lvs. often more or less opposite, all shaggy-haired. Fls. in dense cymes, bright blue, with stamens fixed very near top of corolla; style projecting.

❀ Stony places. S.E. Alps; Apuan Alps; N. Apennines. May–July.   563

ONOSMA L. GOLDEN DROP. Narrow-lvd. perennials and biennials with tubular corolla, yellow in alpine species, with short, equal teeth; no scales in throat; cymes leafy. Plants covered in stiff erect hairs. Fruit of 4 carpels. The species are very similar, and nomenclature is extremely confused.

O. echioides L. GOLDEN DROP. Perennial, forming tufts of stiff erect stems 10–40 cm. tall terminated by a branching fl.-head of 2–3 cymes, curving over so that fls. point sideways or down. Lvs. narrow spoon-shaped at base, lance-shaped on stem. Fls. yellow, 2 cm. long, with projecting style; anthers 1 cm. long. Calyx deeply lobed and growing in fruit to 2½ cm. long. Hairs of plant carried on smooth tubercles.

The name *Onosma echioides* has been much misused and it is doubtful whether the plant now so named, after recent research, is alpine at all. The plant described above, and illustrated, is presumably **O. bubanii** *Strob.*, an alpine-level endemic of the Spanish Pyrenees. *O. vaudensis Gremli* occurs in one place in the Rhone valley near Aigle.
⁂ Dry stony places, preferring limestone. To 1700 m. May–June.   **569**

O. helveticum (*A. DC.*) *Boiss.* Perennial, 20–50 cm. tall, with woody rootstock, forming tufts of narrow, almost strap-shaped lvs. at base, and linear-lance-shaped lvs. on the erect stems. Cymes crook-shaped so that the fls. point upwards. These are yellow, 2–2½ cm. long, with projecting style, anthers 6–8 mm. long. Hairs of tubercles downy with star-shaped hairs. Subspecies have been named which differ in minor characters.   *
⁂ Stony and sandy places. To 2440 m. Pyrenees (doubtful record); S.W. Alps. May–June.   **570**

O. arenaria *W. & K.* Biennial, much branched from the base, with 30–50 cm., very leafy stems; lvs. narrow-elliptic. Fls. often pointing upwards in more or less curved cymes, the pale yellow corolla barely exceeding calyx, 12–16 mm. long (*ssp.* **pyramidata** *Br.-Bl.*) or 20–24 mm. long (*ssp.* **pennina** *Br.-Bl.*).
Stony and sandy places. To 1700 m. *Ssp. pyramidata:* French Alps. *Ssp. pennina:* C. Alps (Switzerland, Piedmont). May-June.

CERINTHE L. HONEYWORT. Perennials and biennials, with tubular corolla tapering slightly towards apex, yellow or bicoloured, with equal teeth; no scales in throat; cymes leafy. Plants virtually hairless, often waxy, with fleshy oval lvs. clasping the stem. Fruit of 2 carpels.

C. glabra *Mill.* (C. alpina *Kit.*). SMOOTH HONEYWORT. Perennial, 20–40 cm. tall. Lvs. quite smooth. Corolla 9–12 mm. long, about ⅓ longer than hairless calyx; yellow with purplish brown patches forming a band near the short, outwardly recurving tooth-like lobes. Anther filaments short.
⁂ Meadows, damp woods, on limestone. 1000–2650 m. Pyrenees; Alps; Apennines. May–July.   **571**

C. minor L. LESSER HONEYWORT. Biennial or rarely perennial, 15–60 cm. tall. Lvs. with small raised tubercles and often white blotches. Corolla 10–14 mm. long, about ⅓ longer than the toothed, ciliate calyx; pale yellow, sometimes blotched midway with purplish brown, cut almost halfway into pointed, normally converging lobes which make the fl. look conical.
Ssp. **auriculata** (*Ten.*) *Domac:* fls. purplish, half the normal size, with swollen lobes which do not converge.

Var. **maculata** *All. & Vis.*: fls. larger, yellow with purplish blotches midway, and purple lobes.

✤ Meadows, fields, waste places, on limestone. 1300–2200 m. Alps. *Ssp. auriculata:* S.W. French and Maritime Alps. *Var. maculata:* S. Alps. May–July.   **572**

ECHIUM *L.* E. **vulgare** *L.* VIPERS BUGLOSS. Biennial, 30–90 cm. tall, very bristly. Lvs. to 15 cm. long, lance-shaped to oblong. Fls. in short dense cymes, elongating in fruit, together forming a large terminal cluster (panicle). Fls. 15–18 mm. long, pinkish or purplish in bud, bright blue when open, funnel-shaped with straight tube, lobes unequal so symmetrical in vertical plane only. 4 or 5 stamens, and style, projecting. A very variable plant.

✤ Meadows, arid places, debris. To 1800 m.; adventitious to 2300 m. Pyrenees; Alps. (Britain.) July–September.   **573**

ANCHUSA *L.* ALKANET. Annuals or perennials, usually bristly or hairy. Fls. 5-parted, regular; calyx cleft; corolla with straight tube, terminal lobes, and scales in the throat. Fruit wrinkled, but not with spines or hooks as in *Cynoglossum* and *Lappula*.

A. barrelieri (*All.*) *Vitm.* Perennial, 25–60 cm. tall. Lvs. thick, ovate-lance-shaped, with 1 prominent vein; basal lvs. tapering into long stalk; covered with flattened hairs. Buds pink, fls. bright blue, ½ cm. long, 1 cm. across; corolla tube shorter than calyx, which is lobed almost to base. Fls. in short cymes elongating in fruit, on slender often branching stems, forming a loose, airy head.

✤ Woods, fields. To 2300 m. Maritime Alps, mainly Italian; N. Apennines. May–July.   **567**

A. officinalis *L.* Annual, 30–60 cm. tall. Lvs. lance-shaped, covered with spreading hairs. Fls. blue to purple, 1 cm. across, in dense terminal heads of several compact cymes. Corolla tube barely longer than calyx, which is lobed to middle.

✤ Meadows, gravels, debris, preferring limestone. To 1800 (2300) m. E. Pyrenees; Alps. Rare and local. (Britain: probably casual.) May–September.

LYCOPSIS *L.* L. **arvensis** *L.* (**Anchusa arvensis** (*L.*) *Bieb.*). SMALL BUGLOSS. Very similar to *Anchusa* in fl., but corolla tube bent. Annual or biennial, 15–50 cm. tall, with stout erect stem; plant bristly with hairs with bulbous bases. Lvs. to 15 cm. long, wavy, lower tapering into long stalk. Fls. bright blue, 5–7 mm. across, with abruptly bent tube; scales in throat. Cymes compact, forming fairly dense heads.   *

✤ Fields, waste places, on acid soils. To 1700 m.; adventitious to 2290 m. Alps. (Britain.) May–July.   **566**

PULMONARIA *L.* LUNGWORT. Perennials with creeping rhizomes. Fls. in compact terminal cymes. Calyx tubular or bell-shaped, enlarging and widening in fruit; 5-angled at base. Corolla regular, funnel-shaped, with 5 tufts of hairs alternating with the lobes, above or around the anthers which are fixed to the sides of the tube; no scales in throat. Lvs. grow markedly after fl. time and the summer lvs. may differ from the basal ones at fl. time. A confusing genus with ill-defined species: *Flora Europaea* describes several further alpine species.

P. angustifolia *L.* (including **P. azurea** *Bess.*). AZURE LUNGWORT. Plant covered with harsh stiff hairs mingled with glandular ones. Lvs. long and narrow, lance-shaped, tapering into relatively short stalk; summer lvs. 5–10 times longer than broad, up to 20–30 cm. long, not blotched. Fls.

12–20 cm. long, first red or purple, then sky-blue.

✵ Woods, meadows, on acid soils. To 2620 m. Pyrenees; Alps; W. Apennines. April–July. **575**

P. tuberosa *Schrank.* Similar to *P. angustifolia* in basic characters, and sometimes treated as a subspecies; both spring and summer lvs. 4–5 times longer than wide, to 10–15 cm. long, rarely white-blotched. Fls. first pink or red, then cobalt blue to deep violet. *

✵ Woods, meadows. To 2000 m. Pyrenees; W. and C. Alps. April–July. **576**

P. longifolia *Bast.* Similar to *P. angustifolia* in basic characters and sometimes treated as a subspecies; summer lvs. 10–15 times longer than broad, up to 40–60 cm. long, white-blotched. Fls. first red, then deep violet.

✵ Woods, meadows. To 2000 m. Pyrenees. (Britain.) April–July.

P. officinalis *L.* COMMON LUNGWORT. 10–30 cm. tall. Plant covered with hard stiff hairs. Basal lvs. to 10 cm. long, 1½ times as long as broad, with distinct stalk, pointed, often heart-shaped at base, often heavily white-spotted. Corolla 13–18 mm. long, 10 mm. across, first pink, then blue.

✵ Damp open woods, preferring limestone. To 1900 m. Jura; Savoy; E.C. and S. Alps. Rare. (Britain.) March–May. **577**

P. montana *Lej.* MOUNTAIN LUNGWORT. 20–40 cm. tall. Lvs. soft, shining, with soft hairs, very glandular; stems and calyxes sticky. Basal lvs. 10–15 cm. long, 4–6 cm. broad, with winged stalk 20–30 cm. long. Lvs. normally unblotched; two Eastern Alps subspecies which do not exceed 1500 m. have blotched lvs. Corolla 1½–2 (2½) cm. long, first pink, then lilac blue to bright blue.

✵ Meadows, woods. To 1900 m. Pyrenees; Alps. April–May. **574**

VERBENACEAE

The insignificant lilac-flowered *Verbena officinalis* L., the VERVAIN, may reach 1500 m.

LABIATAE—MINT FAMILY

Annual or perennial herbaceous plants, occasionally shrubs; stems often square; lvs. opposite. Fls. mainly in clusters in axils of bracts (floral lvs.), often gathered to form a ring or 'whorl' of fls. around the main stem; sometimes a number of these whorls together on a stem give the appearance of a spike. Fls. sometimes solitary in axils. Corolla tube usually well developed, basically with 5 lobes, the upper 2 often joined together forming a single lobe, the other 3 lobes forming a lower lip. Calyx often with 2 lips, the upper usually with 3 teeth, the lower with 2. Stamens 4, rarely 2 (*Salvia*), attached to the corolla tube. Style branched into 2. Characteristic fruit of 4 nutlets (also in *Boraginaceae*, but this family has alternate lvs.).

This is usually an easily recognisable family. Some members are aromatic, and many are cultivated for their culinary and perfumery properties, e.g. mint, thyme and lavender.

330

LAVANDULA *L.* **L. angustifolia** *Ehrh.* **(L. officinalis** *Chaix,* **L. vera** *DC.*). LAVENDER. A bushy plant, woody at the base, 30–60 cm. tall, greyish green, aromatic. Lvs. linear to longish-oval, much longer than wide, edges rolled under; older lvs. green. Fls. in whorls up the stem, forming stiff upright spikes, lavender blue in colour, stems and bracts greyish in the spike. Corolla tube much longer than the calyx. Stamens 4, 2 long, 2 short, all enclosed in the corolla tube.

Ssp. **pyrenaica** *(DC)* Guinea is a form with very narrow lvs. and slender compact spikes, from the E. Pyrenees.

✿ Warm, stony hillsides, slopes, preferring limestone. To 1800 m. E. Pyrenees; French Alps. Widely cultivated for perfume. June–July.　**583**

CALAMINTHA *Mill.* Aromatic perennials with fls. in small stalked clusters in axils of bracts which resemble the basal lvs. Calyx straight-tubed, 5-toothed, hairy inside. Corolla straight-tubed, 2-lipped. Stamens 4, shorter than corolla. Style branches with lobes of different size. Nutlets smooth, oval.

Included in some floras in *Satureja,* which has fls. in few-fl. axillary whorls forming a 1-sided spike.

C. grandiflora *(L.) Moench.* **(Satureja grandiflora** *Scheele*). LARGE CALAMINT. 20–50 cm. tall. Lvs. toothed, triangular, stalk 1–2 cm. long, blade 3–7 cm. long, 2–7 cm. wide. Fls. large, 3–4 cm. long, crimson. Calyx 1–1½ cm. long.

✿ Woods, on humus. To 2100 m. Pyrenees; Alps. (Britain: garden escape.) July–September.　**602**

C. alpina *(L.) Lam.* **(Acinos alpinus** *(L.) Moench,* **Satureja alpina** *Scheele*). ALPINE CALAMINT. 10–30 cm. tall, with slender stems. Lvs. oval or narrow, firm, usually toothed, veins marked. Fls. large, 1–3 in axil of each bract, to 2 cm. long, bright violet

(rarely white or pink), longer than the calyx, which is constricted in the middle. Plant aromatic when dried.　　*

✿ Screes, stony places, woods, meadows, mainly on limestone. To 2550 m. Pyrenees; Alps; Apennines. June–September.　**603**

C. ascendens *Jord.* **(C. officinalis** *auct.,* **Satureja calamintha** *Scheele,* **S. ascendens** *(Jord.) Druce*). COMMON CALAMINT. 30–60 cm. tall; stems hairy. Lvs. oval to round-oval, to 3½ cm. wide, stalked, toothed, hairy. Fls. to 1½ cm. long, lilac or violet with dense spots on lower lip, to reddish purple. Calyx sometimes purple-tinted, hairy.

✿ Woods, stony places, preferring limestone. To 1600 m. Alps. (Britain.) July–October.

ACINOS *Mill.* **A. arvensis** *(Lam.) Dandy* **(Satureja acinos** *(L.) Scheele,* **Calamintha acinos** *(L.) Clairv.*). BASILTHYME. Annual, sometimes perennial. Stems erect, 10–40 cm. tall, hairy. Lvs. small, ½–1½ cm. long, stalked, oval to narrow-oval, slightly pointed and toothed, almost hairless. Fls. 1 cm. or

1233. *Acinos arvensis.* Flower head.

more long, up to 8 in axillary whorls, making a lax terminal cluster. Corolla violet, with white markings on lower lip.

❋ Fields, dry slopes, railway tracks, preferring limestone. To 2000 m. Alps. (Britain.) June–September. **1233**

THYMUS *L.* THYME. Aromatic, shrubby plants. Fls. in heads or spikes of few-fld. whorls. Corolla 2-lipped. Calyx 2-lipped, upper with 3 teeth, lower with 2 lobes. Stamens 4, longer than the corolla. Nutlets oval, smooth.

T. serpyllum *L.* WILD THYME. A low shrub, seldom over 7 cm. tall, with horizontal creeping branches up to 50 cm. long, the flowering shoots in rows on the last season's branches. Stems hairy, slightly 4-sided. Lvs. firm, thickish, oval, blunt-tipped, hair-fringed on edges, surfaces either hairy or not. Fls. in a head, pale pink, rose-purple, or purple.

There are a great many variants within this species, many of which have now been given specific status. The differences are mainly in the type of hairiness of the stems, stem shape, cylindrical, round or square, and the shape of the lvs.

❋ Dunes, open woods, dry grassland, scrub. To 3000 (3300) m. Pyrenees; Alps; Apennines. (Britain to 1240 m.) April–September. **604**

T. polytrichus *A. Kern. ex Borb.* HAIRY THYME. Now considered a subspecies of *T. praecox* *Opiz*. The hairs on the stems are longer on the corners and short on the faces. The stems are hairy right to the top, though sometimes hairless at the base. Upper lvs. almost round, $\frac{1}{2}$–1 cm. long, hairless at least on the upper surface. Lowest lvs. much smaller, spoon-shaped. Creeping stems very long and rampant.

❋ Rocks, meadows. To 3000 m. C. and E. Alps. May–September. **605**

ORIGANUM *L.* **O. vulgare** *L.* MARJORAM. An aromatic perennial, 30–80 cm. tall, branched, slightly hairy. Lvs. stalked, rounded-oval, very slightly toothed, slightly hairy on both surfaces. Fls. in dense ovoid clusters. Corolla rose-purple, to 1 cm. long, longer than the calyx, with 2 lips. Calyx with 5 equal teeth. Stamens 4.

❋ Woods, banks, meadows. To 2030 m. Pyrenees; Alps; Apennines. (Britain.) July–September. **1120**

MENTHA *L.* MINT. Herbaceous perennials, pleasantly aromatic. Fls. very small, in whorls in lf.-axils, forming a cluster or spike. Corolla white to purple, 4-lobed, tube shorter than bell-shaped or tubular 5-toothed calyx, which has up to 13 nerves. Stamens 4, almost the same length. Nutlets oval, smooth, round at top. The species of this genus are very variable and cross freely. Many are cultivated as flavouring herbs.

M. arvensis *L.* (**M. longifolia** *Host.*). CORN MINT. A variable perennial 10–60 cm. tall; stems branched, slightly hairy. Lvs. oval to round, toothed or slightly wavy on edges, usually more or less hairy. Fls. in widely spaced whorls. Corolla lilac, outside hairy. Calyx hairy, with 5 short, equal teeth. Stamens protruding from corolla. Hybridises readily.

❋ Swampy places, arable fields, ditches, paths. To 1800 m. Alps. (Britain.) July–October.

M. aquatica *L.* WATER MINT. A strongly aromatic, variable perennial, 15–90 cm. tall; stems often reddish, more or less hairy. Lvs. generally hairy on both sides, oval to round-oval, toothed to wavy-edged, stalked. Fls. in a 1–3 whorled head, often with up to 3 whorls below in lf.-axils. Corolla violet to lilac. Stamens protruding.

Calyx and stalks hairy. Hybridises
readily.
✤ Watersides, damp ground. To 1700
m. Pyrenees; Alps. (Britain.) July–
October.

M. longifolia (*L.*) *Huds.* (**M. sylvestris**
L.). HORSE MINT. A moderately pungent
perennial, with creeping underground
stems. Upright stems 60–90 cm. tall,
more or less hairy. Lvs. oblong, 3–8
cm. long, 1–3 cm. wide, pointed,
toothed, green, usually hairy above,
thickly hairy below, giving a greyish
felt-like appearance, rounded or nearly
so at the bottom, stalked. Fls. lilac in a
cylindrical spike 3–10 cm. long. Stamens
usually protruding. Calyx and stalks
hairy.
✤ Fields, hedges, damp places, ditches.
To 1920 m. Alps. (Britain: doubtful
native.) July–October.

M. spicata *L. em. Huds.* (**M. viridis**
L.). SPEAR MINT. A strongly aromatic
perennial 30–90 cm. tall; stems hairless.
Lvs. oblong or narrowing towards the
pointed tip, toothed, hairless on both
sides, or with few hairs below, stalkless
or nearly so. Fls. lilac, hairless, in
terminal cylindrical spikes. Calyx and
stalks hairless, rarely calyx teeth hairy.
Stamens protruding.
✤ Damp, waste places. To 1900 m.
Pyrenees; Alps. Uncommon. (Britain:
introduced, now widely naturalised.)
July–October.

HYSSOPUS *L.* **H. officinalis** *L.*
HYSSOP. An aromatic perennial, slightly
woody at base, 20–60 cm. tall; stems
hairless or very hairy. Lvs. widely
oblong to linear, 1½–2½ cm. long,
bluntish tipped. Fls. brilliant blue-
violet, 1–1½ cm. long, in long, dense,
terminal, rather 1-sided spikes; usually
erect but rarely somewhat sprawling
(*var.* **decumbens** *J. & F.*). Corolla
2-lipped, stamens 4. Calyx with 15
nerves and 5 practically equal teeth.

Nutlets smooth, roundly triangular in
shape.   *
  The typical alpine plant, *ssp.* **montana**
J. & F., seldom exceeds 20 cm., and is
bright green and quite hairless.
✤ Dry, warm, stony or rocky places,
preferring limestone. Rare. Cultivated
herb, and ornamental. To 2000 m. S.
and W. Alps. *Ssp. montana:* French Alps
only (rare). (Britain: introduced.) June–
September.   601

H. aristatus *Godr.* Similar to *H.
officinalis*, but bracts ending in a fine
whitish 1–2 mm. point. Fls. reddish
blue, in a compact, short head.   *
✤ Rocks, stony places. To 1900 m. C.
and E. Pyrenees. Rare. June–September.

DRACOCEPHALUM *L.* DRAGON-
HEAD. Perennials. Fls. long, in long,
fairly dense terminal clusters or spikes.
Anthers woolly. Calyx 2-lipped, the
upper lip with 3 teeth, the central one
much larger than the other 2.

D. ruyschiana *L.* (**D. hyssopifolium**
Mart.). NORTHERN DRAGONHEAD. 10–30
cm. tall, stems hairless. Lvs. narrow to
broadly linear, hardly stalked, hairless.
Fls. blue-violet; corolla tube straight,
2½–3 cm. long.
✤ Dry grassland, open woods. 1200–
2200 m. Pyrenees (very rare); W. and C.
Alps (rare). June–September.   589

D. austriacum *L.* PONTIC DRAGON-
HEAD. 15–30 cm. tall, very woolly-
hairy. Lvs. deeply divided into 3–5
linear segments. Fls. deep violet,
corolla tube curved, 3–4 cm. long.
✤ Dry grassland, warm stony places,
preferring limestone. To 2000 m. E.
Pyrenees (probably extinct); French
Alps (extremely rare); C. Alps. May–
June.   590

NEPETA *L.* Herbaceous perennials.
Fls. in whorls in lf.-axils, forming a
terminal spike, white or rose-pink.
Corolla 2-lipped, upper lip flat. Calyx

with 5 teeth. Stamens 4, protruding, 2 middle ones longest.

Besides the species described, *N. cataria L.*, the common CATMINT, may reach 1530 m. in the Alps.

N. nepetella *L.* (**N. lanceolata** *Lam.*). 30–80 cm. tall. Lvs. lance-shaped, under 2 cm. wide, short-stalked, whitish grey below. Fls. whitish to flesh-pink, in whorls of 4–6 forming slender clusters. Corolla with long hairs, tube longer than woolly-hairy calyx. ❧ Arid, stony places, streamside gravels. To 1700 m. Pyrenees (rare); Alps. July–August. **1126**

N. latifolia *DC.* 80–150 cm. tall. Lvs. oval-oblong, 8–10 cm. long, 4 cm. wide. Stem and lvs. more or less velvety. Fls. bluish, occasionally reddish, very numerous in well-spaced whorls, forming a long, interrupted spike. ❧ Meadows, pine-forest clearings. To 1700 m. E. Pyrenees. Uncommon. July–September.

PRUNELLA *L.* (**BRUNELLA** of some authorities). Herbaceous perennials. Fls. in a dense terminal, oblong spike. Corolla 2-lipped, upper hooded, lower curved upwards. Calyx 2-lipped, upper with 3 short teeth, lower with 2 long ones. Stamens 4, protruding. Nutlets smooth, oblong.

P. vulgaris *L.* (**P. reptans** *Dum.*, **Brunella officinalis** *Crantz*). COMMON SELFHEAL. A usually slightly hairy plant to 30 cm. tall. Lvs. oval to oblong, 2–5 cm. long, slightly toothed or not toothed at all, stalked. Fls. violet, occasionally white or pink, to 1½ cm. long. Calyx often tinged with purple, with long white hairs. ❧ Woods, dry meadows, preferring limestone. To 2400 m. Pyrenees; Alps; Apennines. Norway to 1220 m. (Britain to 840 m.) June–October. **593**

P. grandiflora *Jacq.* (**Brunella alpina** *Thunb.*). LARGE SELFHEAL. 10–30 cm. tall. Lvs. oval, contracted below, 3–5 cm. long, slightly toothed, stalked. Fls. 2–2½ cm. long, violet-blue, in spike 3–5 cm. long. Upper lip of calyx with 3 almost equal teeth, lower lip scarcely divided or toothed. *
❧ Dry meadows, woods, hillsides, particularly on limestone. To 2400 m. Pyrenees; Alps; Apennines. June–August. **592**

SIDERITIS *L.* Perennials with small white or yellow fls. in dense spikes, the corolla shorter than calyx, which is spiny with 5 straight teeth as long as tube; style with 2 lobes, the lower wide and short, clasping the base of the upper.

S. hyssopifolia *L.* (including **S. alpina** *Vill.*). A sub-shrub 10–40 cm. tall. Lvs. green, hairy, upper ones oval to linear, occasionally slightly toothed, not spreading far from stem; lower lvs. smaller. Fls. in short, oblong clusters, among bracts more obviously toothed than stem lvs. Corolla pale yellow; calyx flaring out like a bell. Nutlets oblong, round-tipped. ❧ Stony places, dry slopes, river gravels, preferring limestone. To 1800 m. Pyrenees; Alps. July–August. **1123**

S. endressii *Willk.* Sometimes considered a subspecies of *S. hyssopifolia*, but only 8–15 cm. tall, very woody, lvs. close together, small, with inrolled edges, very white-woolly. Fl. clusters rounded. ❧ Stony places. To 1800 m. C. and E. Pyrenees. July–August.

STACHYS *L.* WOUNDWORT. Herbaceous annuals and perennials, often with a disagreeable smell when crushed. Lvs. not divided, occasionally rosetted at base. Fls. in axillary whorls; corolla yellow or purple, 2-lipped, upper lip concave but not hooded. Calyx bell-shaped with 5 usually equal teeth. Stamens 4, inner pair shortest.

Besides the species described, *S. palustris* L., the MARSH WOUNDWORT, with purple fls., reaches 1600 m.; *S. recta* L., with pale yellow fls., 2250 m.; and *S. sylvatica* L., the HEDGE WOUNDWORT, with dark red fls., 1700 m.

S. alpina L. ALPINE WOUNDWORT. A hairy perennial 40–100 cm. tall. Lvs. oval to round, wide near base, 4–18 cm. long, 3–9 cm. wide, with toothed margins; stalks to 10 cm. long. Fls. hairy, dull reddish purple, to 2 cm. long, many in whorls. Calyx hairy.
✼ Open woods, damp stony places, preferring limestone. To 1950 m. Pyrenees; Alps; Apennines. (Britain: rare.) June–October. **595**

S. germanica L. (**S. tomentosa** *Gat.*, **S. polystachya** *Ten.*). DOWNY WOUNDWORT. A white-cottony perennial or biennial 30–80 cm. tall. Lvs. to 12 cm. long, upper stalkless or almost so, lower long-stalked, oblong-oval to oval, wider near base, edges round-toothed, veins prominent. Fls. pale reddish pink. Calyx with silky hairs, half length of corolla tube.
✼ Wood-sides, copses, screes, stony places. To 1740 m. Tyrol. (Britain: rare.) June–September. **594**

S. densiflora *Benth.* (**S. monieri** (*Gouan* P. W. Ball, **Betonica hirsuta** L.). ALPINE BETONY. Perennial, 10–30 cm. tall; stems with long, bristly, yellow hairs. Lower lvs. rosetted, long-stalked, oval, with bluntish tip, few teeth on edges, green below. Stem lvs. of up to 3 pairs, scarcely stalked. Fls. in a tight cluster, purplish (seldom white). Corolla 2 cm. long, upper lip slightly longer than stamens. Calyx 1–1½ cm. long, with obvious veins.*
✼ Meadows, preferring limestone. To 2400 m. C. Pyrenees; Alps; Apennines. July–August. **596**

S. officinalis (*L.*) *Trev.* (**Stachys betonica** *Benth.*, **Betonica officinalis** L.). BETONY. Very similar to *S. densiflora*, but stems not hairy, or softly hairy (not bristly yellow hairs as in *S. densiflora*), 20–60 cm. tall. Calyx ½–1 cm. long; corolla purplish red, to 1½ cm. long, the upper lip much longer than the stamens.
✼ Light woods, meadows, heaths, copses, preferring acid soils. To 1800 (2050) m. Pyrenees; Alps; Apennines. (Britain.) June–October.

S. alopecuros *Benth.* (**Betonica alopecuros** L.). YELLOW BETONY. Similar to *S. densiflora* and *S. officinalis*, but fls. pale yellow. 20–50 cm. tall. Lvs. rosetted at base, 3–6 cm. long, 2–4 cm. wide, white-hairy below. Fls. in a dense spike.
✼ Stony, grassy places, scrub, on limestone. To 1950 (2280) m. E. and C. Pyrenees; Alps. (Britain.) June–August. **1125**

LAMIUM L. DEADNETTLE. Annual or perennial herbaceous plants. Fls. in dense whorls in lf.-axils, bracts (fl. lvs.) similar to the lower lvs. Corolla tubular, widening at the top, with 2 lips, upper one concave forming a hood, lower lip of 3 lobes, the middle one the largest. Calyx bell-shaped or tubular. Anthers hairy. Nutlets roundly triangular, flattened at the top.

L. album L. WHITE DEADNETTLE. A hairy perennial 20–60 cm. tall. Lvs. oval to round, 2–7 cm. long, stalked, edges quite heavily toothed or jagged, tip pointed. Fl. whorls spaced well apart. Corolla white, to 2 cm. long, upper lip hairy, outer lobes of lower lip with 2–3 teeth. Calyx tube bell-shaped, to 1 cm. long, with teeth a little longer than the tube.
✼ Paths, roadsides, waste places, railway lines, hedgerows. To 2270 m. Pyrenees (rare); Alps (rare in W.);

Apennines. (Britain.) April–November.
1122

L. maculatum *L.* SPOTTED DEAD-NETTLE. A variable perennial 10–80 cm. tall, similar to *L. album*, but the slighter darker green lvs. have a central whitish area, and are more pointed at the top. Corolla pink to purplish pink; calyx teeth shorter.
✲ Paths, hedgerows. To 2020 m. Pyrenees; Alps; Apennines. (Britain: introduced.) April–October.

L. amplexicaule *L.* HENBIT DEAD-NETTLE. A hairy annual, 5–25 cm. tall. Lvs. oval to round, rounded or lobed at the base, with toothed edges, and long stalks (to 5 cm. long in the lower lvs.). Bracts similar, sometimes larger and lobed, occasionally wider than long, without stalks, their bases partly clasping the stem. Fl. whorls few, well spaced. Corolla pinkish purple, usually to 1½ cm. long. Calyx tubular, densely silky-hairy, to 1 cm. long, tube usually longer than the teeth.
✲ Paths, cultivated and waste ground, walls. To 2550 m. Pyrenees; Alps; Apennines. (Britain.) April–December.
591

L. purpureum *L.* RED DEADNETTLE. A hairy annual, sometimes red- to purple-tinged, 10–45 cm. tall. Lvs. stalked, oval, heart-shaped at base, with evenly toothed edges. Fl. lvs. similar. Fl. spike compact; corolla pinkish purple. Calyx about ½ cm. long, hairy, bell-shaped.
✲ Paths, walls, cultivated ground. To 2476 m. Alps; Apennines. (Britain.) March–December.

GALEOBDOLON *Adans.* **G. luteum** *Huds.* **(Lamium galeobdolon** (*L.*) *L.*). YELLOW ARCHANGEL. A slightly hairy perennial, 20–60 cm. tall. Lvs. more or less triangular, pointed at tip, squarish or rounded at base, with un-

evenly toothed edges, 4–7 cm. long, stalked, often white-blotched. Fls. in dense axillary whorls. Corolla bright yellow, sometimes with brownish markings, to 2 cm. long, 2-lipped, upper lip hooded, lower 3-lobed. Calyx to 1 cm. long, bell-shaped, with 5 nearly equal teeth. *
✲ Woods, hedgerows. To 1980 m. Pyrenees; Alps. (Britain.) April–July.
1121

GALEOPSIS *L.* HEMPNETTLE. Herbaceous annuals. Fls. in terminal and axillary clusters and whorls. Corolla 2-lipped, upper lip hooded, lower 3-lobed, with 2 cone-like protuberances at the base; tube conical. Calyx shorter than corolla tube, with 5 more or less unequal spiny teeth, tube bell-shaped. Nutlets triangular, rounded at the top.

G. ladanum *L.* **(G. intermedium** *Vill.*). 10–50 cm. tall, lvs. broad, 1–3 cm. long, oval-oblong, toothed, with 3–7 obvious teeth on each side. Corolla rose-purple, tube hardly longer than the green, hairy calyx.
✲ Fields, stony places, railway lines. To 2400 m. Pyrenees; Alps; Apennines. (Britain: introduced, rare.) July–October.
586

G. angustifolia *Ehrh. ex Hoffm.* **(G. ladanum** *auct.*). NARROW-LEAVED HEMP-NETTLE. Sometimes considered a subspecies of *G. ladanum*, which it much resembles. 10–80 cm. tall. Stems not swollen at the nodes, hairy or not. Lvs. linear to oblong, with 1–4 teeth on each side, 1½–8 cm. long, under 1 cm. wide, pointed at tip, short-stalked, often hairy. Corolla bright reddish purple, 1½–2½ cm. long, tube longer than the tubular, hairy calyx which sometimes has white, flattened hairs.
✲ Fields, stony places. To 2000 m. Pyrenees; Alps. (Britain.) July–October.
1124

G. tetrahit L. COMMON HEMPNETTLE. 10–100 cm. tall, stiffly hairy. Lvs. 2½–10 cm. long, roundly-oval to longish-oval, toothed, slightly hairy. Corolla white, pink or purple with darker markings, tube not much longer than the calyx, which has stiff hairs.
✤ Woods, fields, paths, hedgerows. To 2310 (2660) m. Pyrenees; Alps; Apennines. (Britain.) July–October. **587**

G. pyrenaica Bartl. PYRENEAN HEMP-NETTLE. 10–50 cm. tall. Lvs. oval, round or square at the base, with even short teeth on edges, velvety-hairy, at least below. Corolla purplish, much longer than the velvety-hairy calyx.
✤ Debris, gravels, on acid soil. To 2200 m. E. Pyrenees. August–September. **588**

HORMINUM L. **H. pyrenaicum** L. DRAGONMOUTH. Perennial, with woody stock, 10–30 cm. tall. Stems usually without lvs. Lower lvs. stalked, 3–6 cm. long, 2–5 cm. wide, rounded-oval with pointed tip and toothed edges. Fls. 4–6 to a whorl, on one side of stem, to 1½ cm. long, violet; calyx hairless. Stamens 4.
✤ Open woods, stony places, dry meadows, on limestone. 1000–2450 m. C. Pyrenees; Alps (very rare in French Alps, often abundant to E.). June–August. **600**

SALVIA L. SAGE, CLARY. Under-shrubs and herbaceous plants, alpines perennial. Fls. in a loose terminal spike of axillary whorls. Corolla with 2 lips, upper lip usually concave, lobes unequal. Calyx bell-shaped, 2-lipped, upper with 3 teeth, the lower with 2. Stamens 2. Nutlets roundly triangular, smooth.

S. glutinosa L. STICKY SAGE. A strongly aromatic, sticky, hairy herbaceous perennial, 40–80 cm. tall. Lvs. triangular, 8–16 cm. long, 5–12 cm. wide, pale

green, with toothed edges. Fls. yellow 3–4 cm. long.
✤ Clearings, copses, preferring limestone. To 1800 m. E. Pyrenees; Alps; Apennines. June–September. **597**

S. pratensis L. MEADOW CLARY. A hairy, aromatic perennial, 30–100 cm. tall. Lower lvs. 7–15 cm. long, triangular heart-shaped to oblong, unevenly toothed, wrinkled, long-stalked; stem-lvs. smaller, to 3 pairs, top ones stalkless. Corolla violet-blue, upper lip hooded, 1½–2½ cm. long (sometimes only female fls. appear; these are usually less than 1 cm. long). Calyx hairy, bell-shaped, tube about ½ cm. long.
✤ Dry grassland, debris. To 1920 m. Pyrenees (uncommon); Alps. (Britain.) May–August. **598**

S. verticillata L. WHORLED CLARY. A hairy, unpleasant-smelling perennial, 30–80 cm. tall. Lvs. oval-heart-shaped, with unevenly toothed edges, sometimes deeply lobed, stalked. Corolla 1–1½ cm. long, violet, the base of the tube pinched into a short claw-like projection. Calyx bell-shaped, ½ cm. long, the middle tooth of upper lip shortest.
✤ Paths, dry grassland, gravelly places. To 2380 m. C. and S. Alps. (Britain: introduced.) May–August. **599**

SCUTELLARIA L. **S. alpina** L. ALPINE SKULLCAP. Perennial, 10–30 cm. tall, hairy. Lvs. small, oval, blunt-tipped, with toothed edges. Bracts very thin, pale or violet. Fls. in compact quadrangular clusters at the top of the stems. Corolla 2–3 cm. long, bright blue-violet, occasionally purple or white. Calyx glandular-hairy.
✤ Limestone rocks and screes. 1000–2500 m. Pyrenees; Alps; Apennines. June–August. **582**

TEUCRIUM L. GERMANDER. Perennial herbaceous plants, with fls. in spikes or clusters. Corolla with 1 lip

having 5 lobes, the 4 upper short.
Calyx tubular or bell-shaped, 5-toothed.
Nutlets roundly-oval, smooth or
marked.

Besides the species described, *T.
chamaedrys* L., the WALL GERMANDER,
and *T. lucidum* L., both with purplish
fls., may reach 1800 m.

T. montanum L. ALPINE PENNYROYAL,
MOUNTAIN GERMANDER. With 5–25 cm.
slender, creeping stems, woody at base,
forming circular mats. Lvs. linear, 1–2
cm. long, to ½ cm. wide, with slightly
toothed edges. Fls. yellowish white in
terminal clusters. Calyx hairless, green.
❧Rocks, stony places, dry meadows,
on limestone. To 2350 (2900) m.
Pyrenees; Alps; Apennines. Local.
May–August. **585**

T. pyrenaicum L. PYRENEAN GER-
MANDER. With 5–20 cm. slender creeping stems, woody at the base, with
long soft hairs. Lvs. green on both
sides, round to oval, the uppermost
surrounding the oval clusters of purple-
red fls., with yellowish white lower
lobes.
❧ Rocks, dry slopes, on limestone. To
2000 m. Pyrenees; Dauphiné Alps
(rare). June–August. **584**

AJUGA L. Herbaceous annuals or
perennials. Fls. few to many in whorls,
sometimes in a terminal cluster. Corolla
2-lipped, lower lip of 3 obvious lobes,
the upper very short. Calyx bell-
shaped, 5-toothed. Nutlets egg-shaped,
with net-like markings.

A. chamaepitys (L.) *Schreb.* GROUND-
PINE. A sprawling annual, 5–20 cm.
tall, hairy, smelling of pine when
crushed. Lvs. 2–4 cm. long, sticky, the
upper cut into 3 linear, bluntish lobes.
Lower lvs. soon withering. Fls. 2 to a
whorl, in axils of lvs. Corolla yellow
red spots on lower lip, as long as
hairy, bell-shaped calyx, 1–1½ cm. long.
❧ Fields, dry slopes, preferring cal-

careous soils. To 1600 m. Alps. (Britain.)
April–October. **581**

A. reptans L. COMMON BUGLE. A
perennial with creeping runners; fl.
stems 10–30 cm. tall. Stems hairy on 2
opposite sides. Basal lvs. rosetted, 4–7
cm. long, oval or oblong, sometimes
slightly hairy, long-stalked. Upper stem-
lvs. shorter, hardly stalked, few. Upper
bracts tinged blue. Fls. in a terminal
spike. Corolla blue, occasionally pink
or white. Calyx bell-shaped, teeth
shorter than the tube, to ½ cm long.
❧ Poor fields, open woods. To 2000
m. Alps; Apennines. (Britain.) April–
July. **580**

A. genevensis L. BLUE BUGLE. Perennial, 10–40 cm. tall. Stems white-hairy
on 2 sides or all round. Lower lvs.
5–12 cm. long, rounded oval, with
toothed margins, long-stalked, hairy,
withering before flowering. Upper
stem-lvs. oblong, short-stalked, a little
smaller. Upper bracts blue-tinged. Fls.
in a terminal spike, bright blue. Calyx
bell-shaped, to ½ cm. long.
❧ Wood clearings, dry meadows,
preferring calcareous soils. To 2230
(2750) m. Pyrenees; Alps; Apennines.
(Britain: introduced.) May–August. **579**

A. pyramidalis L. PYRAMIDAL BUGLE.
A uniquely pyramidal, upright perennial, 10–30 cm. tall. Stems hairy all
round. Lower lvs. hairy or nearly
hairless, rounded oval, blunt-tipped,
slightly toothed, short-stalked, persisting at flowering. Stem-lvs. oval-
oblong, with very short stalks or none.
Bracts large, longer than fls., deep
violet or reddish purple, surrounding
the terminal spike of pale violet-blue
fls. Calyx nearly 1 cm. long, teeth
longer than the tube.
❧ Meadows, stony places, scrub, on
acid or alluvial soils. 1300–2800 m.
Pyrenees; Alps; Apennines. Norway to
1130 m. (Britain.) April–August. **578**

SOLANACEAE—NIGHTSHADE FAMILY

Several members of the Nightshade Family sometimes grow at altitudes above 1500 m. They are as follows: *Atropa belladonna* L., the DEADLY NIGHTSHADE (**1234**), to 1650 m.; *Hyoscyamus niger* L., the COMMON HENBANE, to 1860 m. (**1235**); *Lycium barbarum* L. (*L. halimifolium* Mill.), the BOX THORN or DUKE OF ARGYLL'S TEA-PLANT, to 1800 m.; *Solanum dulcamara* L., the WOODY NIGHT-SHADE, to 1700 m.; *S. nigrum* L., the BLACK NIGHTSHADE, to 1740 m. All these are British natives (*Lycium* naturalised). *Atropa* and *Hyoscyamus* are especially likely to be found in and around alpine villages.

The curious *Scopolia carniolica* Jacq., with pendant golden bells, sometimes included in Alpine floras, only attains 1000 m. (**1236**).

The TOMATO, *Solanum lycopersicum* L., is cultivated to 1800 m., and the POTATO, *S. tuberosum* L., to 2020 m. *Nicotiana rustica*, a form of TOBACCO, is cultivated to 1850 m.

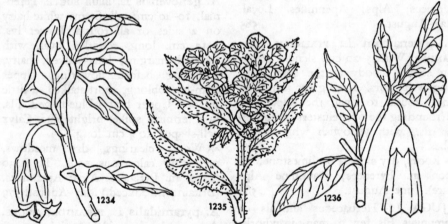

Solanaceous plants. 1234. *Atropa belladonna.* 1235. *Hyoscyamus niger.* 1236. *Scopolia carniolica.*

SCROPHULARIACEAE—FIGWORT FAMILY

Alpine representatives mainly herbaceous (rarely shrubby); occasionally partially parasitic, e.g. *Pedicularis, Rhinanthus, Euphrasia.* Fls. solitary, or in clusters, or in long spikes. Corolla joined into a tube at least at the base, with 5 usually even lobes (sometimes 4, one absent; *Veronica*), or lobes reduced to 2 lips (*Antirrhinum*). The base of the corolla tube is sometimes developed into a pouch (*Antirrhinum*) or a spur (e.g. *Linaria, Chaenorrhinum*). Calyx 4–5-lobed. Stamens usually 4 or 5 (sometimes 2, e.g. *Veronica*), attached to the corolla. Occasionally the fifth stamen is a sterile one, a 'staminode', e.g. in *Scrophularia.* Style simple or two-lobed. Fruit a 2-celled capsule with numerous seeds.

This family contains genera of greatly differing appearances, e.g. *Euphrasia, Verbascum, Rhinanthus*. Certain genera are extremely difficult to determine specifically and many species which are very much alike go to similarly high altitudes, e.g. in *Veronica, Euphrasia*. Such genera often hybridise fairly readily also.

Besides the genera described, the tiny *Limosella aquatica* L. may reach 1830 m.

VERBASCUM L. MULLEIN. Mostly biennials (as in all species described) with a basal rosette, and tall upright leafy fl. stems; lvs. alternate, not divided. Fls. in long spikes. Corolla with 5 more or less equal petals, united into a very short tube. Calyx 5-lobed. Stamens 5, lower pair longer than remaining three, filaments all or upper 3 hairy.

V. nigrum L. (**V. lanatum** *Schrad.*). DARK MULLEIN. 50–120 cm. tall. Stems hairy (hairs star-shaped), square. Lvs. darkish green above, paler beneath, densely hairy, heart-shaped, wavy-edged. Lower lvs. 10–30 cm. long, long-stalked, upper lvs. stalkless or nearly so. Corolla yellow, occasionally cream, with dark purplish spots towards centre. All filaments covered in purple-maroon hairs. Capsule oval, longer than calyx.

❀ Dry, open places, banks, railway lines. Rather rare. To 1800 m. Pyrenees; Alps. (Britain.) July–September. **607**

V. chaixii *Vill.* Very similar to *V. nigrum*, but has yellow fls. with violet to purple throat, filaments with purple hairs, and cylindrical stems.

❀ Woody clearings, dry places, fields, paths, preferring calcareous soils. To 1800 m. Pyrenees; Alps. Rare. June–September.

V. pulverulentum *Vill.* (**V. floccosum** *W. & K.*). HOARY MULLEIN. 50–120 cm. tall, covered with dense white-woolly hairs which can be rubbed off, giving a greyish blotchy appearance. Stems not ridged or grooved. Lvs. broadly oval-

oblong, lower ones 20–50 cm. long, short-stalked, upper ones usually stalkless, smaller, all hairy on both surfaces. Fls. in branched spikes. All filaments covered in whitish hairs. Capsule oval, longer than calyx.

❀ Stony, waste places, paths, ditches. To 2000 m. Pyrenees; Alps. (Britain: rare.) July–August. **608**

V. lychnitis L. WHITE MULLEIN. 30–150 cm. tall, covered in whitish hairs; similar to *V. pulverulentum*, but stems angled, and lvs. almost hairless on upper surface. Fls. yellow with whitish hairs on all filaments.

❀ Clearings, gravelly, dry places, preferring acid soils. To 1800 m. Pyrenees; Alps; Apennines. (Britain: the common form, *var.* **album** (*Mill.*) *Druce*, having white fls.; the yellow form known only in Somerset.) June–September.

V. thapsus L. AARON'S ROD. 30–200 cm. tall, with thick white-woolly covering. Lvs. oval-oblong, lower ones 15–45 cm. long, with slightly winged stalks, upper lvs. smaller, with their bases lying against the main stem down almost to the next lf. Fls. in dense spike, yellow, petals concave. Lower pair of filaments hairless or nearly so, upper three with yellow-whitish hairs. Capsule oval, longer than calyx.

❀ Dry, gravelly places, copses. To 1850 m. Pyrenees; Alps. Norway to 850 m. (Britain.) July–September.

V. crassifolium (Lam.) Murb. (**V. montanum** *Schrad.*). MOUNTAIN MULLEIN. Like *V. thapsus*, and nowadays considered a subspecies, but a less robust

plant, with lvs. tapering gradually into a long stalk; lf. bases against main stalk for only half distance to next lf. Upper lf. surfaces finely white-hairy, lower often yellowish-hairy. Stamen filaments white-woolly. Capsule as long as calyx.
❀ Stony places, scrub. To 2100 m. Pyrenees; C. Alps; Apennines. June. **606**

ANTIRRHINUM *L.* Plants herbaceous. Lvs. undivided, upper ones often alternate on stem, lower opposite. Fls. stalked, yellow, red, pink, purplish (never blue), in axils of lvs., forming terminal spikes. Corolla with a long broad tube pouched at the base, 2-lipped, the upper lip with 2 lobes, the bottom lip with 3 lobes and a projection (throat-boss) which closes mouth of the corolla tube. Stamens 4. Cells of capsule unequal in size. Differs from the otherwise similar *Linaria* in having no spur.

A. sempervirens *Lapeyr.* ROCK SNAP-DRAGON. A sprawling or hanging plant with brittle 10–25 cm. stems; covered in short hairs, with small leathery oval lvs., ½–1 cm. long, which persist over winter. Fls. to 2 cm. long, white or pink-flushed, with golden throat-boss; calyx shorter than fl. stalks.
❀ Rocks, stony places. To 2000 m. French and Spanish C. Pyrenees. June–September. **613**

A. molle *L.* SOFT SNAPDRAGON. Similar to *A. sempervirens*, but lvs. 1–2 cm. long, not leathery, and not persisting over winter; whole plant woolly-hairy. Fls. to 3 cm. long on stalks shorter than calyx.
❀ Rocks. To 1500 m. Mainly Spanish Pyrenees (Andorra, Catalonia). May–August. **614**

ASARINA *Tourn. ex Mill.* **A. procumbens** *Mill.* (**Antirrhinum asarina** *L.*). CREEPING SNAPDRAGON. With flexible, sprawling stem 10–60 cm. long;

plant sticky-downy. Lvs. all opposite, 3–6 cm. long, round to kidney-shaped with wavy margins. Fls. 3–4 cm. long, whitish yellow streaked with red, throat-boss yellow, scented. Capsule hairless, shorter than calyx.
❀ Rocks, stony places, walls, preferring acid soils. To 1800 m. C. and E. Pyrenees. April–September. **615**

LINARIA *Mill.* TOADFLAX. Herbaceous plants. Lvs. undivided, upper ones sometimes alternate, usually all opposite or in whorls. Fls. in terminal spikes or more compact clusters, similar to those of *Antirrhinum*, but corolla with spur, violet-blue, whitish or yellow, base of tube a long slender curved spur. Capsule with 4–10 openings at top.

L. alpina (*L.*) *Mill.* ALPINE TOADFLAX. Normally annual or biennial, but usually perennial at higher altitudes; a sprawling, hairless, blue-green plant with 10–20 cm. stems; fl. stems upright. Lvs. strap-shaped to oval, lying close to the stem, stalkless. Fls. blue-violet, usually with an orange central projection or occasionally a white one; some older authorities refer to these as varieties or subspecies, but they are inconstant from seed. Capsule ovoid, much longer than the calyx; seeds winged.
❀ Screes, rocks, gravels. 1500–3800 m. Pyrenees; Alps; Apennines. July–August. **612**

L. italica *Trev.* (**L. angustissima** (*Lois.*) *Borb*) ITALIAN TOADFLAX. An erect 20–50 cm. plant, blue-green, hairless. Lvs. narrow strap-shaped, pointed. Fls. in a terminal spike, corolla 16–22 mm. long with a long down-pointing spur, citron-yellow, orange at the throat. Calyx lobes short, hairless.*
❀ Grassland. 500–2200 m. W. Alps. July–August. **609**

L. perrieri Ry. is similar and, like *L. italica*, often considered a subspecies of *L. vulgaris*. It has spoon-shaped lvs. and 3–3½ cm., golden yellow fls. It is found only in the Val d'Isère (French Alps) from 1600–2000 m. *

L. pyrenaica DC. (**L. supina** (*L.*) *Desf. ssp.* **pyrenaica** *Duby*). PYRENEAN TOADFLAX. Very similar to *L. italica*, but smaller and strongly glandular-hairy in upper part. The fls. are larger (18–26 mm.) with long arching spur, the calyx lobes longer and hairy, and fl. stalks very short.
❀ Hillsides, grassland. To 2000 m. Pyrenees. May–September. **610**
    The sprawling *L. supina* itself may reach 2000 m.

L. vulgaris *Mill.* COMMON TOADFLAX. Very similar to previous three species, but a stouter plant, 30–80 cm. tall, lvs. thicker, fl. spur practically straight. Capsule oval, twice length of calyx.
❀ Paths, fields, stony and grassy places. To 1600 m. Pyrenees; Alps. Norway to 870 m. (Britain.) May–September.

L. repens (*L.*)*Mill.* (**L. striata** *DC.*, **L. monspessulana** (*L.*) *Mill.*). STRIPED TOADFLAX. An upright plant 15–80 cm. tall, bright green or bluish, hairless. Lvs. strap-shaped. Fls. usually stalkless, in loose head, white or yellowish with lilac veins, and yellow throat, and short blunt spur. Capsule oval to spherical, a little longer than calyx.
❀ Dry places, paths, walls, clearings. To 2300 m. Pyrenees; Alps. (Britain.) June–September. **611**

CYMBALARIA *Baumg.* **C. pallida** (*Ten.*) *Wettst.* (**Linaria pallida** *Ten.*). A sprawling plant with flexuous, hairy stems. Lvs. round to kidney-shaped, lightly lobed. Fls. solitary in lf.-axils, 15–20 mm. long, azure-violet, on long stalks. Calyx lobes equal, short. Differs

from *Linaria* in having capsule with 2 pores.
❀ Dry and stony places. To 2100 m. C. Apennines. June–August. **1131**

CHAENORHINUM (*DC.*) *Lange.* **C. origanifolium** *Fourr.* (**Linaria origanifolia** *DC.*). A compact annual, biennial or perennial with many upright to semi-sprawling 8–25 cm. stems, slightly sticky, hairy. Lvs. round to oval-oblong, lower ones opposite. Fls. ½–1½ cm. long, bluish purple with orange-yellow throat-boss. Differs from *Linaria* in having open throat.
❀ Old walls, stony places, screes, preferring limestone. Uncommon. To 1500 m. Pyrenees. April–July. **616**

ERINUS *L.* **E. alpinus** *L.* A tufted perennial with erect 5–15 cm. stems. Lowest lvs. in rosette; stem-lvs. alternate; about 1½ cm. long, wedge-shaped with bluntish tips narrowing at base to fairly short stalks, with wavy, toothed edges. Fls. in terminal clusters or spikes, rosy to purple-violet, rarely white; corolla of 5 spreading lobes with deeply notched tips, and a slender narrow tube about as long as calyx. Stamens 4. Capsule ovoid, shorter than calyx.
❀ Rocks, screes, grassland, preferring limestone. Local. 1000–2400 m. Pyrenees; Alps; Abruzzi. (Britain: introduced.) May–October. **617**

SCROPHULARIA *L.* FIGWORT. Herbaceous biennials or perennials with square stems and opposite lvs. Fls. in lf.-axils in leafy clusters or spikes, usually dull in colour. Corolla of 5 small lobes, the two lower ones joined at the bottom, tube not pouched or spurred. Calyx of 5 lobes. Stamens 4, with sometimes a sterile fifth one. Capsule opens along its side.

S. vernalis *L.* YELLOW FIGWORT. Biennial or perennial, 30–80 cm. tall, with soft glandular hairs. Lvs. 4–15

342

cm. long, thin, stalked, round-oval to heart-shaped with pointed tip, edges deeply toothed. Clusters compact, of numerous fls. with leafy bracts. Corolla greenish yellow, lobes small, almost equal, no sterile stamen, other stamens finally protruding. Fl. stems shorter than calyx.

❧ Cool, shady places, waste ground. To 1800 m. Pyrenees; Alps; Apennines. Rare. (Britain: introduced.) April–July.

1127

S. pyrenaica *Benth.* PYRENEAN FIGWORT. A hairy perennial 10–40 cm. tall with hollow stems. Lvs. greenish yellow, slightly longer than wide, with bluntish tip and scalloped edges. Fls. nearly 1 cm. long, yellowish with reddish markings on edges. Edges of calyx lobes papery. Sterile stamen circular.

❧ Shaded rocks. To 1900 m. Pyrenees. Rare. June–July. **1130**

S. scopolii *Hoppe* (**S. auriculata** *Scop.*, **S. glandulosa** *W. & K.*, **S. alpestris** *Gay*). A hairy perennial 40–100 cm. tall; stems solid, or nearly so. Lvs. thin, greyish white, rounded-heart-shaped, pointed, with toothed margins. Fls. brownish red, to 1½ cm. long, no lvs. in inflorescence. Calyx green, hairless.

❧ Damp places, woods, preferring acid soils. To 2300 m. Pyrenees; Alps; Apennines. June–August. **1128**

S. hoppei *Koch.* ALPINE FIGWORT. 10–50 (80) cm. tall. Lvs. many times deeply divided almost to the nerves, often purplish. Fls. in a cylindrical spike, dark violet-purple with white markings; stamens protruding from corolla. Fl. stalk as long as calyx or longer. *

Nowadays considered only a sub-species of the variable *S. canina* L., which is not normally an alpine plant.

❧ Stony places, screes, preferring limestone. To 2156 m. Pyrenees; Alps; Apennines. June–August. **1129**

S. nodosa *L.* COMMON FIGWORT. A more or less hairless, clear green plant 50–150 cm. tall with square, solid, sharp-angled stems. Lvs. uncut, oblong-oval with sharp-pointed tip, stalked. Fls. reddish brown. Sterile stamen represented by a heart-shaped scale. Capsule conical.

❧ Damp places, usually by rivers or streams. To 1850 m. Pyrenees; Alps. (Britain.) June–September.

VERONICA *L.* SPEEDWELL. Herbaceous plants, perennial unless specified, with opposite lvs. Fls. blue, seldom white or pink, either solitary in lf.-axils, or in axillary or terminal spikes. Corolla with 4 lobes, the upper larger than the rest, and a very short tube. Calyx 4- or rarely 5-lobed. Stamens 2.

A number of rather weedy, basically lowland species exceed 1500 m. They include *V. agrestis* L., the FIELD SPEEDWELL, to 1800 m.; *V. arvensis* L., the WALL SPEEDWELL, to 2100 (2565) m.; *V. officinalis* L., the COMMON SPEEDWELL, to 2140 m.; *V. polita* Fries., to 2084 m.; *V. scutellata* L., the MARSH SPEEDWELL, to 1800 m.; and *V. urticifolia* Jacq. to 1900 m. All these except *V. polita* and *V. urticifolia* are British natives.

V. beccabunga *L.* BROOKLIME. Hairless, with creeping rooting stem and fleshy upright 20–60 cm. stems. Lvs. rather fleshy, oblong to oval, round at base, bluntish-tipped, short-stalked. Fls. in loose spikes of 10–30, in axils of lvs. Corolla blue, nearly 1 cm. across. Calyx lobes narrow-oval, pointed. Capsule round, shorter than calyx.

❧ Boggy places, streams, ponds. To 2470 m. Pyrenees; Alps; Apennines. (Britain.) May–September. **618**

V. spicata *L.* SPIKED SPEEDWELL. 8–60 cm. tall, grey-downy, with slightly woody rhizome and upright flowering stems. Lower lvs. stalked, oval to roundish, upper ones stalkless, nar-

rower, mostly with wavy or wavy-toothed margins. Fls. many in a long, pointed, terminal spike. Corolla blue-violet, tube relatively long. Capsule roundish, as long as calyx lobes.
❧ Dry places, grassland, edges of woods. To 2040 m. Pyrenees; Alps; Apennines. (Britain.) July–November.
620

V. teucrium L. LARGE SPEEDWELL. To 100 cm. tall, usually hairy. Lvs. round-ish-oval, narrowing towards base, on short stalks. Fls. blue, 10–13 mm. across, in large, open terminal spikes. Calyx 5-lobed, small. Capsule longer than calyx. *
❧ Grassland, clearings, dry hillsides, preferring limestone. To 1780 m. Pyrenees; Alps; Apennines. June–August.
621

V. ponae Gouan (**V. gouani** Mor.). 20–50 cm. tall, hairy. Lvs. large, stalkless, pointed heart-shaped, toothed. Fls. small, blue or lilac, on stalks in loose spikes. Capsule twice as long as calyx, heart-shaped, hairy.
❧ Damp rocks, cool woods. 1200–2500 m. Pyrenees. June–August.
619

V. chamaedrys L. GERMANDER SPEED-WELL. A sprawling plant with stems rooting at nodes; fl. stems 20–40 cm. tall, hairless except for two opposite lines of long white hairs along their length. Lvs. oval to triangular, 1–2½ cm. long, stalkless or with short stalks, edges unevenly toothed, hairy, dullish green. Fls. in loose, long-stalked spikes from lf.-axils. Corolla to 1 cm. across, bright blue with white centre. Filaments and style blue. Calyx lobes narrow-oval, hairy. Capsule shorter than calyx, hairy.
❧ Clearings, paths, meadows, culti-vated ground. To 2270 m. Pyrenees; Alps; Apennines. Norway to 1100 m. Britain.) March–July.
623

V. fruticulosa L. SHRUBBY SPEEDWELL. A variable plant: lower part hairless, more or less woody, with creeping hairy stem. Erect stems 5–20 cm. tall. Lvs. oval, slightly toothed at edges, lower lvs. usually smaller than the upper ones. Fls. pink to blue with reddish markings, usually solitary in lf.-axils, in very loose clusters, which are glandular. Capsule oval, glandular, longer than calyx.
❧ Rocks, screes, meadows, on lime-stone. To 2800 m. Pyrenees; Alps. June–September.
624

V. fruticans Jacq. (**V. saxatilis** Scop.). ROCK SPEEDWELL. Similar to V. fruti-culosa, and sometimes regarded as a subspecies. 5–10 cm. tall; fls. brilliant blue with red-purple throat; fl. spike and capsule hairy, not glandular.
❧ Rocks, screes, meadows, preferring acid soils. To 3000 m. Pyrenees; Alps; Apennines. Norway to 1750 m. July–September.
633

V. allionii Vill. A creeping, slightly blue-green plant with 10–30 cm. stems. Lvs. slightly leathery, thickish, rounded oval with very short stalks. Fls. blue in compact spikes; corolla lobes narrow. Capsule slightly dented at top.
❧ Dry meadows, on granite and schists. 1800–2700 m. Alps. Uncommon. July–August.
626

V. nummularia Gouan (also written **nummularifolia**). A low, tufted plant with tortuous woody stock and creeping 5–15 cm. stems. Lvs. ½–1 cm. long, oval to round, hairless, except on edges. Fls. small, few, blue or pink, in compact little heads. Capsule slightly dented.
❧ Schistous rocks and screes. 1800–2500 m. Pyrenees. June–August.
625

V. serpyllifolia L. THYME-LEAVED SPEEDWELL. Creeping, with 10–30 cm., rooting, hairy stems, woody at base, and upright fl. stems. Lvs. light green,

344

round-oval to oblong, 1-2 cm. long, edges often slightly wavy, almost or completely stalkless, hairless. Fls. in loose, often long, terminal spikes, white or pale blue with darker blue lines. Anthers grey-violet. Capsule hairy, wider than long, about equalling calyx.
Ssp. **apennina** *Tausch.* has bright blue fls. and is downy-glandular.   *
❋ Grassy, cool shady places. To 2500 m. Pyrenees; Alps; Apennines. Norway to 1350 m. *Ssp. apennina:* E. Pyrenees; N. Apennines (very rare). (The species in Britain.) May–October.   **622**

V. bellidioides *L.* A tufted, glandular-hairy plant with creeping basal stems and 5-20 cm. erect fl. stems; basal lvs. in a rosette; stem-lvs. opposite, stalkless, round to oval spoon-shaped, rarely toothed on edges. Fls. in a small terminal cluster, violet-blue with white markings; anthers pale purple. Calyx of 4 unequal lobes.
❋ Damp meadows, peaty places, often on acid soils. 1420-3000 m. Pyrenees; Alps; Apennines. July–August.   **630**

V. lilacina *Towns.* Very similar to *V. bellidioides*, and nowadays considered a subspecies, but fls. pale blue-lilac with white marks, lvs. distinctly wavy-edged, and calyx 4-7 unequal lobes.
❋ Damp meadows, preferring acid soils. Pyrenees; Alps. To 3000 m. July–August.   **631**

V. alpina *L.* ALPINE SPEEDWELL. Erect, 2-10 (15) cm. tall, hairy in upper part. Lvs. oval, sometimes toothed, shortly stalked, on fl. stem. Fls. 4-12 in a compact terminal spike, dull blue. Capsule oval to round, hairless, longer than calyx.
❋ Stony places, meadows. 1500-3000 (3500) m. Pyrenees; Alps; Apennines. Norway to 1960 m. (Britain.) July–August.   **632**

V. pumila *All.* (**V. alpina** *var.* **australis**

Wahl.). Resembles *V. alpina*, to 10 cm. tall, but has elliptic lvs. held erect, close to the stem, with long hairs on the edges. Fls. small, in a tight cylindrical cluster; capsule, calyx and upper stem all hairy.   *
❋ Moist meadows, snow-beds. To 1800 m. Norway. July.

V. aphylla *L.* Erect, usually almost stemless, ½-3 (6) cm. tall, with all lvs. in basal rosettes, rounded to narrow-oval, stalkless. Stems and lf. margins hairy. Fls. relatively large, ½-1 cm. long, 2-5 in a loose head, lilac to blue suffused or veined pink. Capsule purplish, glandular.
❋ Rocks, meadows, snow-beds, preferring limestone. 1200-3000 m. Pyrenees; Alps; Apennines. July–September.   **634**

PAEDEROTA *L.* Very similar to *Veronica*, and sometimes included in that genus. It differs in having a distinctly 2-lipped, scarcely open, cylindric corolla and 5-lobed calyx; stamens 2. The fls. are in short pyramidal spikes. Stems with lvs. in opposed pairs (decussate). Species perennial.

P. lutea *Scop.* (**P. egeria** *L.*, **Veronica lutea** (*Scop.*) *Wettst.*). A hairy, dark green, erect plant 10-30 cm. tall. Lvs. stalkless or short-stalked, long-triangular with sharply toothed margins. Fls. in a fairly short terminal spike. Corolla 1-1½ cm. long, straw-coloured. Calyx tube narrow with thin lobes, hairy.
❋ Rock crevices. 1000-2100 m. E. Alps from Tyrol eastwards. June–August.   **628**

P. bonarota *L.* (**P. caerulea** *L.f.*, **Veronica bonarota** (*L.*) *Wettst.*). A hairy, light green or bluish, erect plant 8-25 cm. tall. Lvs. round to widely oval, narrowing towards the stalk, edges widely toothed. Fls. 1-1½ cm. long, blue-lilac to darkish blue-purple, anthers and stigma dark blue. Calyx hairy, with long narrow lobes.

❀ Rock crevices. To 2500 m. S. and E. Alps (not Switzerland). June–August.
627

DIGITALIS *L.* FOXGLOVE. **D. grandiflora** *Jacq.* (**D. ambigua** *Murr.*). LARGE YELLOW FOXGLOVE. A stout, erect, hairy, 40–100 cm. perennial with large, stalkless, long-triangular, opposite lvs. Fls. solitary in lf.- or bract-axils, forming a long, loose, terminal spike. Corolla 3–4 cm. long and 1½–2 cm. wide, conical, with 4 slightly spreading lobes, pale yellow outside, cream with maroon markings inside, hanging more or less on same side of stem. Poisonous.

❀ Open woods, clearings, stony places. Uncommon. To 2000 m. Pyrenees; Alps. June–August.
636

MELAMPYRUM *L.* COW-WHEAT. Annuals with usually undivided, opposite lvs. Fls. in leafy spikes. Corolla tubular, 2-lipped, lower lip with 3 lobes, with projection nearly closing mouth of tube. Calyx tubular, 4-lobed. Capsule flattened, with 1–4 oval seeds.

Besides the species described, *M. arvense* L., *M. cristatum* L. and *M. nemorosum* L., which include spectacular forms with bright-coloured fls. and bracts, may reach 1500 m.

M. pratense *L.* COMMON COW-WHEAT. A very variable species, with spreading to erect branches, 8–60 cm. tall, hairless to stiffly hairy. Lvs. stalkless or with short stalks 1½–10 cm. long, narrow, triangular to oval, pointed. Fls. in axils of green lf.-like bracts, all turned to the same side of the stem and held almost horizontally. Corolla 1–2½ cm. long, whitish to deep yellow, occasionally with red or purple margins, mouth almost closed. Calyx ½ length of the corolla tube. Capsule usually 4-seeded.

The usual alpine form, *ssp.* **alpestre** (*Brugg.*) *Ronn.*, is typically unbranched and only 10–15 cm. tall.

❀ Open woods, clearings, peat bogs. To 2250 m. E. Pyrenees; Alps. Rare at alpine levels. (Britain.) June–September.
629

M. sylvaticum *L.* WOOD COW-WHEAT. 5–35 cm. tall, more or less branched, slightly to densely hairy. Lvs. like those of *M. pratense*. Fls. in 1-sided spike, nearly upright, deep yellow, seldom pale yellow, mouth wide open, lower lip bent backwards. Calyx as long as corolla tube. Capsule usually 2-seeded.

❀ Woods, meadows. To 2500 m. Pyrenees; Alps. Norway to 1350 m. (Britain.) July–September.

ODONTITES *Gilib.* Annuals with opposite lvs. Fls. small, in 1-sided, terminal spikes. Corolla 2-lipped, the lower lip 3-lobed, upper lip shorter. Calyx tubular, 4-lobed. Reputedly semiparasitic.

O. lutea (*L.*) *Reichb.* (**Euphrasia lutea** *L.*). 10–30 (50) cm. tall. Lvs. stalkless, narrow, the lower ones saw-toothed, the upper ones not. Fls. in spikes, terminal and axillary, among bracts longer than the bright yellow, open-mouthed corolla, edged with small hairs. Calyx hairless. Capsule longer than calyx.

The typical alpine form, *ssp.* **lanceolata** *Reichb.*, is a rather squat, spreading plant.
                                                    *
❀ Dry meadows, waste places, among crops; on limestone. To 1800 m. Pyrenees; Alps. July–September. **635**

O. verna (Bellardii) Dumort. (**Euphrasia odontites** *L.*). 20–50 cm. tall. Similar to *O. lutea*, but lvs. wider, all with toothed edges, narrowing at base. Fls. reddish pink.

Ssp. **verna** (*Bell.*) *Hayek*: branches erect. Fl. May–June.

Ssp. **serotina** (*Dumort.*) *Corb.*: branches spreading. Fl. Aug. – Oct. ❀ Grassland, hillsides, paths. To 1800 m. E. Pyrenees; Alps. August–October.

WULFENIA *Jacq.* **W. carinthiaca** *Jacq.* An erect perennial 20–40 cm. high with basal lvs. in a rosette, round-oval, narrowing at base into a short stalk, darkish green, paler beneath. Fl. stems stout, slightly hairy, with small alternate, stalkless lvs.; all lvs. with wavy edges. Fls. in a dense spike; corolla tube 5-lobed, dark purple-blue outside, light blue inside. Calyx with 5 long lobes and very short tube. Capsule spherical to oval, as long as calyx. ❀ Moist humus-rich places. 1000–2000 m. Carinthia. Very local. July–August. **640**

TOZZIA *L.* **T. alpina** *L.* A frail, symmetrically branched perennial 10–50 cm. tall. Stems square, fleshy, brittle, hairless except on angles. Lvs. opposite, stalkless, soft, oval to round, edges slightly wavy, bases clasping stem. Fls. in loose heads, golden yellow with red to purple markings at throat. Calyx of 4 (5) unequal lobes. Capsule globular, one-seeded. Reputedly semi-parasitic upon *Petasites, Adenostyles, Mulgedium,* etc. ❀ Damp meadows, streamsides. Uncommon. 1000–2000 m. Pyrenees; Alps. June–July. **637**

BARTSIA *L.* (sometimes spelt **BARTSCHIA**). Perennials with opposite lvs. Fls. in terminal spikes. Corolla tube with two lips, the upper forming a hood, the lower 3-lobed. Stamens 4. Capsule broad. Seeds few, large with prominent ribs or wings. Reputedly semi-parasitic.

B. alpina *L.* ALPINE BARTSIA. A very hairy plant 10–30 cm. tall with upright, unbranched stems. Lvs. stalkless, 1–2 cm. long, oval to round, bluntish-tipped. Fls. in short spikes among large purplish leafy bracts. Corolla dull purple, hairy. Capsule almost twice length of calyx. ❀ Damp meadows, snow-beds. 1100–2700 (3100) m. Pyrenees; Alps. Norway to 1960 m. (N. British mountains to 1000 m.) June–August. **638**

B. spicata *Ram.* Very similar to *B. alpina,* 15–40 cm. tall, hairy, with reddish stems; bracts barely as long as calyx, narrow. Corolla reddish purple. Capsule barely longer than calyx. ❀ Limestone rocks. C. Pyrenees. Rare. August–September. **639**

EUPHRASIA *L.* EYEBRIGHT. Annuals; lvs. small, opposite or upper ones alternate; stems with stiff white hairs. Fls. stalkless, forming a terminal spike. Calyx bell-shaped, 4-lobed. Corolla 2-lipped, upper lip 2-lobed, lower lip 3-lobed, with white, purple or blue markings and yellow throat. Stamens 4. Reputedly semi-parasitic. A confusing group with many very similar species, and also numerous hybrids. Detailed descriptions are only given of a few. Besides those mentioned *E. frigida* Pugsl. reaches 1700 m. in Norway and there are several further alpine species in Italy.

Plant glandular-hairy on bracts and calyx

E. rostkoviana *Hayne.* COMMON EYEBRIGHT. Slender, 10–20 (40) cm. tall, often with reddish tinge. Stem branching from base. Lvs. ½–1 cm. long, bright green, thinnish, with very obvious venation, and glandular hairs on both surfaces; round to oblong with toothed edges. Fls. in terminal heads. Corolla 9–11 mm. long, white with yellow centre, upper lip lilac or mauve-tinted. Capsule elliptic to oblong, hairy. ❀ Meadows, heaths, stony places, open woods. To 3000 m. Pyrenees;

Alps; Apennines. (Britain.) July–October. **643**

E. hirtella *Jord.* is also glandular-hairy; it has 5–7 mm. fls., white-striped violet, and is found from 1300–2300 m. in all the European mountains.

Plants not glandular

E. minima *Jacq.* DWARF EYEBRIGHT. A slender plant 2–12 (25) cm. tall. Lvs. and bracts ½–1 cm. long; lvs. round to oval with toothed edges, hairy. Fls. few in short terminal clusters. Corolla 5–6 mm. long, with upper lip blue to purple (seldom white or violet), lower lip yellow. Calyx lobes pointed. Capsule hairy.

✤ Stony places, meadows, preferring acid soils. To 3250 m. Pyrenees; Alps; Apennines. July–September. **644**

E. alpina *Lam.* ALPINE EYEBRIGHT. 5–20 cm. tall. Lvs. dense, staying close to the stem, stalkless, oval to oblong, hairy. Fls. 9–11 mm. long, in short clusters; upper lip blue, white or purple-striped, lower lip white, throat yellow.

✤ Meadows, on acid soils. Uncommon. To 2750 m. Pyrenees; Alps; Apennines. May–September. **645**

Fls. of similar size are found in:

E. picta *Wimm.*: fls. 9–11 mm. long, white touched with blue, throat yellow; rare from 1400–2500 m. in Alps.

E. portae *Wettst.*: fls. 9 mm. long, upper lip striped purple-blue, lower white, throat yellow; to 2300 m. in Alps.

E. stricta *Host.*: fls. (6) 8–10 mm. long, pale violet with blue veins, throat yellow; plant to 40 cm. or more tall; uncommon from 2000–2600 m. in Alps and Apennines.

E. versicolor *Kern.*: fls. 9–11 mm. long, whitish to blue, striped blue or violet; bracts with dark edges; uncommon to 2700 m. in Alps.

E. salisburgensis *Funck.* SALZBURG EYEBRIGHT. A hairless, blue-green to bronze plant 5–25 cm. tall. Lvs. longer than wide, with 2–4 deep teeth. Fls. in loose spikes: upper lip bluish, reddish or tinted with yellow, lower lip white, violet-veined; throat yellow. Fls. 6–8 (10) mm. long. Capsule hairless.

✤ Stony or grassy places, open woods, on limestone. To 2600 (3300) m. Pyrenees; Alps; Apennines. (Britain.) July–September. **646**

E. pulchella *Kern.* is a usually small plant with lvs. having 1–3 teeth, fls. about 8 mm. long, blue or white with yellow throat, rare from 1750–2370 m. in Alps.

RHINANTHUS *L.* (**ALECTORO-LOPHUS** *auct.*). YELLOW-RATTLE. Annuals. Fls. in terminal spikes among lf.-like bracts, yellow, the upper lip of the corolla forming a pronounced beak or hood. The calyx is large, more or less circular, flattened in one plane, swelling and becoming rather papery in fruit. Stamens 4 in upper lip of corolla. Seeds winged, large, few.

This is a very critical genus in which many very similar species reach high altitudes. Hybridisation also occurs. Numerous subspecies or varieties have been named in each species. Besides the species described, *R. freynii* Stern. and *R. ovifugus* Chab. reach 2300–2500 m. in Italy.

R. alectorolophus *Poll.* (**R. major** *Ehrh.*, **R. hirsutus** *Lam.*, **Alectorolophus hirsutus** *All.*). GREATER YELLOW-RATTLE. Light green, 20–80 cm. tall. Stem hairy. Lvs. to 7 cm. long, tapering, with toothed edges. Fls. 8–15 in a head; bracts greenish yellow. Corolla yellow, 2 cm. long: upper lip with 2 violet teeth; mouth usually closed. Calyx hairy on ribs.

✤ Meadows, sandy places. To 2300 m. Pyrenees; Alps; N.W. Apennines. (Britain.) May–September. **641**

R. aristatus *Čel.* (**R. angustifolius** *Gmel.*, **A. angustifolius** (*Gmel.*) *Heyn.*).

5–50 (80) cm. tall. Stem with blackish lines. Lvs. linear, 2–10 mm. wide, lower ones with wavy toothed edges. Corolla 18 mm. long, deep yellow with violet teeth, mouth open. Calyx hairless. Different forms flower at varying seasons.
❀ Meadows, thickets. To 2500 m. Alps. June–September.   642

R. antiquus *S. & T.* (A. antiquus *Stern.*). Stem usually unbranched, (5) 10–15 cm. tall. Lvs. lance-shaped. Corolla 15 mm. long, yellow, with 2 long teeth.
❀ Grassy slopes. 1800–2500 m. Bergamasque Alps. Rare. July.

R. minor *Ehrh.* (A. minor (*Ehrh.*) *Wimm. & Grab.*). YELLOW-RATTLE. A very variable species 5–30 cm. tall, stems sometimes spotted. Corolla 15 mm. long, bright yellow with very short violet or whitish teeth, mouth more or less open.
❀ Paths, grassland. To 2000 (2300) m. Pyrenees; Alps; Apennines. Norway to 1400 m. (Britain.) May–September.

PEDICULARIS *L.* LOUSEWORT. Herbaceous plants, perennial unless otherwise specified, usually semi-parasitic. Lvs. radical and also sometimes alternate on fl. stems, composed of numerous opposite lobes or segments, sometimes connected along the midrib by a thin piece of tissue (pinnatifid), sometimes cut to midrib (pinnatisect); the lobes sometimes further divided. Fls. more or less numerous in terminal clusters (spikes or racemes), with usually lf.-like bracts among them. Calyx tubular or bell-shaped, becoming swollen in fruit, with 2–5 more or less lf.-like lobes. Corolla 2-lipped: upper lip curving, typically helmet- or beak-shaped, sometimes conical or tubular, with 0, 2 or 4 small teeth towards apex; lower lip 3-lobed. Stamens 4, concealed in upper lip. Style 1, usually projecting.

Numerous hybrids have been recorded.

Flowers yellow or bicoloured red/brown and yellow, upper lip blunt-ended, with short or no beak

P. sceptrum-carolinum *L.* MOORKING. A stout plant 30–60 cm. tall with a large basal rosette of pinnatifid lvs.; lobes short and broad. Fl. stems numerous, often leafless. Fls. well spaced in an oblong head over 3 cm. long. Calyx brownish green. Corolla over 3 cm. long, yellow or buff, the lips often completely closed, but if open basal lip reddish. Bracts leafy, often almost as long as calyx.
❀ Moist meadows, fens, willow thickets. Sub-alpine and rare in Germany and Austria. Norway to 1200 m. July–August.   647

P. lapponica *L.* LAPLAND LOUSEWORT. With creeping rhizome and thin erect 10–20 cm. leafy stems. Lvs. to 4 cm. long and 1 cm. wide, with very broad midrib and small toothed lobes. Fls. yellow, rose-scented, radiating at the top of the stem, held almost horizontally; lower lip of corolla twisted. Calyx small, bell-shaped, barely lobed, brown.
❀ Damp meadows, heaths. To 1700 m. Norway. July–August.   648

P. flammea *L.* RED-HOODED LOUSEWORT. 5–10 cm. tall. Lvs. mostly basal, pinnatisect with neat lobes. Fls. small, in a spike, dark yellow with purple-red tip to upper lip, bracts short. Calyx bell-shaped, short-lobed.
❀ Meadows, heaths, gravels, on acid soils. N. Norway to 1320 m., S. Norway to 1100 m. Very rare. July.   649

P. oederi *Vahl.* 5–20 cm. tall, with stem-lvs. Fls. bright yellow with red tip to upper lip; bracts as long as fls. Calyx bell-shaped, with short narrow teeth; hairy.

✻ Meadows, rocks, preferring limestone. Mt. Cenis; E. Alps. Rare in Europe. Norway to 1960 m. July–August. **652**

P. petiolaris *Ten.* (including **P. friderici-augusti** *Tomm.*). A stout plant, with woody stock, 10–40 cm. tall, with very ferny pinnatisect lvs., the lobes longest at the base and themselves with subsidiary divisions. Fls. to 2½ cm. long, in a tight leafy head. Calyx hairy, irregularly cut into 3 + 2 narrow lance-shaped lobes. Corolla yellow or rarely pinkish. ✻ Meadows. To 2260 m. C. and S. Apennines. May–July. **650**

P. comosa *L.* CRESTED LOUSEWORT. 10–40 cm. tall. Not unlike *P. petiolaris* in lvs. and fl.-head; fls. to 2½ cm. long, lemon-yellow or whitish yellow. Calyx bell-shaped, with short, equal, broad-triangular lobes, lightly hairy especially on veins and edges. Corolla with short, wide beak prolonged into 2 teeth. *Ssp.* **asparagoides** *Lap.* has reddish fls. in a looser head. ✻ Meadows. 1400–2270 m. Pyrenees; W. Alps; Apennines. *Ssp. asparagoides:* E. and C. Pyrenees. June–August. **651**

P. foliosa *L.* LEAFY LOUSEWORT. A stout plant 20–60 cm. tall, with very long, ferny, doubly pinnatisect lvs. and 2½ cm. yellow fls. in a dense head with leafy bracts much longer than fls. Calyx bell-shaped, with short triangular lobes hairy on edges. ✻ Wet meadows, streams, preferring limestone. 1200–2500 m. Pyrenees; Alps; Apennines. July–August. **653**

P. hacquetii *Graf.* Sometimes considered a subspecies of *P. foliosa.* A very stout plant 30–120 cm. tall, with long, ferny doubly pinnatisect lvs., the side lobes themselves deeply dissected; lowest lvs. on very long stalks.

Fls. in a dense, cylindrical head with long leafy bracts. Calyx densely woolly with small triangular lobes. Corolla pale sulphur yellow, erect and almost without beak. ✻ Meadows, on limestone. 1200–1700 m. S.E. and E. Alps; Abruzzi. July–August.

Flowers yellow; upper lip prolonged into a curved, truncated beak

P. barrelieri *Reichb.* (**P. adscendens** *Gaud.*). 20–40 cm. tall, with neat pinnatisect lvs.; stem-lvs. short. Fls. straw-yellow, 16 mm. long, in a long loose spike, with short, leafy bracts. Calyx tubular, with triangular lobes, shortly hairy on edges only. Corolla crook-shaped, beak long and slender. * ✻ Meadows, on limestone. 1800–2300 m. W.C. Alps; N. Apennines. July–August. **655**

P. elongata *Kern.* Similar to *P. barrelieri*, 15–35 cm. tall; bracts very short. Calyx tubular, with linear, slightly lf.-like, fringed lobes a quarter of its length. Corolla erect, broad at top, with fairly long, slender beak. ✻ Meadows, on limestone or dolomite. 1300–2300 m. S.E. Alps. July–August. **654**

P. tuberosa *L.* Similar to *P. barrelieri*, but distinctly smaller, 10–25 cm. tall; fls. 20 mm. long, pale yellow; bracts very short. Calyx tubular-bell-shaped, with recurving, linear, deeply fringed, lf.-like lobes ⅓ to ¼ of its length. Corolla crook-shaped, with conical beak. Several rather similar forms have been named. ✻ Dry meadows, stony places, occasionally gravels, on acid soils. 1200–2900 m. Pyrenees (rare); Alps; Apuan Alps; N. and C. Apennines. June–August. **662**

Flowers pink or red, with short beak; calyx lobes leaf-like

P. palustris *L.* RED RATTLE, MARSH

LOUSEWORT. Annual or biennial, 8–50 (80) cm. tall, branching from base into erect unbranched stems. Lvs. 2–4 cm, long, of oblong outline, pinnatisect; bracts similar but smaller. Fls. widely spaced, projecting rather horizontally. Calyx slightly swollen, often reddish, with 2 short, broad lobes. Corolla 2–2½ cm. long, purplish pink or pale pink; upper lip with 4 small teeth.

⚜ Marshes, wet meadows and heaths, usually on acid soil. To 1800 (2300) m. Pyrenees; Alps. Norway to 960 m. (Britain to 900 m.) May–September. **656**

P. sylvatica L. COMMON LOUSEWORT. Perennial or biennial, making sprawling branches from the base, the central one erect, 8–15 (25) cm. tall; with tap-root. Lvs. to 2 cm. long, of oblong outline, pinnatisect with widely spaced lobes; bracts similar. Calyx swelling rapidly in seed, with 4 small lf.-like teeth and 1 strap-shaped tooth. Corolla 2–2½ cm. long, pink, upper lip with 2 teeth near tip.

⚜ Damp woods, meadows and heaths, marshes. To 1700 m. Alps. Uncommon. (Britain to 1000 m.) April–July. **659**

Flowers pink or red, with short beak; calyx lobes triangular, not leafy

P. hirsuta L. HAIRY LOUSEWORT. 5–15 cm. tall with woolly upper stem and calyx. Basal lvs. pinnatisect; stem-lvs. long, narrow, oblong, with rounded lobes, bracts similar. Calyx tubular, with short narrow lobes. Corolla flesh pink, upper lip often darker than lower.

⚜ Damp places, snow-beds. To 1380 m. Norway. June. **657**

P. rosea *Wulf.* PINK LOUSEWORT. (2) 8–15 cm. tall, with long pinnatisect basal lvs. and often none, or 1–3 only, on the hairy stem. Fls. in a tight head with few bracts. Calyx woolly, with narrow lobes. Corolla rose-pink, with upper lip darker.

⚜ Granite and schistous rocks. 1600–2700 m. Pyrenees (one locality); French Alps; E. Alps. (Not Switzerland.) Rare. July–August. **658**

P. recutita L. A stout, hairless plant 20–60 cm. tall, with large lance-shaped pinnatifid lvs. Fls. densely packed in a columnar head. Calyx with teeth as wide as long. Corolla rusty purple (rarely greenish); upper lip almost tubular, with no real beak nor teeth.

⚜ Damp meadows and scrub, marshes. (1000) 1500–2500 m. Alps. Local. July–August. **669**

P. verticillata L. WHORLED LOUSEWORT. The only lousewort with lvs. in whorls of 4. Erect, 5–20 (30) cm. tall, with purplish red fls. in a short, tight head. Calyx somewhat swollen, carrying erect hairs, and with broad, short lobes.

⚜ Damp meadows. (900) 1500–3090 m. Pyrenees; Alps; Apuan Alps; N. and C. Apennines. June–August. **660**

Flowers pink or red, with long, cylindrical beak. Stems typically leafy

P. incarnata *Jacq. non* L. (**P. rostratospicata** *Crantz*). FLESH-PINK LOUSEWORT. 15–45 cm. tall, with stiff, hairless stem. Lvs. pinnatisect, stem lvs. almost as long as basal ones. Fls. in an elongated spike with bracts of 3 linear segments. Calyx woolly, with narrowly triangular teeth. Corolla 13 mm. long, bright pink with deeper helmet; beak long and narrow, close to the wide lip with side lobes larger than central one.*

⚜ Damp meadows, on acid soils. 1500–2700 m. Pyrenees: Mt. Canigou only; Alps. Uncommon. July–August. **661**

P. portenschlagii *Saut.* (**P. geminata** *Geb.*). 2–8 cm. tall, with long, narrow, pinnatisect lvs. Fls. few in a loose head with leafy bracts. Calyx hairy on veins; lobes lightly toothed. Corolla rose-red, 25 mm. long, with relatively short beak in crook form, angular on lower

and narrow, tapering into calyx.
✴ Stony places, meadows, on both
limestone and primary formations.
1700–2600 m. E. Austrian Alps. June–
August.   **664**

P. gyroflexa *Vill.* TUFTED LOUSEWORT.
10–30 cm. tall, with downy stem. Lvs.
also downy, doubly pinnatisect (side
lobes also indented); stem-lvs. few and
relatively small. Fls. stalkless in a head
with leafy bracts. Calyx woolly-hairy
with more or less lf.-like lobes. Corolla
rose-red, with short, broad, rounded
beak, smallish lip and short tube.
✴ Meadows, preferring limestone.
1600–2800 m. Pyrenees (very rare); S.
Alps (Switzerland and Tyrol only).
July–August.   **668**

P. praetutiana *Lev.* is a C. Italian
lousewort now considered a ssp. of
P. gyroflexa, but with stalkless fls.

P. elegans *Ten.* Sometimes considered
a variety of *P. gyroflexa* and resembling
it, but hairless, with sparsely lobed lvs.
and calyx lobes only slightly toothed or
notched; fls. with distinct footstalks.
✴Meadows. To 2350 m. C. and S.
Apennines. July–August.   **673**

P. rostrato-capitata *Crantz* (**P. rostrata**
L. in part, **P. jacquinii** *Koch*). BEAKED
LOUSEWORT. A striking plant, 5–20
cm. tall, hairless, with pinnatisect lvs.
of lance-shaped outline, often suffused
with purplish red, stem-lvs. few and
relatively short. Fls. 3–15 in a dense
head with leafy bracts. Calyx bell-
shaped, downy on veins only, with
lf.-like lobes ⅓ to ¼ length of whole.
Corolla 2½ cm. long, with long, down-
pointing, conical, glossy purplish beak,
broad tube, and very large pink lip hairy
on the margins.
✴ Meadows, on limestone. 1140–2800
m. E. Alps from E. Switzerland. June–
August.   **666**

*Flowers pink or red, with long cylindrical
beak. Stems usually leafless; leaves in a
rosette; plants often dwarf*

P. kerneri *D.T.* (**P. raetica** *Kern.,* **P.
rostrata** *L.* in part, **P. caespitosa** *Sieb.*).
RHAETIAN LOUSEWORT. A rather sprawl-
ing plant 5–10 cm. tall with a dense
rosette of narrow pinnatisect lvs. Fl.
stems slender, with 2 lines of hairs.
Fls. on stalks as long as calyx, in a head
with short leafy bracts. Calyx more or
less downy, long bell-shaped, with
rather unequal, lf.-like, reflexing lobes.
Corolla 2 cm. long, deep pink, rarely
white, the helmet bent backwards
before projecting into a slender conical
beak.
✴ Damp meadows, on acid soils. 1200–
3350 m. Pyrenees; W. and C. Alps.
June–September.   **667**

P. cenisia *Gaud.* MT. CENIS LOUSEWORT.
10–20 cm. tall, with arching stems. Lvs.
pinnatisect, narrow. Fls. 4–10, almost
stalkless, in a short head with leafy
bracts. Calyx rotund, with woolly hairs,
and 5 lightly toothed lobes, 4 long, 1
very short and narrow. Corolla about
2 cm. long; helmet dark purple, straight-
backed, recurving sharply to the long,
narrow, almost cylindrical beak; lip
pink.
✴ Meadows. 1500–1600 m. French and
W. Swiss Alps; N. Apennines. Rare.
July–August.   **665**

P. asplenifolia *Floerke.* FERN-LEAVED
LOUSEWORT. 2½–8 cm. tall, with relatively
long, narrow, pinnatisect, short-lobed
lvs. Stem woolly. Fls. almost stalkless,
in a small head with leafy bracts.
Calyx bell-shaped, very woolly, with
notched, rather lf.-like lobes. Corolla 17
mm. long, rose-red, darker on the
somewhat angular helmet and narrow
almost cylindrical beak, nearly at right
angles to tube.
✴ Meadows, debris, rocks, on primary

352

formations. 1900–2800 m. E. Alps from
E. Switzerland. July–August.   672

P. mixta *Gren.* A low plant with
narrow pinnatisect lvs. and 12–30
almost stalkless fls. in leafy-bracted
spikes almost half as long as the 10–20
cm. stems, sprawling then abruptly
erect. Calyx relatively broad, with
woolly hairs and short, barely notched
lobes. Corolla very small, bright pink,
with arching, neatly rounded helmet and
slender conical beak.
✿ Damp meadows. 1400–2800 m. C.
and E. Pyrenees. June–August.   671

P. pyrenaica *Gay.* PYRENEAN LOUSE-
WORT. Rather resembling *P. mixta*, but
stems with 2 lines of hairs, pink fls.

4–10 in the head, and calyx almost or
entirely hairless.
✿ Meadows, woods, streamsides. 1500–
2800 m. Pyrenees. Uncommon. June–
August.   670

Flowers stemless

P. acaulis *Scop.* STEMLESS LOUSEWORT.
The only lousewort without fl. stems:
fls. clustered on footstalks shorter than
calyx among the large, pinnatisect,
broad-lobed lvs. Calyx narrow bell-
shaped, woolly, with long lf.-like lobes.
Corolla rose-red, 12–18 mm. long, with
short blunt helmet, no beak. Roots
tuberous.
✿ Meadows, debris. 1900–2700 m. S.
and E. Alps (not Switzerland). (March)
July–August.   663

OROBANCHACEAE—BROOMRAPE FAMILY

Herbaceous annual to perennial plants which contain no chlorophyll and are
full parasites. Fls. in compact terminal spikes on upright scaly stems. Corolla
2-lipped, tube curved. Stamens in 2 pairs. Calyx tubular, 2–5-toothed. Fruit
a dehiscent 2-valved capsule. Seeds small, many.
   In some older works *Lathraea* is included in *Scrophulariaceae*.

LATHRAEA *L.* **L. squamaria** *L.*
TOOTHWORT. A stout, upright perennial
with scaly rhizome and 8–30 cm. scaly
fl. stem, white or pale pink. Fls. with
short stalks in bract axils on a 1-sided
spike, which first droops then straight-
ens. Corolla white tinged with pale
purple, little longer than the glandular-
hairy calyx which has 4 wide, triangular
lobes. Parasitic on various woody roots,
notably Hazel (*Corylus*) and Elm (*Ulmus*).
✿ Cool woods. To 1600 m. Alps.
Uncommon. (Britain.) March–May. 681

OROBANCHE *L.* Root parasites,
annual to perennial, with underground
tubers attached to roots of host,
producing upright scaly flowering
stems. Fls. stalkless in terminal spikes.
Corolla with curved tube, 2-lipped,

lower 3-lobed, upper 2-lobed. Calyx
2-lipped, 4–5-toothed.
   Besides the species described the
following may reach 1600 m.: *O.
caryophyllacea* Sm., the CLOVE-SCENTED
BROOMRAPE, with yellowish, brown-
tinged fls., parasitic on *Asperula* and
Galium; *O. laserpitium-sileris* Reut., with
violet fls., on *Laserpitium*; and *O. major*
L., with pink, then yellow fls., on *Centaurea* and *Scabiosa*.

O. purpurea *Jacq.* (**O. arenaria** *auct.*,
O. caerulea *Vill.*, **Phelipaea purpurea**
(*Vill.*) *Mey.*). PURPLE BROOMRAPE. Stem
stout, bluish, occasionally branched,
15–45 cm. tall, glandular-hairy above,
with few narrow scales below. Fls. in
loose spike. Corolla 18–30 mm. long,
dull purplish blue, yellowish at base,

twice length of calyx. Anthers hairless; stigma whitish. Calyx tubular with 4 narrow, pointed lobes, hairy. Parasitic on *Compositae*, notably *Achillea mille-folium*, *Artemisia*, *Cirsium*.

✤ Waste places. To 1800 m. Alps. Rare. (Britain: rare.) June–July. **674**

O. arenaria *Borkh.* **(Phelipaea arenaria** *Walp.*). SAND BROOMRAPE. Not unlike *O. purpurea*, but 20–60 cm. tall, more slender, with bluish, slightly hairy corolla 26–35 mm. long; anthers woolly-downy, stigma yellow; calyx with lobes longer than slender tube, and prominent bracts. Parasitic on *Artemisia campestris*, *Anthemis*, *Eryngium*.

✤ Alluvial river flats. To 1800 m. Alps. June–July. **675**

O. teucrii *Hol.* GERMANDER BROOM-RAPE. Fl. stems 10–40 cm. tall, slender, hairy, brownish yellow. Bracts few, pointed, slender. Fls. in loose head. Corolla 2–3 cm. long, purplish red-brown, glandular-downy, hairy on edges. Calyx short, pointed. Parasitic on *Teucrium*.

✤ Scrub, rocky places. To 1900 m. Pyrenees; Alps. Uncommon. June–July. **678**

O. flava *Mart.* YELLOW BROOMRAPE. Stems 15–60 cm. tall, stoutish, dull brownish yellow. Bracts same colour, few, slender. Corolla 2 cm. long, ochre-yellow, upper lip reddish brown. Parasitic on *Petasites*, *Tussilago*, *Adenostyles*.

✤ Stony places. To 1700 m. Alps. Rare. June–July. **680**

O. salviae *F. Schultes.* SAGE BROOM-RAPE. Stem 20–55 cm. tall, light brownish yellow, much swollen at the base. Bracts few, wide-based, slim-pointed. Corolla 12–23 mm. long, light yellow or fawn, inside light cream. Parasitic on *Salvia*, especially *S. glutinosa*.

✤ Dry places, meadows, To 1200 m. Alps. Rare. June–July. **679**

O. alba *Steph.* **(O. epithymum** *DC.*, **O. rubra** *Sm.*). THYME BROOMRAPE. A variable plant with stems 8–25 (35) cm. tall, thickish, dull reddish yellow, with many similar coloured bracts at base, entirely glandular hairy. Fls. few in loose spike, clove-scented. Corolla 15–20 mm. long, pale reddish yellow to purplish red, slightly glandular-hairy. Calyx 2-lipped. Filaments glandular above, hairy below. Parasitic on *Thymus* and other *Labiatae*, and also on cultivated beans and peas. The pallid form illustrated is more common on the Continent; the British form is usually purplish red.

✤ Woods, grassland. To 1800 m. Alps. (Britain.) April–August. **676**

  O. hellebori *Mieg.* is an orange-fl. ssp., parasitic on *Helleborus*, very rare in the Pyrenees.

O. reticulata *Wallr.* **(O. scabiosae** *Koch*), SCABIOUS or NETTED BROOM-RAPE. Stem 30–90 cm. tall, red-brown, bracts slightly darker. Corolla 15–22 mm. long, brown-violet or purple, occasionally pallid, with many glands, the inside of the corolla darker red-brown. Stigma purple. Parasitic on *Knautia*, *Scabiosa*, *Carduus*, *Cirsium*, *Aconitum*.

✤ Fields, stony places. To 2500 m. Pyrenees; Alps. Uncommon. (Britain: local.) June. **677**

O. loricata *Reichb.* **(O. artemisiae** *Gren.*). MUGWORT BROOMRAPE. Stem 20–40 cm. tall, swollen at base, bluish violet, with numerous bracts of the same colour. Corolla violet or purple. Calyx narrow at base. Parasitic on *Artemisia campestris* and *A. glutinosa*.

✤ Hillsides. To 2200 m. E. Pyrenees; Alps. Rare. May–July.

GESNERIACEAE—GLOXINIA FAMILY

This family occurs mainly in the Tropics and Subtropics and many of its members are well-known greenhouse ornamentals. There is a very small group of species from the north temperate zone, including one alpine representative in our area.

RAMONDA *Rich.* **R. myconi** *Reichb.* (**R. pyrenaica** *Rich.*, **Verbascum myconi** *L.*). A hairy perennial, 5–15 cm. tall. Lvs. in a flat rosette, to 6 cm. long, dark green, corrugated, with a distinct covering of hairs above and a dense woolly covering of orange hairs beneath, broadly oval, edges roundly toothed, narrowing at the base to a wide stalk. Corolla blue to violet, of 5 slightly unequal round petals which are joined below to form a very short tube. Calyx small. Anthers yellow. Fls. usually solitary, but sometimes grouped on long slender stems. Fruit a 2-celled capsule.
✲ Shady rock crevices. Local. To 1800 m. W. and C. Pyrenees. June–August.
690

LENTIBULARIACEAE—BUTTERWORT FAMILY

Insectivorous plants of bogs or wet places (*Pinguicula*) or growing in water (*Utricularia*). Calyx 5-lobed or 2-lipped. Corolla of one piece, with a projecting spur; 2-lipped, the upper lip 2-lobed, the lower more or less 3-lobed. Stamens 2, fixed to the lower part of the corolla. Stigma typically stalkless. Fruit a capsule.

PINGUICULA *L.* BUTTERWORT. Herbaceous plants with uncut lvs. all in a basal rosette, usually almost flat on the ground, yellowish green, with inrolled margins, and covered with sticky glands which trap and digest insects. Fls. solitary on slender leafless stalks. Calyx with 5 unequal lobes. Corolla with 5 distinct lobes, open at the mouth. The plants may overwinter as a rosette or as a rootless bud.

P. alpina *L.* ALPINE BUTTERWORT. Lvs. 2–3 cm. long, elliptic to lance-shaped. Fl. stalk 5–10 (15) cm. tall. Fl. only 8–10 mm. long, whitish, occasionally red-flushed, with yellow to orange spot in the mouth. Spur fat and conical, down-pointing, 2–4 mm. long.
✲ Damp meadows, streamsides, rocks. To 2600 m. Pyrenees; Alps. Norway to 1150 m. (Britain: recorded in Ross, now thought to be extinct.) May–August. **682**
P. gavei *Bvrd.* is like *P. alpina*, and usually considered a subspecies; it is identical except that the fl. is violet or lilac with yellow spur. It is very rare in Savoy at 700–800 m.

P. vulgaris *L.* COMMON BUTTERWORT (**683**). Lvs. 2–8 cm. long, ovate to oblong. Fl. stalk 5–10 (15) cm. tall. Calyx lobes broad, rather oblong, with upper lip divided not beyond middle.

Corolla 15–22 mm. long, including the long thin spur, directed back or slightly down; violet, usually with a small white patch at the mouth; fl. wide, shallow vertically.

Var. **alpicola** *Reichb.* (684): has fls. twice as large and lvs. elliptic.

⚘ Bogs, wet meadows, wet heaths, wet rocks and debris. To 2300 m. *Var. alpicola:* 1200–2300 m. Pyrenees; Alps; Apennines. Norway to 1600 m. (Britain to 1050 m.) May–July. **683, 684**

P. leptoceras *Reichb.* (**P. grandiflora** *auct., non Lam.*). Like *P. vulgaris* in general, fl. stalk 6–10 cm. tall, fl. 2–3 cm. long, including blunt, cylindrical, down-pointing spur, with pronounced lobes and as deep vertically as broad; violet-blue with large hairy white patch in mouth and on central lobe of lower lip. Lower lobes sometimes overlapping.

⚘ Marshes, wet places, damp meadows. To 2500 m. Pyrenees (very rare); French Alps (very rare); C. Alps to Tyrol. May–July. **688**

P. grandiflora *Lam.* LARGE-FLOWERED BUTTERWORT (**686**). Lvs. 3–5 cm. long, oval-oblong. Fl. stalk 8–15 (20) cm. tall. Upper lip of calyx divided nearly to base. Corolla purplish violet, usually with white patch in mouth, 2½–3 cm. long including the 1 cm. long, pointed, backwards-directed spur, which is occasionally forked; lobes of lower lip often wavy, shown splayed out in illustration but in nature usually touching or even overlapping.

Ssp. **reuteri** (*Genty*) *Schind.* (*var.* **pallida** *Gaud., var.* **rosea** *Mutel.*) (687): fls. lilac-pink. *

Other minor variations have also been given names.

⚘ Bogs, wet meadows, wet rocks. To 2500 m. Pyrenees; French Alps; French and Swiss Jura. (S.W. Ireland to 900 m.) April–June (August). **686, 687**

P. longifolia *Ram.* Lvs. 3–20 cm. long, ½–2½ cm. wide, pointed. Fls. 3–4 cm. long, half the length being the thin, arching spur; lilac-purple, with white zone and yellowish hairs right across the very deep lower lip.

⚘ Wet rocks, wet meadows, streamsides. To 1600 m. French and Spanish E. Pyrenees. Very rare. July. **689**

Ssp. **reichenbachiana** (*Schind.*) *Casper* is an equally rare geographical race with smaller lvs. and fls., the sepals very narrow, from the Maritime Alps (Roja valley) and C. & N.W. Italy.

P. villosa *L.* DOWNY BUTTERWORT. A minute species with small brownish lvs., fl. stalk to 5 cm., fls. only 7 mm. long, pale violet with 2 yellow spots on lower lip.

⚘ Damp places, typically in sphagnum bog. To 1050 m. Norway. July. **685**

P. norica *Beck.* A curious butterwort with blue-violet fls. 9–10 mm. long, resembling *P. leptoceras* from the front, but with spur replaced by sac-shaped swelling entirely enclosed in the calyx.

⚘ Wet meadows. N. of E. Alps. Very local. July.

UTRICULARIA *L.* BLADDERWORT. **U. minor** *L.* LESSER BLADDERWORT. The only species of this genus of aquatic plants to reach alpine levels. Lvs. submerged, cut into thread-like sec-

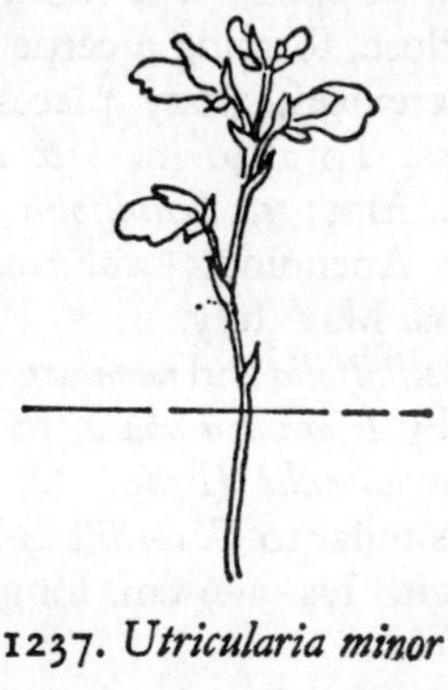

1237. *Utricularia minor*

tions, bearing 2 mm. bladders which trap and digest microscopic organisms. Fls. carried above water, 2–6 on a 4–15 cm. stalk; corolla 6–8 mm. long, pale yellow with brown lines, with 2 entire lips and very short blunt spur; very like those of a *Linaria*.

⚘Ponds, ditches, bog-pools. To 1850 m. Jura; Alps. Norway to 1000 m. (Britain to 700 m.) June–September.

1237

U. vulgaris L., *U. intermedia* Hayne and *U. ochroleuca* R. Hartm. attain 800–900 m. in Norway.

GLOBULARIACEAE

Perennial herbaceous plants or small shrubs, with alternate, undivided lvs. Fls. small, in dense globular heads. Corolla tubular, normally with 2 lips, upper lip of 2 lobes, lower lip larger, of 3 lobes. Calyx 5-lobed. Stamens 4, nearly equal in length. Fruit a 1-seeded nut.

GLOBULARIA L. Fls. blue; calyx teeth linear; stigma simple. The only European genus.

G. cordifolia L. A creeping, more or less hairless shrublet with erect fl. stems carrying no lvs., but sometimes 1 or 2 scales. Fls. grey-blue, in solitary, slightly flattened heads. Lvs. with more or less tapering stem, 1–10 cm. long.

Ssp. **cordifolia** (*L.*) *Hayek* (691): (15) cm. tall. Lvs. indented or 3-toothed at tip, 5–7 mm. wide; rosettes wide-spreading.

Ssp. **bellidifolia** (*Ten.*) *Hayek*: 5 (10) cm. tall. Lvs. rounded or shortly pointed at tip. Otherwise like *ssp. cordifolia*.

Ssp. **nana** *Lam.* (692): 1–2 cm. tall. Lvs. blunt-tipped, 2–4 mm. across; rosettes close, forming a carpet.

⚘Rock crevices, stony places, screes, dry slopes. To 2630 m. *Ssp. cordifolia*: W. and C. Alps; *ssp. bellidifolia*: S.E. and E. Alps; Apennines; *ssp. nana*: Pyrenees; Alps. May–July. **691, 692**

Sspp. *bellidifolia* and *nana* are now considered, by *Flora Europaea*, to be sspp. of *G. meridionalis* (*Podp.*) *O. Schwarz*, which is similar to *G. cordifolia* but more robust, with lvs. 2–9 cm. long and 2–5 mm. wide.

G. incanescens *Viv.* A perennial with woody stock and 3–6 cm. fl. stems. Lvs. on these and on sprawling non-fl. stems are almost round to spoon-shaped, slightly pointed and narrowing abruptly into stalk, white-mealy. Fls. pale blue; calyx hairy.

⚘Rocks. To 2000 m. Apuan Alps; N. Apennines. May–August. **693**

G. nudicaulis L. A hairless, tufted perennial, 10–30 cm. tall. Basal lvs. long-oval or spoon-shaped, tapering gradually into stalk, rounded at tip or slightly indented, dark green. Stem without lvs., but with a few scales. Fls. blue in a dense terminal head, 1½–2½ cm. across; corolla with a single 3-lobed tip.

⚘Open woods, meadows, stony places, preferring limestone. Uncommon. To 2673 m. Pyrenees; Alps; Apennines. June–August. **694**

A form not usually exceeding 5–10 cm. tall and with fl. heads not more than 12 mm. across, from the Pyrenees, has been named **G. gracilis** *Ry. & Richt.*

G. aphyllanthes *Crantz* (**G. willkommi** *Nym.*, **G. vulgaris** *L.*). A tufted herbaceous plant, 10–25 cm. tall.

Basal lvs. long-stalked, 3-veined, veins nearly parallel, blunt-tipped or indented, seldom with 3 teeth, green. Stem-lvs. small, stalkless, pointed. Fls. blue in a globular head 1–1½ cm. across. *
❋Meadows, stony places, especially in dry places. To 1650 m. Alps. May–June.
695

G. tenella *Lange*. Similar to *G. aphyllanthes*, and sometimes considered a subspecies: a smaller plant with bluish,

white-dotted lvs. and fl. heads only 5–8 mm. across. *
❋Meadows, stony places. To 1600 m. C. Pyrenees. Very rare. May–June.

G. linnaei *Ry*. Another close relation of *G. aphyllanthes*, with stiff, wavy-edged lvs., the basal at least ending in 1–5 spiny teeth. Stems 20–40 cm. tall, fl. heads 14–16 mm. across. *
❋Meadows, stony places. To 1650 m. E. Pyrenees. Rare. May–June.

PLANTAGINACEAE—PLANTAIN FAMILY

Herbaceous perennials with a basal lf. rosette in the species described. Fls. very small, clustered in heads or spikes on a usually leafless stem. Fl. parts usually in 4's. Corolla tubular; stamens fixed to tube, protruding filaments long, anthers large.

PLANTAGO *L*. PLANTAIN. Characters of the family. Fruit a capsule.
Besides the species described, 3 familiar plantains may reach considerable heights: *P. lanceolata* L. to 2302 m.; *P. major* L. to 2800 m.; and *P. media* L. to 2450 m.

P. atrata *Hoppe* (**P. montana** *Lam*.). 4–12 cm. tall; stems hairy or not. Lvs. green, hairless or hairy, widely linear to oval, 3–5-veined. Fls. few, brownish green, in a spike ½–1½ cm. long.
❋ Meadows, stony places, preferring calcareous soils. 1500–2500 m. Pyrenees; Alps; Apennines. May–August.
1138

P. fuscescens *Jord*. A silky-hairy plant 10–40 cm. tall. Lvs. all basal, 5–7-veined, lance-shaped, with pointed tips, tapering gradually at the base, densely hairy. Fls. many, reddish green, in an oblong spike 1–2 cm. long, with large oval bracts at the base. *
❋ Meadows, dry stony places. To 2500 m. W. and S. Alps. Very local. May–August.

P. alpina *L*. ALPINE PLANTAIN (**1135**). 3–15 cm. tall, with soft, thin, linear, 3-

veined lvs. (black when dry), hairless or slightly downy. Fls. whitish green in a narrow-oblong spike to 2½ cm. long; bracts short.
Var. **capitellata** *Ram*. (**1136**): a tufted, 2–6 cm. plant with round heads of 3–6 greenish fls. Lvs. with cottony down around their bases. Considered a subspecies of *P. recurvata* by some authors.
❋ Meadows, rarely scree. To 2500 (3350) m. Pyrenees; Alps. Uncommon. *Var. capitellata*: Pyrenees only. July–August.
1135, 1136

P. serpentina *Vill*. 8–40 cm. tall, with short linear lvs. to ½ cm. wide, hairy and rarely toothed at edges, 3–5-veined, slightly blue-green, leathery, edges hairy. Fls. whitish in a 2½–6 cm., pointed spike. *
❋ Poor meadows, screes, gravels, rocks, preferring clay and calcareous soils. To 2415 m. Alps; Apennines. June–August.

P. recurvata *L*. (**P. carinata** *Schrad*.). A tufted 10–25 cm. plant with short-branched rootstock carrying lvs. only at branch ends. Lvs. narrow, grass-like, stiff, lower ones curved back, rarely with toothed edges, without noticeable veins, triangular at tip. Fls. greenish in a narrow, 3–4 cm. cylindrical spike. *

❋ Meadows, rocks, screes, preferring acid soils. To 2600 m. E. Pyrenees; Maritime Alps. May–September.

P. monosperma *Pourr.* A whitish-

hairy 3–12 cm. plant. Lvs. long-oval, silky-downy, lying more or less flat on the ground. Fls. reddish in an oval-oblong spike to 1 cm. long.

❋ Damp meadows, gravels, stony places. 1500–2800 m. Pyrenees. July–August. **1137**

RUBIACEAE—BEDSTRAW FAMILY

Alpine representatives herbaceous perennials. Lvs. simple, undivided, with stipules similar in appearance to the lvs., whorled (arranged in a ring around the stem). Fls. very small, in loose clusters either in lf. axils or terminal; parts in 4–5's. Corolla funnel-shaped with lobes more or less upright, or spreading above a short tube. Calyx very small, usually of separate sepals or forming a circular ridge. Stamens the same number as the corolla lobes and alternating with them. Styles 2. Fruit dry, 2-celled.

GALIUM *L.* BEDSTRAW. Lvs. and lf.-like stipules in whorls of 4–10. Fls. in lax clusters, terminal and in lf.-axils. Corolla shortly tubed with (3) 4 (5) spreading lobes; calyx a minute circular ridge. Stamens 4, protruding; styles 2, short. Fruit of 2 parts each with 1 seed.

Many species of this generally weedy and insignificant genus exceed 1500 m. Among them are *G. anisophyllon* Vill., to 2900 m.; *G. mollugo* L., to 2100 m.; *G. pumilum* Lam., to 2600 m.; *G. rubrum* L., to 2000 m.; *G. uliginosum* L., to 2100 m.; and *G. saxosum* (Chaix) Breistr. to 2500 m.

G. cruciata (*L.*) *Scop.* (**Valantia cruciata** *L.*, **Cruciata laevipes** *Opiz*). CROSSWORT, MUGWORT. A slender plant with creeping root, 15–70 cm. tall. Stems leafy, branched near the base, hairy, 4-sided, sprawling. Lvs. with 3 veins, to 2½ cm. long, 4 in a ring, hairy on both surfaces, yellowish green, oval, the largest lvs. usually situated towards the middle of the stem. Fls. in a lax spreading cluster of about 8, stalked, in

lf. axils. Corolla shortly tubed with 4 pointed lobes, pale yellow. Fruit more or less spherical, becoming black. *

❋ Meadows, hedgerows, open woods, preferring calcareous soils. To 2300 m. Alps; Apennines. (Britain.) April–June. **1132**

G. verum *L.* LADY'S BEDSTRAW. A slender plant with creeping stolons, with upright to sprawling 15–100 cm. stems, hairless or sparsely hairy; stems bluntly 4-angled with many upright branches. Lvs. 8–12 in a ring, linear, pointed, 1-veined, ½–2½ cm. long, dark green, upper surface rough, lower surface softly hairy, the lf. edges rolled under. Fls. bright yellow, in a loose, branched leafy head. Corolla lobes 4. Fruit minute, becoming black. Plant becomes black on drying.

❋ Meadows, hillsides, hedge-banks, paths. To 2000 m. At alpine levels in C. Alps. Norway to 1100 m. (Britain.) July–September. **696**

G. boreale *L.* NORTHERN BEDSTRAW. A stiff upright plant, 20–45 cm. tall, with hairy or hairless, 4-sided stems. Lvs.

4 in a ring, to 4 cm. long, 3-veined, oblong-oval, bright green, rough on edges. Fls. white, in a loose terminal cluster, corolla lobes broadly pointed at tip. Fruit small, thickly hairy and bristly, olive-brown. Plant becomes black on drying.

✤ Open woods, marshy meadows, scrub, preferring calcareous soils. Uncommon. To 2200 m. Alps. Norway to 1100 m. (Britain.) May–August. **1133**

G. baldense *Spreng.* TYROL BEDSTRAW. A sprawling plant 2–10 cm. tall. Lvs. 8–10 in a ring, bright green, fleshy, smooth on edges, long-oval, veins hardly visible. Fls. whitish yellow in a terminal cluster of 3–5; petals blunt at tips. Fruit minute. Plant becomes black when drying.

✤ Stony grassland, rocky places, preferring limestone. 1700–2700 m. Alps; Apennines. July–September. **697**

The Eastern race of this plant has been named *G. noricum* Ehrend.

G. helveticum *Weigel.* SWISS BEDSTRAW. A sprawling, more or less hairless plant 5–8 cm. tall. Lvs. 4–8 in a ring, oblong-oval, fleshy, veins hardly visible, lf. edges with hooked prickles which grip the surrounding vegetation. Fls. whitish yellow, corolla lobes pointed. Fruit about 3 mm. long. Plant yellowish on

drying when growing on granite, black when growing on limestone.

✤ Screes, meadows. Uncommon. To 3216 m. Alps. June–August. **698**

ASPERULA *L.* WOODRUFF. Herbaceous perennials, with lvs. and lf.-like stipules in whorls. Fls. in loose clusters; parts in 4's. Differs from *Galium* in the corolla shape, which is funnel-like, the lobes not exceeding the tube.

Several species of this insignificant genus exceed 1500 m., including *A. aristata* L. and *A. cynanchica* L. to 2000–2100 m.

A. hirta *Ram.* A more or less hairy plant, 8–20 cm. tall. Lvs. to 1½ cm. long, stiff, 6 in a ring, 1-veined. Fls. small, rose-pink, stalkless, in heads surrounded by lvs.; tube longer than the lobes. Fruit smooth.

✤ Rocks, stony places. Rare. To 2600 m. W. and C. Pyrenees. July–August. **699**

A. hexaphylla *All.* A sprawling, generally hairless plant, 8–20 cm. tall. Lvs. linear, short, 6 in a ring. Fls. in a terminal head, rose-pink, corolla tube to 5 times the length of the lobes. Style forked, longer than the corolla. Fruit smooth.

✤ Limestone rocks. To 2000 m. Maritime Alps. June–July. **700**

CAPRIFOLIACEAE—HONEYSUCKLE FAMILY

Alpine species shrubs or undershrubs with opposite lvs. and fls. in pairs or clusters. Corolla tubular with 5 lobes, or 2-lipped. Stamens fixed to corolla tube, alternating with the lobes. Fruit a drupe, achene or berry.

Besides the species described *Viburnum lantana* L., the WAYFARING TREE, reaches 1600 m. in the Engadine and Tyrol.

LINNAEA *L.* L. **borealis** *L.* TWIN-FLOWER. An evergreen, creeping, perennial undershrub, with slender downy stems 5–7 (15) cm. tall. Lvs. to 1½ cm.

long, broadly oval to roundish, toothed towards the top, slightly hairy, narrowing abruptly to a short stalk. Fls. palest pink, fragrant, pendulous, in pairs on

short stalks; corolla bell-shaped with 5
lobes; stamens 4. Fruit an achene.
✤ Moss and humus in conifer forests.
1200–2200 m. Alps: rare. Norway to
1200 m. (Britain: very rare.) June–
August. 717

LONICERA L. HONEYSUCKLE. Alpine
species perennial shrubs (none of the
familiar climbing species reaches alpine
levels). Lvs. undivided. Fls. stalkless in
pairs, each on a long stem, in lf.-axils.
Corolla either 2-lipped (upper lip of 4
lobes, lower of 1 lobe) or of 5 almost
equal lobes. Calyx of 5 small teeth.
Stamens 5. Fruit a berry.

L. nigra L. BLACK-BERRIED HONEY-
SUCKLE, ST. FRANCIS' WOOD. 60–150 cm.
tall; young branches hairless. Lvs.
elliptic, sometimes pointed, veins
opaque; hairless. Corolla strongly pink-
flushed, 2-lipped, hairless, faintly
scented, to 1 cm. long on hairless, 3–4
cm. stalks. Fruit black, to 1 cm. across,
not joined except slightly at base.
✤ Woods, scrub, stony places. To 1800
m. Pyrenees; Alps. May–July. 712

L. coerulea L. BLUE-BERRIED or MOUN-
TAIN HONEYSUCKLE. 60–80 cm. tall;
young branches hairy. Lvs. oval, with
blunt tips, hairy on lower surface,
shortly stalked. Corolla yellowish white,
hairy outside, 5-lobed, 1–1½ cm. long;
fl. stalk hairy, much shorter than fl.
The bases (ovaries) of the paired fls. are
fused completely so there is 1 calyx
below the 2 fls. and consequently there
appears to be only 1 blue-black, 1 cm.
berry to the pair of fls.
✤ Woods, scrub, occasionally bogs,
preferring acid and humus-rich soils.
1350–2630 m. Pyrenees; Alps. May–
July. 713

L. alpigena L. ALPINE HONEYSUCKLE,
CHERRY WOODBINE. 100–150 cm. tall.
Lvs. oblong with a short point, to 10
cm. long by 4½ cm. wide, shiny on

lower surface, hairy on edges. Corolla
darkish red, to more than 1½ cm. long,
with 2 very obvious lips, shiny, hairless.
Calyx and ovaries fused. Berries fused
together (very rarely separate to centre),
shiny, bright red, twice as wide as long.
✤ Woods, scrub, stony places, preferring limestone. To 2300 m. Pyrenees;
Alps; Apennines. May–July. 714

L. xylosteum L. (Caprifolium xylosteum *Gaertn.*). FLY HONEYSUCKLE. 100–
200 cm. tall, with greyish, downy
branches. Lvs. oval or elliptic, pointed,
greenish grey, downy mostly on undersurface, with short stalks. Paired fls.
yellowish white, sometimes red-tinged,
on downy stalks to 2 cm. long. Corolla
2-lipped, lips longer than tube, 1–1½
cm. long, downy outside. Berries bright
red, not joined or only slightly so at
base.
✤ Woods, hedgerows, scrub, preferring
limestone. To 1800 m. Pyrenees; Alps.
May–June. 715

L. pyrenaica L. (Caprifolium pyrenaicum *Lam.*). PYRENEAN HONEY-
SUCKLE. 50–100 cm. tall. Lvs. smallish,
bluish, slightly leathery, elliptical,
pointed or not, veins a little transparent; shortly stalked, hairless or nearly
so. Fls. whitish tinged with pink,
fragrant. Corolla long-tubed, with 5
short, nearly equal, hairless lobes. Fl.
stalks almost as long as fls. Berries
bright red, not joined or only slightly at
base.
✤ Rocks, woods, mainly on limestone.
To 1500 m. Pyrenees. May–July. 716

SAMBUCUS *Tourn. ex Linn.* S. racemosa L. ALPINE or RED ELDER. A
hairless shrub to 4 m. tall. Lvs. of 2–3
paired leaflets with a terminal one, 4–8
cm. long, elliptic, pointed, toothed;
each leaflet with a small stalk, the whole
lf. with a fairly long main stalk. Fls.
greenish yellow, in a dense ovoid
cluster. Fruit scarlet drupes.

⚘ Shady woods, among rocks, on light and sandy soils. To 2050 m. Pyrenees; Alps; Apennines. (Britain: introduced.) April–June. 719

S. nigra L., the COMMON ELDER, with white fls. in flat-topped clusters followed by black fruit, reaches 1580 m. in Valais.

ADOXACEAE

A family of a single species, with no obvious relationship, though at one time included in *Caprifoliaceae*.

ADOXA *L.* **A. moschatellina** *L.* MOSCHATEL, TOWNHALL CLOCK, FIVE-FACED BISHOP. A small green perennial 5–10 (15) cm. tall with a creeping rhizome. Basal lvs. deeply lobed and divided into oblong to oval lobes, long-stalked, light green. Stem-lvs. 2, opposite, to 1½ cm. long, also lobed and divided, short-stalked. Stems upright, unbranched, terminating in a single head of normally 5 small, light green fls., 1 on top and 4 facing outwards. Corolla 5-lobed (terminal fl. of cluster with 4), calyx 3-lobed (terminal fl. with 2). Stamens yellow, (4) 5 (anthers split, appearing as 8–10). Fruit a green drupe, but seldom formed.

⚘ Shady rocks, shady damp woods, hedgerows. To 2370 m. Pyrenees; Alps; Apennines. Local. Norway to 1160 m. (Britain to 1300 m.) March–June. 718

VALERIANACEAE—VALERIAN FAMILY

Herbaceous perennials, occasionally woody at the base, rhizomes sometimes strong-smelling. Lvs. opposite or basal. Fls. small, in clustered heads or loose spikes. Corolla tubular, sometimes spurred or pouched at base, with (3) 5 spreading lobes. Stamens 1–3. Calyx toothed or in a continuous ring, becoming feathery in fruit. Fruit a nut in our species.

VALERIANA *Tourn. ex Linn.* Plants with a bitter taste and rather unpleasant smell. Lvs. sometimes deeply divided with opposite lobes. Fls. in a terminal cluster or spike. Corolla funnel-shaped, slightly pouched at the base, lobes 5, unequal. Stamens 3. Fruit with a feathery pappus.

Besides those described, *V. dioica* L. and *V. tuberosa* L. occasionally reach 1800 m.

V. pyrenaica *L.* PYRENEAN VALERIAN. An upright, hairy, dark green plant with ridged 70–140 cm. stems. Lvs. 10–25 cm. long, 8–20 cm. broad, more or less oval, deeply and irregularly toothed, with pointed tip; usually undivided, but upper lvs. have 1 large terminal leaflet and about 2 smaller ones. Fls. pink in a dense head of several stalked clusters. Fruit to about ½ cm. long, linear.

⚘ Woods, shady places. Uncommon. To 2400 m. Pyrenees. (Britain: introduced, naturalised in places.) June–August. 702

V. officinalis *L.* VALERIAN. A variable, upright, more or less hairless, 20–150 cm. plant; stems furrowed, sometimes hairy below. Lvs. to 20 cm. long, lower ones stalked, deeply divided into 5–23 oval lobes with slightly toothed edges, stem-lvs. small, nearly stalkless, lobes narrow, slightly toothed. Fls.

reddish pink in a dense head of several stalked clusters. Fruit less than ½ cm. long.
✤ Damp woods and meadows, watersides, stony places. To 2400 m. Pyrenees; Alps; Apennines. (Britain.) May–September. **703**

V. hispidula *Boiss.* A slender 40–60 cm. plant, sometimes considered a subspecies of *V. officinalis*, but entirely white-hairy; basal lvs. only 2 cm. long, 1 cm. wide, stem-lvs. of 5–9 small leaflets.
✤ Damp stony places and meadows. To 2000 m. N. Pyrenees. Very rare. June–July.

V. tripteris *L.* THREE-LEAVED VALERIAN. 10–50 cm. tall. Lvs. greyish green to blue-green; lower lvs. stalked, broadly oval, with large rounded teeth; stem-lvs. smaller, stalked, divided into about 3 leaflets. Lvs. below fl. head (bracts) stalkless, linear. Fls. pink, several stalked clusters forming a head. Fruit hairless.
✤ Woods, damp stony places, watersides, preferring limestone. To 2600 m. Pyrenees; Alps; Apennines. June–August. **704**

V. montana *L.* MOUNTAIN VALERIAN. 20–50 cm. tall, with slightly hairy stems arising from an odorous, woody stock. Basal lvs. roughly oval, with very slightly toothed edges and long stalks; glossy bright green. Stem-lvs. shortly stalked, narrowly oval, pointed, edges more toothed. Fls. pale pink to white, in short-stalked clusters forming a dense terminal cluster.
✤ Woods, rocks, screes, chiefly on limestone. To 2620 m. Pyrenees; Alps; Apennines. April–July. **706**

V. globulariifolia *Ram. ex DC.* (**V. apula** *Pourr.*). A tufted 10–20 cm. plant. Basal lvs. oval, pointed, tapering sharply into stalk. Stem-lvs. deeply

divided into 3–7 narrow segments. Fls. pink in a small, fairly compact head.
✤ Limestone rocks. To 2200 m. Pyrenees. Uncommon. June–August. **711**

V. saliunca *All.* A tufted, hairless 5–15 cm. plant, with woody stock. Basal lvs. undivided, oval-oblong, blunt-tipped, tapering gradually into stalk. Stem-lvs. similar but smaller. Fls. pink in a small compact cluster, with lance-shaped bracts below. Fruit nearly 1 cm. long, hairless but with a feathery pappus.
✤ Rocks, screes, stony grassy places, preferring limestone. 1800–2600 m. E. Pyrenees; Alps; Abruzzi. Rare. July–August. **710**

V. supina *L.* DWARF VALERIAN. A tufted, hairless 3–15 cm. plant, with creeping woody stock. Basal lvs. hairy on edges, round-oval, pointed, narrowing to a short stalk, sometimes toothed, hairy on edges; stem-lvs. usually 1 pair, stalkless, narrow-oval. Fls. pink in a dense terminal head with several linear bracts below. Fruit to ½ cm. long, crowned with a long feathery pappus.
✤ Stony places, watersides, snow-beds, preferring limestone. 1800–2900 m. E. Alps. Rare. July–August. **708**

V. celtica *L.* CELTIC SPIKENARD. A tufted 5–15 cm. plant with slender, hairy, scaly, odorous rhizome. Lvs. narrow, blunt-oblong, undivided, mainly basal, a few on the stems which are the same but smaller. Fls. yellowish with red markings in small whorls forming a small, interrupted spike. Pappus short; fruit with distinct 'horns' at end.
✤ Stony places, rocks, meadows, preferring acid soils. 2000–2800 (3580) m. Alps. Local. July–August. **705**

V. saxatilis *L.* ROCK VALERIAN. A tufted, hairless 5–30 cm. plant, stems furrowed. Basal lvs. long-stalked, long-

oval with slightly toothed, sparsely hairy edges. Stem-lvs. usually 2, long and narrow, shortly stalked or stalkless, undivided. Fls. white in small long-stalked clusters forming a very loose, elongated head.
❋ Stony, rocky places, preferring limestone. To 2500 m. C. and E. Alps. June–August. **709**

V. elongata *Jacq.* A hairless 5–25 cm. plant, with rhizome odorous and slender, stem furrowed. Basal lvs. round, pointed, not toothed nor cut, with very long stalks; stem-lvs. larger, short-stalked, round-triangular, with coarsely toothed edges. Fls. yellow in small axillary clusters forming a loose spike.
❋ Screes, rocky clefts, near snow-line, on limestone. 1800–2200 m. Austrian Alps. June–August. **707**

CENTRANTHUS *DC.* (**KEN-TRANTHUS** *Neck.*). **C. angusti-folius** *DC.* (**Valeriana angustifolia** *All.*). A hairless, blue-green perennial, 30–80 cm. tall. Lvs. linear, 8–15 cm. long, to ½ cm. wide, one pair growing out of another and thus sometimes giving the appearance of a symmetrically divided lf.; stalkless with 1 central vein. Fls. reddish pink, occasionally white, fragrant, in small stalked clusters forming a terminal head. Corolla tube ½–1½ cm. long, with spreading lobes and distinct spur, as long as the ovary, on one side at base; 1 stamen projecting. Fruit crowned with a tuft of hairs.
❋ Stony, rocky places, screes, preferring calcareous soils. To 2000 m. E. Pyrenees; Alps. May–August. **701**

DIPSACACEAE—SCABIOUS FAMILY

Herbaceous annuals, biennials or perennials. Lvs. divided or not, opposite, in whorls or in rosettes. Fls. in a dense terminal head with collar of involucral bracts (floral lvs.) below. Each floret has a more or less cup-like epicalyx around the true calyx and corolla. Corolla tubular, sometimes curved, with 4–5 lobes. Calyx small, of 4–5 segments, deeply lobed or cup-shaped. Stamens 4, alternating with the corolla lobes. Stigma 2-lobed or single on a slender style. Fls. sometimes of one sex only. Fruit dry, 1-seeded.

CEPHALARIA *Schrad.* **C. alpina** *Schrad.* ALPINE SCABIOUS. A hairy perennial 60–120 cm. tall. Basal lvs. of 9–15 segments, paired, with a terminal segment, all being oval, pointed, hairy, with toothed edges. Stem-lvs. smaller, hairy, sometimes undivided or divided with fewer segments, which are almost linear with the terminal one much larger than the others. Fls. yellow, in dense globular heads 2–3 cm. wide on long slender stalks. Fls. normally with equal lobes, the outer fls. occasionally with larger lobes. Bracts scaly, in many rows. The only yellow alpine scabious.
❋ Meadows, scrub, woods, screes, stony places. To 1800 m. W. Alps; N. Apennines. July–August. **724**

SUCCISA *Haller.* **S. pratensis** *Moench* (**S. praemorsa** (*Gilib.*) *Asch.*, **Scabiosa succisa** *L.*). DEVILS-BIT SCABIOUS. An upright or sprawling perennial, sometimes hairy, 15–100 cm. tall. Basal lvs. in rosettes, to 30 cm. long, oblong-oval to widely oval, tapering to a short stalk, usually slightly hairy; stem-lvs. similar but narrower. Fls. mauve to dark purple, rarely white, in semi-spherical clusters 1½–2½ cm. across, with long, leafy, purple-tipped bracts. Receptacle carrying scales almost as long as corolla, and epicalyx furrowed (thus differing from *Knautia*). Heads either of hermaphrodite fls. or only of female ones, the latter usually in smaller heads. Anthers red-purple, protruding, in the hermaphrodite fls. Fruit to ½ cm. long, softly hairy.

✤ Meadows, damp woods. To 2400 m. Pyrenees; Alps. Apennines. (Britain.) July–October.　　　**725**

KNAUTIA L. Annuals or perennials. Lvs. paired, opposite. Fl. heads flat, on long stalks. Corolla 4–5-lobed, unequal, those of the outer fls. often larger than the central ones; calyx shortly cup-shaped with many (8–16) teeth. Receptacle with bristly hairs but no scales and epicalyx compressed, not furrowed (thus differing from *Succisa*).

Besides the species described there are many others, basically very similar, which reach considerable altitude, some being very localised. These include *K. arvernensis* (Briq.) Szabo, with 3–4 cm. purplish fl. heads, to 2000 m. in Pyrenées, Alps; *K. brachytricha* Briq., with 3 cm. rose-red heads, from 1500–1900 m. in Tyrol*; *K. godeti* Reut., with 3–3½ cm. mauve heads, to 2000 m. in E. Pyrenees; *K. longifolia* (W. & K.) Koch, with 4–6 cm. purplish violet heads, from 1400–1900 m. in C. and S. Alps; *K. sixtina* Briq., with 2½–3½ cm. violet heads, from 1600–2000 m. in W. Alps; and *K. subcanescens* Jord., with 3½–4 cm. mauve heads, and downy stems, from 1800–2200 m. in W. Alps.

K. sylvatica *Duby* (**Scabiosa sylvatica** L.). WOOD SCABIOUS. A hairy perennial 30–100 cm. tall. Lvs. variable on the same plant, hairy, oblong-oval, stalkless, tapering suddenly or becoming con-stricted towards the base, edges toothed. Stem-lvs. many, green on both surfaces. Fls. pink-lilac or lilac-purple in a head 2½–4 cm. across.　　　*

✤ Meadows, woods, scrub. To 2000 m. Pyrenees; Alps. June–September.　**722**

K. baldensis *Kern.* (**K. magnifica** *Boiss. & Orph. var.* **baldensis** *Szabo*). MONTE BALDO SCABIOUS. A slightly hairy perennial with 20–80 cm. stems. Basal lvs. long-oval, pointed, usually stalked; stem-lvs. stalkless. Fls. purple, reddish violet or rose-pink, in heads 1½–3 cm. across.

✤ Meadows. To 2000 m. E. Alps; N. Apennines. July–August.　　**723**

SCABIOSA L. SCABIOUS. Herbaceous perennials. Lvs. opposite, some deeply divided. Fl. heads flattened or slightly domed, on long slender stalks. Outer fls. with enlarged corolla lobes. Receptacle carrying scales much shorter than fls.; epicalyx developed into a papery, pleated funnel-shaped cup.

Besides the species described, *S. graminifolia* L., with pale violet 3–6 cm. heads, reaches 1800 m. in Alps and (rarely) Pyrenees; *S. vestina* Facch., with lavender 1½–2 cm. heads, reaches 1900 m. in S. Tyrol.

S. lucida *Vill.* SHINING SCABIOUS. A usually hairless plant 10–30 cm. tall; fl. stem usually unbranched. Lower lvs. widely oval, with shallow rounded teeth, narrowing to a stalk; upper lvs. deeply divided with a large, broad terminal leaflet and small linear, toothed, lateral leaflets; the topmost stem lvs. entirely of small leaflets. All lvs. hairless, usually glossy. Fls. rose-lilac, violet or deep mauve, in a 1–2 cm. head. Calyx cup-shaped with 5 very narrow teeth.

✤ Dry meadows, stony places. To 2700 m. Pyrenees; Alps; Apennines. June–September.　　　**720**

S. pyrenaica *All.* PYRENEAN SCABIOUS.

Similar to and perhaps synonymous with *S. lucida*, but 20–40 cm. tall, whitish-hairy with smaller lvs., the terminal leaflet rounder, not pointed; and the fls. are a clear blue-lilac.

❀ Dry meadows, stony places. To 2000 m. Pyrenees; S.W. Alps. June–September. **721**

CAMPANULACEAE—BELLFLOWER FAMILY

Mainly herbaceous plants, sometimes with milky sap. Lvs. undivided, usually alternate. Fls. in clusters or single, often showy. Corolla either with a short tube or characteristically bell-shaped, white, yellow, blue, violet, purple. Stamens the same number as corolla lobes and alternating with them. Calyx tube joined to the ovary. Ovary 2–10-celled. Fruit fleshy or a capsule.

The genera *Phyteuma* and *Jasione* begin to resemble *Compositae* in having their many fls. in dense heads; their way of pollination is also similar.

CAMPANULA L. BELLFLOWER, HAREBELL. Usually herbaceous perennials. Fls. either solitary, in loose clusters, or in spikes, blue or purple, rarely yellow or white. Corolla and calyx lobes 5; corolla bell-shaped or shortly tubed. Stamens 5, stigmas 3–5. Fruit a 3–5-celled capsule dehiscing by pores (openings).

Besides the species described, *C. bononiensis* L. may reach 1500 m., *C. latifolia* L., 1600 m., and *C. patula* L., 1600 m.

C. barbata L. BEARDED BELLFLOWER. A hairy, rosetted perennial, 10–40 cm. tall. Rosette lvs. long, oval, roughish with wavy edges; stem-lvs. similar but smaller, few. Stem sturdy, hairy, carrying the pendulous, 1½–3 cm. bells on one side. Corolla pale blue, sometimes white, with an obvious fringe of hairs around the edge of the lobes. Calyx lobes triangular and pointed.

❀ Meadows, stony places, open woods, heathland, preferring acid soils. To 2980 m. Alps. Norway: subalpine. June–August. **726**

C. alpina *Jacq.* ALPINE BELLFLOWER. A hairy, rosetted perennial with long taproot and branching, erect fl. stem to 15 cm. tall. Lvs. oval, shiny, edges slightly toothed. Fls. lilac to lavender-blue, slightly pendulous, on long stems, up to 10 forming a loose pyramidal cluster. Corolla 17–27 mm. long, fringed with hairs on the slightly recurved lobes. Stigma 3-lobed. Calyx long, hairy and curved back when mature.

❀ Stony, rocky places. 1250–2400 m. E. Alps. July–August. **728**

C. spicata L. SPIKED BELLFLOWER. A rosetted biennial, 20–100 cm. tall, with stout fleshy root. Lvs. oblong, slightly toothed, rough. Fls. in a long-pointed cluster, purple, lilac or bluish, stalkless. Corolla 17–22 mm. long, densely hairy in the throat. Calyx broad, rough, hairy, not recurved.

❀ Pastures, stony slopes, rocks, usually on schist. 1500–2400 m. Alps; Apennines. July–August. **730**

C. thyrsoides L. (also spelt **thyrsoidea**). YELLOW BELLFLOWER. A rosetted, roughly hairy biennial, 20–30 cm. tall. Lvs. long, narrow, rough. Fls. stemless, pale yellow in a dense, clustered head, round-topped till fully expanded. Corolla tube 17–22 mm. long, with recurved lobes. Calyx smooth, hairy on edges, not recurved. Stigma 3-lobed, projecting from corolla. *

❀ Meadows, screes, stony places, on calcareous and schistous soils. 1500–2720 m. Alps. July–September. **731**

C. glomerata L. CLUSTERED BELL-FLOWER. A hairy, rosetted perennial to 60 cm. tall. Lvs. of rosette stalked, rounded–oval, with toothed edges. Stem-lvs. stalkless, bases partly clasping the stem, lower stem-lvs. sometimes with short stalks. Fls. in a terminal cluster, violet, blue-purple, seldom white. Corolla tube funnel-shaped, 1½–3 cm. long. A variable plant.

❀ Open woods, meadows, mainly on limestone. To 1700 m. Alps. (Britain.) June–August.

C. foliosa *Ten.* A rosetted, softly hairy plant, very similar to *C. glomerata*, but generally larger. Basal lvs. long-stalked, the stalks slightly winged. Fls. stalkless in a globular cluster, violet to purple, hairy within, lobes not much recurved, to 3 cm. long. Stigma slightly longer than corolla, 3-lobed. Calyx with long upright hairy lobes.

❀ Woods, scrub. To 1800 m. Apennines. July–August. **727**

C. speciosa *Pourr.* PYRENEAN BELL-FLOWER. A hairy, rosetted plant, typically biennial but sometimes longer-lived, to 50 cm. tall, very like a dwarf form of the Canterbury Bell, *C. medium*. Rosette lvs. long, narrow, bristly, with wavy-toothed edges. Fls. bell-shaped, 3–5 cm. long, each on a long slender stalk held more or less upright, blue-violet, forming a loose pyramidal cluster.

❀ Stony places, screes, preferring limestone. To 1600 m. Pyrenees. Local. July. **729**

C. rapunculoides L. CREEPING BELL-FLOWER. A slender perennial 20–60 (100) cm. tall, forming large colonies with creeping rhizomes. Basal lvs. long-stalked, rough, triangular-oval, with raggedly toothed edges. Stem-lvs. stalkless. Erect stems shortly branched, with 2–3 cm. long, deep violet to purple, sometimes white, pendulous, funnel-shaped fls. Calyx sharply recurved, with narrow, almost linear lobes.

❀ Fields, woods, cultivations, preferring calcareous soils. To 2020 m. Alps; Apennines. (Britain: introduced.) July–August. **735**

C. trachelium L. BATS-IN-THE-BELFRY. A rosetted perennial to 100 cm. tall. Lvs. long-stalked, bristly-hairy, with deeply, roughly toothed edges. Stem-lvs. stalkless or nearly so, bristly with toothed edges. Stems often branched. Fls. 3–4 cm. long, (1–)2–3 together on short stalks forming loose clusters, blue or white (white forms found more commonly on granite). Calyx very dark green, sometimes looking almost black, bristly.

❀ Stony places, open woods, scrub, edges of fields. To 1700 m. Pyrenees; Alps. (Britain.) June–September.

C. persicifolia L. PEACH-LEAVED BELL-FLOWER. A hairless perennial, 50–100 cm. tall. Basal lvs. linear-oval, gently toothed (similar to peach lvs.), slender, long, sometimes with short stalk. Fls. usually out-facing, shortly stalked on unbranched stems. Corolla blue-violet, rarely white, roundly bell-shaped, 2½–4 cm. long, nearly as wide.

❀ Fields, scrub, hedgerows, vineyards. To 2000 m. Alps. (Britain: introduced.) May–August. **732**

C. caespitosa *Scop.* TUFTED BELL-FLOWER. A compact, tufted perennial 10–30 cm. tall, with a taproot. Rosetted basal lvs. broadly lanceolate, to 3 cm. long, pointed, with few teeth on the edges, shortly stalked. Stem-lvs. linear, not toothed, stalkless. Stems slender,

angled, with the pendulous fls. nearly always carried towards the top on slender stalks. Corolla much longer than wide, bell-shaped, constricted at the throat, with very short lobes, light blue, 1–1½ cm. long. Calyx lobes linear. Anthers pink, pollen red or violet.   *
❀ Rocks, scree, on limestone. To 2100 m. E. Alps. August–September.   **744**
This species has been confused with *C. cochleariifolia* (see below), but is, as a rule, taller, without the running rootstock, and has very distinct constricted bells.

C. cochleariifolia *Lam.* (**C. pusilla** *Haenke,* **C. bellardii** *All.,* **C. pumila** *Curt.*). FAIRY'S THIMBLE. A very variable rosetted, mat-forming perennial to 20 cm. tall, with a thin root growing freely in and along rock cracks. Lvs. shiny, in small rosettes, roundly-oval, toothed, with longish stalks. Stems upright, wiry, carrying up to 6 long-stalked, semi-pendulous fls. Fls. bell-shaped, 12–20 mm. wide and long, lobes short, rounded, blue, violet, lilac or white. Calyx smooth, lobes outspread.
❀ Screes, rocky places, streamsides, walls, preferring limestone. To 3400 m. Pyrenees; Alps; Apennines. June–August.   **739**

C. rotundifolia *L.* (**C. diversifolia** *Dum.,* **C. heterophylla** *Gray,* **C. minor** *Lam.*). HAREBELL, SCOTTISH BLUEBELL. Perhaps the most widely known and distributed species of *Campanula,* this is also an extremely variable one, and many forms have been named. A spreading, rosetted perennial with underground stolons. Basal lvs. long-stalked, roundish oval, with wavy-toothed margins. Stems lying along the ground, then rising, heights varying from 10–60 cm. Lvs. on the prostrate part of the stem stalked, long-oval, pointed, toothed or not; lvs. on up-

right part of stem stalkless, narrow-linear, pointed, not toothed. Fls. either solitary or in a loosely branched cluster. Fls. variable, upright, pendulous or partly so, stalks slender. Corolla bell-shaped, lobes recurved, pointed; blue (seldom white), 12–20 mm. long.
❀ Rocks, screes, meadows, open woods, river gravels. To 2156 m. Pyrenees; Alps; Apennines. Norway to 1920 m. (Britain.) May–November. **737**

C. linifolia *Scop.* (**C. schleicheri** *Suter*). FLAX-LEAVED BELLFLOWER. Sometimes considered a subspecies of *C. rotundifolia.* A loosely tufted, rosetted perennial, 10–35 cm. tall. Basal lvs. small kidney-shaped, long-stalked. Stems partly sprawling then becoming upright. Stem-lvs. many, linear or narrowly oval, stalkless with hairs on edges, lower lvs. occasionally slightly toothed. Stems slender, bearing 1 to 6 fls. in a loose cluster. Fl. buds pendulous, fls. more or less so, on very fine stalks, round bell-shaped, to 3 cm. long, purplish-blue, occasionally paler, rarely white. Calyx lobes long, sometimes as long as the corolla. Fruit pendulous.   *
❀ Stony places, meadows, preferring limestone. To 2000m. E. Alps; Appenines. July–August.   733

C. scheuchzeri *Vill.* Similar to *C. linifolia,* and also sometimes considered a subspecies of *C. rotundifolia.* To 40 cm. tall. Stem-lvs. linear, stalkless, not as numerous, lower lvs. long, narrow with toothed edges. Stems hairless. Fls. borne singly. Corolla broadly bell-shaped, lobes recurved, violet to purple-blue, 2–3 cm. long.
❀ Meadows, stony places, alluvial soils. 1400–3400 m. Pyrenees; Alps; Apennines. July–August.   **738**

C. rhomboidalis *L.* A hairy, rosetted perennial of the *C. rotundifolia* group, with thickish root and 30–70 cm. hollow stems. Lvs. oval, pointed, with toothed edges and long slender stalks. Stem-lvs. stalkless or nearly so . becoming broadly oval or rhomboid, sometimes hairy, paler in colour on lower surface. Fls. on shortish stalks, more ·or less pendulous, purple-blue, in a loose cluster. Corolla broadly bell-shaped, to 2 cm. long, lobes slightly recurved. Calyx smooth, hardly recurved.

✤ Meadows, woods. To 2200 m. Pyrenees; Alps. Rare. June–August. **734**

C. elatinoides *Mor.* A greyish-hairy, tufted perennial, with leafy stems sprawling and creeping in and around rock crevices. Lvs. round-oval, sharply toothed, long-stalked. Fls. in lf. axils all along the stem, forming a many-fld. cluster. Corolla deeply lobed, resulting in star-shaped, bright blue, very hairy fls. to 2 cm. across. Calyx lobes awl-shaped, very hairy. Stigma greatly protruding.

✤ Rocky places, screes. To 2000 m. N. Italian Alps, between Lakes Como and Garda only. July–September. **736**

C. allionii *Vill.* (C. alpestris *All.*). A creeping, sprawling perennial with a spreading underground stolon. Lvs. narrow lance-shaped, stalkless, hairy, forming small rosettes. Upright, hairy stems to 7 cm. (rarely more) arise from these rosettes each bearing a single fl. (sometimes 2), and occasionally 1 or 2 small stalkless, narrow, hairy stem lvs. Fls. out-facing, fully bell-shaped, 3–4 cm. long, and almost as wide, deep to pale blue, rarely white. Calyx tube small, hairless, the lobes linear, curved back, hairy on margins. Fruit pendulous. *

✤ Rocks, screes, stony places, preferring granite. 1400–2800 m. W. Alps. Rare. July–August. **740**

C. raineri *Perp.* A hairy perennial to 10 cm. tall, with a woody rootstock which grows in and along rock crevices. Lvs. in tufts, greyish-green, hairy, stalkless or nearly so, round-oval,

pointed and gently toothed, edges hairy. Stems with a few similar, stalkless lvs. Fls. usually solitary, upward-facing, light blue, conical-bell-shaped, $2\frac{1}{2}$–3 cm. long and 3–4 cm. across, with short oval lobes which recurve slightly. Stigma shorter than corolla. Calyx lobes long, upright, broadly oval, pointed, slightly toothed, half the length of the corolla.

✤ Rocks, screes, stony places, on limestone. 1300–2200 m. C. Alps. Local. August–September. **745**

C. morettiana *Reichb.* (**C. filiformis** *Mor.*, **C. tridentina** *Poll.*). DOLOMITES BELLFLOWER. A perennial, 5–8 cm. tall, closely allied to *C. raineri*, but smaller; tufted, softly grey-hairy. Basal lvs. ivy-shaped with indentations on the edges. Stem-lvs. roundish oval, not toothed. Fls. usually solitary, large, upward-facing, bell-shaped, 2–3 cm. long, violet-blue, lobes recurved with a small tuft of hairs at the end of each. Calyx lobes broad, outspread, with hairy edges.

✤ Rock crevices, cliffs, stony places. 1500–2300 m. E. Alps. Rare. August–September. **746**

C. cenisia *L.* MONT CENIS BELL-FLOWER. A dwarf plant with 1–5 cm. sprawling stems, with numerous sterile runners forming rosettes, and solitary fls. at the tips of older shoots. Lvs. oval, bluish, rather fleshy, ciliate. Fls. slaty blue, starry 1–$1\frac{1}{2}$ cm. across, corolla cut into strap-like lobes almost to its base. Fruit erect.

✤ Screes, rocky ridges, stream-gravels, usually avoiding limestone. 2000–3090 m. W. Alps. Rare . July–September. **748**

C. pulla *L.* A rosetted perennial, to 8 cm. tall, rosettes forming a carpet. Lvs. shortly stalked, shiny, round-oval. Stems slender; stem lvs. smaller, oval, pointed, stalkless. Fls. solitary, purple, pendulous, long bell-shaped, 17–22 mm. long. Calyx lobes long, linear, smooth not recurved.

⚜ Stony, grassy places, heaths, usually on limestone, sometimes on schists. 1500–2200 m. E. Alps. July–August. **747**

C. excisa *Schleich*. PERFORATE BELL-FLOWER. A slender, delicate, usually hairless perennial to 12 cm. tall. Lvs. narrow, linear, edges not toothed, the basal lvs. sometimes a little shorter and broader, the stem-lvs. longer and pointed. Fls. solitary, pendulous, bright blue or sometimes lilac-blue, narrow-bell-shaped, 2–3½ cm. long. Corolla lobed to a third of its length, the lobes slightly wavy, narrowing at their base to give the impression of a circular perforation. Calyx fully recurved, lobes narrow lance-shaped, sometimes a little hairy.

⚜ Crevices, shady, rocky, stony places, screes, near springs, preferring granite. Extremely local. 1400–2340 m. C. Alps. June–September. **741**

C. zoysii *Wulf.* (sometimes spelt **zoisii**). CRIMPED BELLFLOWER. A delicate, tufted plant to 10 cm. tall. Basal lvs. roundish-oblong, edges few-toothed, sometimes hairy, short-stalked, shiny. Stem-lvs. stalkless or shortly stalked, small, roundish oblong to linear. Stems carrying 1 to 6 light blue, stalked fls., unmistakable in shape, the crimped, flask-shaped 8–9 mm. corolla becoming narrowly constricted at the neck, just below the short lobes which form a frilled collar. Stigma shorter than corolla. Calyx to ¼ length of corolla, slightly recurved.

⚜ Rock crevices, screes, often near water, preferring limestone . To 2300 m. Julian and Karawanken Alps. Rare. July–August. **743**

C. uniflora *L.* NORTHERN BELLFLOWER. A slender, velvety-hairy perennial 2–10 cm. high with thick, fleshy taproot and many leafy stolons. Basal lvs. stalked, rounded-oblong; stem-lvs. shortly stalked, narrow-oval, the upper ones slightly toothed. Fls. solitary, pendulous, fl. 1 cm. long, clear mid-blue, tube narrow, lobes not opening out and recurving. Calyx nearly as long as the corolla, also not opening out. Fruit capsule longer than the fl., held stiffly erect.

⚜ Dry exposed ridges, *Dryas*-heaths. To 1580 m. Norway. July. **742**

EDRAIANTHUS *A.DC.* (*Aug.*) (sometimes written **HEDRAIANTHUS**). **E. graminifolius** *A.DC.* (**Wahlenbergia graminifolia** *A.DC.*). Very similar to *Campanula*, differing only in having seed capsules opening at the top, not at the base. A rosetted, tap-rooted perennial 5–20 cm. tall, usually with up to 3 upright stems arising from the rosette. Basal lvs. 1–4 cm. long, linear to club-shaped, pointed or blunt, edges not toothed. Stem-lvs. upright, few, linear, 2½ cm. or more long, bases partly clasping the stem. Fls. in globular clusters of up to 6, each cluster on one stem, with a collar of long, narrow bracts. Fls. 1–2 cm. long, blue or violet, funnel-shaped, lobes roundish, curved back, hairless outside, hairy within. Calyx tube hairless, lobes hairy, upright, not recurved, oblong, pointed. Capsule smooth, oval, 2-celled. *

⚜ Rocks, stony places. 1500–1800 (2280) m. Austrian Alps (Krain region only); C. and S. Apennines. May–August. **749**

PHYTEUMA *L.* Herbaceous perennials with many usually small fls. forming a dense oblong or round head, below which are bracts of often characteristic shape. Corolla and calyx 5-lobed. Corolla divided almost to the base, into linear lobes, at first joined at the top forming a tube, later dividing and spreading, whitish, yellowish white, blue, violet or purple; stigmas linear, 2–3, protruding distinctly out of the corolla. The buds are curved. Fruit a capsule, 2–3-celled.

Many of the species are rather similar and difficult to distinguish; the fls. may vary in colour; and they are also botanically confusing since so many of the names have been applied to several different species by various authorities.

Flower head cylindrical or oval, not round

P. spicatum L. SPIKED RAMPION. A sturdy hairless plant, 30–80 cm. tall, with fleshy, swollen root. Basal lvs. oval-triangular, pointed, toothed, long-stalked, lf.-blade continuing down part of the stalk. Lower stem-lvs. stalked and sometimes larger than the basal lvs., upper lvs. oval to linear, unstalked. Fls. in a cylindrical head to 6 cm. long, normally yellowish or greenish white but occasionally pale or bright blue or deep violet.
✤ Woods, preferring limestone. To 2110 m. Pyrenees; Alps. Norway to 1000 m. (Britain: probably introduced.) May–July. **752**

P. halleri *All.* (**P. ovatum** F. W. *Schmidt*). DARK RAMPION. A robust plant, 50–100 cm. tall. Basal lvs. large, inverted heart-shaped with raggedly toothed edges, long-stalked. Lower stem-lvs. similar in shape, but much smaller, shortly stalked; upper lvs. narrower, small. Fls. purple-blue in an oblong-cylindrical head to 6 cm. long.*
✤ Woods, scrub, meadows. To 2400 m. Pyrenees; Alps; Apennines. July–August. **750**

P. betonicifolium *Vill.* A slightly hairy plant 25–70 cm. tall. Basal lvs. lance-shaped, truncated or slightly heart-shaped at base, long-stalked. Stem-lvs. small, many, linear. Base of stem sometimes hairy, the upper part

usually not. Fls. pale blue to lilac in an oval head to 4 cm. long.
✤ Meadows, stony places. To 2650 m. C. and E. Pyrenees; Alps; Apennines. May–August. **751**

P. pyrenaicum *Schulz.* (including **P. cordifolium** *Schulz* and **P. betonicoides** *Schulz*). A fairly robust plant, 20–45 cm. tall. Basal lvs. long-triangular, with toothed edges; lower stem-lvs. stalked, long, narrowly triangular, similar to basal lvs. but smaller; upper stem-lvs. linear, stalkless, toothed. Fls. dull slaty blue to bright blue in a cylindrical to rounded head up to 7½ cm. long and 2–3 cm. wide; bracts long, linear to narrowly triangular.
✤ Woods, meadows, stony, bushy slopes. To 2100 m. Pyrenees. May–August.

P. scorzonerifolium *Vill.* A mainly hairless plant, 30–90 cm. tall. Basal lvs. not, or shortly, stalked, very long and narrow, to 15 cm. long and 1½ cm. broad, with toothed edges. Stem-lvs. short, linear, toothed. Fls. lilac-blue in a cylindrical head to 5 cm. long.
✤ Open woods, meadows. To 2200 m. E. Pyrenees; Alps; Apennines. June–July. **754**

P. scaposum *Schulz.* Similar to *P. scorzonerifolium*, 25–45 cm. tall, but lvs. mostly rosetted at base, narrowly oval, with tapering point and tapering into stalk. Fls. lilac-blue in a cylindrical head 5–6 cm. long. *
✤ Woods, meadows. 1600–2500 m. Alps. June–September. **755**

P. michelii *All.* 25–40 cm. tall. Basal lvs. long-stalked, oval-triangular, pointed, sometimes slightly hairy. Fls. blue-lilac in a shortly oval head.
✤ Meadows. 1500–2300 m. W. Alps. July–August. **756**

P. balbisii *A.DC.* (**P. cordatum** *Balb.*). A slender plant 10–25 cm. tall, hairy or not. Lvs. heart-shaped, long-stalked, lightly toothed. Fls. pale blue in an ovoid or oblong head; bracts much shorter than the fls.   *

❧ Rocks. To 2000 m. Maritime and Ligurian Alps. Rare. July–August. 753

Flower head round

P. orbiculare *L.* ROUND-HEADED RAM-PION. 15–50 cm. tall. Basal lvs. rosetted, heart-shaped to triangular, edges toothed, long-stalked; lower stem-lvs. similar, shorter-stalked, much narrower; upper lvs. stalkless, bases clasping the stem. Fls. blue in a squat, globular head; bracts lance-shaped, fairly broad. ❧ Meadows, scrub, stony places, preferring limestone. To 2600 m. Pyrenees; Alps; Apennines. May–October. 758

P. sieberi *Spreng.* DOLOMITES RAMPION. Usually a low plant, 2–10 cm. tall, occasionally to 30 cm. Lvs. lance-shaped, sometimes heart-shaped at base, toothed; lower lvs. stalked, upper stalkless. Fls. blue in a globular head; bracts broad, ovate or rhomboidal, toothed. ❧ Meadows, stony places, on limestone and dolomite. 1600–2600 m. E. Alps. July–September. 757

P. scheuchzeri *All.* HORNED RAMPION. 12–45 cm. tall. Basal lvs. rosetted, of two types, triangular heart-shaped or long, linear-oval, both with toothed edges and long stalks, slightly bluish. Stem-lvs. long, oval-linear, lower shortly stalked, upper not so much, both with toothed edges. Fls. blue in a rather flattened spherical head; bracts long, narrow, pointed, extending well beyond the fl. head, though often curved downwards towards stem. ❧ Rocks, stony places. To 2580 (3600) m. Alps; Apennines. June–July. 763

P. charmelii *Vill.* PYRENEAN RAMPION. A slender-stemmed plant 10–20 cm. tall; stems hairy. Basal lvs. of 2 kinds,

heart-shaped to round, and long-oval, pointed, both long-stalked with toothed edges. Stem-lvs. linear, shortly stalked or not. Fls. blue in a large roundish head 1–1½ cm. wide; bracts long, narrow, toothed, extending beyond the head. ❧ Limestone rocks. To 1900 m. C. and E. Pyrenees (rare); Alps; Apennines. July–August. 759

P. hedraianthifolium *R. Schulz.* (**P. carestiae** *auct.*). RHAETIAN RAMPION. 2–18 cm. tall, distinctive because of the lvs. which are long, linear, toothed, with each tooth ending in an elongated point. Lower stem-lvs. stalked, upper ones not, but all of similar length; bracts under fl. heads similar, long, dry and needle-like, another distinctive feature. Fls. blue in a squat globular head. ❧ Rocks, stony places. 1800–3100 m. C. Alps (E. Switzerland, W. Tyrol). Rare. July–August. 760

P. hemisphaericum *L.* A tufted plant 2–10 (30) cm. tall. Lvs. long, linear, stalkless. Stem-lvs. linear, smaller, few. Fls. blue in a flattish globular head, 1½–2 cm. wide; bracts triangular, toothed. ❧ Meadows, stony places, screes, moraines, on acid and humus-rich soils. To 2900 (3618) m. Pyrenees; Alps; Apennines. July–August. 761

P. humile *Schleich.* DWARF RAMPION. A small tufted plant, 1–12 cm. tall. Lvs. linear, 1–6 cm. long, 2–4 mm. broad. Stems usually carrying 1 lf. and the round squat head of blue fls. Bracts round at their base, linear with toothed edges. ❧ Rocks, stony meadows, moraines. Very local. 1800–3250 m. Pennine Alps (C. Switzerland and N. Italy). July–August. 768

P. comosum *L.* DEVIL'S CLAW. Biggest fld. of all the Rampions and quite distinctive. A tufted plant 5–15 cm. tall with sprawling leafy stems; basal lvs. kidney-shaped, stem-lvs. broadly lance-shaped, all bright green, glossy and with large pointed teeth. Fls. each 16–20 mm. long, much swollen at the base, contracting into a long, very narrow tube; up to 20 in a head, pale pink to violet-red, tube violet, stigma much protruding. *

❀ Rock crevices, on limestone and dolomite. To 2000 m. S.E. and E. Alps. July–August. **764**

Pauciflorum group: typically dwarf tufted plants with thick rootstocks and lvs. in rosette. 4 very similar races have been named, though it would probably be better to reduce them to 2 (*P. pauciflorum* and *P. globularifolium*).

P. pauciflorum L. A tufted perennial 2–6 (10) cm. tall. Lvs. obtuse lance-shaped, tapering to their base, sometimes lightly toothed. Fls. deep violet-blue, 5–8 in round heads. Bracts broad-triangular.

The form **typicum** R. *Schulz* (illustrated) is more elongated than the others.

❀ Rocks, stony places, screes, on granite. 1700–3400 m. C. and E. Alps. July–September. **766**

P. confusum Kern. TONGUE-LEAVED RAMPION. Very close to *P. pauciflorum*, and by some authorities considered synonymous. 1–15 cm. tall, with lvs. widening noticeably towards the tip. Fls. dark blue in a broad round head; bracts with hairs on backs and tips.

❀ Rocks, stony places. 1700–2800 m. E. Alps. July–September. **762**

P. pedemontanum R. *Schulz*. PIEDMONT RAMPION. Now considered synonymous with *P. globularifolium*, although in the past it has been considered a form of *P. pauciflorum*; it appears to be a

distinct geographical race. 1–5 cm. tall, with tongue-like lvs. sometimes only 1½ cm. long, occasionally toothed, often 'hooded' by the inrolling of margins at the tip. Fls. few in a small head, blue-violet; bracts rounded-triangular, exceeding the head.

❀ Rocks, stony meadows, on granite. 1300–2600 (4010) m. Pyrenees; C. Alps. July–September. **765, 1238**

1238. *Phyteuma pedemontanum.* Leaves showing typically inrolled upper margins.

P. globularifolium S. & H. Very similar to *P. pedemontanum*, but lvs. spoon-shaped, with rounded or spatula-like blade and distinct stalk; 1–5 cm. tall. A very variable plant.

❀ Rocks, screes, stony meadows, on granite and volcanic rock. 2000–3000 m. E. Alps. July–September. **767**

JASIONE L. SHEEPSBIT. Herbaceous perennials. Fls. many, in a dense terminal cluster, small, stalkless or nearly so, blue, rarely white. Corolla with 5 narrow spreading lobes. Calyx tubular, with 5 lobes. Fruit a capsule.

J. perennis Lam. SHEEPSBIT. A rosette-forming plant 2–50 cm. tall, with leafy creeping sterile stems, usually slightly hairy. Lvs. oblong-oval, edges seldom toothed, sometimes hairy. Fls. in a globular head with leafy bracts, shorter and broader than the lvs., forming a collar beneath. Calyx hairless. Stems carrying the fl. head without lvs. in the upper part. *

✤ Rocks, stony places, dry meadows, preferring acid soils. To 1900 m. Pyrenees. July–September. 769

J. humilis *Loisel.* DWARF SHEEPSBIT. Like a dwarf version of *J. perennis*: a compact tufted perennial, 3–6 cm. high, bristly-hairy, with creeping leafy stems. Lvs. small, oval, stalkless or nearly so. Fls. in a spherical cluster. Calyx hairy on edges. Stems carrying the fl. heads leafy. *

✤ Screes, meadows, on acid soils. To 2500 m. C. and E. Pyrenees. July–August. 770

COMPOSITAE—DAISY FAMILY

The largest of all plant families (over 900 genera and 14,000 species) is correspondingly well represented in the mountains.

The small fls. (*florets*) are arranged in characteristic heads, flat to conical, resembling one large fl., each surrounded by distinctive, more or less sepal-like bracts in 1 or more rows (*involucre*). Between the individual florets and the involucre is the fleshy *receptacle*, which is in effect the swollen end of the stalk.

There are two kinds of floret, the *disk-floret* in which the corolla is short and tubular, and the *ray-floret* in which one side of the corolla is prolonged into a strap-shaped 'petal' or is sometimes thread-like. In some genera all of the florets may be disk-florets, e.g. thistles (*Carduus*, etc.); in others all ray-florets, e.g. dandelion (*Taraxacum*); in some there are central disk-florets and marginal ray-florets, e.g. daisy (*Bellis*).

The stamens, where present, are 5, fixed to the corolla; the anthers, often of distinctive shape, are frequently joined to form a cylinder around the single style, which branches into 2 arms. The 1-celled ovary is below the corolla (inferior) and results in an *achene*, sometimes bristly for dispersal purposes. There is no calyx to the individual florets as in most other flowers; it is frequently replaced by a *pappus* of hairs (as in the dandelion 'clock'), which usually remains fixed to the seed for wind dispersal, or can be in the form of scales, teeth or bristles, on a membrane-like ring; or the calyx can be entirely absent.

Besides variable arrangements of the sexes in different ranks of florets, the phenomenon known as *apomixis* sometimes occurs. This means that seeds are produced without fertilisation. This is particularly pronounced in *Hieracium* (p. 397), but also occurs in other genera. Any mutations ('sports') which occur in apomictic offspring are not bred out as occurs in cross-breeding populations. Thus apomixis can result in an often very large number of stable races appearing, which perpetuate themselves and never interbreed, thus deserving specific rank although they may not differ greatly from the parent.

Some species have milky juice.

Although most of the species are instantly recognisable as Composites, the distinctions between genera are often minute and even microscopic. The

374

family can be divided fairly conveniently into *Tubuliflorae*, in which some or all of the florets are disk-florets (pp. 374–394) and *Liguliflorae*, in which they are all ray-florets (pp. 394–398), starting with *Prenanthes*.

In this volume many species have had to be omitted for lack of space, but indications of such omissions are given throughout. Genera which are omitted altogether include *Arctium* L., the BURDOCKS, several species of which exceed 1500 m.; *Bellis perennis* L., the COMMON DAISY, which reaches 2400 m.; *Eupatorium cannabinum* L., the HEMP AGRIMONY (1700 m.); *Matricaria* L., the MAYWEEDS, several species of which exceed 1750 m.; *Mycelis muralis* (L.) Dum., the WALL LETTUCE (1900 m.); *Picris hieracioides* L., the HAWKWEED OXTONGUE (1900 m.); *Sonchus arvensis* L., the FIELD MILK-THISTLE (1830 m.) and *S. oleraceus* L., the SOW-THISTLE (1800 m.); and *Calycorsus stipitatus* (Jacq.) Rausch. (2450 m.).

SOLIDAGO *L.* **S. virgaurea** *L.* GOLDEN-ROD. The alpine form is *ssp.* **alpestris** (*W. & K.*) *Gaud.* A variable, erect perennial 6–20 cm. tall, with lance-shaped lvs. tapered at both ends, and numerous groups of 1–3 stalked, yellow fl. heads in the axils and at the end of the stem, forming a loose spike. Fl. heads 1½–2 cm. across, with few, strap-shaped ray-florets.
Ssp. **minuta** (*L.*) *Arc.* (*ssp.* alpestris (W. & K. (Hayek) is 5–20 cm. tall with only 1–3 fl. heads on long stalks.
✿ Dry woods, clearings, stony places. 1000–2800 m. (*ssp. minuta* above 1500 m.). Pyrenees; Alps; N. Apennines. Norway to 1800 m. (Britain to 1170 m.) July–October. **774**

BELLIDIASTRUM *Cass.* **B. michelii** *Cass.* (**Aster bellidiastrum** (*L.*) *Scop.*). FALSE DAISY. A perennial 10–35 cm. tall much resembling an enlarged, very robust common daisy. Lvs. all basal, in a rosette, with rounded or diamond-shaped lvs. toothed in upper part and tapering into downy stalks. Fl. heads 2–4 cm. across, solitary on long downy stalks, with white or pinkish ray-florets. Bracts in 2 rows. *
✿ Clearings, stony or sandy places, meadows. To 2800 m. Alps; Apennines. (March–)June–September. **1146**

ASTER *L.* Perennials. Fl. heads with 1 row of usually large blue, red or white ray-florets surrounding a relatively small yellow disk; receptacle flat, covered with small pits edged with a toothed membrane. Involucre of many rows of overlapping green or scaly bracts. Pappus with 2–3 rows of hairs of equal size.

A. alpinus *L.* ALPINE ASTER. 5–15 (40) cm. tall, with fl. heads normally solitary, 3½–4½ cm. across, ray-florets violet, purple or mauve, rarely white. Lvs. mainly basal, a few on the stem, usually hairy, somewhat spoon-shaped, tapering into stalk.
✿ Dry meadows, stony places, rocks. To 3185 m. Pyrenees; Alps; Apennines. July–September. **772**

A. pyrenaeus *DC.* 40–60 cm. tall, with 1–5 purple-rayed fl. heads 5 cm. across on an erect, leafy stem. Lvs. broadly lance-shaped, lightly toothed, partly clasping the stem. Bracts with a long point.
✿ Damp meadows, stony places. To 2000 m. Pyrenees. Rare. July–September. **773**

ERIGERON *L.* FLEABANE. Lvs. spirally arranged. Fl. heads small, with narrow, often thread-like ray-florets in several rows. Involucre of narrow green bracts of similar size, scarcely overlapping. Receptacle convex, pitted, the pits not toothed at edges. Pappus usually of 1 main row of hairs. Besides the species described, the lanky, usually 1-fld. *E. neglectus* Kern. grows from 1600–2600 m., and its relation *E. borealis* (Vierh.) Simm. reaches 1600 m. in Norway and 1180 m. in Scotland. *E. gaudinii* Brügg. reaches 2300 m.

E. acer *L.* (also spelt **acris** and **acre**). BLUE FLEABANE. Annual or biennial, (6–)15–60 (100) cm. tall; the alpine form is ssp. **angulosus** *Gaud.* This has an angular, more or less hairy, reddish stem with several fl. heads 6–13 mm. wide, on variable stalks, the ray-florets not spreading, mauve. Lvs. lance-shaped, tapering at each end. * ✣ Moraines, glacial streams. To 2300 m. Alps. Norway to 1200 m. (Britain.) May–September. **1145**

E. atticus *Vill.* A stout, stiff, erect, downy perennial (15)25–60 cm. tall, with short branches carrying 1–3 fl. heads each. Heads 2½–3½ cm. across, with violet ray-florets, not spreading, and yellow disk; thread-like florets between ray and disk. Lvs. shortly spoon-shaped, lower ones usually shrivelled at fl. time. ✣ Meadows, stony places. To 2200 m. Alps. July–September. **1144**

E. polymorphus *Scop.* Perennial (2)5–30 (40) cm. tall, slightly downy; lvs. ciliate, narrowly oblong to spoon-shaped. Fl. heads usually solitary, 1½–2 cm. across, with spreading mauve ray-florets and yellow or reddish disk; no thread-like florets. A variable plant.* ✣ Short turf, stony places. To 3000 (3600) m. Pyrenees; Alps; Apennines. July–September.

E. alpinus *L.* ALPINE FLEABANE.

Perennial, 2–20 (40) cm. tall, coarsely downy; lvs. hairy, narrow spoon-shaped. Fl. heads often solitary, sometimes up to 5 on stem, 2–3 cm. across, with spreading pink or red ray-florets and yellow or reddish disk; many thread-like florets between ray and disk. ✣ Meadows, stony places, open woods. 1500–3057 m. Pyrenees; Alps; C. Apennines. July–September. **775** **E. pyrenaicus** *Ry.* is 2–10 cm. tall, with very narrow lvs. and usually 1 fl. head: Pyrenees.

E. uniflorus *L.* Perennial, 2–8 (12) cm. tall; lvs. narrow-spoon-shaped, thick, ciliate; stem hairy. Fl. heads solitary, 1–1½ cm. across, rarely more, with more or less spreading, very narrow, white or mauve-pink ray-florets; involucre woolly. Pappus as long as the fruit. ✣ Humus-rich meadows, stony places, screes, moraines. 1200–3000 (3750) m. Alps; Apennines. Norway to 2000 m. Uncommon. July–September. **776**

E. frigidus *Boiss.* Similar to *E. uniflorus*, but fl. heads 2½ cm. across, ray-florets wider and longer, bright violet; pappus twice as long as fruit. ✣ Meadows, stony places. 1750–2900 m. E. Pyrenees. Uncommon. July–August.

E. unalaschkensis (*DC.*) *Vierh.* Perennial, 5–12 cm. tall, with hairy, spoon-shaped, long-stalked, mostly basal lvs. Stems and involucre carrying dark hairs. Fl. heads 1–1½ cm. across, with white ray-florets turning bluish, short, not spreading; disk yellow. * ✣ Snow-beds, debris, on limestone. To 1400 m. Norway. July–August. **777**

ANTENNARIA *Gaertn.* Perennials with uncut, narrow lvs.; plants covered with whitish hairs. Fls. in small tubular heads, themselves gathered into clusters; involucre bracts stiff and dry, white or coloured, often petal-like. Sexes often on different plants. Fl. heads of female plants with thread-like, tubular florets, with pappus hairs in many rows. Fl. heads of male plants with broader tubular florets, apparently carrying both sexes but female part typically sterile, the pappus of a few hairs thickened near the top.

A. dioica (*L.*) *Gaertn.* (Gnaphalium dioicum *L.*) CATSFOOT. 5–20 cm. tall, with creeping woody stock and leafy, rooting runners. Fl. shoots unbranched. Lvs. 1–4 cm. long, mostly in rosettes at ends of runners, rounded-spoon-shaped; stem-lvs. narrow-lance-shaped, pointed, pressed to stem; all lvs. white-woolly below, with a few hairs above. Fl. heads 2–8, short-stalked, in a tight terminal cluster (umbel); on female plants 12 mm. across, with pink to red bracts; on male plants 6 mm., with white, occasionally pink bracts.
⚘ Meadows, heaths, dry open woods, usually on poor, acid soils. To 3010 m. Pyrenees; Alps; Apennines. Norway to 2000 m. (Britain: to 1000 m. in Scotland.) May–July. 771

A. alpina (*L.*) *Gaertn.* ALPINE CATSFOOT. Very similar to *A. dioica*, 5–12 cm. tall, but lvs. downy above, woolly below; fl. heads small, bracts greyish brown; male plants rare.
⚘ Meadows, heaths. To 2200 m. Norway. July–August.

A. carpatica (*Wahl.*) *Bluff & Fing.* (Gnaphalium carpaticum *Gaertn.*). CARPATHIAN CATSFOOT. 5–20 cm. tall, making no runners. Lvs. tapering to both ends. Lvs. and stem white-woolly. Fl. heads 6–8 mm. long, 2–6 together, brown or blackish, with pointed bracts. Female plants with long silky pappus.
⚘ Meadows, stony places, rock ledges, on acid soils. 1500–3100 m. Pyrenees; Alps. July–August. 1139

LEONTOPODIUM *Cass.* Perennials with fl. heads surrounded by long lvs.

forming a starry pattern, thickly white-woolly, which is why the plants are sometimes called FLANNEL-FLOWER. Pappus hairs club-shaped.

L. alpinum *Cass.* EDELWEISS. 5–20 cm. tall, with 2–10 fl. heads surrounded by 5–9 long lvs. Plant white-woolly, but upper surface of narrow-lance-shaped lvs. often green and almost hairless.
⚘ Meadows, stony places, occasionally rock crevices, preferring limestone and schist. To 3400 m. Pyrenees; Alps; Ligurian Apennines. July–September. 779

L. nivale *DC.* SNOW EDELWEISS. A shorter plant than *L. alpinum*, with short, spoon-shaped lvs., white-woolly on both surfaces. *
⚘ Meadows, stony places, rocks. To 2450 m. Abruzzi. July–September. 780

GNAPHALIUM *L.* CUDWEED. Annuals or perennials, with spirally arranged, usually white-woolly lvs. Fl. heads small, gathered into various kinds of cluster, both terminal and axillary. Both sexes present. Bracts scaly, in several overlapping rows, as long as florets, usually spreading in fruit. *
Besides the species described, the annual *G. uliginosum* L. reaches 1600 m. in Tyrol only.

G. supinum *L.* DWARF CUDWEED. A tufted perennial, 2–12 (20) cm. tall, with thin creeping stock, short non-fl. and erect or sprawling fl. stems. Lvs. narrow-lance-shaped to very narrow on stems, to 2 cm. long, woolly on both sides. Fl. heads bell-shaped, 6 mm. long, 1–7 in a short terminal spike. Bracts in 2–4 rows, the outermost about two-thirds length of inner, with brown edges and central stripe, spreading in fruit.
⚘ Damp meadows, snow-beds, stony places, moraines, preferring acid soils. 1400–3400 m. Pyrenees; Alps; C.

Apennines. Norway to 2000 m. (N. Britain: montane.) July–September.

1140

G. hoppeanum *Koch.* A slender perennial, 2–10 cm. tall, not forming tufts; stems erect and usually solitary. Lvs. narrow-lance-shaped, all about the same length, to 6 cm. long, grey-downy on both sides. Fl. heads rounded, 5–7 mm. long, 1–5 in a short spike. Bracts in 3–4 rows, the outermost one-third length of inner, blackish brown at tips, not spreading in fruit.

❋ Stony meadows, screes, on limestone. 1500–2650 m. Alps; Apennines. July–August.   **1141**

G. sylvaticum *L.* WOOD CUDWEED. A stout perennial 8–70 (100) cm. tall, with short woody stock, short non-fl. and erect fl. stems. Rosette and lower stem-lvs. 2–8 cm. long, narrow-lance-shaped, tapering to a narrow stalk-like base; upper stem-lvs. 4–5 mm. wide, decreasing in length up the stem; all lvs. hairless above, woolly below. Fl. heads egg-shaped, 6 mm. long, solitary or in clusters of 2–8, the whole forming a long, loose, narrow spike ½ length of stem. Bracts with central green stripe and red or brownish-black tip.

❋ Open woods, clearings, poor grassland, heaths, on humus-rich and acid soils. To 2500 m. Pyrenees; Alps; Apennines. Norway to 1200 m. (Britain.) July–September.   **1143**

G. norvegicum *Gunn.* HIGHLAND CUDWEED. Like *G. sylvaticum*, but only 8–30 cm. tall, with stem lvs. 1½–2 cm. wide, decreasing in length only among the fl. heads of the compact spike of 6–7 mm. heads, solitary or 2–3 together. Bracts with brown central stripe and edges.

❋ Meadows, heaths, open woods, stony places, cliffs, preferring acid soils. 1200–2800 m. Pyrenees; Alps. Norway to 1780 m. (Britain: to 1200 m. in Scotland.) July–September.   **1142**

ANTHEMIS *L.* CHAMOMILE. Annuals or perennials, usually strongly aromatic, with ferny, spirally arranged lvs. divided 1–3 times into narrow subsegments. Fl. heads usually solitary, with flat to conical receptacle; usually with strap-shaped ray-florets (female or sterile), normally white in alpine species, and yellow, tubular disk-florets (hermaphrodite); most florets with narrow, stiff scales at the base (thus differing from *Chrysanthemum* which has none). Bracts overlapping, blunt, usually stiff and dry. Fruit ribbed, round; no pappus of hairs.

Besides the species described, the CORN CHAMOMILE, *A. arvensis* L., a common field weed, reaches 1950 m. in Valais and 2300 m. adventitiously. *A. elegans* Jan is an endemic of the C. and S. Apennines to 2260 m.; *A. aetnensis* Schouw is a pink-rayed endemic of Mt. Etna, Sicily, to 2800 m. See also *Achillea oxyloba*, p. 378.

A. montana *L.* (including **A. carpatica** *W. & K.*). MOUNTAIN DOG-DAISY. Perennial, 5–25 cm. tall, with woody stock, more or less downy. Lvs. 3 times divided into narrow finger-like segments; stem-lvs. reduced to scales. Fl. heads usually solitary, 3–4 cm. across, with truncated, often notched rays. Bracts with blackish edges.   *

❋ Dry slopes, stony places, screes. To 2000 (2600) m. Pyrenees; Apennines. July–September.   **1147**

A. barrelieri *Ten.* (**Achillea barrelieri** *Sz.*). Perennial, to 12 cm. tall, all greysilky. Basal lvs. in rosette, ellipticoblong in outline, divided twice into short, relatively broad segments. Stem-lvs. similar, smaller. Fl. heads solitary, with short truncated rays, not spreading. Bracts woolly.   *

❋ Meadows, stony places. To 2350 m. C. and S. Appenines. May–August.

1148

378

A. elegans *Jan* (**A. mucronulata** *Bert.*).
Similar to *A. barrelieri*: a slender, more
or less hairless plant with smaller lvs.
divided into narrow pointed segments;
fl. heads with fewer, broader rays. *
✿ Meadows, stony places. To 2260 m.
C. and S. Apennines. May–August.

ACHILLEA. MILFOIL, SNEEZEWORT.
Normally perennials, often aromatic,
with spirally arranged lvs. usually
divided into subsidiary leaflets on each
side of the midrib (pinnatisect). Fl.
heads in flattish clusters (corymbs),
occasionally solitary, with flat or slightly
convex receptacle; ray-florets strap-
shaped, short and broad, white, pink or
red, female; disk-florets tubular, white
or yellow, hermaphrodite. Florets with
narrow stiff scales at the base (thus
differing from *Chrysanthemum* which has
none). Fruit not ribbed, truncated at
top, flat (this is the basic character
separating *Achillea* from *Anthemis* which
has round, ribbed seeds, although,
except for *Achillea oxyloba*, all alpine
species have a flat cluster of several fl.
heads).
　　Besides the species described, the
SNEEZEWORT, *A. ptarmica* L., reaches
1700 m. (Engadine), and its smaller
form *A. pyrenaica* Sibth. 1800 m.
(Pyrenees).

A. oxyloba (*DC.*) *Schultz* (**Anthemis
alpina** *L.*). ALPINE SNEEZEWORT. 8–30
cm. tall, with a creeping stock and lvs.
of elliptic outline cut into long, narrow,
finger-like segments. Fl. head solitary
on a slender stem carrying some lvs.,
2–3 cm. across, with white ray-florets
6–10 mm. long, and pale yellow disk.
✿ Stony meadows, rocks, cliffs, on
limestone. 1600–2800 m. S. of E. Alps.
July–September. 1149

A. atrata L. (**A. atrata** L. *ssp.* **halleri**
Crantz, **A. halleri** *Crantz*). 8–30 cm.
tall, slightly hairy, not strong-smelling,
with 3–15 (25) fl. heads in a loose, more

or less flat cluster; heads 11–18 mm.
across, with 6–12 broad, short, white
ray-florets and whitish disk. Lvs. rather
dark green, without gland-pits, broad-
elliptic in outline, deeply divided into
irregular, pointed segments 1 mm. wide,
usually themselves cut into 2–5 forks.
✿ Damp screes, moraines, streamlets,
on limestone. 1700–3000 m. (4270 m. on
Finsteraarhorn.) Alps (very rare in W.).
July–September. 1153

A. clusiana *Tausch* (**A. atrata** L. *ssp.*
clusiana (*Tausch*) *Heim.*). Very similar
to *A. atrata*, but lvs. neater, more
divided, with more, finer segments. Fl.
heads smaller.
✿ Damp screes, moraines, streamlets,
on limestone. To 2700 m. N.E. Alps.
July–September. 1154

A. moschata *Wulf.* MUSK MILFOIL. 7–20
cm. tall; similar to *A. atrata*, but bright
green, strongly aromatic and with
gland-pits on the lvs., which are
normally only once divided into long,
pointed segments, sometimes slightly
toothed. Fl. heads 3–25 in a cluster,
10–14 mm. across, with 6–8 white ray-
florets. Bracts brown-edged. *
✿ Rocks, gravels, moraines, dry
meadows, on acid soils. 1450–3400 m.
Alps (very rare in W.). July–September.
1152

A. nana L. DWARF MILFOIL. A tufted,
strong-smelling plant 5–10 (20) cm.
tall, covered with thick greyish wool.
Lvs. narrow-elliptic in outline, tapering
at both ends, divided into fairly broad,
more or less toothed segments. Fl.
heads 5 or more in a dense rounded
cluster, each 1 cm. across, dirty white,
with 5–8 short, rounded rays. Bracts
black-edged.
✿ Rocks, screes, moraines, gravels, on
granite and schist. 1700–3800 m. Alps;
Abruzzi (local). July–September. 1156

A. clavennae L. (2)10–25 cm. tall,
with creeping stock. Lvs. long-elliptic

in outline, divided into relatively few, widely spaced, often toothed segments, all covered in short silvery-silky hairs. Fl. heads 5 or more in a loose, rather long-stalked cluster, each 1–2 cm. across, with 5–9 short, round, pure white rays and off-white disk.

✤ Rocks, screes, on limestone. 1500–2500 m. Monte Baldo; E. Alps. July–September. 1151

A. erba-rotta *All.* (commonly spelt **herba-rotta** or **herba-rota**). 10–20 cm. tall, aromatic on bruising. Distinctive with its narrowly spoon-shaped, pitted lvs., those of the sterile stems in rosettes, tapering into a stalk and toothed at tip; stem-lvs. stalkless, often with small teeth all along edges, those at the base often longer than the rest. Fl. heads few in a cluster, each 1½ cm. across, with 4–7 white rays. Several sub-species now recognised.

✤ Rocks, meadows, on acid soils. S.W. Alps. 2000–3200 m. July–August. 1155, 1239

1239. *Achillea erba-rotta.* Stem-leaf, enlarged.

A. macrophylla *L.* LARGE-LEAVED SNEEZEWORT 30–90 cm. tall, with broad-lance-shaped lvs. cut into 5 narrow lance-shaped, sharp-toothed segments. Fl. heads 13–15 cm. across, with 5 white rays and white disk, 6–12 forming a flat 3–4 cm. cluster with stalks of very unequal lengths.

✤ Damp woods, gullies, and by shady rocks, in humus-rich soil. To 2500 m. Alps, mainly W. and S., less common to E.; N. Apennines. July–September. 1150

A. tanacetifolia *All.* (**A. distans** *W. & K.*). TANSY MILFOIL. A stout, hand-some, slightly downy plant 20–120 cm. tall, with long-creeping rootstock and large lvs. of broad-lance-shaped outline, divided into broad, toothed segments with smaller ones between, the stem lvs. tending to clasp the stem with sub-sidiary leaflets. Fl. heads 5 mm. across, numerous in convex clusters, several on long branches merging to form a head 10 cm. or more wide; rays 5, white, rose-red or purplish, disks off-white.*

✤ Scrub, open woods, poor grassland. To 2500 m. Alps. (Britain: escaped.) July–September. 781

A. millefolium *L.* YARROW, COMMON MILFOIL. This familiar 8–60 cm. plant is like *A. tanacetifolia*, but smaller, the lvs. much smaller and neater, narrow lance-shaped in outline; the fl. heads 4–6 mm. across, white, rarely pink or red, in heads with only 1 main stalk.

✤ Meadows, hedgerows, paths, railway lines, waste and stony places. To 2450 (3100) m. Pyrenees; Alps; Apennines. Norway to 1350 m. (Britain.) July–September. 782

A. virescens (*Fenzl*) *Heim*. Very like *A. millefolium*, 20–60 cm. tall, with rather loose clusters of 4 mm. fl. heads with pale yellow rays and whitish disk.

✤ Meadows, stony places, scrub. To 1900 m. Monte Baldo. July–October.

A. chamaemelifolia *Pourr*. Similar to *A. millefolium*, 15–60 cm. tall, but with lvs. cut into 7–13 narrow, pointed, well-separated segments, all roughly the same size and usually sickle-shaped. Fls. white, in a loose head.

✤ Rocks, stony places. To 1700 m. E. Pyrenees. June–August.

CHRYSANTHEMUM *L.* Alpine species perennials with spirally ar-ranged, more or less cut lvs. Fl. heads solitary or in flattish clusters (corymbs), with rounded involucre of overlapping, dry-edged bracts; receptacle usually flat. Strap-shaped ray-florets usually present, yellow or white, rarely pink, female; disk-florets tubular, compressed, yellow or white, hermaphrodite; no scales among florets (thus differing from *Anthemis* and *Achillea*). Pappus absent or reduced to a small rim on the top of the fruit.

Older floras refer to the species described under *Leucanthemum* Tourn., retaining *Chrysanthemum* for the yellow-rayed species.

The species are often variable and the demarcations between them are treated differently by various authors; many subspecies have been described in some cases.

Besides the species described the TANSY, *C. vulgare* (L.) Benth. (*Tanacetum vulgare* L.), with very aromatic foliage and yellow, rayless fl. heads, and the lanky *C. corymbosum* L., with small white fl. heads in long-stalked clusters, both reach 2000 m.

C. alpinum L. ALPINE MOON-DAISY. A tufted plant with weak, sprawling, partly erect 5–15 cm. stems, sparsely woolly-hairy. Lvs. variable (see below); stem-lvs. usually narrow lance-shaped. Fl. head solitary, 2–4 cm. across, with 8–12 mm. rays, lightly notched at tip, normally white but occasionally pink-flushed; disk golden. Bracts blunt, green with brown edge. *

Var. **hutchinsiifolium** (*Murr.*) *Vierh.*: lvs. broadly oblong in outline, with distinct narrow stalk, cut into several nearly opposite, pointed segments of similar size (**1240 a**).

Var. **minimum** (*Vill.*) *Koch:* lvs. of spoon-shaped outline, with up to 5 segments, sometimes reduced to large teeth; lf. stalk densely hairy, swelling towards base which clasps stem. Fl. heads small (**1240 b, c**).

Var. **pseudotomentosum** (*F. & B.*) *Vier.*: like *var. minimum*, but lvs. woolly.

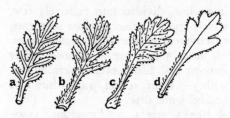

1240. *Chrysanthemum alpinum:* variation in leaf form. a, *var. hutchinsiifolium;* b, c, *var. minimum;* d, *var. cuneifolium.*

Var. **pyrenaicum** *Vier.*: like *var. minimum*, but lvs. hairless and deeply cut.

Var. **cuneifolium** (*Murr.*) *Vier.*: lvs. with very long, tapering, hairy stalk, and only 3–5 coarse teeth on rhomboidal blade (**1240 d**).

✷ Short turf, rocks, screes, moraines, gravels, on acid soils. 1800–2800 (3827) m. *Var. cuneifolium:* E. Alps. *Var. hutchinsiifolium:* Pyrenees; Alps; Apennines. *Var. minimum:* Pyrenees; W. Alps. *Var. pseudotomentosum:* W. Alps. *Var. pyrenaicum:* Pyrenees. July–August.

1161, 1240

C. pulverulentum *Pers.* DOWNY MOON-DAISY. Similar to *C. alpinum*, but lvs. entirely silky-downy, only 3–5-lobed, lower ones rather truncated, tapering into stalk. Ray-florets yellow or reddish in inner third. Disk-florets with flattened tube. Bracts pointed. *

✷ Meadows, stony places. Around 2000 m. E. Pyrenees. Rare. July–August.

1160

C. atratum *Jacq. non* L. (**C. coronopifolium** *Vill.*). SAW-LEAVED MOON-DAISY (**1157**). A mat-forming plant with partly sprawling (3)10–40 cm. stems, and long, narrow, brittle, fleshy lvs. typically of jagged outline with 3–7 large teeth, tapering into a winged stalk, dark green. Fl. head solitary, white-rayed, $2\frac{1}{2}$–$4\frac{1}{2}$ cm. across, exceptionally 6–9 cm.

Bracts black-edged. Fruit with a 3-lobed ring at top. *
Var. **ceratophylloides** *All.* (1158): lvs. reduced to strap-shaped lobes and a midrib, very long-stalked.
Var. **tridactylites** *Fiori* (1159): lvs. lance-shaped to reversed-triangular, with about 5 blunt lobes, tapering into extremely long stalk.
See also note under *C. leucanthemum.*
⚜ Rocks, screes, river gravels, on granite. To 2840 m. Alps. Uncommon. *Var. ceratophylloides:* Basse Alpes, Maritime Alps; N. and C. Apennines. *Var. tridactylites:* C. and S. Apennines. July–September. **1157-59**

C. leucanthemum L. MOON-DAISY, DOG-DAISY. A very variable plant with many named forms or subspecies, including a montane one called *C. atratum* L. non Jacq. This familiar 20–70 cm. plant with 2½–5 cm. fl. heads solitary on very long branches, or sometimes on single fl. stems, has lvs. varying from very narrow and lightly toothed to broad, deeply and jaggedly toothed, but normally long-spoon-shaped in outline. Rays white; disk yellow. *
Small forms of *C. leucanthemum* can be mistaken for large forms of *C. atratum,* the main difference being the mat-forming habit and sprawling stems of the latter, while the former has no lobed ring at the top of the fruit.
⚜ Meadows, open woods, paths, banks, To 2686 m. Pyrenees; Alps; Apennines. Norway to 1000 m. (Britain.) (May–)June–August(–November).
C. maximum Ram., the familiar hardy perennial chrysanthemum of gardens looking like a giant form of *C. leucanthemum* with 6–9 cm. fl. heads, occurs in the Pyrenees at sub-alpine levels.

ARTEMISIA L. Perennials, sometimes sub-shrubby, often pungent or aromatic, with spirally arranged lvs, cut almost or quite to midrib into many narrow segments. Fl. heads small, usually in spike-like racemes, occasionally solitary. All florets tubular, the outer, if present, female, the disk-florets hermaphrodite. Involucre cylindrical or round, with many overlapping bracts; receptacle more or less flat, without scales. Pappus absent.
Besides the species mentioned, *A. absinthium* L., the WORMWOOD, reaches 2580 m., and *A. vulgaris* L., the MUG-WORT, 1830 m.; both are British natives. In the Pyrenees the Iberian species *A. aragonensis* Lam. and *A. chamaemelifolia* Vill., both very rare, reach 2000 m. and 2400 m. respectively. The latter also occurs in the S.W. Italian Alps.

A. genipi *Web.* (**A. spicata** *Wulf.*). GENIPI. A silver-woolly, aromatic plant forming a tuft of 5–10 (30) cm. stems. Lower lvs. of 3 main divisions, often further 3-lobed; upper stem-lvs. smaller and stalkless. Fl. heads spaced along upper stem to form a loose spike, arching at summit, each 3–8 mm. across, dark-coloured. Bracts woolly, dark-edged. Genipi is a liqueur made from this plant.
⚜ Rocks, screes, moraines. 2000–3800 m. Pyrenees; Alps; Abruzzi. Uncommon. July–September. **1162**

A. nitida *Bert.* Very like *A. genipi,* silky-woolly, 10–30 cm. tall, with 6–8 mm. fl. heads usually on one side of the stem only.
⚜ Rocks, stony places. 1300–2000 (2400) m. E. Alps; Apuan Alps. August–September.

A. eriantha *Ten.* (**A. petrosa** (*Baum.*) *Jan*). Similar to *A. genipi* and sometimes considered a subspecies, but with larger, usually leaning fl. heads, which are tawny-woolly; the stem-lvs. are larger and have larger lobes.
⚜ Rocks, screes, on granite. 2000–3135

m. Maritime Alps; N. and C. Apennines.
Uncommon. July–September.

A. nivalis *Br.-Bl.* A tiny, hairless, green
version of *A. genipi*, sometimes considered a subspecies or hybrid, with
greenish fl. heads 2–3 mm. across, and
stem-lvs. strap-shaped, undivided.
✣ Rocky crests. Around 3400 m.
Swiss/Italian Alps: Valais/Val d'Here-
mence only. August–September.

A. mutellina *Vill.* **(A. laxa** *(Lam.)*
Fritsch.). YELLOW GENIPI. 5–15 cm. tall:
like *A. genipi*, silver-woolly, but lower
lvs. with long stalks, divided into 5 main
lobes themselves often further cut;
stem-lvs. distinctly stalked; fl. heads
downy, 4–5 mm. across, with brown-
edged bracts, few in a loose spike.   *
✣ Rocks, screes, moraines, on acid
soils. 1300–3700 m. Pyrenees; Alps; N.
Apennines. Uncommon or rare. July–
September.   **1164**

A. borealis *Pall.* **var. nana** *Gaud.*
ARCTIC MUGWORT. Now considered a
subspecies of *A. campestris* L. A green,
usually hairless, scentless perennial 10–
20 cm. tall, with woody stock and lvs.
divided and subdivided into long narrow
lobes, the upper stem-lvs. reduced to a
strap; stalks long, winged. Fl. heads
greenish, 5–6 mm. across, 15–20 in
spikes or long clusters, elongating and
becoming spaced out as they age.
✣ Rocks, screes, gravels. 1500–2800 m.
W. Alps (very rare); C. Alps. July–
August.   **1163**
A. campestris L. and its *ssp. alpina*
(DC.) Fritsch are undistinguished plants,
both found up to 2000 m.

A. atrata *Lam.* DARK ALPINE WORM-
WOOD. A green, hairless, scentless plant
10–40 cm. tall; lvs. dotted with glands.
Lower lvs. fern-like, with side lobes,
themselves divided, at right angles to
midrib, and a long stalk furrowed on
the underside. Fl. heads greenish,

brown-bordered, 8 mm. across, very
short-stalked, numerous in a long
narrow spike.
✣ Stony places, dry grass, on acid
soils. 1800–2400 m. Cottian Alps; E.
Alps. Very rare and local. July–August.
    1165
A. glacialis *L.* GLACIER WORMWOOD. A
white-woolly, very aromatic, tufted
5–15 cm. plant. Lvs. all stalked, with 5
divisions, very finely 3-lobed. Fl. heads
4–6 cm. across, golden yellow, usually
2–9 in a tight terminal head, sometimes
also 1–3 in the upper lf. axils. Bracts
white-cottony, brown-edged.
✣ Exposed rocks, screes, moraines.
1900–3200 m. W. Alps. Very rare.
July–August.   **785**

A. norvegica *Fr.* NORTHERN WORM-
WOOD, NORWEGIAN MUGWORT. A white-
woolly, aromatic, tufted 10–25 cm.
plant with very stout rootstock. Lvs.
rounded in outline, to 3 cm. long, with
wide, long stalk and about 5 divisions,
themselves 3-lobed. Fl. heads 12 mm.
across, bright yellow, often solitary, up
to 3, down- or side-facing.
Ssp. **scotica** *Hulten:* 3–6 cm. tall,
with lvs. not over 2 cm. long; fl. head
typically solitary.
✣ Dry, exposed ridges, screes, on
mineralised and limestone formations.
To 1640 m. Norway. *Ssp. scotica:*
Scotland, 600–900 m., very local. July–
September.   **786**
TUSSILAGO *L.* **T. farfara** *L.* COLTS-
FOOT. The only species. A perennial
with thick tuberous underground runners and 5–15 cm. fl. stems bearing
scale-like pointed lvs., appearing before
basal lvs. Fl. heads solitary, bright
primrose yellow, with up to 300 very
narrow female ray-florets and a few
male disk-florets. Bracts many, green or
purplish, long and narrow, in 1 main
row, with upper stem-scales forming an
uneven lower rank. Pappus of long

hairs in several rows. Fl. stems elongating in fruit. Basal lvs. more or less rounded, 10–20 cm. across, with shallow, blackish-toothed lobes.

✤ In all kinds of habitat: at high altitudes typically in shingle and similar stony places. To 2640 m. Pyrenees; Alps; Apennines. Norway to 1390 m. (Britain to 1250 m.) February–May (–August at high altitudes). **778**

HOMOGYNE *Cass.* Perennials arising from a slender scaly rhizome, with round to kidney-shaped basal lvs. and long slender stems with few, small lvs. and usually solitary, terminal fl. heads. Florets all tubular, of two kinds, with stigmas typically protruding. Bracts long, narrow, in a single row. Pappus of several rows of hairs. Fl. stems elongating in fruit.

H. alpina (*L.*) *Cass.* ALPINE COLTSFOOT. 10–30(40) cm. tall. Basal lvs. 2–4 cm. across, almost circular to kidney-shaped, heart-shaped at base, round-toothed, dark green and hairless above, often purplish below, with long hairy stalk. Fl. stem woolly, with 1–2 very small, slightly clasping lvs. Fl. head 10–15 mm. long, reddish or violet; bracts purplish red.

✤ Damp meadows, open woods, streamlets. To 3260 m. Pyrenees; Alps; Apuan Alps; N. and C. Apennines. (Britain: introduced, very rare.) May–August. **783**

H. discolor *Cass.* Very similar to *H. alpina* and has been considered a subspecies, but lvs. more coarsely toothed, white-downy below; stem not woolly at base; lower stem-lvs. usually broad and markedly clasping.

✤ Damp meadows. To 2400 m. E. Alps. June–August. **784**

H. sylvestris (*Scop.*) *Cass.* Very similar to the other species, but lvs. more deeply lobed, the central 1 or 3 lobes with 3 distinct teeth. Fl. head smaller.

✤ Meadows, scrub. To 2000 m. S.E. Alps. May–June.

PETASITES *Mill.* BUTTERBUR. Perennials with invasive subterranean rhizomes, often in fl. before the lvs. appear. Fl. heads small, in clusters (spike-like racemes or panicles), of two kinds, one with mostly male fls. and a few female, sometimes rayed at margins; the other with mostly female, thread-like fls. and a few sterile ones, apparently hermaphrodite, in centre. Bracts in 2–3 uneven rows. Pappus of long, thin hairs. Fl. stems elongating in fruit.

The predominantly male and female plants, which differ in appearance, were in some cases treated as separate species by earlier authors.

P. hybridus (L.) G., M. & S. (*P. officinalis* Moench), the BUTTERBUR, with lvs. up to 150 cm. across, can reach 1800 m. (E.C. Alps).

P. albus (*L.*) *Gaertn.* (**Tussilago alba** *L.*, including **T. racemosa** *Hoppe*). WHITE BUTTERBUR. 10–30 (70) cm. tall. Fl. heads on stalks of unequal length, in a rounded cluster; stem with a few long, narrow, yellowish or pale green scales. Heads whitish, the male much larger and more rounded than the female; stigmas deeply 2-lobed, protruding. Lvs. 15–30 (100) cm. across, greyish below with green veins, round in outline, heart-shaped at base, with large lobes, the whole margin cut into small teeth; stalk flattened, lightly furrowed on top.

✤ Streamsides, gullies, damp woods, waste places. To 2200 m. Pyrenees; Alps. (Britain: introduced.) March–May. **1167**

P. paradoxus (*Retz.*) *Baumg.* (**P. niveus** *Baumg.*, including **Tussilago nivea** *Vill.* and **T. paradoxa** *Retz.*). ALPINE BUTTERBUR. 20–30 (60) cm. tall. Fl. stem with large overlapping scales. Fl.

384

heads white or pinkish, short-stalked, in a long, egg-shaped cluster, tighter in male plants. Stigmas deeply 2-lobed, protruding. Lvs. white below, triangular in outline, longer than broad, not heart-shaped at base, with indistinct, irregular lobes and many small teeth.
✲ Stream-beds, avalanche gullies, stony places, damp open woods. To 2600 m. Pyrenees; Alps. March–May(–August at high altitudes). **1169**

P. frigidus (*L.*) *G., M. & S.* 20–30 (50) cm. tall. Fl. stem with few, well spaced, often large, clasping brown scales. Male fl. heads pink, with a few short, strap-shaped ray-florets; female yellowish white. Lvs. 5–10 cm. across, white-downy below, rounded to triangular in outline, with pronounced fairly regular lobes, no small teeth.
✲ Wet meadows, snow-beds, streamsides. To 1750 m. Norway. June. **1168**

ADENOSTYLES *Cass.* Perennials with large lvs., long slender stems, and numerous small, oblong, pink to purplish fl. heads of tubular hermaphrodite florets with protruding stigmas; corolla with distinct spreading lobes. Bracts few, in 1 row. Pappus of long slender hairs in several rows. Named under *Cacalia* L. in older floras.

A. alliariae (*Gouan*) *Kern.* (**A. albifrons** *Reichb.*, **A. albida** *Cass.*). 60–100 (200) cm. tall. Lvs. white-cottony below; lower lvs. to 50 cm. across, rounded-triangular, irregularly lobed and toothed; stem-lvs. clasping stem, the lower with distinct little 'ears'. Stem branching, with purplish fl. heads in short-stalked clusters grouped on branches of unequal length. Fl. heads narrowly cylindrical, to 1 cm. long, of 3–6 florets each, with 3–5 bracts.
✲ Streamsides, wood margins, scrub.

To 2670 m. Pyrenees; Alps, July–August. **1170**
A. pyrenaica *Lange.* Similar to *A. alliariae* and now regarded as *ssp.* **hybrida** (*Vill.*) Tutia; lvs. downy but not white-cottony below; heads with 10–25 florets and 8–9 bracts.
✲ Streamsides, scrub. To 2500 m. Pyrenees. July–August.
A. glabra (*Mill.*) *DC.* (**A. alpina** *Bl. & F.*, **A. viridis** *Cass.*). 30–60 (80) cm. tall. Lvs. green and virtually hairless, not large, broadly triangular, somewhat heart-shaped at base, with small regular teeth. Stem-lvs. without clasping 'ears'. Fl. heads 1 cm. long, usually of 3 florets, pale red or reddish mauve, on unbranched stems. *
✲ Screes, gravels, meadows, damp open woods. To 2500 m. Alps; Apennines. July–August. **1171**
A. leucophylla (*Willd.*) *Reichb.* (**A. tomentosa** (*Vill.*) *S. & T.*, **A. candidissima** *Cass.*). 20–30 (60) cm. tall. Lvs. white-cottony below, often above also, smaller than in the other species, broadly triangular, markedly heart-shaped at base, with relatively large, fairly regular teeth; stem-lvs. with distinct stalk. Fl. heads rounded, peach-pink to blood-red, with 12–32 florets and 8 bracts, on unbranched stems.
✲ Screes, stony places, meadows, preferring acid soils. 1900–3100 m. W. Alps. July–August. **1172**

BUPHTHALMUM *L.* **B. salicifolium** *L.* (including **B. grandiflorum** *L.*). YELLOW OX-EYE. A slender perennial 30–70 (150) cm. tall, with stems branched in upper part, each branch with a single fl. head; lvs. to 10–12 cm. long, thin, soft, hairless, lance-shaped, tapering at each end especially to the stalk-like base, toothed; the upper ones clasping the stem and with a long point. Fl. heads 3–5 cm. across, with bright yellow rays and disk. Fruit winged; pappus reduced to a circular, sharp-toothed ridge.

✲ Woods, stony places, marshes. To 2040 m. Alps; N. Apennines. June–July. **796**

Telekia speciosissima *Less.* (B. speciosissimum *Ard.*) is a similar plant with much broader lvs. clasping the stem, which reaches 1600 m. in the Italian Alps.

ARNICA *L.* **A. montana** *L.* ARNICA. A stout, glandular-downy, aromatic perennial 20–60 cm. tall. Basal lvs. in rosette; stem-lvs. much smaller, opposite, in 1–2 pairs, oblong-lance-shaped with lightly waved edges. Fl. heads usually solitary, sometimes 2–4, terminal, 7–8 cm. across, orange-yellow, often untidy. Involucre bracts in 2 equal rows; pappus of 1 row of hairs.

✲ Unmanured meadows, open woods, on acid soils. To 2830 m. Pyrenees; Alps; N. Apennines. May–August. **795**

DORONICUM *L.* (also *Vaill.*) (including **ARONICUM** *Neck.*). Perennials with irregularly swollen rootstock, spirally arranged lvs., and large flat yellow fl. heads. Bracts green, in 2–3 equal rows; receptacle convex. Ray-florets strap-shaped, in 1 row, female; disk-florets tubular, hermaphrodite; disk small in proportion to rays. Pappus of 1–2 rows of hairs.

The species are similar and names overlap a good deal. Some species were originally named under *Arnica*.

Besides the species described, the often cultivated LEOPARDS-BANE, *D. pardalianches* (L.) Jacq., is occasionally found up to 1700 m.

D. austriacum *Jacq.* (D. scorpioides *W. & G.*). AUSTRIAN LEOPARDS-BANE. 30–150 cm. tall, with short rootstock. Basal lvs. withered at fl. time; stem leafy, with lvs. larger in upper part than near base, lance-shaped, lightly toothed, enlarging at base into stem-clasping lobes. Fl. heads usually many on the branched stem, 5–6 cm. across.

✲ Open woods, shaded meadows, streamsides, preferring acid soils. To 2000 m. Pyrenees; Alps; Apennines. July–August. **787**

D. clusii *(All.)* *Tausch.* (Aronicum clusii *Hausm.*). TUFTED LEOPARDS-BANE. A rather slender 8–40 cm. plant with stout rootstock and solitary 3½–6 cm. fl. head on stem thickened just below it. Lvs. soft, more or less hairy, lightly toothed, narrow-diamond-shaped, lower ones tapering into long stalk, upper stalkless.

✲ Stony places, stony meadows, snow-beds, moraines, on primitive rocks. 1600–2800 (3500) m. C. and E. Alps. July–September. **788**

D. glaciale *(Wulf.)* *Nym.* (D. clusii var. glaciale *Tausch*, Aronicum glaciale *Reichb.*). GLACIER LEOPARDS-BANE. Very like *D. clusii*, but dwarfer, 5–25 cm. tall, with narrower, more distinctly toothed lvs., the upper distinctly stem-clasping. Fl. heads 3–4½ cm. across.

✲ Poor, stony turf, snow-beds, moraines, boulder-slopes. 1600–2900 m. E. Alps. July–August.

D. grandiflorum *Lam.* (D. jacquini *Tausch*, **D. halleri** *Tausch*, **D. scorpioides** *W. & L.*, Aronicum scorpioides *Koch*). LARGE-FLOWERED LEOPARDS-BANE. 6–50 cm. tall, with strong, oblique rootstock (sweet-tasting). Lvs. mostly basal, oval, heart-shaped or abruptly truncated at base, regularly but lightly toothed; stem-lvs. clasping; lvs. hairy on edges. Fl. head solitary, 4–6 (8) cm. across, on stem thickened just below it.

✲ Screes, rocks, debris, stony meadows. 1300–2560 (3450) m. Pyrenees; Alps. July–August. **789**

D. viscosum *Nym.* Similar to *D. grandiflorum*, but 8–20 cm. tall, sticky-glandular all over, with 5–8 cm. fl. heads. *

🌿 Screes, debris, rocky meadows. E. Pyrenees. Very rare. To 2500 m. July–August.

D. columnae *Ten.* (**D. cordatum** (*Wulf.*) *Schultz-Bip.*, **D. orientale** *Reichb.*, **D. wulfenianum** (*Lam.*) *P.F.*). HEART-LEAVED LEOPARDS-BANE. 15–60 cm. tall, with rootstock covered with fine threads and retaining the debris of old lvs. Lvs. mostly basal, the lowest smallest, triangular heart-shaped, with distant teeth, very long-stalked. Stem-lvs. oblong-lance-shaped, markedly stem-clasping. Fl. head 3½–6 cm. across, solitary on long stem.

🌿 Stony places, scrub, open woods, on limestone. To 2300 m. S.E. and E. Alps; Apennines. May–August. **790**

SENECIO *L.* RAGWORT, GROUNDSEL. Alpine species all herbaceous perennials with spirally arranged lvs. Fl. heads yellow, either solitary, or few on branched stems, or in flattish clusters (corymbs). Ray-florets strap-shaped, female; disk-florets tubular, hermaphrodite. Bracts in 1 main row, with a few short outer ones. Pappus of unbranched hairs.

A very large genus of which many species reach alpine levels. Only a few of the taller, coarser ones are described here; the more noteworthy species are the low-growing, white-downy group.

Among the less distinguished tall species are *S. brachychaetus* DC., to 2500 m.; *S. cacaliaster* Lam. and *S. crispatus* DC., to 1900 m.; *S. nemorensis* L., to 2200 m.; *S. rupestris* W. & K., to 2300 m. The two GROUNDSELS, *S. viscosus* L. and *S. vulgaris* L., the latter a troublesome weed, reach 2200 (2500) m. *S. aethnensis* Jan is a glaucous-leaved endemic from Mt. Etna, to 2000 m.

Plants typically 15 *cm. tall or much more, not white-felted*

S. alpinus (*L.*) *Scop.* ALPINE RAGWORT. 30–70 cm. tall, with oval, more or less pointed, doubly saw-toothed lvs., heart-shaped at base, a little longer than broad, long-stalked towards base of stem. Fl. heads 3–4 cm. across, in rather uneven, flattish clusters on stalks of very varying length. *

🌿 Meadows, streamsides, wood margins. To 2150 m. Alps. July–September. **791**

S. ovirensis (*Koch*) *DC.* Similar to *S. alpinus* with woolly-hairy stem, 20–60 cm. tall. Lvs. narrowing into short stalk, except topmost ones; oval to oblong, rounded-toothed. Fl. heads 3–4 cm. across, 3–10 in a neat head.

🌿 Open woods, scrub, by cow-huts. To 2000 m. E. Alps. May–July. **794**

S. doronicum *L.* CHAMOIS RAGWORT. A variable plant often divided into subspecies, with silky-woolly 20–60 cm. stem. Lvs. oblong to narrow lance-shaped, the upper much smaller, usually downy, stem-clasping, well spaced. Fl. heads 4–6 cm. across, 1–3 (7) on long stalks.

Var. **arachnoideus** *Sieb.* (**S. arachnoideus** *Scop.*): lvs. broad lance-shaped; fl. heads to 6 cm. across, with broad rays long in proportion to disk.

🌿 Meadows, stony turf, woods, preferring limestone. To 3100 m. Pyrenees; Alps; Apennines. *Var. arachnoideus:* to 2260 m. E. Alps; C. and S. Apennines. July–August. **792**

S. tournefortii *La Peyr.* Similar to *S. doronicum*, 20–80 cm. tall, with 2–5 (1–12) fl. heads 3–4 cm. across. Lvs. broader, tapering evenly to both ends, upper ones not clasping stem, close together; lvs. glossy, bright green. *

🌿 Meadows, damp hollows, rocks. Pyrenees. 1300–2000 m. July–August. **793**

S. abrotanifolius *L.* 15–40 cm. tall, with long woody rootstock. Lvs. slightly or not hairy, twice or thrice divided into very narrow segments, dense especially around the base of the stem. Fl. heads 2½–4 cm. across, untidy, 2–5 (typically 3) on short stalks, orange-yellow to orange-red. ✤ Open woods, scrub, stony places. To 2700 m. S. and E. Alps. July–September. **797**

Plants less than 20 cm. tall, lvs. white-felted at least when young

S. uniflorus *All.* ONE-FLOWERED ALPINE GROUNDSEL. 5–15 cm. tall, normally with 1 (rarely 2–4) golden to orange fl. head, 2–3 cm. across, with 7–15 rays. Basal lvs. toothed or round-lobed, long-spoon-shaped, tapering to a long stalk; upper lvs. long and narrow. Lvs. variable. ✤ Thin turf, rocks, stony places, on acid soils. 1900–3618 m. S.C. Alps. Very local. July–September. **798**

S. incanus *L.* GREY ALPINE GROUNDSEL. 3–15 cm. tall. Fl. heads about 13 mm. across, 6–10 in a head, with 3–5 rays. There are three geographical races.

Ssp. **incanus** (799): usually not exceeding 10 cm. tall; fls. 6–8 in a neat rounded head, usually opening flat. Lvs. thin, narrow lance-shaped, tapering into long stalks, more or less deeply cut into relatively broad, rounded, nearly equal segments with distinct gaps between them; oldest lvs. sometimes hairless and green.

Ssp. **insubricus** (*Chen.*) *Br.-Bl.* (800): like *ssp. incanus*, but lvs. more oval, segments more irregular, broader and often overlapping.

Ssp. **carniolicus** (*Willd.*) *Br.-Bl.* (801): a taller plant than the two other subspecies, to 15 cm.; fl. heads paler yellow, up to 10 in a less tidy, longer-stalked head, often not opening fully. Lvs. lightly cut into irregular but seldom overlapping lobes, gradually tapering into stalk; older lvs. rapidly losing their grey down. ✤ Meadows, stony places, moraines, on acid soils. 1700–3498 m. *Ssp. incanus:* W. Alps, into Switzerland and N. Apennines. *Ssp. insubricus:* W. Swiss Alps, Bergamasque Alps: extremely local. *Ssp. carniolicus:* E. Alps. July–September. **799–801**

S. leucophyllus *DC.* WHITE ALPINE GROUNDSEL. Very like *S. incanus*, and probably best regarded as another geographical race. 10–20 cm. tall, very white-downy, with 12–16 fl. heads in a tight head. Lvs. thick, oval in outline, cut into irregular-toothed lobes broader at apex than base. ✤ Rocks, stony places, on acid soils. 1500–2700 m. E. Pyrenees; Cevennes. August–September. **802**

Plants 10–70 cm. tall, white-cottony

S. capitatus (*Wahl.*) *DC.* 15–30 (70) cm. tall, with oblong-elliptic lvs., basal ones tapering gradually into stalk. Stem unbranched, with 2–10 short-stalked fl. heads, normally 2–3 cm. across, gold to orange-red. ✤

Ssp. **campestris** *DC.*: fls. golden yellow; bracts green; 10–70 cm. tall.

Ssp. **capitatus** (803): fls. yellow, orange or red; bracts brownish purple; 18–30 cm. tall.

Ssp. **pyrenaicus** *G.G.*: fls. without ray-florets; lvs. very narrow; 30–50 cm. tall. ✤ Meadows, rocky slopes. 1800–2500 m. *Ssp. campestris:* Maritime Alps: rare. *Ssp. capitatus:* Alps, Abruzzi. *Ssp. pyrenaicus:* Pyrenees: rare. July–August, **803**

CARLINA *L.* Perennials with spiny lvs. cut into roughly opposite lobes. Florets all tubular, hermaphrodite, the heads having the appearance of a row of ray-florets because the inner bracts resemble rays; these are hard, coloured, glossy, open out only in dry weather and close the head in wet. Outer bracts lf.-like. Pappus of 1 row of feathery hairs.

Flower heads very large, typically solitary and stemless

C. acaulis *L.* STEMLESS CARLINE THISTLE (**1173**). Perennial, typically with rosette flat on the ground (but see variety below), with radiating lvs. to 30 cm. long and 6 cm. across, with distinct stems cut into narrow toothed divisions, sometimes slightly silky-hairy. Fl. head solitary, stemless, in centre of rosette, 5–10 (13) cm. across, with the interior bracts silvery-white on top, green or purplish below. *Var.* **alpina** (*Jacq.*) *Beck* (*var.* **caulescens** *Lam.*, **C. subacaulis** *DC.*, *var.* **caulescens** *DC.*) (**1174**): ALPINE CARLINE THISTLE: with stout stems 20–40 (70) cm. tall, the upper stem-lvs. radiating widely around the fl. head. Multi-headed forms occasionally appear.   *
⚜ Poor meadows, stony slopes, open woods, preferring limestone. To 2800 m. Pyrenees; Alps; Apennines. July–September.   **1173–74**

C. acanthifolia *All.* Perennial, forming a huge rosette flat on the ground, with closely packed lvs. to 30 cm. long or more, 9 cm. across; central lvs. without distinct stalk. Lvs. white-velvety below and sometimes on top. Fl. head solitary, stemless, in centre of rosette, 12–14 cm. across.
Ssp. **acanthifolia**: inner bracts silvery white or pale yellow, next row with branching, intercrossing spines; lvs. downy on top.
Ssp. **cynara** *Pourr.*: inner bracts bright yellow, next row with simple spines. Lvs. nearly hairless on top.
⚜ Meadows, dry and stony places, preferring limestone. To 1800 m. *Ssp. acanthifolia*: E. Pyrenees, Cevennes,

French Alps. *Ssp. cynara:* Pyrenees, Cevennes. July–September.   **1175**

Flower heads small and clustered

C. vulgaris *L.* COMMON CARLINE THISTLE. A very spiny biennial 10–60 cm. tall, with a basal rosette which withers when the stiff fl. stalk appears. Lvs. 7–13 cm. long, cottony-downy especially below, narrow-lance-shaped, with numerous stiff spines; stem-lvs. clasping. Heads 2–5 in a cluster (corymb), 2–4 cm. across, with inner bracts long and narrow, spine-tipped, straw-yellow, outer bracts green or purplish, cottony.
⚜ Meadows, stony places, open woods, preferring chalk and limestone. To 1740 m. Alps. (Britain.) July–September.

C. stricta *Ry.*: almost identical to *C. vulgaris* and best regarded as a sub-species: lvs. almost hairless, held close to the stem, with small teeth and spines. 1500–2500 m.; Savoy, very rare.

JURINEA *Cass.* **J. bocconi** *Guss.* (including **J. humilis** *DC.*, **J. gouani** *Ry.*). A rosette-forming perennial with very short or no fl. stem; lvs. oblong in outline, cut into narrow, pointed, well separated parallel lobes, white-cottony below, greyish and pitted on top. Fl. head pinkish red, solitary in centre of rosette, 2–3 cm. across (rarely 1½ cm.); florets all tubular; bracts narrow, pointed, arching outwards at tip. Pappus of many toothed hairs in several rows, forming a ring at the base.   *
⚜ Dry slopes, on limestone. To 2000 m. Pyrenees. June–August.   **804**

BERARDIA *Vill.* **B. subacaulis** *L.* (**Onopordum rotundifolium** *All.*). A curious, entirely white-woolly, rosette-forming perennial with shortly stalked, rhomboid to rounded, rarely toothed lvs. to 10 cm. long. Fl. head solitary, to 6 cm. long and 4 cm. wide, in the centre of the rosette, stalk usually very

short but occasionally 5–15 cm. long; fls. whitish, projecting beyond the large, long-pointed, triangular, cottony bracts. Pappus of toothed hairs, twisted at the base.
❋ Stony places, screes, debris, on limestone and schist. 1500–2500 m. W. Alps (Maritimes to Dauphiné). Rare and local. July–August. **809**

SAUSSUREA *DC.* Perennials with spirally arranged, non-spiny lvs. and fl. heads either solitary or in clusters (corymbs). Florets all tubular, hermaphrodite, the anthers projecting and conspicuous. Receptacle flat; bracts in many overlapping rows. Pappus with 1 row of persistent hairs and an inner, deciduous row forming a ring.

S. alpina (*L.*) *DC.* (Serratula alpina *L.*). 5–50 cm. tall, with scaly horizontal rootstock, making rosettes on short branches; fl. stems leafy, unbranched, grooved and sometimes woolly. Rosette lvs. narrow-oval to lance-shaped; stem lvs. narrower, widely spaced, not exceeding the fl. heads, lower ones with winged stalks, upper stalkless, all lvs. more or less toothed, white-cottony below. Fl. heads in a small dense cluster on short or no stalks, fragrant, purplish, 1½–2 cm. long; anthers dark purple; inner bracts with long hairs.
❋ Meadows, stony places, ridges. 1500–3000 m. C. and E. Pyrenees; Alps. Norway to 2100 m. (Britain: to 1300 m. in Scotland.) July–September. **806**

S. depressa *G. & G.* Resembling a dwarf form of *S. alpina* and nowadays considered a subspecies, but with semi-prostrate 3–9 cm. stems, lvs. close together, much broader, more triangular, with pronounced teeth; fls. purplish blue, very rarely white.
❋ Debris, screes, on acid rocks. W. Alps. To 3100 m. July–September. **805**

S. discolor (*Willd.*) *DC.* (S. alpina *var.* lapathifolia *Fiori*, **Serratula discolor**

Willd.). 5–35 cm. tall. Lvs. long-triangular, lower truncated or heart-shaped at base, without wings on stalk, upper lance-shaped, stem-clasping; all lvs. irregularly toothed, white-cottony below. Fls. 3–8 in a tight cluster, fragrant, dark rose-red to violet.
❋ Rock crevices, debris, on granite. 1400–2800 m. Alps. July–September. **808**

S. pygmaea (*Jacq.*) *Spreng.* (Cnicus pygmaeus *L.*, **Carduus pygmaeus** *Jacq.*). A rosette-forming plant (3)5–20 cm. tall, with vertical rootstock and long narrow pointed lvs. 3–7 cm. long, 3–8 cm. wide, sometimes with distinct teeth, notches or wavy edges, sometimes entirely plain-sided, densely covering the woolly stem. Fl. head solitary, 2–4 cm. long, to 3 cm. broad, violet-purple.
❋ Rock crevices, screes, stony places, on limestone. 1600–2550 m. E. Alps (not Switzerland). July–August. **807**

CARDUUS *L.* Annuals to perennials with spirally arranged, sometimes divided, usually spiny lvs. Stems often branched; fl. heads solitary or clustered with usually spiny-tipped, overlapping bracts in many rows. Receptacle very bristly and deeply pitted. Florets all tubular, hermaphrodite. Pappus of rough hairs in many rows, joined at base.

Besides the species described, several others reach alpine levels: *C. carlinae-folius* Lam. and *C. medius* Gouan are both truly alpine, ranging from 1800–2500 m.; others occasionally seen above 1800 m. are *C. acanthoides* L., to 3000 m., *C. chrysacanthus* Ten., to 2300 m. (C. and S. Apennines), *C. crispus* L., to 1900 m., and *C. nutans* L., the MUSK THISTLE, to 2500 m.

C. carlinoides *Gouan.* PYRENEAN THISTLE. A white-downy perennial 20–50 cm. tall, with winged, much branched, very spiny stem. Lvs. long and narrow, cut into divisions almost

reduced into yellowish, very prickly spines. Fl. head 1½–2 cm. long, rose-red, purplish or white, in dense clusters.
❀ Screes, stony places, meadows. To 2200 m. Pyrenees. July–September. 810

C. defloratus L. ALPINE THISTLE. A slender perennial (10)20–80 (100) cm. tall, with at most 3 branches, leafless and wingless in upper part; lvs. long, narrow, cut into fairly regular, toothed, spiny lobes of very varying size. Fl. heads solitary, leaning sideways when mature, 1½–2½ (4½) cm. across, rose-red to purplish, egg-shaped, the florets finally spreading outwards. Bracts of very unequal lengths, short-spined.
❀ Meadows, stony slopes, open woods. To 3000 m. Pyrenees; Alps; Apennines. June–October. 811

C. personatus (L.) Jacq. MOUNTAIN THISTLE. A stout perennial 50–200 (270) cm. tall, with short branches; stem winged and with very short spines. Lvs. soft, white-cottony below, oval lance-shaped, tapering to both ends, with many small irregular teeth and non-spiny hairs, Fl. heads several, 1½–2 cm. across, purplish red, virtually stalkless, in tight clusters. Bracts very narrow, not spiny, lower spreading almost as widely as florets at maturity.
❀ Meadows, damp woods, streamsides, on limestone. To 2300 m. Alps; N. and C. Apennines. July–August. 812

CIRSIUM *Mill.* Alpine species perennials with spirally arranged, variously divided, usually prickly lvs. Fl. heads solitary or clustered. Florets all tubular, hermaphrodite or female. Fl. heads otherwise as in *Carduus*, but pappus of feathery hairs in many rows, joined at base; many species have previously been named under *Carduus*.
Besides the species described several less distinctive of these thistles may reach 2000 m.

C. spinosissimum (L.) *Scop.* SPINIEST THISTLE. A perennial 20–50 (120) cm. tall, branching, with long, fairly narrow deeply cut, very spiny, more or less downy lvs, crowded on the stem, the upper stem clasping and surrounding the dense cluster of whitish to yellow 2–2½ cm. fl. heads. Bract spines longer than the very conspicuous bracts.
❀ Meadows, stony places, screes, favouring damp places. To 3100 m. Alps. July–September. 814

C. glabrum *DC.* Similar to *C. spinosissimum*, but 10–40 cm. tall, not downy; upper stem-lvs. not clasping, bract spines shorter than bracts.
❀ Rivers, ravines, damp places, To 1800 m. W. and C. Pyrenees. July–September.

C. eriophorum (L.) *Scop.* WOOLLY THISTLE. A stout biennial to perennial 60–150 cm. tall, with thick taproot; stem woolly, furrowed, wingless, branching. Lowest lvs. up to 60 cm. long, stalked, upper stalkless, partly clasping; all lvs. white-woolly below, oval-oblong in outline, deeply cut into narrow, well-spaced, spine-tipped lobes of similar size. Upper lvs. may or may not exceed the fl. head, which is basically rounded but may be narrower or broader than high, usually 4–7 cm. across, woolly, with broad, triangular, spine-tipped bracts in many rows; florets reddish purple, occasionally white.
❀ Waste and stony places, paths, scrub. To 2100 m. Pyrenees; Alps; Apennines. (Britain: an endemic subspecies to 700 m.) July–September. 815

C. erisithales (*Jacq.*) *Scop.* (**C. ochroleucum** *DC.*). A perennial 30–150 (200) cm. tall, with slender, usually unbranched stems, leafless in upper part. Lvs. few, dark green, cut nearly to midrib into fairly even, pointed, toothed, barely spiny segments, and with distinct clasping lobes at base. Fl. heads often 1, or 2–5, lemon-yellow, rarely purplish red, to 3 cm. across. ✳ Woods, stony slopes, meadows, streams, preferring calcareous soils. To 2000 m. Cevennes; Alps. July–September. **816**

C. heterophyllum (*L.*) *All.* MELANCHOLY THISTLE. A stout perennial 50–150 cm. tall, with usually unbranched, grooved, wingless, woolly stem, Lower lvs. 20–40 cm. long, 4–8 cm. wide, elliptic lance-shaped, with fine teeth, long-stalked; lower stem-lvs. with stem clasping lobes at base, and often several upward-pointing segments; upper lvs. narrow, undivided; all lvs. soft, white-felted below, softly prickly on edges. Fl. heads often 1, sometimes 2–3, 3½–5 cm. long and 2 cm. across, red-purple, with long, spreading, deeply divided florets. Bracts purple-tinged.   ✳ ✳ Damp meadows and woods, marshes, gullies, on acid soils. To 2350 m. Pyrenees; Alps. Norway to 1680 m. (Britain to 1000 m.) June–August. **817**

C. acaulon (*L.*) *Scop.* (**C. acaule** (*L.*) *Web.*). STEMLESS THISTLE. A rosette-forming perennial with stalked, oblong lance-shaped lvs. 10–15 cm. long, 2–3 cm. wide, cut almost to midrib into rounded, spiny lobes. Fl. head normally stalkless (very seldom on stalk to 30 cm.—*var.* **caulescens** *DC.*), 3–5 cm. long and broad, with bright red-purple florets and purplish, spiny-tipped bracts.   ✳ ✳ Dry and over-grazed meadows, waste places, denuded slopes, preferring calcareous soils. To 2550 m. Pyrenees; Alps; N. and C. Apennines. (Britain.) July–September. **813**

ONOPORDUM L. (also spelt **ONOPORDON**). O. acaulon L. A virtually stemless biennial with a rosette of 5–25 cm. lvs., white-cottony, deeply slashed and very spiny, rising upwards around

the 1–3 (12) whitish, 1½ cm. fl. heads. Receptacle pitted; involucre bracts numerous, hard and spiny; florets all tubular, hermaphrodite; pappus of many rows of hairs. ✳ Dry slopes, stony places. To 1900 m. Pyrenees. Local. July–August. **1166**

O. acanthium L., the tall, handsome SCOTCH THISTLE, is often sub-alpine, and attains 1500 m. in Tyrol.

SERRATULA L. SAW-WORT. Non-spiny perennials with spirally arranged lvs. and fls. either grouped (corymbs) or solitary. Receptacle flat, with many chaffy scales among the florets which are all tubular; sexes variously arranged. Pappus of many rows of stiff, rough hairs, the outermost shortest, not joined at base.

S. tinctoria L. *ssp.* **macrocephala** (*Bert.*) *Rouy.* (*var.* **alpina** *G. & G.*). ALPINE SAW-WORT. 10–40 cm. tall, with seldom-branching stems carrying lvs. elliptic in outline, divided into many small, opposite, toothed segments and 1 large, broad lance-shaped terminal one; the lower lvs. stalked. Fl. heads purplish, occasionally whitish, 6–12 mm. across, 15–20 mm. long, on very short stalks forming a dense terminal cluster; bracts violet. ✳ Stony places, scrub. 1600–2400 m. Pyrenees; Alps; N. Apennines. (The species in Britain.) July–October. **1241**

S. lycopifolia (*Vill.*) *Kern.* (**S. heterophylla** *Desf.*, **Carduus lycopifolius** *Vill.*). 40–90 cm. tall, with creeping stock. Lvs. at base of slender stem varying from pointed-elliptic and slightly toothed, to deeply and jaggedly cut into irregular segments. Fl. head solitary, 2½–4 cm. long, with neat round involucre and spreading red-purple fls. ✳ Meadows, scrub. To 1800 m. E. Pyrenees (doubtful record); S.W. Alps. June–July. **1242**

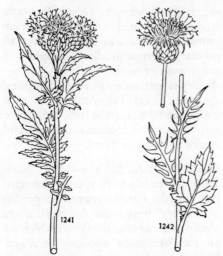

1241. *Serratula tinctoria ssp. macrocephala*
1242. *S. lycopifolia.*

CENTAUREA *L.* KNAPWEED. Alpine species perennials, non-spiny, with spirally arranged lvs. Fl. heads characterised by the rounded involucre of many overlapping bracts each ending in a scaly or membraneous appendage which is variously cut, toothed, spiny, hairy or comb-like, its shape often being the diagnostic feature. Florets in alpine species mainly tubular, hermaphrodite, with a few large, outspread, outer neuter florets, the ligule often divided. Pappus of rough hairs in several rows, not joined at base. Seeds flattened, smooth, unridged.

Besides the species described the following exceed 1500 m.: *C. transalpina* Schleich. ex DC., to 2200 m.; *C. debeauxii* G. & G. ssp. *thuillieri* (*C. pratensis* Thuill.) and *C. jacea* L., to 2000 m. The annual CORNFLOWER, *C. cyanus* L., is recorded to 1780 m. as a field weed.

C. montana *L.* MOUNTAIN CORNFLOWER. A variable plant 10–80 cm. tall, typically with bluish or greyish, narrow-lance-shaped, sometimes slightly toothed lvs. tapering at both ends and running down the stem at the base so that the stem appears continually winged (sometimes only partly so: **C. semidecurrens** *Jord.*). Fl. head solitary, 6–8 cm. across, blue to blue-violet; marginal florets few, with several strap-shaped, pointed segments. Bracts 2–2½ cm. long, oblong, with a pointed crest of dark hair-like teeth.

⚜ Meadows, woods, rocks. To 2124 m. Pyrenees; Alps; Apennines. May–July (October). **818, 1243**

C. scabiosa *L.* *ssp.* **alpestris** (*Hegets.*) *Hayek* (var. **alpina** *Gaud.*). ALPINE KNAPWEED. A variable plant 20–70 cm. tall, seldom branched, with stiff, well-spaced lvs. of roughly broad-lance-shaped outline, cut to midrib into wide-spaced lance-shaped lobes; lower lvs. stalked. Fl. head usually solitary, 4–5 cm. across, pale to deep pink or purplish; marginal florets many, with several very fine segments. Bracts 18–22 mm. long, oblong, with a dark arrow-shaped appendage fringed with long hairs.

⚜ Meadows, scrub, open woods. To 2600 m. Pyrenees; Alps; N. and C. Apennines. (The species in Britain.) July–August **819, 1244**

C. nervosa *Willd.* PLUME KNAPWEED. A greyish plant, usually with several fl. heads on the stout (5)10–40 cm. stem. Lvs. narrow-lance-shaped, tapering into the stem, rough at edges, more or less deeply toothed, teeth pointing towards tip. Fl. head 6–8 cm. across, purplish red; marginal florets many, long, with several fine segments. Bracts 2–2½ cm. long, narrow-elliptic, surmounted by an appendage like a recurving feather, longer than the bract, with long, spreading, brownish hairs, giving the involucre a densely hairy appearance.*

⚜ Meadows, scrub. To 2600 m. Alps; N. Apennines. July–August. **820, 1245**

C. uniflora *Turra.* Very similar to *C. nervosa* in general appearance, but always with 1 fl. head, lvs. not toothed, whitish, soft. Bracts shorter, elliptic, with a broad, partly solid, partly feathery appendage a little longer than broad. ✤ Meadows, scrub. 1500–2500 m. W. Alps. Rare. July–August. **1246**

C. raetica *Moritzi*. RHAETIAN KNAPWEED. Very like *C. nervosa*, 10–50 cm. tall, but lvs. with more, smaller teeth. Fls. purple-red. Bracts 12–15 mm. long, elliptic, waisted, with feathery appendage about as long, not recurving.* ✤ Open woods, scrub. To 2200 m. S.C. Alps. Local. July–August. **1247**

C. phrygia L. WIG KNAPWEED. Not unlike *C. nervosa*, but a stouter, 15–80 cm. plant with lance-shaped lvs. not markedly tapering at base, very lightly and regularly toothed, with pronounced midrib. Fl. head deep purple. Bracts 1½–2 cm. long, narrow-elliptic, surmounted by a dark, rhomboidal, recurving appendage as long, with feathery hairs forming a triangle. ✤ Shady, grassy slopes, scrub, woods. To 2200 m. C. and S.C. Alps; N. and C. Apennines. July–September. **1248**

RHAPONTICUM *Lam.* (also *Adans.*). Very stout perennials with large solitary heads; florets all tubular, hermaphrodite. Involucre of large overlapping bracts with membranous edges or appendages. Pappus of fragile toothed hairs in several rows, the innermost longer than the rest. Seeds flattened, with a longitudinal ridge on each side.

This genus is now included in *Leuzea* DC. Before that some botanists replaced it in *Centaurea*, but it is not only distinct by reason of the pappus, bract and seed characters quoted above, and by having no ray florets, but visually so on account of the huge size, and it seems worth while maintaining it as a separate genus.

R. cynaroides *Less.* (**Serratula centauroides** (*L.*) *P.F.*, **S. cynaroides** *DC.*, **Centaurea rhapontica** L. in part, **Cnicus centauroides** L.). CARDOON KNAPWEED. 80–120 cm. tall, seldom branched, with rosy purple fl. head 6–7 cm. across, and very large lvs., finely hairy on top, white-cottony below, cut almost to midrib into wide lobes, themselves further divided on lowest lvs. Bracts brown, narrow, pointed, toothed on edges. * ✤ Steep rocky ridges. Pyrenees. Rare. To 2000 m. August–September. **821**

R. scariosum *Lam.* (**Centaurea scariosa** *Rouy*, **C. rhapontica** L. in part, **Serratula rhaponticum** *DC.*). GIANT KNAPWEED. 40–100 cm. tall, with rosy purple fl. head 5–7 cm. across. Lvs. very

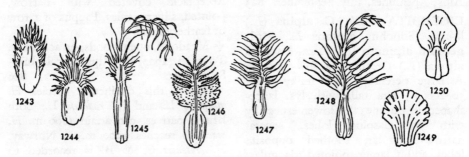

Involucral bracts in *Centaurea* and *Rhaponticum*. 1243. *C. montana*. 1244. *C. scabiosa ssp. alpestris*. 1245. *C. nervosa*. 1246. *C. uniflora*. 1247. *C. raetica*. 1248. *C. phrygia*. 1249. *R. scariosum*. 1250. *R. heleniifolium*.

large, lance-shaped, lowest about 4 times longer than broad, upper narrower, lightly toothed, greyish below. Bracts brown, rounded, with hairs on the irregularly notched membrane.   *

✤ Damp meadows, rocks, on granite. 1400–2600 m. Alps. Rare. July–September.   **822, 1249**

R. heleniifolium *G. & G.* (**R. lyratum** (*Bell.*) *Hayek*, **Centaurea heleniifolia** *Schultz*, also *Rouy*). Similar to *R. scariosum*, and often considered a subspecies. 60–150 cm. tall, often branched; lvs. much broader, rather truncated at base, white-cottony below. Bracts hairless and with whitish, usually entire membranes.   *

✤ Damp meadows, rocks, on limestone. 1400–2200 m. Alps. Rare. July–September.   **1250**

PRENANTHES *L.* **P. purpurea** *L.* (**Chondrilla purpurea** *Lam.*). 30–150 (230) cm. tall with bluish, somewhat fiddle-shaped, lightly toothed lvs. clasping the stem with rounded basal lobes. Fl. heads violet or purplish red, to 2 cm. across, typically hanging at the ends of stalks of varying lengths, the whole forming a very open, conical inflorescence. Fls. 2–5 in a head; pappus of toothed hairs.

✤ Damp woods, in the shade of rocks, streamsides. To 2040 m. Pyrenees; Alps; Apennines. July–September.   **823**

CICERBITA *Wallr.* **C. alpina** (*L.*) *Wallr.* (**Sonchus alpinus** *L.*, **Mulgedium alpinum** (*L.*) *Less.*, **Lactuca alpina** (*L.*) *Gray*). BLUE SOW-THISTLE. A large perennial with milky juice, 50–200(+) cm. tall, with lvs. lanceshaped in outline, the lower especially with stem-clasping lobes, several narrow-triangular, toothed opposite lobes, and 1 larger, pointed-triangular, toothed terminal lobe. Fl. heads pale blue, 2–3 cm. across, stalked, in a narrow, sometimes slightly branched

spike (raceme) which has reddish glandular hairs on the stalks and purplish bracts. Pappus of toothed hairs.

✤ Woods, rocks, in moist places. To 2200 m. Pyrenees; Alps; N. Apennines. (Britain: very rare.) July–September.   **824**

LACTUCA *L.* **L. perennis** *L.* MOUNTAIN LETTUCE. A perennial with milky juice, 20–70 cm. tall, with thick stems and soft blue-green lvs., long-oblong in outline, deeply divided into narrow segments, clasping the stem with narrow lobes; upper stem-lvs. small and linear. Fls. blue or lilac, 3–4 cm. across, forming a flattish head. Fruit black, with a long beak carrying the pappus of toothed hairs.

✤ Open stony places, fields. To 2120 m. Alps; Apennines. May–August. **825**

Lactuca sativa L., the edible LETTUCE, is cultivated to 2500 m. One or two other, weedy species just exceed 1500 m.

HYPOCHOERIS *L.* **H. uniflora** *Vill.* GIANT CATS-EAR. A stout perennial 15–50 (80) cm. tall, with pale green, lanceshaped, lightly toothed lvs. mainly in rosette. Stem with 3–5 lvs., densely hairy, thick, swelling markedly below the tapering, almost conical involucre of many overlapping rows of lance-shaped bracts. Fl. head yellow, 4–5 cm. across. Receptacle covered with narrow, pointed, silvery scales. Pappus of 1 row of feathery hairs.

✤ Meadows, open woods, on acid soils. To 2600 (2900) m. Alps. Local. July–September.   **826**

Besides this distinctive species *H. maculata* L. and *H. radicata* L., both British natives, can attain 1800 m. *H. maculata* reaches 1200 m. in Norway. *H. cretensis* C. & B. is recorded to 2150 m. in C. and S. Apennines.

APOSERIS *Necker.* **A. foetida** (*L.*) *Less.* A slender perennial 5–25 cm. tall, with lvs. all in rosette, oblong in outline, cut almost to midrib into regular, opposed, triangular, toothed lobes. Fl. head golden yellow, 2½–3 cm. across, with relatively few florets; bracts narrow, pointed, in 1 row; pappus absent.

❀ Woods, scrub, meadows, streamsides, preferring limestone. To 2200 m. Alps; Apuan Alps; Apennines. Local. June–August. **827**

SCORZONERA *L.* VIPERGRASS. Alpine species perennials with milky juice, thick cylindrical rootstocks, and long erect fl. stems. Lvs. almost all basal, long and more or less narrow, sheathing at base. Fl. heads usually solitary, fairly large, opening out flat only in full sun, with many rows of overlapping bracts; pappus long, narrowly conical, of several rows of feathery hairs and sometimes a few unfeathered hairs.

S. rosea *W. & K.* PINK VIPERGRASS. 15–60 cm. tall, with dark brown hairs on rootstock, and very long, flat lvs. 3–4½ mm. across, some on the stem. Fl. head pink, to 5 cm. across when open. *

❀ Meadows, scrub, open woods, stony places, on limestone. To 2000 m. S.E. Alps. June–August. **829**

S. aristata *Ram.* BEARDED VIPERGRASS. 10–50 cm. tall, with scales on rootstock. Lvs. very long and narrow, all basal or sometimes 1 on the usually cottony stem. Fl. head golden yellow, 3–4 cm. across when open.

❀ Meadows, on limestone. To 2300 m. Pyrenees; S.C. and E. Alps; Apuan Alps; N. Apennines. July–August. **830**

S. austriaca *Willd.* AUSTRIAN VIPERGRASS. 5–40 cm. tall, with many blackish hairs on rootstock. Lvs. variable, narrow-oval to lance-shaped, exceptionally to 4–5 cm. across (*var.* **latifolia**

Vis.); stem-lvs. small, linear. Fl. head golden yellow, 2–4 cm. across.

❀ Rocks, arid meadows, copses, preferring limestone. To 2800 m. Pyrenees (*var. latifolia* only); W. Alps (at subalpine levels in E. Alps). May–July. **831**

S. humilis *L.* DWARF VIPERGRASS. Very like *S. austriaca*, but rootstock not hairy; fl. heads 2–5 cm. across.

❀ Damp meadows, marshes, clearings, heaths. To 1700 m. Tyrol (common at sub-alpine levels elsewhere). (Britain: dubiously native.) May–July.

TRAGOPOGON *L.* **T. pratensis** *L.* GOATSBEARD, JACK-GO-TO-BED-AT-NOON, MEADOW SALSIFY. Annual, biennial or perennial, 30–70 cm. tall, with long brown taproot; closely related to *Scorzonera*, but has involucre of only 1 row of very long pointed bracts, joined at base, which may project beyond the florets of the bright golden yellow, 4–6 cm. fl. heads. These close at midday or in dull weather: the closed fl. is narrowly conical. Lvs. narrow-lance-shaped, with long point, sheathing at base; stem-lvs. similar, stem-clasping. Pappus of 1 row of hairs, densely feathery, including 5 unfeathered hairs, the whole forming a large feathery ball when fruit matures.

❀ Meadows, damp places, roadsides. To 2565 m. Pyrenees; Alps; Apennines. (Britain.) May–July(October). **832**

T. dubius Scop. reaches 2130 m. in the Apennines.

CREPIS *L.* HAWKSBEARD. A very large genus with many rather similar alpine species; only a few examples are described. Alpine species perennial, with spirally arranged lvs.; stems often branched; fl. heads often in clusters. Florets usually yellow; bracts many, equal-sized, usually in 1 main row; receptacle flat, with pits edged by teeth or hairs. Pappus of unbranched hairs in several rows. Many of the species have previously been named under *Soyeria*, ~~.nd~~ and also *Hieracium*.

C. pontana (*L.*) *DT.* (**C. montana** *Tausch.*). MOUNTAIN HAWKSBEARD. A downy perennial 20–60 cm. tall, with stout stem thickening under the 4–5½ cm. yellow fl. head. Involucre covered in long yellowish hairs. Lvs. oblong, with small pointed teeth, more or less stem-clasping. *

❀ Meadows, open woods, preferring limestone. 1100–2500 m. Alps. June–August. **828**

C. raetica *Hegets.* PLUMED HAWKSBEARD. Normally 2–6 cm. tall, with fl. stem barely longer than lvs., exceptionally to 30 cm. Stem unbranched, thickened below involucre, both covered with long soft yellowish hairs. Fl. head yellow, to 3 cm. across. Lvs. almost all basal, oblong to elliptical, more or less toothed. *

❀ Stony places, screes, thin turf. 2000–3000 m. W. Alps (very rare); C. Alps (Switzerland, Tyrol). July–September. **836**

C. terglouensis (*Hacq.*) *Kern.* (also spelt **terglovensis**). TRIGLAV HAWKSBEARD. 2–7 cm. tall; stem unbranched, leafy, and thickened below involucre. Upper part of stem, upper stem lvs. and involucre covered with dark hairs. Fl. head yellow, to 5 cm. across. Lvs. raggedly cut into deep lobes pointing towards base.

❀ Stony places, debris, on limestone. 1800–2860 m. C. and E. Alps. July–August. **837**

C. aurea (*L.*) *Cass.* GOLDEN HAWKSBEARD. 5–30 cm. tall; stem slender, seldom branched, virtually leafless. Fl. heads 2–3 cm. across, usually orange-yellow to reddish (despite the name); involucre covered with long black or yellowish hairs. Lvs. in an often massive basal rosette, smooth and shiny, lance-

shaped in outline with many short lobes pointing towards base.

❀ Short turf, stony places, gravels, preferring acid soils. To 2900 m. Alps; Apennines. June–September. **838**

C. pygmaea *L.* PYGMY HAWKSBEARD. 2–15 cm. tall, with long underground runners and forking stem. Fl. heads pale to golden yellow, to 2 cm. across, the involucre usually hairy. Lvs. few, not in rosette, thick, often reddish, sometimes cottony-haired, with often very long, wavy-winged stalks and oval or heart-shaped, toothed blades.

❀ Damp screes, rocky slopes, on acid soils and schist. 1600–3000 m. Pyrenees; W. Alps; Abruzzi. July–August. **839**

C. jacquinii *Tausch.* ROCK HAWKSBEARD. 5–30 cm. tall, often branched near the top of the slender, leafy stem. Fl. heads yellow, about 2 cm. across, with relatively few, broad-rayed florets. Lvs. long and narrow, the upper ones especially reduced to the midrib and narrow, irregular lobes.

❀ Stony places, avalanche gullies. To 2970 m. E. Alps. July–August. **841**

C. incarnata (*Jacq*). *Tausch.* PINK HAWKSBEARD. 8–30 (60) cm. tall, branching near the top of the slender, leafless stem. Fl. heads less than 2 cm. across, flesh-pink or white, occasionally yellow (*var.* **lutea** *Tausch.*), 2–7 in individual loose clusters (corymbs). Lvs. in basal rosette, narrow-elliptic, tapering into short stem, more or less toothed.

This plant is now renamed *C. praemorsa* (*L.*) Tausch ssp. *dinarica* (G. Beck) P. D. Sell.

❀ Meadows, stony places. To 1800 m. S. and S.E. Alps. *Var. lutea* only in Switzerland (Tessin). May. **840**

TARAXACUM (*L.*) *Boehm.* DANDELION. The COMMON DANDELION, *T. officinale* Weber, is a widespread plant, extremely variable owing mainly to apomictic increase (see p. 373). Many forms of this, and of the very similar, narrower-leaved T. *palustre* (Lyons) DC., have been named. Although often treated as subspecies, it is perhaps easier to consider them as separate entities. Several are high alpines; three are described as examples. All have solitary fl. heads on unbranched stems, with pitted receptacle and pappus of many rows of rough hairs. Besides these, T. *cornutum* Dt., with curiously hooked bracts, reaches 2050 m. in Norway.

T. alpinum *Hoppe* (**T. officinale** *Web. ssp.* **alpinum** (*Hoppe*) *Chev.*). ALPINE DANDELION. Perennial, 5–20 cm. tall, with lvs. in rosette, soft, lance-shaped, jaggedly cut into lobes pointing towards base. Fl. head 2½–3 cm. across, yellow, with outer row of bracts recurving like a row of hooks, often dark green. *

⁂ Meadows, debris, snow-beds. 1200–3350 m. Pyrenees; Alps; Apennines. July–September. **833**

T. pacheri *Schultz-Bip.* (**T. officinale** *ssp.* **reichenbachii** *Hut.*). BRENNER DANDELION. 2–6 cm. tall, with orange or red-streaked fl. heads 1½ cm. across.
⁂ Dry heaths, sheep pastures. 2000–2900 m. C. and E. Alps. July–September.

T. schroeteranum *Handel-Maz.* (**T. palustre** (*Lyons*) *DC. ssp.* **schroeterianum** (*S.-B.*) *Breistr.*). A slender perennial 3–35 cm. tall; fl. stem often prostrate; lvs. with few, triangular lobes. Fl. heads small.
⁂ Marshes. To 2750 m. Alps. July–September.

LEONTODON L. HAWKBIT. Perennial, rosette-forming plants with a single fl. head on unbranched stems. Fls. yellow. Bracts in several over-lapping rows; receptacle pitted; pappus usually of 2 rows of hairs, the outer plain, inner feathery.

Besides the species described, the common L. *autumnalis* L. may reach 2616 m., and L. *hispidus* L., 2700 m. Both are British natives; the first attains 1000 m. in Scotland and Ireland, and 1600 m. in Norway. Other species reaching alpine levels are L. *crispus* Vill., to 2500 m.; L. *croceus* Haenke, to 2280 m.; and L. *incanus* (L.) Schrank, to 2250 m.

L. montanus *Lam.* MOUNTAIN HAWK-BIT. 3–10 cm. tall, with fairly stout, hairy stem carrying a short, thick involucre covered with long blackish hairs. Fl. head 2–3 cm. across. Lvs. lance-shaped to elliptic, more or less toothed or lobed, usually hairless.
⁂ Stony meadows, gravels, on lime-stone and schist. 1750–2925 m. Alps; Apennines. July–August. **834**

L. pyrenaicus *Gouan.* PYRENEAN HAWK-BIT. 10–30 cm. tall, with slender stem carrying a few scale-like lvs. Fl. heads often orange-yellow, 2–2½ cm. across. Lvs. narrow-elliptic, lightly toothed, sometimes with a few hairs.
⁂ Meadows, stony places, scrub, on acid soils. To 3000 (3250) m. Pyrenees; Alps; Apuan Alps; N. Apennines. June–August. **835**

HIERACIUM L. HAWKWEED. Perennials with lvs. spirally arranged or in basal rosettes; fl. heads typically clustered, but sometimes solitary. Bracts in several irregular, overlapping rows. Receptacle with toothed- or hairy-edged pits. Florets typically yellow, but sometimes orange or red. Pappus of 1 or 2 rows of stiff hairs.

Owing to apomictic increase (see p. 373) there is a fantastic number of stable forms of *Hieracium* which can be treated as species: at a conservative estimate there are 260 in Britain alone, and at least 10,000 in the North Temperate regions of the world. Most of the alpine species are dull, rather similar plants which are difficult to identify, and only 5 are described here, although there are at least 50 which exceed 2000 m., and several which reach 3000 m., including the common British weed *H. pilosella* L., the MOUSE-EAR HAWKWEED, which also attains 1230 m. in Norway.

H. humile *Jacq.* DWARF HAWKWEED. 5–30 cm. tall, covered with stiff hairs, with lvs. in basal rosette and slender, slightly forked, often zigzag stem with a few lf.-like bracts. Lvs. very variable, typically elliptic in outline and cut into unequal, jagged lobes with upper quarter or third uncut. Fl. head yellow, 2–2½ cm. across.
✤ Limestone and feldspar rocks. Pyrenees; Alps; C. and S. Apennines. To 2500 m. June–August. **842**

H. alpinum *L.* (including **H. pumilum** *Hoppe*). ALPINE HAWKWEED. (5)10–20, (35) cm. tall, covered with soft, whitish black-based hairs and black-based glands. Lvs. mostly basal, deep green, narrow-elliptic, more or less toothed. Stem fairly stout, with 1 or 2 small lvs., and usually a solitary yellow fl. head to 3 cm. across. Involucre large, swollen, very hairy.
✤ Rocks, meadows, screes, on acid soils. To 3255 m. Alps; Apuan Alps; N. and C. Apennines. (Britain: Scottish mountains.) July–August. **843**

H. holosericeum *Back.* SHAGGY HAWKWEED. Like *H. alpinum*, but only 5–15 cm. tall, with very long white, black-based hairs. Lvs. pale green.
✤ Rocks, screes. To 3000 m. Alps. (Britain: montane.) July–August.

H. lanatum *(L.) Vill.* (**H. tomentosum** *All.*). WOOLLY HAWKWEED. 10–50 cm. tall, with thick, oblong to rhomboid, entirely white-cottony lvs., sometimes lightly toothed, almost all basal. Stems stout, slightly branched, with small lf.-like bracts. Fl. heads yellow, 2½–3 cm. across, usually 3–7 per branch.
✤ Rocks, debris, clearings, dry places. To 2000 (2450) m. W. Alps (only Valais in Switzerland); Apuan Alps. May–July. **844**

H. aurantiacum *L.* GRIM THE COLLIER, DEVIL'S PAINTBRUSH, DIRTY DICK, ORANGE HAWKWEED. 20–50 cm. tall, hairy all over. Lvs. mostly basal, narrow-oblong, dark green. Stem with few, smaller lvs., unbranched except at top where short stalks carry 1–6 brick-red fl. heads 1½ cm. across in a tight cluster.
✤ Meadows, preferring acid soils and schist. To 2600 m. Alps. (Britain: naturalised.) June–August. **845**

CONIFER TRIBE

Mainly evergreen trees, rarely shrubs, with resin. *Larix* deciduous among European species. Male fls. in catkins or cones, female fls. in cones which are solitary or 2–4 together. Fruit a fleshy berry or cone.

TAXACEAE—YEW FAMILY

TAXUS *L.* **T. baccata** *L.* YEW. The only European species. A tree to 20 m. tall, with a very broad, thick trunk and many irregularly arranged branches of differing sizes. Leafy from base. Bark flaky, thin, red-brown. Lvs. in a flat, spreading row on either side of stems, linear, flat, to 3 cm. long, dark green, paler underneath, with obvious midrib on both sides; lf. edges rolled under, tip with a short sharp point. Sexes on separate plants. Male fls. in small cones clustered in lf. axils at ends of branches, scales reddish brown, pollen yellow. Female fls. solitary or paired in lf. axils. Fruit a characteristic, bright red fleshy cup (*aril*), containing 1 large hard seed up to 1 cm. across. Poisonous.

❊ Woods, chalk downs, limestone screes; seldom on acid soils. To 1800 m. Pyrenees; Alps; Apennines. (Britain.) Flowers, March–April; fruit, August–September. **875**

PINACEAE—PINE FAMILY

Trees, seldom shrubs, with many branches in regular whorls. Lvs. long and narrow, smooth or very slightly toothed, arranged spirally around the stem. Male and female fls. in cones of many spirally arranged scales; male small, usually grouped near shoot tips, pollen normally yellow; female large and usually woody. Seeds usually winged.

This family is much cultivated.

ABIES *Mill.* **A. alba** *Mill.* SILVER FIR. A pyramidal tree 20–50 m. tall. Bark green, smooth when young, becoming ridged, greyish and scaly when old. Twigs grey, downy. Lvs. 1–3 cm. long, shiny dark green, silvery grey beneath, stalks very short, tips notched. Male cones with reddish brown scales. Female cones upright, green ripening to brown, cylindric, to 14 cm. long, scales closely overlapping, bracts protruding between scales and curved back.

❊ Woods, forests. 800–2100 m. Pyrenees; Alps; Apennines. (Britain: introduced, cultivated.) Flowers, April–May; fruit, October. **876**

PICEA *A. Dietr.* **P. abies** (*L.*) *Karst.* (**P. excelsa** *Link*). NORWAY SPRUCE. A pyramidal tree to 60 m. tall. Bark brown, scaly, twigs reddish or yellowish brown, hairless or slightly downy, deeply grooved. Lvs. almost 4-sided, 1–2 cm. long, tips with a short hard point. Lf. bases inserted in a prominent, short, woody projection which remains after lvs. have fallen. Male cones with brown scales. Female cones cylindrical, pendulous, 8–15 cm. long, dark reddish brown; scales thin, unevenly toothed at the tip.

❊ Forests. To 2200 m. Pyrenees; Alps; Apennines. Norway to 1160 m. (Britain:

introduced and cultivated.) Flowers, April–June; fruit, October. **877**

LARIX *Mill.* **L. decidua** *Mill.* (**L. europaea** *DC.*). LARCH. A roughly pyramidal, deciduous tree to 50 m. tall, with roughly horizontal branches, bark grey-brown. Twigs either short, developing tufts of 30–40 bright green, 1–3 cm. lvs. at their tips each year, or long, hairless, and when young yellowish green, with spirally arranged lvs. Lvs. flat-pointed, narrow, turning yellow in autumn. Male cones spaced along twigs. Female cones upright, at first bright pink, seldom cream, with recurved bracts, maturing into egg-shaped, pale brown cones, 2–3½ cm. long, with wide, rounded scales.
✤ Open forests, or isolated on slopes. To 2500 m. Alps; Apennines. (Britain: introduced and cultivated.) Flowers, March–June; fruit, September–October. **878**

PINUS *L.* Evergreen trees with branches in regular circles around the trunk, typically pyramidal, sometimes broad and low (*P. mugo* forms), older trees sometimes becoming wider at the top. Bark rough, ridged or flaky. Lvs. grouped, 2, 3 or 5 together, long and narrow, their bases enclosed in a short brownish, scaly shoot which drops off with the lvs. Male cones yellowish brown. Female cones fairly large and woody, ripening over 2–3 years. Cone scales large, thick and hard in alpine species.

P. cembra *L.* AROLLA PINE. An often irregularly shaped, roughly pyramidal tree to 18 (25) m. tall. Young twigs olive green, rough. Lvs. stiff, 5–14 cm. long, needle-like, 3-sided, blue-green on the 2 inner faces, in groups of 5. Female cones very distinctive, pinkish violet when young, dark violet-brown when mature, upright, 1–4 at the ends of branches, roundly-oval, 4–10 cm. long, 3–6 cm. wide.
✤ Open woods, stony places. 1200–2585 m. Alps. Local. May–June. **881**

P. nigra *Arnold* (**P. laricio** *Poir.*). AUSTRIAN PINE, BLACK PINE. A tree to 50 m. with pyramidal crown; branches shortish, spreading, irregular. Old bark rough, thick, deeply grooved, dark grey to brown. Twigs lightish brown, with old persistent lf.-bases giving a rough scaly appearance. Lvs. paired, dark green, stiff, needle-like, 8–16 cm. long, sometimes twisted. Cones irregularly pyramidal, 5–8 cm. long, yellowish, shiny, scales sometimes with a small point or prickle.
This is a very variable species, and many races have been named at various times. The typical alpine form is ssp. **nigra** (*var.* **austriaca** *Höss.*). Ssp. **salzmannii** (*Dunal*) *Franco* (including **P. pyrenaica** *Willk.*) is a smaller tree of loose habit which has soft blue-green lvs. not sharply pointed, reddish or orange twigs and cones 4–6 cm. long.
✤ Forests. To 1800 m. Ssp. *nigra:* Alps. *Ssp. salzmannii:* Pyrenees, Cevennes. (Britain: introduced.) May–June. **882**

P. sylvestris *L.* SCOTS PINE. A very variable tree 3–50 m. tall; older trees often having a flattened crown. Bark on the lower part of the trunk deeply and irregularly grooved into long plates, on the upper part orange to bright red-brown. Young twigs greenish-brown. Lvs. paired, mainly twisted, 3–10 cm. long, stiff, blue-green. Female cones solitary or in pairs, stalked, 3–8 cm. long, egg-shaped, not always regular, green at first, eventually brown.
✤ Mountainsides. 1800–2320 m. Pyrenees; Alps; Apennines. Norway to 1300 m. (Britain.) May–June. **884**

P. mugo *Turra* (**P. montana** *Mill.*). MOUNTAIN PINE. A variable, often contorted shrub up to 3½ m. tall, often forming impenetrable thickets. Older bark greyish brown, unevenly fissured, scaly. Twigs pale green, hairless. Lvs. paired, slightly twisted, curved towards branch, to 4 cm. long, with hard, pointed tip and minutely toothed edges. Male cones brown. Female cones upright to slightly pendulous, single or 2–3, roundly oval or oblong-oval, to 6 cm. long, 4 cm. wide, variously coloured.

The tree-like forms originally described under this name are now considered as a separate species, P. uncinata Mill. (see below). There are also hybrids between the two.

Var. mugo: A broad, bushy shrub with partly sprawling, angular branches. Cones regularly shaped, horizontal and spreading or curved downwards, conical or oval-conical, yellowish brown maturing to dark greenish brown, ends of cone scales often with a prickle.

Var. pumilio (*Haenke*) *Zenari* (**P. pumilio** *Haenke*): a hybrid with P. *uncinata*: a broad sprawling shrub with upright branches. Lvs. short, upright or spreading at ends of twigs. Cones regularly shaped, roundly oval to globular, upright at first, then becoming horizontal to pendulous, violet-purple maturing to dark yellowish brown.
⚘ Stony places, crags, screes, peaty bogs, often on margins of taller forests.

To 2700 m. E.C. and E. Alps; N. and C. Apennines. May–June. **883**

P. uncinata *Mill.* (**P. mugo** *var.* **rostrata** (*Ant.*) *Goud.*) A tree with erect trunk up to 25 m. tall; other characters as for P. *mugo*, but cones narrower, 5–7 cm. long, 2–3 cm. wide, irregularly shaped, horizontal or pendulous.

Var. rotundata (*Link*) *Ant.*: a hybrid with P. *mugo*: a large shrub or small bushy tree.
⚘ Stony places, screes, peaty bogs, often on margins of taller forests. To 2700 m. Pyrenees; C. and W. Alps. May–June.

P. leucodermis *Antoine* (**P. heldreichii** *Christen.* *var.* **leucodermis** (*Ant.*) *Markgr.* *ex Fitsch.*). BOSNIAN REDCONE PINE. A pyramidal tree to 20 m. tall, with rather flat crown. Trunk straight, upright; old bark ash-grey and fissured. Young twigs greyish-white with lvs. only at their ends. Lvs. paired, stiff, often curved inwards, glossy, pale green when young, becoming darker, 5–11 cm. long, tip blunt or prickly, edges sparsely, minutely toothed. Cones ovoid, singly or 3 together, 6–8 cm. long, 2–3 cm. wide, yellowish to dark brown, scales ending in a sharp keel.
⚘ Stony places, crags, forming forests. To 2270 m. S. Apennines. May–June.

CUPRESSACEAE

Alpine representatives evergreen trees or shrubs. Lvs. either needle- or scale-like, opposite or whorled. Cones small, scales whorled or opposite, pollen yellow.

JUNIPERUS *L.* Bark thin, shed in long strips. Lvs. scale-like or needle-like. Female cones of 3–8 scales which, when ripening, become fleshy and berry-like.

J. communis *L.* JUNIPER. Mountain forms shrubs. Bark red-brown. Lvs. needle-like, whorled in 3s, darkish green with a broad whitish band above, tip with a spiny point. Male cones cylindrical, to 1 cm. long. Female cones ('berries') blue-black with white 'bloom', to ½ cm. long, slightly oblong.

Ssp. hemisphaerica (*Presl*) *Nym.*:

MOUNTAIN JUNIPER: a spreading shrub 1–6 m. tall. Lvs. ½–2 cm. long, 1 cm. wide, spreading.

Ssp. nana (*Willd.*) *Syme* (*var.* saxatilis *Pallas*, J. nana *Willd.*, J. sibirica *Burgesdorf*) (**879**): DWARF JUNIPER: a spreading, rather sprawling shrub only 10–15 cm. tall. Lvs. upright, thick, 4–8 mm. long, 2 mm. wide, tip suddenly narrowing to a shorter point.

(*Ssp. communis*, the narrow upright 15 m. tree familiar in S. Europe, is not alpine.)

✲ Rocky and stony places, moors. *Ssp. hemisphaerica:* to 2500 m. Alps. Norway to 1730 m. (Britain to 1400 m.) Flowers, May–June; fruits, mature second or third year.

Ssp. nana: to 3570 m. (the highest-altitude woody plant in Europe).

Pyrenees; Alps; Apennines. (Britain.) Flowers, June–July; fruit, mature second or third year. **879**

J. sabina *L.* SAVIN. Shrub to 5 m. tall, spreading and sprawling, rarely upright. Older bark red-brown, peeling. Branches spreading out or up, tips always curving upright. Twigs close together, thin; lvs. on young plants needle-like; adult lvs. very small, overlapping in 4–6 rows, long-pointed, blue-green, very pungent-smelling. Male cones yellow-brown, in lf. axils. Female cones ('berries') 4–6 mm. long, bluish-black with a white 'bloom'.

✲ Rocks, stony places, meadows, woods. To 3000 m. Pyrenees; Alps; Apennines. Flowers, April–June; fruit, the first season or the following spring. **880**

FLOWERLESS PLANTS

EQUISETACEAE—HORSETAIL FAMILY

Herbaceous, spore-bearing perennials with a creeping, often very deep-penetrating rhizome. Upright stems either sterile or fertile, all green, or fertile stems colourless, furrowed, sometimes branched from the base. Branches, when present, like the stem, or very slender and in axillary whorls (rings) from the nodes (stem divisions). Lvs. minute, joined together to form toothed sheaths above the nodes, the number of teeth corresponding to the number of stem furrows. The spore-bearing structure, carried at tops of stems, is a group of whorled, small, globular bodies in a cone-like spike.

EQUISETUM L. The only genus: characters as for family. Aerial stems either dying down or persisting throughout the winter.

Besides the species described, *E. silvaticum* L., the WOOD HORSETAIL, reaches 1800 m., and *E. arvense* L., the COMMON HORSETAIL, 2500 m. Both are British natives.

E. fluviatile L. (E. limosum L., E. heliocharis Ehrh.). WATER HORSE-TAIL. Upright stems 50–140 cm. tall, fertile and sterile ones alike, appearing together, both green with 10–30 fine furrows, unbranched or with whorls of uneven branches. Branches upright, slender, hollow, usually 5-angled. Lf. sheaths green, to 1 cm. long, teeth small, black at least at the tip, narrow, pointed, almost flattened. Spike 1–2 cm. long, brownish.

🔹 Shallow, still water, ponds, ditches, lake edges. To 2500 m. Alps; Apennines. Norway to 1325 m. (Britain to 1000 m.) May–August. **846**

E. pratense *Ehrh.* FIELD HORSETAIL. Fertile and sterile stems differing, but appearing together. Sterile stems 20–60 cm. tall, upright, green, rough, with 8–20 deep furrows. Lf. sheaths just under 1 cm. long, teeth pointed, flattened, brown with a very dark rib. Branches many, upright, spreading to slightly drooping, with 3–4 furrows; lf. sheaths pale, teeth 3–4, pointed-triangular. Fertile stems 10–25 cm. tall, unbranched, colourless, lf. sheaths loose, many, creamish-white, teeth 10–20, pale to brownish, ribs dark. After dispersal of the spores the fertile stem may become branched and green. Spike oval, 1½–4 cm. long, red-brown.

🔹 Woods, damp pastures, grassy banks, stream edges. To 2150 m. Alps. Norway to 1350 m. (Britain.) April–June. **847**

E. palustre L. MARSH HORSETAIL, PADDOCK PIPES, CAT-WHISTLE. Sterile and fertile stems alike, appearing together, upright or sprawling, 10–60 cm. long, less than ½ cm. across, green, usually branched, branches sometimes unequal, roughish, with 4–8 deep furrows. Branches upright to spreading, rather short, furrows 4–5, smooth. Lf. sheaths ½–1½ cm. long, loose, green, teeth 4–8, flattened, triangular, dark to blackish with tissue-like edges. Sheaths on branches with 4 short, black-tipped teeth. Spike dark bluish-brown, 1–3 cm. long, oblong with blunt top.

🔹 Damp, marshy places, bogs, woods, meadows. To 2000 (2445) m. Alps;

Apennines. Norway to 1325 m. (Britain to 1000 m.) May–August. **848**

E. variegatum *Schleich.* VARIEGATED HORSETAIL. Sterile and fertile stems alike, upright or sprawling, 15–60 cm. long, green, unbranched or branched at the base, carrying no whorls of branches, furrows 4–10, each ridge having a double row of minute swellings, surface rough. Lf. sheaths green, slightly loose, with a dark ring at the top, thin, dry, whitish with black centres, round-triangular or lance-shaped-triangular, tip pointed then falling away leaving a blunt top, with 4 ribs. Spike dark blackish green, just under 1 cm. long. A variable plant.
⚘ Damp, sandy, gravelly places. To 2500 m. Pyrenees; Alps; Apennines. Norway to 1500 m. (Britain.) April–September. **849**

E. hyemale *L.* DUTCH RUSH. Sterile and fertile stems similar, upright, 30–150 cm. tall, bluish green, unbranched, with 10–30 furrows, ridges with a double row of minute swellings, rough. Lf. sheath to 1 cm. long, quickly becoming whitish with a dark ring at the top and bottom, dropping early leaving a round-lobed edge to the sheath. Spike dark greenish-brown, ½–1½ cm. long.
⚘ Damp woods, streamsides, sandy soils. To 2600 m. Alps; Apennines. Norway to 1300 m. (Britain.) March–August. **850**

LYCOPODIACEAE—CLUBMOSS FAMILY

Herbaceous spore-bearing perennials with small lvs. The spore-bearing structures (*sporangia*) are all alike and are borne on the upper surfaces at the base of certain lvs. called *sporophylls*. These particular lvs. either look the same as the ordinary lvs. and grow intermingled with them, or appear completely different and grow clustered together to form 'cones' on the ends of some of the upright stems.

LYCOPODIUM *L.* CLUBMOSS. Originally considered the only European genus. *Flora Europaea* now refers *L. selago* to *Huperzia* Bernh. and *L. alpinum* to *Diphasium* C. Presl.

L. annotinum *L.* Stems irregularly branched, 30–60 cm. long, creeping and rooting, with many upright branches 10–25 cm. tall. Lvs. spirally arranged, 4–6 mm. long, usually more on the branches than on the main stem, somewhat spreading, narrow lance-shaped, tipped with a stiff short point, dull green, edges sometimes slightly toothed. Cones borne singly on branches, stalkless, 1½–3 cm. long.

⚘ Coniferous woods, moors. To 2400 m. Alps; Apennines. Norway to 1600 m. (Britain.) June–September. **853**

L. selago *L.* FIR CLUBMOSS. With sprawling, rooting stem base and upright, regularly branched 5–30 cm. stems. Lvs. ¼–1 cm. long, spreading to upright, dull green, lance-shaped, tip pointed, edges sometimes minutely toothed. Sporangia in axils of lvs. appearing the same as the ordinary lvs.
⚘ Woods, meadows, rock ledges, heaths, moors. To 3080 m. Pyrenees; Alps; Apennines. Norway to 1940 m. (Britain to 1400 m.) June–October. **854**

L. alpinum *L.* ALPINE CLUBMOSS.

With stems 15–50 cm. long, sprawling and rooting, greatly branched, carrying upright branches to 7 cm. Lvs. bluish green, to ½ cm. long, separated on the main stems, very close together and arranged in 4 rows on the branches; oblong to lance-shaped, pointed, sometimes with a translucent, short broad point, concave, hairless, edges untoothed. Sporangia forming cones which are 1–2 cm. long, usually solitary and stalkless on the ends of the upright branches.

⚘ Rocky grasslands, heathland, preferring acid soils. To 2900 m. Pyrenees; Alps; Apennines. Rare. Norway to 1600 m. (Britain to 1300 m.) June–September. **855**

L. clavatum L. STAGSHORN CLUBMOSS, COMMON CLUBMOSS. Stems mainly all sprawling, branched, 30–100 cm. long, only the fertile branches upright, 10–25 cm. tall. Lvs. bright green, arranged spirally, dense, pressed against or curved in towards the stem, linear, edges minutely toothed, terminating in a long, white, wavy fine point. Sporangia in yellowish or brownish cones, 2–5 cm. long, singly or in pairs (occasionally 3) on the ends of long stalks which are covered with scale-like lvs.

⚘ Heathland, woods, grassland, preferring acid soils. To 2500 m. Alps; Apennines. Rare. Norway to 1200 m. (Britain to 920 m.) June–October. **856**

SELAGINELLACEAE

Herbaceous perennials with creeping branches and upright fertile stems. Lvs. small, of 2 sorts, arranged spirally or in 4 ranks, with a small flap-like appendage at the base called a 'ligule'. Sporangia male and female, borne on the upper surface at the base of some lvs. which form 'cones', the small male sporangia usually in the upper part, the larger female ones in the lower.

SELAGINELLA *Beauv.* The only genus. Characters as for the family.

S. selaginoides (*L.*) *Link* (Lycopodium selaginoides *L.*, S. spinosa *Beauv.*, S. spinulosa *A.Br.*). Stems sprawling, 3–15 cm. long, sterile branches short, fertile branches longer, both more or less upright, 2–6 cm. long. Lvs. arranged spirally, to ½ cm. long, either spreading or close to the stem, lance-shaped, pointed, stiffly hairy on the edges. Cones stalkless, borne singly, 1–1½ cm. long. Cone lvs. like the sterile ones but larger, colour a little paler or brownish.

⚘ Damp, stony pastures. To 2900 m.

Pyrenees; Alps. Uncommon. Norway to 1520 m. (Britain to 1200 m.) June–August. **851**

S. helvetica (*L.*) *Link* (Lycopodium helveticum *L.*). Stems creeping, branched, fertile stems 3–10 cm. tall. Lvs. in 4 ranks, those of the 2 upper ranks smaller than the 2 lower ranks, both pointed, widely oval. Lvs. of the fertile branches longer, spirally arranged, growing close against the stem. Cones slender, yellowish, cone lvs. oval, pointed.

⚘ Damp woods, pastures, stony places. To 2500 m. Alps. Rare. May–September. **852**

FILICES—FERN TRIBE

Perennial rhizomatous plants with undivided or very deeply divided green lvs. Reproducing by means of spores contained in *sporangia* which are arranged in variously shaped groups called *sori*, situated either on the undersides of the lvs. or on spikes separate from the lvs.

The plants described exclude most of the 'ferny' species such as *Thelypteris phegopteris*, no. 874, which is illustrated as an example. These are rather unrewarding to identify, and include numerous other species of *Thelypteris* and *Athyrium*; among the latter *A. alpestre* Clairv. attains 3200 m. Other ferns exceeding 1500 m. are *Phyllitis scolopendrium* (L.) Newm., the HARTS-TONGUE FERN, to 1800 m., and *Pteridium aquilinum* (L.) Kuhn, the BRACKEN, exceptionally to 2100 m. *Adiantum capillus-veneris* L., the MAIDENHAIR FERN, reaches 1500 m. in Italy.

There is much nomenclatural confusion in the tribe; some species have been named under six or more different genera. Synonyms have been kept to the minimum here.

Modern authorities divide the tribe into a number of small families: here it is only separated into two, *Polypodiaceae* and *Ophioglossaceae*.

POLYPODIACEAE—POLYPODY FAMILY

Rhizomes hairy or scaly. Lvs. more or less deeply divided, with sori on the undersides.

CYSTOPTERIS *Bernh.* Rhizome softly scaly. Lvs. triangular in outline, deeply divided into small lobes. Sori stalked, arranged along the sides of the veins, round and dome-shaped.

C. fragilis (L.) *Bernh.* (C. regia (L.) *Desv.*, C. dentata (*Sm.*) *Desv.*). BRITTLE BLADDER-FERN. A tufted plant arising from a short, sprawling, thickish rhizome with lance-shaped scales. Lvs. 5–45 cm. long, narrowly triangular, more or less upright, divided into up to 15 pairs of leaflets, themselves again divided into roundish toothed segments. Lf. stem as long as rest of lf., slender and quite brittle, dark brown at the bottom and sometimes scaly, to pale greenish brown above. Sori in rows on both sides of the midrib. A variable sp. often divided into subspecies.

✲ Woods, screes, walls, rocky places, preferring limestone. 1200–3000 m. Pyrenees; Alps; Apennines. Norway to 1700 m. (Britain to 1300 m.) July-August. **862**

C. montana (*Lam.*) *Desv.* MOUNTAIN BLADDER-FERN. A delicate plant having a slender, black, creeping rhizome with few scales. Lvs. 10–40 cm. long, broadly triangular, deeply divided into triangular segments themselves further twice divided into toothed segments. Main stalk long, dark brown with a few oval scales below, pale green above. Sori small, spread apart, on either side of the veins.

⚜ Screes, damp calcareous soils. To 2500 m. Pyrenees; Alps; Apennines. Norway to 1280 m. (Britain to 1200 m.) July–August. **863**

WOODSIA *R.Br.* Small tufted plants with short scaly rhizomes. Lvs. lance-shaped in outline, divided into short leaflets. Sori on undersurface of lvs., round, domed, small.

W. ilvensis (*L.*) *R.Br.* Rhizome more or less upright, slightly scaly above. Lvs. more or less upright, 5–15 cm. long, narrowly triangular in overall outline, divided into 7–15 pairs of lobed leaflets, the lowest pair sometimes slightly shorter than the rest. Lower surfaces of the lvs. thickly covered with hairs and pale brown scales; sori borne near the edges of the leaflets. Lf. stems pale reddish brown to green, hairy with brown scales.
⚜ Crevices, preferring acid soils. To 2600 m. Alps. Rare. (Britain.) July–August. **858**

W. alpina (*Botton*) *Gray* (**W. hyperborea** (*Lilj.*) *R. Br.*). Lvs. 3–15 cm. long, pointed-oblong in outline, divided into 7–15 pairs of round-triangular, toothed leaflets. The undersurface and stem with few hairs or scales.
⚜ Rock crevices. To 2600 m. Pyrenees; Alps. Norway to 1400 m. (Britain to 1000 m.) July–August. **859**

W. glabella *R. Br.* Similar to the other species but much smaller. Lvs. 2–12 cm. long, more or less hairless, delicate, transparent, bright green or yellowish green, stem pale.
⚜ Rocky, shady crevices, preferring limestone. 1600–2000 m. Alps. Very rare. July–August.

THELYPTERIS *Schmidel.* **T. phegopteris** (*L.*) *Sloss.* (**Dryopteris phegopteris** (*L.*) *C. Chr.*). BEECH FERN. A typically 'fern-like' plant which has quantities of synonyms. Rhizome long,

slender, creeping, with brown scales when young. Lvs. triangular in outline, curving backwards and downwards from the stem. Lf. divided into numerous leaflets, themselves lobed nearly to their midribs, thinnish, dull green, more or less hairy on both surfaces with the edges inclined to bend under. Lf. stem upright, slender, brittle, scaly at the top and base and with long white hairs. Sori small, round, near the edges on the undersides of the lvs.
⚜ Shady, rocky, damp places, woods, preferring acid soils. To 2500 m. Pyrenees; Alps; Apennines. (Britain to 1230 m.) July–September. **874**

POLYSTICHUM *Roth.* **P. lonchitis** (*L.*) *Roth.* (**Aspidium lonchitis** (*L.*) *Sw.*, **Dryopteris lonchitis** (*L.*) *O. Ktze.*). HOLLY FERN. Rhizome sturdy, upright. Lvs. 10–60 cm. long, strap-shaped in outline, but tapering towards the base as well as the top, divided into 20–40 pairs of leaflets 1–3 cm. long, oval to oval lance-shaped with toothed edges and a roundish projection at the base of the upper edge near the midrib; dark green on the upper surface, lower surface paler, slightly scaly, rather leathery in texture. Stems 1–10 cm. long, with oval red-brown scales. Sori usually on the upper leaflets in a row along each side of their midribs.
⚜ Screes, rock crevices, woods. To 3000 m. Pyrenees; Alps; Apennines. Norway to 1500 m. (Britain to 1200 m.) July–September. **864**

P. aculeatum (*L.*) Roth. (*P. lobatum* (Huds.) Sw.), the HARD SHIELD FERN, occurs in the Alps and Apennines to 2200 m.

CETERACH *DC.* **C. officinarum** *DC.* (**Asplenium ceterach** *L.*). RUSTY-BACK. A tufted plant with a short more or less upright rhizome, covered with dark scales. Lvs. narrow-oval in outline, 3–20 cm. long, tapering slightly at the base, divided into short rounded segments more or less alternate on each side of midrib, leathery, dull green on top, completely covered with rust-brown overlapping scales and sori on lower surface. Stalk 1–5 cm. long, scaly. Sori linear, in a row along one or both sides of the veins.

❀ Old walls, sunny screes, rock crevices. To 2000 m. Alps. (Britain.) April–October. **857**

ASPLENIUM L. Rhizome scaly. Lvs. variously divided. Sori linear to oval, on the veins.

A. viride *Huds.* GREEN SPLEENWORT. Rhizome creeping, shortish, with dark scales. Lvs. light green, narrow, oblong-oval, 5–30 cm. long, divided into 4–40 round to oval, hairless, more or less overlapping lobes with deeply toothed edges. Stem dark brown to blackish at base, green above. Sori oblong to linear in rows along one or both sides of the veins nearer the midrib than the edge of the lobes.

❀ Screes, rock crevices, on limestone. To 3015 m. Pyrenees; Alps; Apennines. Norway to 1700 m. (Britain to 1050 m.) June–September. **870**

A. trichomanes L. MAIDENHAIR SPLEENWORT. A slender, tufted plant, not unlike *A. viride*, with dark green, linear lvs. 4–35 cm. long, divided into 15–40 paired oval to oblong lobes well spaced out along the midrib; stem dark green to blackish, with a fine brown wing. Sori linear-oblong, mainly along the branches of the main vein.

❀ Rocky crevices, shady walls. To 2250 m. Pyrenees; Alps; Apennines. Norway to 800 m. (Britain.) May–October.

A. septentrionale (*L.*) *Hoffm.* FORKED SPLEENWORT. A tufted plant with creeping rhizome. Lvs. darkish green, 4–15 cm. long, forking into 2 (3) reversed-wedge-shaped lobes, occasionally unequal in size, tapering gradually into the much longer stems. Sori narrow-linear, covering most of the undersurface of the lvs.

❀ Rock crevices, screes, preferring acid soils. To 2800 m. Pyrenees; Alps; Apennines. Norway to 1100 m. (Britain to 1000 m.) June–October. **872**

A. seelosii *Leybold.* Similar to *A. septentrionale*, but the lvs. are 2–10 cm. long, divided into 3 broader, toothed segments, the edges of which are curled under, narrowing abruptly to long slender stalks. Sori linear, mainly along the veins of the undersides of the lvs.

❀ Crevices and cavities of overhanging cliffs, on dolomite. To 2600 m. E. Alps. July–August. **1251**

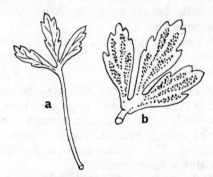

1251. *Asplenium seelosii.* a, leaf; b, leaf underside enlarged, showing sori.

A. ruta-muraria L. WALL RUE. A tufted plant with short creeping rhizome. Lvs. leathery, oval-triangular in outline, dark, drab green apart from the base of the stalks which are blackish, divided into rounded wedge-shaped, toothed segments, to 3 cm. across. Sori linear, situated on the veins towards the base of the segments, finally merging into each other.

❀ Screes, rocks, walls, mainly on limestone. To 2900 m. Pyrenees; Alps; Apennines. (Britain.) June–December. **873**

A. adiantum-nigrum L. BLACK SPLEEN-WORT. A tufted plant with creeping, sprawling rhizome. Lvs. slightly leathery, bright green, 10–50 cm. long, narrow- to oval-triangular in outline, deeply divided, with up to 15 pairs of leaflets. Lower leaflets largest, stalked, deeply divided again into toothed lobes; the upper leaflets usually just lobed and toothed. Lf. stalk long, blackish, scaly at the base. Sori linear to oblong-linear, covering most of the surface of the lateral veins, closer to the midrib than the edge of the lobes, sometimes merging.
✢ Screes, old walls. To 1750 (2450) m. Alps; Apennines. Rare. (Britain.) July–August.   871
A. cuneifolium *Viv.* (**A. serpentini** *Tausch.*) is very similar to *A. adiantum-nigrum* and has been considered a subspecies; it has fewer, narrower leaflets, and occurs to 2000 m. in Alps, Apennines.

BLECHNUM L. **B. spicant** (*L.*) *Roth.* (**Lomaria spicant** (*L.*) *Desv.*) HARD FERN. With a short, stoutish, upright, brown-scaly rhizome and many somewhat leathery lvs. in tufts, the central fertile ones more or less upright, the outer sterile ones spreading. The latter are not unlike those of *Polypodium vulgare*, narrow-lance-shaped, 10–50 cm. long, the 1–2 cm. lobes overlapping, midrib green and hairless. Stalk short, dark brown, scaly at the base. The central fertile lvs. are 15–75 cm. long, deeply divided, with a blackish midrib, and sori in a line along either side of the midrib.
✢ Damp woods, heaths, moors, preferring acid soils. To 2900 m. Pyrenees; Alps; Apennines. Norway to 1000 m. (Britain to 1300 m.) June–September.

CRYPTOGRAMMA R. *Br.* **C. crispa** (*L.*) *Hook. & Bauer* (**Allosurus crispus** (*L.*) *Bernh.*). PARSLEY FERN. A thickly tufted plant with short rhizome and both fertile and sterile lvs. Fertile lvs. central, 10–30 cm. long, having deeply and finely divided narrow-oblong segments and a very long stalk; sori oblong, on the tips of the veins of the undersurface. The outer sterile lvs. are triangular in outline, deeply divided but with much wider, wedge-shaped segments.
✢ Screes, stony places, on acid soils. To 3000 m. Pyrenees; Alps; Apennines. Norway to 1550 m. (Britain to 1300 m.) July–September.   861

POLYPODIUM L. **P. vulgare** L. POLYPODY. With a stoutish creeping scaly rhizome, sometimes above ground. Lvs. rather leathery, dullish green, 5–45 cm. long, lance-shaped or oblong in outline, cut almost to the midrib, into 10–25 pairs of lobes up to 10 cm. long. Sori round or oval, sometimes yellow, in rows on either side of the main veins.
✢ Screes, walls, bases of tree trunks. To 2780 m. Pyrenees; Alps; Apennines. Norway to 1200 m. (Britain to 900 m.) July–December   860

OPHIOGLOSSACEAE

Plants with upright, fleshy, underground rhizome. Lvs. stalked, 1 or more, fertile ones of 1 sterile blade and 1 or more fertile spikes standing above sterile blade. Sporangia in 2 rows along the edges of the spikes.

OPHIOGLOSSUM *L*. **O. vulgatum**
L. ADDERS-TONGUE. Lf. usually 1
upright, 8–20 (4–45) cm. long. Sterile
blade undivided, oval-lance-shaped to
pointed-oblong, bright fresh green.
Fertile spike stalked, narrow, unbranched, to 7 cm. long.
✢ Damp meadows. To 2000 m. Pyrenees (rare); Alps; Apennines. (Britain.)
May–August.   865

BOTRYCHIUM *Sw*. Lf. blades deeply
divided and fertile spikes branching.

B. lunaria (*L*.) *Sw*. MOON-FERN, MOON-
WORT. Lvs. usually 1, seldom 2, 5–15
(2–30) cm. long, upright, fresh green.
Sterile blade to 12 cm. long, oblong in
outline, divided into 4–18 semicircular
or fan-shaped lobes with slightly
toothed edges, usually joined to the
fertile spike at about the centre of the
stalk. Fertile spike branched to about
3 times, to 5 cm. long.
✢ Meadows, screes. To 3105 m. Pyrenees; Alps; Apennines. Norway to
1600 m. (Britain to 1120 m.) May–
August.   866

B. multifidum (*Gmel*.) *Rupr*. (**B. terna-
tum** *Thunb*.) Similar to *B. lunaria*, but
the fertile spike is to 6 cm. long, broadly
triangular and with more side branches.
Sterile blade broadly triangular in outline with more oblong, stalked divisions; junction of stalks of sterile and
fertile parts just above ground level.
✢ Meadows. To 1750 m. Alps. August–
September.

B. lanceolatum (*Gmel*.) *Angström* (**B.
palmatum** *Presl*.). 5–20 cm. tall. Sterile
blade yellowish green, short-triangular
in outline, with oblong, lance-shaped,
lobed divisions, joined to the fertile
blade just below the triangular, loosely
branched spike. Stalk two-thirds the
length of the entire plant.
✢ Meadows. 2100–4000 m. Alps. Very
rare and local. To 1200 m. Norway.
June–August.   868

B. boreale *Milde*. 5–12 cm. tall. Sterile
blade long-triangular in outline, divided
into roundish-triangular lobes with
slightly lobed edges, joined to the fertile
blade just below the longer, yellowish,
loosely branched, oval-triangular spike.
✢ Meadows, on calcareous soils. To
1600 m. Norway. July.   867

B. simplex *Hitchc*. 2–15 cm. tall.
Sterile blade oblong, divided into
rounded, slightly overlapping roundish
lobes with sometimes slightly wavy
edges, joined at the base, low down on
main stem, to the fertile narrowly
oblong, few-branched, palish green
spike which much exceeds it.
✢ Damp meadows. To 2400 m. Alps;
Apennines. Very local. May–July.   869

GLOSSARY OF BOTANICAL TERMS

achene   a one-seeded ovary, normally separate from its fellows
actinomorphic   radially symmetrical
adventitious   of a plant occurring in places outside its normal range and habitats
annual   a plant which germinates, flowers, seeds and dies within a year
anther   the part of the stamen containing the pollen grains
apomixis   the production of viable seed without fertilisation
appressed (also **adpressed**)   pressed flat against a surface; usually referring to hairs
auricle   a lobe at the base of a leaf (rarely a petal) which is often ear-like in shape and
    typically clasps the stem
awn   a long stiff bristle-like projection at the end or side of an organ
axil   the angle between a leaf or shoot and a main stem; hence, an axillary growth,
    flower or bud
berry   a fleshy fruit, typically rounded and containing several hard seeds; often
    loosely used (e.g. strawberry, blackberry)
biennial   a plant which germinates and develops in the first year and flowers, seeds
    and dies in the second, though sometimes capable of behaving like an annual
blade   the flattened part of a leaf or petal
bract   a leaf-like or scale-like organ, usually smaller than the true leaves of the plant,
    and in the axils of which flower stems often develop
bulb   an underground storage organ, consisting of separate, fleshy scales
bulbil   a miniature bulb arising among the flowers (as in *Allium*), or in the leaf
    axils (as in *Lilium croceum*), from which new plants can arise
calyx   a collective term for the sepals of a flower
capsule   a dry fruit of at least two carpels, splitting open when ripe
carpel   one female, seed-bearing unit of a flower
cartilaginous   hard, tough tissue, often not green
catkin   a tight, usually hanging spike of small flowers
ciliate   edged with hairs
claw   the narrow basal part of some petals, often hidden inside the calyx
cleistogamic   referring to flowers which never open normally and are self-
    pollinated (as occurring in *Viola, Oxalis*)
cone   the fruit of some trees of the Conifer tribe, consisting of stiff, hard scales
    sheltering the seeds; also used here of the cone-shaped spore-bearing organs of
    some Club-mosses and Selaginellas
corm   a swollen underground stem, not composed of scales like a bulb, usually in
    a tunic; next year's corm is almost always formed on top of the old one
corolla   a collective term for the petals of a flower
cyme   a flower-head in which the growing point is always terminated by a flower,
    and fresh flowers occur on new side growing points. Such clusters are usually
    reversed-cone-shaped, with the oldest flowers at the top and centre
deciduous   losing leaves in winter
decussate   of leaves in opposed pairs with each pair at right angles to the next
dehisce   of seed vessels, to open or split to release the seeds
disk floret   the tubular florets (as opposed to the ray florets) which occupy part
    of or sometimes all the flower-heads of some Composites
drupe   a usually fleshy fruit with one or more seeds each in a hard 'stone'
epicalyx   a calyx-like structure immediately outside the true **calyx**

escaped of a cultivated plant found outside gardens, but not properly naturalised

evergreen not losing all leaves in winter

fall the outer set of petals in Irises, usually larger than the inner and typically out-spread or drooping

family a classificatory term for a group of plants sharing many common characters of the flower (not normally of foliage, habit, etc.)

ferny a word here used loosely to indicate leaves which are long and narrow and divided into many fine, more or less parallel segments as in many Ferns

filament the stalk of the stamen, which bears the anthers

floret a small flower, especially when one of a dense cluster

follicle a dry fruit of one carpel, often swollen and elongated, opening along one side

form (Latin **forma**) a slight but distinguishable variant within a species

genus (plural **genera**) a classificatory term for the main subsections of a family, each genus being composed, usually, of several species

gland a small organ usually containing an oil or resin, which may be in or on the surface, or on a stalk when it is called a glandular hair; often making the plant aromatic or sticky

glaucous bluish or greyish

head a loose term for a dense group of flowers or fruits at the end of one stalk

hep the fruit of a rose; also spelt **hip**

herbaceous of a plant, non-woody, the upper growth usually dying back to ground level in winter; of a plant organ, having the texture and colour of leaves

hood a loose term for the hood- or helmet-shape created by the upper sepal, or three upper sepals together, in orchids, or by the upper petal as in *Pedicularis*

inflorescence a complete flower-head excluding the topmost stem-leaf, including all flowers, stalks and bracts

introduced of an alien plant, introduced deliberately or accidentally into the wild and now fully naturalised as if native

involucre an often calyx-like structure formed by leaf-like bracts surrounding a dense flower-head, as typically in Composites

keel a sharp central edge on an organ; also the combined lower petals of flowers of the Pea family

lanceolate, lance-shaped shaped like a lance-head—much longer than wide, with broad base, narrowing to the tip

lemma the lower of the two flower-bracts in grasses

ligule a small projection where a leaf-blade and its sheath meet, as typically in grasses; also, the strap-shaped extension of a ray floret in Composites

limb the flattened, spreading part of a calyx or corolla which is tubular at the base

linear long and narrow, with sides more or less parallel

lip one perianth segment, or a group of combined ones, forming a flap-like projection distinct from the rest

membranous dry, thin and flexible, not green

midrib the central vein of a leaf

monocarpic flowering and seeding once only, and then dying, usually after more than two years (the term usually excludes annuals and biennials with a specific life)

naturalised of an alien plant which has established itself as if native in the wild

nectary a gland giving off a sugary liquid, usually in the flower to attract insects

node a stem division; a point where a leaf or branch grows from the stem, especially if swollen

nut   a one-seeded fruit with a hard outer shell

nutlet   a small nut-like seed

ob-   as a prefix, inverted, or with the widest part above the middle

ovary   the part of the flower enclosing the ovules

ovate   with an egg-shaped outline, the broadest part at the base

ovule   the structure containing the female germ-cell which after fertilisation becomes the seed

palea   the upper of the two flower-bracts in grasses

panicle   a branched, usually conical, cluster of stalked flowers, the youngest of which are at the top

papillae   small projections

pappus   hairs or bristles which replace the calyx in Composites, and are often retained at the top of the seed

parasite   a plant deriving nourishment from other living plants to which it attaches itself; complete parasites have no green leaves

perennial   living for more than two years and normally flowering every year

perianth   all the floral 'leaves', including both sepals and petals

perianth segment   one floral 'leaf', used especially when petals and sepals are indistinguishable, as in the Lily family

petal   one of the inner floral 'leaves', usually showy and coloured, which together form the corolla

petaloid   petal-like; as noun, a petal-like organ intermediate between petals and stamens

pinnatifid   of leaves cut into lobes in two rows, not as far as the midrib

pinnatisect   of leaves cut into lobes in two rows, mostly to the midrib

plica   a tooth or small lobe between the main corolla lobes of Gentians

pod   a general term for any more or less swollen, dry, splitting fruit of one carpel (section)

pollinium   the structure formed by massed pollen-grains in Orchids

pore   a small opening, typically in a seed pod

procumbent   straggling loosely over the surface of the ground

prostrate   lying more or less close to the surface of the ground

race   (geographical) a localised group of plants differing from other localised groups in minor characters

raceme   an unbranched, usually conical, cluster of stalked flowers, the youngest of which are at the top

ray   one of the stalks of an umbel

ray floret   a floret, tubular at the base, one side of which is elongated into a strap-shape, in the flower-heads of many Composites

receptacle   the often thickened upper part of the stem which carries the flower parts, or the florets in Composites

rhizome   a more or less permanent thickened underground stem

rhombic   roughly diamond-shaped

rosette   a cluster of leaves, typically at ground level, radiating from a central point

runner   a creeping permanent overground stem which roots and forms new plants at its end or nodes

saprophyte   a plant living on dead or decaying organic matter; complete saprophytes have no green leaves

scorpioid cyme   a curving, one-sided spike-like cluster, with the youngest flower at the apex, as in Forget-me-not

sepal one of the outer floral 'leaves', together forming the calyx; usually green but sometimes showy and petal-like, especially if replacing the petals as in *Anemone* or *Clematis*

sessile stalkless

shrub a woody, branching plant with no main trunk

silicula a pod-like fruit of the Crucifer family, often broader than long and never more than twice as long as broad

siliqua a pod-like fruit of the Crucifer family, at least twice as long as broad, usually much more

sinus the cleft between two lobes

sorus (plural **sori**) a group of sporangia in ferns

species (abbreviated sp., plural spp.) a classification term for a group of individual plants, distinct but having similar characters, which will interbreed, and together form a genus

spike a dense, elongated flower-head of stalkless or short-stalked flowers; often used loosely as of narrow elongated panicles; also here of the narrow or cone-like spore-bearing heads of some Horsetails and Ferns

sporangia spore-bearing structures

sporophyll leaves which carry sporangia in Club-mosses

spur a usually hollow, tubular to sac-shaped extension of a petal or sepal, which often contains nectar

stamen the male reproductive organ of a flower, consisting of pollen-bearing anthers and, usually, a filament (stalk)

staminode a sterile or rudimentary stamen with no pollen, sometimes developed in a different way, e.g. as a nectary

standard the broad upper petal of the flower in the Pea family; one of the inner, usually upright perianth segments of an Iris

starry of hairs, branching in a star-shape

stigma the pollen-receptive part of the female reproductive organs of a flower: usually on top of the style, and typically sticky

stipule a scale-like or leaf-like appendage at the base of a leaf-stalk

stolon a creeping stem which roots and produces new plants at the nodes, and eventually decays

style the more or less elongated, stalk-like projection of the ovary, bearing the stigma

subshrub a plant with woody base and herbaceous upper part, like Lavender

subspecies (abbreviated ssp., plural sspp.) a group of plants within a species, with several distinctive characters; often a geographical race

truncate having a square or broad, straight end

tube the fused part of a calyx or corolla

tuber an underground swollen stem which is a storage organ, and is neither a bulb nor a corm

tunic a dry, brownish, usually papery covering around a bulb or a corm

umbel a cluster of stalks arising at the same point from the top of a stem

valve one of the segments into which a seed capsule splits

variety (abbreviated var.) a group of plants within a species with at least one distinctive character such as unusual flower colour

vein strands of conducting and strengthening tissue in a leaf or petal, usually clearly visible

viviparous of a plant, bearing miniature plants, bulbs or offsets which sprout while still on the parent
whorl several organs arising at the same level
wing a thin, projecting extension of an organ such as a pod, calyx or stem; also the side petals of the flowers of the Pea family
zygomorphic of flowers, symmetrical in the vertical plane only, thus divisible into two halves lengthwise

GLOSSARY OF GEOLOGICAL AND HABITAT TERMS

acid of rocks and soil, having an acid reaction; non-alkaline
alkaline of rocks and soil, having an alkaline reaction; non-acid
basalt a fine-textured hard volcanic rock—one form of ancient lava (slightly acid)
basic of rocks, igneous ones containing less than 55 per cent silica (alkaline)
calcareous of rocks such as limestone and chalk composed mainly of calcium carbonate, and/or dolomite (alkaline)
dolomite rock consisting largely of magnesium and calcium carbonates (alkaline). Does *not* effervesce with dilute hydrochloric acid
feldspar a crystalline mineral found in igneous rocks, consisting mainly of aluminium silicates (acid)
gneiss a coarse-textured granite-like rock with a banded appearance due to alternating layers of light-coloured (quartz and/or feldspar) and dark-coloured (mica and/or other ferromagnesian minerals) (acid)
granite a hard, coarse-textured igneous rock made of interlocking crystals of quartz, feldspar and a coloured mineral, which is often mica (acid)
gypsum a hydrated sulphate of calcium occurring in some sedimentary rocks (alkaline). Can be scratched with the fingernail
limestone rock consisting largely of calcium carbonate (alkaline). Scratched by steel and effervesces with dilute hydrochloric acid
micaceous containing mica, a complex silicate containing aluminium and potassium. Both the light and the dark varieties break easily into thin sheets, owing to their perfect cleavage (usually acid)
moraine the rocks and debris deposited by a glacier at its sides and lower end; often fine, compact and damp
quartz silicon dioxide, occurs as crystals, sometimes of large size, in igneous rocks; and as abraded grains in sands. Is not scratched by a penknife (acid)
porphyry an igneous rock, often dark red or purplish, containing large crystals usually of quartz or feldspar in a much finer-grained groundmass, which is usually darker in colour (acid)
primary or **primitive rocks** those of very considerable geological age. They are usually gneissose or granitic and therefore acidic, but locally they may be more calcareous or alkaline
schist of similar composition to gneiss, but much more firmly laminated, so it is apt to flake easily (acid)
scree an accumulation of stones at the foot of a cliff or steep slope; usually rather dry
shale compacted clay, splitting easily into thin layers (acid or slightly alkaline)
siliceous rocks containing abundant silica, as quartz or sand (typically acid)
snow-bed a depression in which snow lies late, resulting in very damp conditions when it melts, although often drying out later

BIBLIOGRAPHY

Acloque, A. *Flore du Sud-Ouest de la France et des Pyrénées* (1904)
Alpine Garden Society. *Quarterly Bulletins* (1930–)
Ardoino, H. *Flore analytique du Département des Alpes-Maritimes* (1867)
Baroni, E. *Guida Botanica d'Italia* (1906, 1955)
Binz, A., and Thommen, E. *Flore de la Suisse* (1941, 1953)
Bonnier, G. *Flore Complete de France, Suisse et Belgique* (1911–35)
Clapham, A. R., Tutin, T. G., and Warburg, E. F. *Flora of the British Isles* (1952, 1962)
Correvon, H. *Atlas de la Flore Alpine* (1901)
Coste, H. *Flore descriptive et illustrée de la France* (1901)
Crook, H. C. *Campanulas* (1959)
Davies, P. & J., and Huxley, A. *Wild Orchids of Britain and Europe* (1983)
Engler, A. *Das Pflanzenreich* (1900–), with special reference to the volume *Saxifragaceae-Saxifraga* (with Irmscher, E.) (1919, 1958)
Farrer, R. *The English Rock Garden* (1918, 1925)
Fenaroli, L. *Flora delle Alpi* (1955)
Fiori, A. *Flora Italiana Illustrata* (1933)
Flahault, Ch. *Nouvelle Flore Coloriée de Poche des Alpes et des Pyrénées* (1906–12)
Fournier, P. *Les Quatre Flores de la France* (1961, 1977)
Gjærevoll, O., and Jørgensen, R. *Mountain Flowers of Scandinavia* (1963)
Grey-Wilson, C. *The Alpine Flowers of Britain and Europe* (1979)
Ingwersen, W. E. Th. *Alpine and Rock Garden Plants* (n.d.)
Irving, W., and Malby, R. A. *Saxifrages or Rockfoils* (1914)
Landolt, E. *Unsere Alpenflora* (1960)
Lid, J. *Norsk Flora* (1952) (latest edition, *Norsk og Svensk Flora*)
Macwatt, J. *The Primulas of Europe* (1923)
Marret, L. *Icones Florae Alpinae Plantarum* (1911–35)
Pitschmann, H., Reisigl, H., and Schiechtl, H. *Bilder-Flora der Südalpen* (1959)
Praeger, R. L. *An Account of the Genus Sedum* (1930)
Praeger, R. L. *An Account of the Sempervivum Group* (1932)
Royal Horticultural Society. *Classified List and International Register of Daffodil Names*
Smith, G. F., Burrow, B., and Lowe, D. B. *Primulas of Europe and America* (1984)
Thommen, E. *Atlas de Poche de la Flore Suisse* (1951)
Thompson, H. S. *Alpine Plants of Europe* (1911)
Thompson, H. S. *Sub-Alpine Plants of Europe* (1912)
Touring Club Italiano. *Conosci L'Italia, II: La Flora* (1958)
Wilkie, D. *Gentians* (1936, 1950)
Wright-Smith, W., and Fletcher, H. R. *The Genus Primula* (1943–48)
Various editors. *Flora Europaea*, (1964–1980)
An invaluable complement to *Mountain Flowers* is *Mountain Flower Holidays in Europe*,
  by Lionel Bacon, Alpine Garden Society (1979)

APPENDIX – CHANGES IN BOTANICAL NAMES

Under the heading 'Authorities and Synonyms' on page 8, reference is made to reasons for the changing of botanical names, and the desirability of following the nomenclature adopted in *Flora Europaea*. The relevant changes embodied in this work, and not stated in the existing text of *Mountain Flowers*, are summarised below. An equals sign (=) indicates that this is the name now recommended.

Text page	Name in Text	New status in Flora Europaea
165	*Gagea villosa*	= *Gagea arvensis* (Pers.) Dumort
166	*Gagea soleirolii*	now spelt *G. solierolii;* = *G. nevadensis* Boiss.
167	*Allium strictum*	now included in *Allium lineare* L.
	Allium montanum	= *Allium senescens* L. ssp. *montanum* (Fries) (F.W. Schmidt) J. Holut
	Allium narcissiflorum var. *insubricum*	= *Allium insubricum* Boiss. & Reuter
	Allium ochroleucum	= *Allium ericetorum* Thore
168	*Fritillaria tenella*	= *Fritillaria orientalis* Adams
	Tulipa didieri	considered to be a naturalised plant = *Tulipa gesnerana* L.
170	*Hyacinthus amethystinus*	= *Brimeura amethystina* (L.) Chouard
	Muscari atlanticum	= *Muscari neglectum* Guss. ex Ten.
171	*Tofieldia pusilla*	The plant in the E. Alps (1800–2200m) is ssp. *austriaca* H. Kunz
	Tofieldia calyculata	var. *glacialis* now = *T. glacialis* Gaud.
172	*Crocus purpureus*	= *Crocus vernus* (L.) Hill. Includes ssp. *vernus*, usually purple, lilac or striped, from Italy eastwards and ssp. *albiflorus* (Kit.) Asch. & Graeb., typically white, from Albania westwards
173	*Iris xiphioides*	= *Iris latifolia* (Mill.) Voss
	Narcissus pseudonarcissus	ssp. *abscissus* and ssp. *bicolor* are now both referred to *Narcissus bicolor* L., and the distinction in trumpet edge ignored
174	*Narcissus juncifolius*	apparently now = *Narcissus requinii* M. J. Roemer
	Dioscorea pyrenaica	= *Borderea pyrenaica* Miègeville. In addition *B. chouardii* (Gauss.) Heslot, with very shiny translucent lvs., is recorded from the valley of the R. Noguera Ribagorzana in the C. Pyrenees
176	*Phleum commutatum*	now included in *P. alpinum* L.
177	*Helictotrichon versicolor*	= *Avena versicolor* (Vill.) Laínz
178	*Eriophorum alpinum*	= *Scirpus hudsonianus* (Michx.) Fernald
182	*Nigritella rubra*	= *Nigritella nigra* (L.) Reichb. ssp. *rubra* (Wettst.) Beauv.
	Leucorchis albida	= *Pseudorchis albida* (L.) A. & D. Love

418

Text page	Name in Text	New status in Flora Europaea
190	*Thesium pyrenaicum*	ssp. *alpestre* O. Schwarz is recorded into N. Yugoslavia
193	*Dianthus neglectus*	= *Dianthus pavonius* Tausch.
220	*Erysimum hieraciifolium*	now spelt *E. hieracifolium*
227	*Thlaspi rotundifolium* ssp. *cepifolium*	now spelt *T. r.* ssp. *cepaefolium*
249	*Ribes schlechtendahlii*	= *Ribes spicata* Robson in With.
251	*Rosa cinnamomea*	= *Rosa majalis* J. Herrmann
	Rosa dumalis	This name is no longer valid. Its components, as suggested in the text, are re-allocated as follows : R. *afzeliana* = R. *vosagiaca* Desportes; R. *coriifolia* = R. *caesia* Sm.
253	*Rosa seraphinii*	now spelt R. *serafinii*
258	*Alchemilla alpina* ssp. *subsericea*	= *Alchemilla subsericea* Reut.
259	*Alchemilla hoppeana* ssp. *asterophylla*	= *Alchemilla plicatula* Gand. (variable)
	Alchemilla hoppeana ssp. *conjuncta*	= *Alchemilla conjuncta* Bab.
	Alchemilla glaberrima	= *Alchemilla fissa* Gunth. & Schumm.
	Alchemilla hybrida	= *Alchemilla glaucescens* Wallr.
	Alchemilla palmata	= *Alchemilla xanthochlora* Rothm.
263	*Sarothamnus purgans*	= *Cytisus purgans* (L.) Boiss.
	Sarothamnus scoparius	= *Cytisus scoparius* (L.) Link
265	*Genista glabrescens*	= *Cytisus emeriflorus* Reich.
	Cytisanthus horridus	= *Echinospartum horridum* (Vahl) Rothm.
	Genistella sagittalis	= *Chamaespartium sagittale* (L.) P. Gibbs
268	*Anthyllis vulneraria* ssp. *coccinea*	= *Anthyllis vulneraria* ssp. *praepropera* (A. Kern.) Bornm.
269	*Astragalus oroboides*	= *Astragalus norvegicus* Weber
271	*Astragalus siculus*	= *Astragalus granatensis* Lam. ssp. *siculus* (Biv.) Franco & P. Silva
272	*Oxytropis foetida*	now spelt *O. fetida* (Vill.) DC.
278	*Erodium petraeum* ssp. *rodiei*	= *Erodium rodiei* (Br.-Bl.) Poirion
	Erodium macradenum	= *E. petraeum* ssp. *glandulosum* (Cav.) Bonn.
279	*Linum alpinum*	= *Linum perenne* L. ssp. *alpinum* (Jacq.) Ock.
287	*Viola calcarata & V. zoysii*	violet-flowered forms of *V. calcarata* are usually ssp. *calcarata;* yellow, blue or white forms are ssp. *villarsiana* (Roem. & Schultes) Merxm. from S. W. Alps; *Viola zoysii* now = *V. calcarata* ssp. *zoysii* (Wulf.) Merxm.
288	*Viola heterophylla*	= *Viola bertolonii* Pio
299	*Chamaepericlymenum suecicum*	= *Cornus suecica* L.
302	*Harrimanella hypnoides*	= *Cassiope hypnoides* (L.) D. Don.
	Arctous alpina	= *Arctostaphylos alpinus* (L.) Spreng.
303	*Vaccinium oxycoccus*	now spelt *V. oxycoccos*
	Erica carnea	= *Erica herbacea* L.
304	*Empetrum hermaphroditum*	now regarded as a ssp. of *E. nigrum*
308	*Primula villosa*	authority should read Wulf. in Jacq.
312	*Androsace alpina* var. *tirolensis*	now spelt *tiroliensis*
312	*Androsace carnea*	Some of the vars. listed are now considered ssp., as follows:

Text page	Name in Text	New status in Flora Europaea
	var. *brigantina*	= ssp. *brigantiaca* (Jord. & Fourr.) I. K. Ferguson
	var. *halleri*	= ssp. *rosea* (Jord. & Fourr.) Rouy
	var. *laggeri*	= ssp. *laggeri* (Huet) Nyman
	var. *puberula*	not recognised in *Flora Europaea*
313	*Soldanella minima*	ssp. *minima*, with fl. fringed to 1/5 of its length, is now recognised; from Monte Majello in C. Appennines
315	*Armeria arenaria* & *A. montana*	both now referred to the polymorphic *Armeria alliacea* (Cav.) Hoffm. & Link.
319	*Gentiana rostani*	now spelt *rostanii*
320	*Gentiana lutea*	ssp. *symphyandra* (Murb.) Hayek from the S. E. Alps has anthers joined in a tube
326	*Lappula myosotis*	= *Lappula squarrosa* (Retz.) Dumont ssp. *squarrosa*
	Lithospermum gastonis	= *Buglossoides gastonii* (Benth.) I. M. Johnson
327	*Onosma helveticum*	now spelt *O. helvetica*
328	*Lycopsis arvensis*	= *Anchusa arvensis* (L.) Bieb.
329	*Pulmonaria tuberosa* Schrank.	Flora Europaea describes great confusion surrounding this plant and allied species
330	*Calamintha alpina*	= *Acinos alpinus* (L.) Moench
	Calamintha ascendens	= *Calamintha sylvatica* Bromf. ssp. *ascendens* (Jord.) P. W. Ball
332	*Hyssopus officinalis* var. *decumbens*	= ssp. *officinlis*
	Hyssopus aristatus	= *Hyssopus officinalis* ssp. *aristatus* (Godr.) Briq.
333	*Prunella grandiflora*	ssp. *pyrenaica* (G.& G.) Bolós has spike to 8cm.
334	*Stachys densiflora*	= *Stachys monieri* (Gouan) P. W. Ball
335	*Galeobdolon luteum*	= *Lamiastrum galeobdolon* (L.) Ehr. & Polat.
340	*Linaria italica*	= *Linaria angustissima* (Lois.) Borb.
341	*Linaria perrieri*	not recognised in *Flora Europaea*
342	*Scrophularia hoppei*	now spelt *hoppii*
343	*Veronica teucrium*	= *Veronica austriaca* L. ssp. *teucrium* (L.) D. A. Webb
344	*Veronica serpyllifolia* ssp. *apennina*	= *Veronica serpyllifolia* ssp. *humifusa* (Dickson) Syme
	Veronica pumila	now included in *Veronica alpina* L.
345	*Odontites lutea* ssp. *lanceolata*	= *Odontites lanceolata* (Gaud.) Reichb.
349	*Pedicularis barrelieri*	= *Pedicularis ascendens* Schleich. ex Gaud.
350	*Pedicularis incarnata*	= *Pedicularis rostratocapitata* Crantz
355	*Pinguicula grandiflora* ssp. *reuteri*	= *Pinguicula grandiflora* ssp. *rosea* (Mutel) Casper
356	*Globularia aphyllanthes*	= *Globularia punctata* Lap.
357	*Globularia tenella* and *G. linnaei*	not recognised as species in *Flora Europaea*
357	*Plantago fuscesens*	now included in *Plantago atrata*
	Plantago serpentina	now regarded as a ssp. *Plantago maritima*
	Plantago recurvata	= *Plantago holosteum* Scop.
358	*Galium cruciata*	= *Cruciata laevipes* Opiz
364	*Knautia brachytricha*	= *Knautia longifolia* (Waldst. & Kit.)

Text page	Name in Text	New status in Flora Europaea
	Knautia sylvatica	= *Knautia dipsacifolia* Kreutz.
365	*Campanula thyrsoides*	ssp. *carniolica* (Sund.) Podl. is recognised as a lax-flowered plant up to 100 cm. from E. Alps & Yugoslavia.
366	*Campanula caespitosa*	now spelt *C. cespitosa*
367	*Campanula linifolia*	= *Campanula carnica* Schiede ex Mert. & Koch; the synonym *C. schleicheri* is now relevant only to *C. scheuchzeri* (below in text)
368	*Campanula allionii*	= *Campanula alpestris* All. (N.B. Calyx in illustration should be much longer)
369	*Edraianthus graminifolius*	A very variable plant. Ssp. *niveus* (G. Beck) Janchen is a white form from W. C. Yugoslavia
370	*Phyteuma halleri*	= *Phyteuma ovatum* F. W. Schmidt
	Phyteuma scaposum	now included in *Phyteuma scorzonerifolium* Vill.
	Phyteuma balbisii	= *Phyteuma cordatum* Balb.
371	*Phyteuma comosum*	= *Physoplexis comosa* (L.) Schur.
372	*Jasione perennis*	= *Jasione laevis* Lam.
373	*Jasione humilis*	= *Jasione crispa* (Pourr.) Samp. ssp. *crispa*
374	*Bellidiastrum michelii*	*Aster bellidiastrum* (L.) Scop.
375	*Erigeron polymorphus*	= *Erigeron glabratus* Hoppe & Hornsch.
	Erigeron unalaschkensis	= *Erigeron humilis* R. C. Graham
376	*Leontopodium nivale*	now considered a ssp. of *Leontopodium alpinum*
	Gnaphalium	The species described are now renamed under *Omalotheca* Cass.
377	*Anthemis montana*	Now referred to *Anthemis cretica* L. Ssp. *saxatilis* (DC.) R. Fernandes is from mts. of S. C. France, calcifuge; ssp. *alpina* (L.) R. Fernandes from Appenines, calcicole. *A. carpatica* is now considered a distinct species, equally variable, from the Pyrenees eastwards, having a woody rootstock
	Anthemis barrelieri	= *Achillea barrelieri* Sz.
378	*Anthemis elegans*	Now referred to *Achillea oxyloba* (DC.) Scultz as ssp. *mucronulata* (Bert.) I. B. K. Richardson
379	*Achillea moschata*	Now referred to *Achillea erba-rotta* All. as ssp. *moschata* (Wulf.) I. B. K. Richardson
	Achillea tanacetifolia	= *Achillea distans* W. & K. ssp. *tanacetifolia* Janch.
380	*Chrysanthemum alpinum &* C. pulverulentum	transferred to *Leucanthemopsis* (Giroux) Heywood
380, 381	*Chrysanthemum atratum &* C. leucanthemum	transferred to *Leucanthemum* Mill. (*C. leucanthemum* = *L. vulgare* Lam.)
382	*Artemisia mutellina*	= *Artemisia umbelliformis* Lam.
384	*Adenostyles glabra*	= *Adenostyles alpina* Bl. & Fing.
385	*Doronicum viscosum*	now referred to *Doronicum grandiflorum* Lam.
386	*Senecio alpinus*	= *Senecio subalpinus* Koch.
	Senecio tournefortii	= *Senecio pyrenaicus* L.
387	*Senecio uniflorus*	= *Senecio halleri* Dandy

Text page	Name in Text	New status in Flora Europaea
	Senecio capitatus	Referred to *Senecio integrifolius* (L.) Clairv. ssp. *capitatus* (Wahl.) Cuf. Ssp. *pyrenaicus* is now named *S. lapeyrousii* Rothm.
388	*Carlina acaulis* var. *alpina*	= ssp. *simplex* (W. & K.) Nyman
	Jurinea bocconi	= *Jurinea humilis* (Desf.) DC.
390	*Carduus personatus*	now spelt *C. personata*
391	*Cirsium heterophyllum*	= *Cirsium helenioides* (L.) Hill
	Cirsium acaulon	returned to *C. acaule*
	Centaurea nervosa	= *Centaurea uniflora* Turra ssp. *nervosa (Willd.) Bonn. & Layens*
393	*Centaurea raetica*	now spelt *C. rhaetica*
	Rhaponticum cynaroides	= *Leuzea centauroides* (L.) J. Holub
	Rhaponticum scariosum	= *Leuzea rhapontica* (L.) J. Holub
394	*Rhaponticum heleniifolium*	= *Leuzea rhapontica* ssp. *heleniifolia* (G. & G.) J. Holub
395	*Scorzonera rosea*	= *Scorzonera purpurea* L. ssp. *rosea* (W. & K.) Nyman
396	*Crepis pontana*	= *Crepis bocconi* P. D. Sell
	Crepis raetica	now spelt *C. rhaetica*
397	*Taraxacum alpinum*	Now referred to the *T. appenninum* Ten. group in Sect. Alpina which includes 23 mostly Alpine species.

INDEX OF LATIN NAMES

This index is of the plants illustrated and gives the plate numbers (in bold figures) and the text pages on which they are described.

For the descriptions of the plants not illustrated, reference should be made to the genus heading. These descriptions are normally placed in the text immediately after the most similar illustrated plants. Synonyms are not indexed owing to space limitations, except those of genera.

An Index of English Names follows on page 425.

INDEX OF ENGLISH NAMES